D0368952

RECENT PROGRESS
IN THE
ENDOCRINOLOGY OF
REPRODUCTION

RECENT PROGRESS

IN THE

ENDOCRINOLOGY of REPRODUCTION

Proceedings of the Conference Held in Syracuse, New York, June 9-12, 1958

Edited by

CHARLES W. LLOYD

Upstate Medical Center
State University of New York
Syracuse, New York

1959

Academic Press Inc., New York and London

Library of Congress Catalog Card Number 59-9809

LIST OF CONTRIBUTORS

VIVIAN J. BEACH, Warner-Lambert Research Institute, Morris Plains, New Jersey

JOHN C. BECK, McGill University Clinic, Royal Victoria Hospital, Montreal, Canada

G. K. BENSON, National Institute for Research in Dairying, Shinfield, Reading, England

BENT G. BÖVING, Department of Embryology, Carnegie Institution of Washington, Baltimore, Maryland

J. B. BROWN, Clinical Endocrinology Research Unit (Medical Research Council), University of Edinburgh, Edinburgh, Scotland

M. C. CHANG, Worcester Foundation for Experimental Biology, Shrewsbury, Massachusetts

A. T. COWIE, National Institute for Research in Dairying, Shinfield, Reading, England

B. A. CROSS, Sub-Department of Veterinary Anatomy, University of Cambridge, Cambridge, England

R. L. ELTON, Division of Biological Research, G. D. Searle & Co., Chicago, Illinois

LUIS FERNANDEZ-CANO, San Marcos University, Lima, Peru, and the Worcester Foundation for Experimental Biology, Shrewsbury, Massachusetts

S. J. FOLLEY, National Institute for Research in Dairying, Shinfield, Reading, England

DWAIN D. HAGERMAN, Department of Biological Chemistry, Harvard Medical School, and the Research Laboratories of the Boston Lying-in Hospital, Boston, Massachusetts

G. W. HARRIS, Department of Neuroendocrinology, Institute of Psychiatry, Maudsley Hospital, British Postgraduate Medical Federation, London University, London, England

H. HELLER, Department of Pharmacology, University of Bristol, Bristol, England

ROBERT KROC, Warner-Lambert Research Institute, Morris Plains, New Jersey

JAMES H. LEATHEM, Bureau of Biological Research, Rutgers University, New Brunswick, New Jersey

JANET W. MCARTHUR, Department of Gynecology, Harvard Medical School, and the Gynecological Service, Massachusetts General Hospital, Boston, Massachusetts

W. V. MACFARLANE, *Sir William MacGregor School of Physiology, University of Queensland, Brisbane, Australia*

WARREN O. NELSON, *Laboratory of the Population Council, The Rockefeller Institute, New York, New York*

PAMELA R. PENNYCUIK, *Sir William MacGregor School of Physiology, University of Queensland, Brisbane, Australia*[1]

ELIJAH B. ROMANOFF, *Worcester Foundation for Experimental Biology, Shrewsbury, Massachusetts*

F. J. SAUNDERS, *Division of Biological Research, G. D. Searle & Co., Chicago, Illinois*

CHARLES H. SAWYER, *Department of Anatomy, School of Medicine, University of California at Los Angeles, and Veterans Administration Hospital, Long Beach, California*

SHELDON J. SEGAL, *Laboratory of the Population Council, The Rockefeller Institute, New York, New York*

BERNARD G. STEINETZ, *Warner-Lambert Research Institute, Morris Plains, New Jersey*

MARTIN L. STONE, *Department of Obstetrics and Gynecology, New York Medical College, Metropolitan Medical Center, New York, New York*

E. THRIFT, *Sir William MacGregor School of Physiology, University of Queensland, Brisbane, Australia*[2]

J. S. TINDAL, *National Institute for Research in Dairying, Shinfield, Reading, England*

PHILIP TROEN, *Department of Medicine, Harvard Medical School, and Department of Medical Research and Yamins Research Laboratory, Beth Israel Hospital, Boston, Massachusetts*

ELEANOR H. VENNING, *McGill University Clinic, Royal Victoria Hospital, Montreal, Canada*

CLAUDE A. VILLEE, *Department of Biological Chemistry, Harvard Medical School, and the Research Laboratories of the Boston Lying-in Hospital, Boston, Massachusetts*

N. T. M. YEATES, *Sir William MacGregor School of Physiology, University of Queensland, Brisbane, Australia*[3]

JOSEF ZANDER, *Universitäts-Frauenklinik, Cologne, Germany*

SIR SOLLY ZUCKERMAN, *Department of Anatomy, The Medical School, University of Birmingham, Birmingham, England*

---

[1] *Present Address:* Department of Zoology, Duke University, Durham, North Carolina.

[2] *Present Address:* General Hospital, Toowoomba, Queensland, Australia.

[3] *Present Address:* Department of Animal Husbandry, University of New England, Armidale, New South Wales, Australia.

FOREWORD

The problem of communication of data, which must be solved if the explosive progress of all research is to continue, challenges the field of endocrinology as forcefully as it does any area of science. This specialty is one in which intimate exchange of knowledge between basic disciplines and clinical areas is essential. Such a plethora of published, to say nothing of unpublished, information has resulted from the recent burgeoning of interest in the endocrine organs that it has become an almost insurmountable task for the investigator to keep abreast of progress in the many specialized areas which contribute to endocrinology. The endocrine journals and meetings view the field through a wide-angle lens, a kind of panorama. The occasional focusing with a higher power on a smaller field is rewarding in that it permits more concentrated delving into detail as well as over-all synthesis of knowledge of a particular facet of endocrinology. This was the purpose of the State University of New York, Upstate Medical Center Dedication Year Conference on the Endocrinology of Reproduction held in Syracuse, New York, in June of 1958.

This conference was planned to bring together basic investigators and clinicians whose primary interests were in the endocrine aspects of reproduction, in an atmosphere which would permit informal, exhaustive, and more or less uninhibited, exchange of information and ideas. Some of the participants were asked to introduce the subjects for discussion by presenting reviews of the present status of their fields of expertise as well as their own investigations. It was hoped that this plan would not only bring up to date workers from different disciplines than those of the speakers but would also provoke stimulating exchange of ideas. These goals were admirably achieved. The fortunate admixture of morphologists, neurologists, physiologists, chemists, and clinicians, not only resulted in suggestions of ways for the clinician to study or treat his patients, who represent the experiments which nature provides, but also intriguing paths of investigation for the non-clinical scientists. In addition to the many elegantly conceived and executed experimental programs which have led to major hypotheses, there were also many important, thought-provoking observations from the laboratory and the clinic which are still too limited or incomplete to be published *in extenso* until some time in the future.

The task of editing the proceedings was eased by the cooperation of all the participants as well as by the lucidity of the speakers and by the wisdom and adroitness of the eight distinguished session chairmen.

The formal presentations are published exactly as they were given. Spelling has been standardized according to American usage. In a few of the figures this could not be done without redrawing them. Therefore, stylistic consistency was sacrificed in the interests of time of preparation. Discussions were corrected by the discussants at the time of the meeting. Any errors are undoubtedly the result of the editing necessary to conserve space and the editor apologizes if his efforts have produced misstatements of fact or loss of eloquence.

The conference itself and the recording of the proceedings in this volume resulted from the encouragement and support offered by the administrative officers of the Upstate Medical Center, in particular, former acting dean W. W. Westerfeld, President Carlyle Jacobsen, assistant dean William Harris, and Messrs. A. J. Carroll and David Sinclair. Miss Julia Lobotsky has carried a major load in proof-reading and redrawing figures and Mrs. Margaret Cooney also helped in redrawing figures. Mmes. Olean Lietz and Katharine Lloyd and Miss Nancy Cochrane performed yeoman service in typing manuscripts. The editor is also grateful to the staff of the Academic Press for their courteous forbearance and cooperation during the difficult gestation of "Recent Progress in the Endocrinology of Reproduction."

This Conference was supported by grants-in-aid from the following sources: Ayerst Laboratories; The Upjohn Company; Smith, Kline & French Laboratories; Warner-Chilcott Laboratories; E. R. Squibb & Sons; State University of New York; G. D. Searle & Company; Ciba Pharmaceutical Products, Inc.; Bristol Laboratories, Inc.; The National Drug Company; Organon, Inc.; Ortho Pharmaceutical Corp.; Wm. S. Merrell Co.

CHARLES W. LLOYD

Syracuse, New York
January, 1959

CONTENTS

ix

Nervous Control of Ovulation[1]

CHARLES H. SAWYER

Department of Anatomy, School of Medicine, University of California at Los Angeles, and Veterans Administration Hospital, Long Beach, California

I. Introduction

The changes in the ovary which culminate in ovulation have been known to be controlled by hormones of the adenohypophysis since the classical work of Smith and Engle (64) reported in 1927. During the past twenty years evidence has been accumulating which reveals that the release of an ovulatory surge of pituitary gonadotropin, here called ovulatory hormone, is stimulated via the central nervous system.

Certain species, which include the rabbit and cat, require the neural stimulus accompanying coitus to induce ovulation. This was first recognized by Heape (34) at the turn of the century, before the essential role of the pituitary hormones had been established. More recent claims that nerve pathways from the brain to the ovary are of crucial significance to ovulation (47) have failed to be confirmed (12), leaving practically unopposed the hypothesis that nervous influences on ovulation are mediated indirectly through the pituitary gland.

The "reflex" ovulators are a very small minority group when compared with the overwhelming population of species that ovulate cyclically or seasonally in a so-called "spontaneous" manner, without an overt neural

[1] The original research presented in this paper was supported in part by grants from the Ford Foundation and the United States Public Health Service (B334 and B1162).

stimulus. The problem of the first two papers is to demonstrate that a process which does not appear to require nervous control is actually controlled by nervous influences through a gland which does not appear to have nerve fibers.

An oversimplified diagram of hypophyseal-ovarian interrelationships is seen in Figure 1. Target organ ovarian steroids are pictured as feeding back directly to the pituitary, as proposed by several early workers including Moore and Price (44) in 1932. The need for the upper arrow (steroids to nervous system), to be discussed in detail below, was first proposed by Hohlweg and Junkmann (35) on the basis that castration

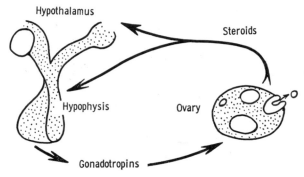

Fig. 1.   Diagram of pituitary-ovarian interrelationships indicating possible sites of action of "feed-back" steroids.

cell formation did not occur in pituitary transplants. Also influencing hypothalamico-hypophyseal mechanisms, though not included in the diagram, are such exteroceptive factors as light, temperature, humidity, nutritional status, and social relationships.

The present paper will attempt to analyze some of the mechanisms involved in nervous system-pituitary-ovarian interrelationships as revealed by modern techniques of electrical stimulation, discrete lesions, blocking agents, and electronic recording of differentially localized activity in cortical and subcortical regions of the brain. Not to be considered a comprehensive review, the report will emphasize recent work in the author's laboratory, some of which has not been published previously. The importance of the hypophyseal portal system, as revealed by stalk section and transplantation experiments, will be reserved for discussion by Dr. Harris (Chapter 2), in whose laboratory so much of the evidence was discovered. For a more complete review of the field to 1955, one is referred to the excellent monograph of Benoit and Assenmacher (7).

II. Hypothalamus

A. RABBIT EXPERIMENTS

Shortly after Marshall and Verney (43) had demonstrated that ovulation could be induced by massive electric currents applied externally to the estrous rabbit's head, Harris (30) and Haterius and Derbyshire (33) independently reported that localized stimulation with weaker currents applied directly to the hypothalamic tuberal and preoptic regions,

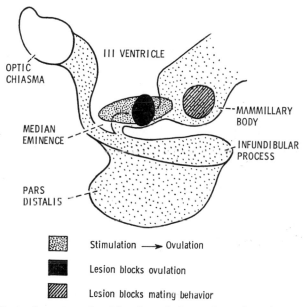

Fig. 2. Sagittal section of rabbit hypothalamic hypophyseal region indicating sites of gonadotropic and behavioral "sex centers."

respectively, was equally effective. During the past twenty years their findings have been confirmed by many groups with a variety of techniques, stimulation parameters, and electrode placements (12, 31, 40, 42, 47, 53). Markee *et al.* (42) reported that the pars distalis was inexcitable electrically to parameters effective in the hypothalamic tuber, a finding quickly confirmed by Harris (31) with his remote control stimulation technique. In a study designed to test the critical site of blocking action of certain drugs, to be discussed below, Saul and Sawyer (53) have recently delineated an elliptical area extending from the rostral end of the mammillary body to the median eminence (Fig. 2), stimulation of which consistently (9/11 cases) evokes ovulation. The stimulation parameters (3.5 volts, 6 per second, 5 millisecond square waves, on-off at 30-second intervals for 30 minutes) were completely ineffective when applied to the preoptic or mid-mammillary regions.

Massive surgical lesions of the female rabbit cerebrum interfered neither with copulation nor the resultant ovulation (8). Small lesions involving the pituitary stalk blocked ovulation (9) or led to ovarian atrophy (30, 36, 66), while basal tuberal lesions in the young rabbit interrupted ovarian development (11, 65). In our laboratory (55, 56, 58) small bilateral electrolytic lesions in the basal tuberal nuclei (Fig. 2) have blocked ovulation with or without inducing ovarian atrophy, but the animals would copulate under the influence of exogenous estrogen. Similar lesions slightly further back, in the mammillary body, did not upset trophic influences on the ovaries, and ovulation could be induced with copper acetate. However, the rabbits remained persistently anestrous, behaviorally, even though supplied repeatedly with exogenous estrogen. Thus, for descriptive purposes, one might assign gonadotropic and behavioral "sex centers" in the female rabbit to the basal tuberal and mammillary regions, respectively.

Mating-induced changes in the electroencephalographic (EEG) activity of the hypothalamus and other regions of the female rabbit brain will be discussed below.

B. CAT EXPERIMENTS

Although the cat is a "reflex ovulator," and the estrous female will ovulate in response to vaginal stimulation with a glass rod, its long anestrous periods have made it less widely used than the rabbit in ovulation experiments. The difficulties were partially remedied when it was found that the anestrous cat could be primed with estrogen and equine gonadotropin (PMS) to the point at which the release of its pituitary gonadotropin could be triggered by the reflex mechanisms (60). Ovarian atrophy in response to basal hypothalamic lesions has been reported (41).

Employing naturally estrous and primed female cats, Porter et al. (49) have recorded dramatic changes in the spontaneous electrical activity of the hypothalamus (Fig. 3) during and following vaginal stimulation. The EEG changes were localized in the anterior and lateral hypothalamus, in and around the medial forebrain bundle, and they could not be evoked in the anestrous cat. They were not motor artifacts for they could be evoked in the curarized animal. Temporally, the changes paralleled in duration the behavioral afterreaction to mating or vaginal stimulation, and it was proposed that they might represent neural correlates either of behavioral activities or of pituitary stimulation.

To test this hypothesis, stimulation and lesioning techniques have been applied to the problem by Robison and Sawyer (52). Estrous female cats under chloralosane anesthesia were stimulated via bipolar electrodes symmetrically placed bilaterally in one of the following regions: medial or lateral anterior hypothalamus, ventromedial nucleus

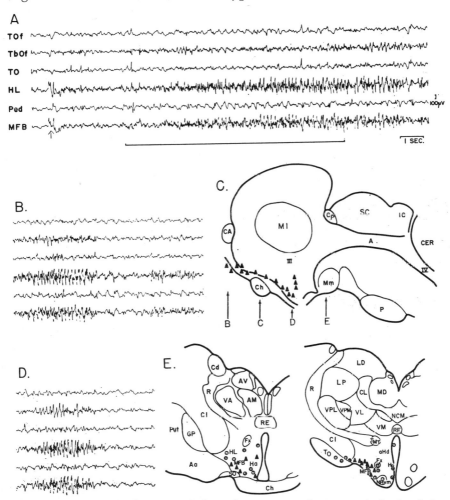

FIG. 3. Selected electroencephalographic tracings during vaginal stimulation (A) and "afterreaction" (B, D) which lasted 3.3 minutes in an estrous cat. Dramatic changes are seen in lateral hypothalamic (HL) and medial forebrain bundle (MFB) channels (C, E). Sagittal reconstruction and cross sections of the cat brain stem showing areas from which altered electrical activity was recorded (solid triangles) and areas failing to show these changes (stippled circles). From Sawyer (58) after Porter *et al.* (49).

or mammillary body. At the end of the half-hour stimulation period (3.5–5 volts, 30 per second, 5 millisecond square waves, 30 seconds on, 30 seconds off) the central tips of the electrodes were used to place electrolytic lesions at the stimulation sites (Fig. 4). Forty-eight or more hours later laparotomy was performed to determine whether or not the experimental procedures had induced ovulation. The cats were then maintained several months to observe the long-term effects of the lesions. It was found that stimulation of the anterior hypothalamic sites failed to induce ovulation, and lesions failed to cause ovarian atrophy; however, the cats became permanently anestrous in spite of treatment with exogenous estrogen. On the other hand, stimulation of either ventromedial or mammillary sites evoked ovulation (12/15 cases), and the lesions induced ovarian atrophy. When supplied extrinsic estrogen, these females would mate normally and show a typical behavioral afterreaction. The results suggest that, whereas the cat gonadotropic "center" is similarly located to its counterpart in the rabbit, the cat reproductive behavioral center lies rostral to that area rather than caudal to it as in the rabbit. The rostral position of the site of integration of sexual behavior in the cat confirms the findings of Ranson's laboratory (23) rather than the proposals of Dempsey and Rioch (16) or Bard (4), which were based on inadequate material.

C. Guinea Pig and Rat Experiments

In these "spontaneously ovulating" forms, anterior hypothalamic lesions block the ovulatory cycle in a state of continuous estrus, as first reported in the guinea pig by Dey (18) and confirmed in the rat by Hillarp (34a), Greer (28), and others. Median eminence lesions in the guinea pig (18) and destruction of the pituitary stalk in the rat (27, 32) induce ovarian atrophy with resulting anestrus. In rats rendered persistent-estrous by hypothalamic lesions or exposure to continuous light, ovulation has been induced by mating (17) or treatment with progesterone (3, 19, 28). In cyclic rats in which the natural release of pituitary ovulating hormone was blocked by appropriately timed treatment with

---

Fig. 4.   A, B.   Anterior hypothalamic lesions which induced permanent anestrus in the female cat in spite of treatment with exogenous estrogen. Stimulation at these sites had failed to cause ovulation and the lesions did not induce ovarian atrophy. C. Ventromedial and D. mammillary lesions which induced ovarian atrophy but did not abolish mating behavior if exogenous estrogen was supplied. Stimulation at these sites had induced ovulation. E. Mid-sagittal reconstruction showing anterior-posterior extent of lesions (A–D). From Sawyer (58) after Robison and Sawyer (52).

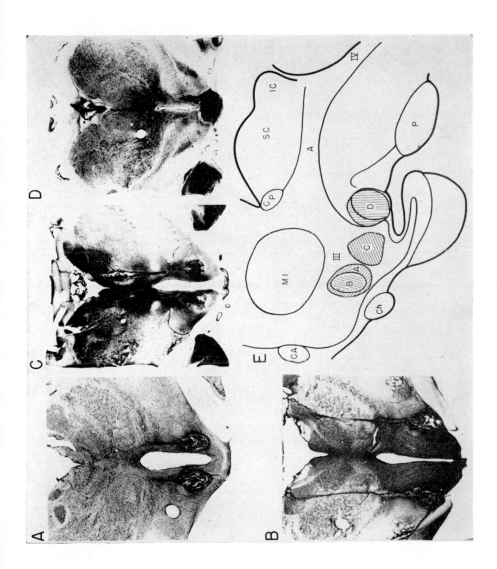

pentobarbital, Critchlow (13) has been able to induce ovulation by electrical stimulation of the ventral hypothalamus.

III. Rhinencephalon

The rhinencephalon or limbic lobe of the brain has so many important anatomical connections with the hypothalamus as to suggest functional interactions. These relationships have been reviewed (25, 50), and a few of the more important pathways are shown diagrammatically in Figure 5. Papez' (48) famous emotional circuit, published in 1937, involved many of these structures. Recently, Adey *et al.* (1, 2) have

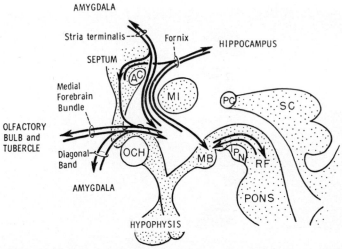

FIG. 5. Some nervous pathways projecting to and from the hypothalamus.

proposed, on the basis of electrophysiological and nerve degeneration studies, that the more important direction of transmission is the reverse of that suggested by Papez, i.e., from fornix ⟶ hippocampus ⟶ entorhinal cortex ⟶ septum ⟶ stria medullaris ⟶ midbrain tegmentum. Green (26) has proposed that afferent impulses affecting pituitary function may reach the basal hypothalamus by the following route: extralemniscal afferents ⟶ lateral hypothalamus ⟶ septum ⟶ precommissural fornix ⟶ hippocampus ⟶ postcommissural fornix ⟶ mammillary body. An alternative route from the hippocampus would go via amygdala ⟶ stria terminalis ⟶ hypothalamus. Nauta (46) has described pathways from the fornix to the arcuate nuclei in the rat.

There is some evidence from stimulation studies that certain rhinencephalic centers may influence ovulation. Koikegami *et al.* (39) induced ovulation in the rabbit by stimulating the amygdala. This has been confirmed in the primed cat (63). In the light-induced persistent-estrous rat, Bunn and Everett (10) induced ovulation by stimulating the amygdala or, in one case, the septum. Tokizane and Sawyer [cf. Sawyer, (56)] were able to confirm Koikegami in the rabbit, though amygdala stimulation results have been much less consistent than in the hypothalamus. More recent unpublished attempts to induce ovulation by direct electrical stimulation of other rhinencephalic areas, including olfactory bulb, septum, and dorsal hippocampus, have been completely negative for ovulation.

Also unsuccessful have been attempts to interfere with copulation-induced ovulation in the rabbit by local destruction of rhinencephalic regions (55). Neither removal of the olfactory bulbs, nor severing the fornix, nor placing large lesions in the septum or amygdala bilaterally, prevented either mating or its consequent ovulation. This does not imply that these areas are functionless in the natural sequence of reflexogenic ovulation, but that there must be, at least, alternate pathways to insure pituitary activation. An artificial system of stimulating the release of ovulating hormone, the intraventricular injection of histamine under weak pentobarbital anesthesia, was shown by both electrical recording and lesioning data to require the integrity of the olfactory bulbs (56). Changes in the spontaneous electrical activity of rhinencephalic areas following copulation will be discussed below.

IV. Brain Stem Reticular Formation

Probably no region of the nervous system has ever attracted more attention over a decade than has the brain stem reticular formation during the past ten years. The reticular core, which extends from the hindbrain at least into the hypothalamus, has been shown by Magoun and his collaborators (24, 45) to play an important functional role in the maintenance of consciousness and a state of alertness. It enters, in an integrative sense, into most of the activities of the central nervous system. Direct electrical stimulation of the reticular formation induces electro-encephalographic (EEG) and behavioral arousal, while large lesions lead to a comatose state. The region is especially sensitive to anesthetics, and agents such as pentobarbital block transmission in this multisynaptic system in dosages too low to affect transmission in the lemniscal classical afferent pathways. Adrenergic (15) and cholinergic (51) components have been proposed for the system, since it may be activated by drugs of these series and blocked by certain antiadrenergic and anticholinergic agents. Under the influence of these agents there may develop a disparity between behavioral arousal and EEG arousal: the animal may remain behaviorally alert while revealing a sleeplike EEG and an elevated threshold of EEG arousal.

Sawyer *et al.* (62) reported that large doses of atropine sulfate would block copulation-induced ovulation in the rabbit if injected rapidly post coitum, and prevent cyclic ovulation in the rat if injected prior to a critical period during the day of proestrus (20). If the drug was injected prior to 2:00 P.M. under controlled lighting conditions, none of the rats ovulated, whereas all of the animals ovulated if injection was withheld until 4:00 P.M. Later, it was found that sedation with barbiturates during this critical period was sufficient to block ovulation (20). Similar effects on ovulation with one or more of these agents have been reported for the hen (68) and the cow (29). More recently, morphine (5) and chlorpromazine (6) have been added to the list of effective agents, and, in ovulation-blocking doses, these agents, as well as atropine and the barbiturates, induce a sleeplike EEG with high-amplitude slow waves and raise the threshold of EEG arousal on direct stimulation of the reticular formation (6, 59). These last two agents are of special interest since morphine has been reported to cause infertility and chlorpromazine to delay ovulation in women (67). The suggestion was made that the afferent impulses responsible for activating the release of pituitary ovulating hormone must traverse the extralemniscal multisynaptic reticular system, or that a certain degree of alertness must be present to permit pituitary activation (59).

Saul and Sawyer (53) have recently designed experiments in the rabbit to localize more precisely the limiting sites of blocking action of agents known to interrupt the reflexogenic or neurogenic release of pituitary ovulating hormone. Estrogen-primed rabbits, unanesthetized other than locally at the surgery sites, were stimulated stereotaxically in various hypothalamic areas at parameters described above. The region positive for ovulation is the heavily stippled area in Fig. 2. However, when atropine sulfate, morphine sulfate, or pentobarbital was injected prior to stimulation, the only rabbits which ovulated were those in which the electrodes were found at histology to have impinged on the median eminence. Under these conditions, ovulation in response to stimulation of the posterior tuberal region was completely blocked. These results place the limiting site of blockade of these agents at the junction of hypothalamus and median eminence (Fig. 6). The reticular formation may be considered as reaching this point. Two other ovulation-blocking drugs, SKF-501 and reserpine, did not block the effectiveness of posterior tuberal stimulation. These agents did not give other indications of blocking the reticular system; their sites of action are not definitely known (6). However, the results afford good evidence that the site of action of SKF-501, an adrenergic blocking agent, is not peripheral at the pituitary gland as had been suggested (61).

A more direct approach to the problem of reticular formation participation in ovulatory mechanisms has recently been made by Critchlow (14). He made large lesions in the rat midbrain before 2:00 p.m. on the day of proestrus and found that these were highly effective in blocking ovulation. However, there was a poor correlation between the development of a comatose condition and blockade of ovulation. On reconstruct-

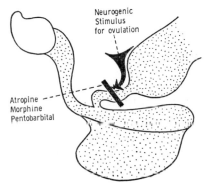

Fig. 6. Suggested site of action of certain drugs in blocking ovulation.

ing and superimposing the lesions, Critchlow observed that the lesion area common to the blocked rats lay ventrally, rostral to the interpeduncular nucleus, involving the mammillary peduncles. Subsequently it was observed that relatively tiny lesions in this region blocked ovulation with a minimal effect on sleep-wakefulness conditions. The results indicate that the "activating system" involved in neurogenic stimulation of the release of ovulating hormone is not identical with the behavioral sleep-wakefulness system, though the former may be even more sensitive to drugs than the latter. Such an explanation would be consistent with the results above, in which drugs affecting the EEG and arousal thresholds did not put the animal to sleep. Locationwise, Critchlow's lesions would lie within the midbrain-hypothalamic projections proposed by Anderson *et al.* (3) as a mesencephalic hypothalamico-pituitary activating system after the anatomical work of Nauta.

V. Effects of Hormones on Thresholds of Nervous and Neuroendocrine Activity

A corollary of some of the data cited above is that both sex behavior and thresholds of pituitary activation are influenced, if not controlled, by the sex steroids. The mechanisms of action of ovarian steroids on these phenomena have been the subject of an intensive investigation in collaboration with Dr. M. Kawakami (37, 38, 57, 58). Somewhat similar studies have been undertaken in France by Faure (21, 22).

The present investigation took as its point of departure the earlier observation (54) that, within a few hours after progesterone treatment of the estrous or estrogenized female rabbit, the threshold of pituitary activation is lowered: at this time, release of ovulating hormone can be induced by mechanical stimulation of the vagina, a procedure quite ineffective in the absence of progesterone. By 24 hours, the pituitary threshold is highly elevated: it is almost impossible to induce ovulation by any means short of supplying exogenous gonadotropin. During the earlier period the rabbit is highly estrous, but by 24 hours it has reached the stage of extreme anestrus with which progesterone is usually associated.

After some preliminary experiments, which included intraventricular injections, the investigation proceeded to study the effects of systemically administered female sex steroids on two types of thresholds in unanesthetized female rabbits with electrodes chronically implanted in several regions of the brain. These were (a) the threshold of EEG arousal on direct stimulation of the reticular formation and (b) the threshold required to induce a peculiar EEG afterreaction on low-frequency stimulation of hypothalamic and rhinencephalic centers. The EEG afterreaction is identical to one observed as a natural sequel to copulation or to vaginal stimulation during the first few hours after progesterone treatment.

Figure 7 illustrates this type of EEG afterreaction, evoked in this instance by 30 seconds of low-frequency stimulation of the lateral mammillary nuclei. Within seconds or minutes, sleep spindles appear in the frontal cortical channel while the animal becomes quiescent and lies down. Suddenly, after several minutes (Fig. 7, D), the record changes

---

FIG. 7. Electroencephalographic afterreaction to low-frequency stimulation of the female rabbit hypothalamus. For explanation, see text. Abbreviations: *FC*, frontal cortex; *LC*, limbic cortex; *SM*, stria medullaris; *SP*, septum; *ML*, lateral mammillary nuclei; *IC*, internal capsule; *VHPC*, ventral hippocampus; *RET*, reticular formation of midbrain.

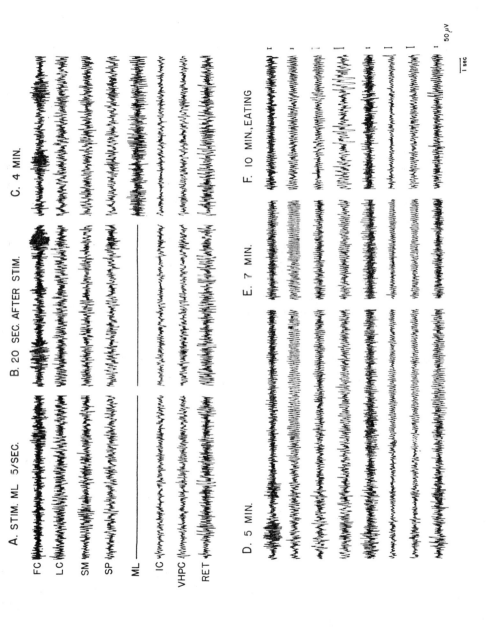

to an apparently hyperaroused EEG condition with a rapid (8 per second) theta rhythm in many channels, especially those with hippocampal projections. Interestingly enough, during this period the rabbit is further depressed rather than alert, stretched out prone and motionless. Within a few minutes it stands and starts eating food or feces. This EEG afterreaction has been evoked by low-voltage stimulation of the hippocampus, amygdala, septum, and olfactory bulbs, as well as various hypothalamic nuclei.

The characteristic changes following progesterone treatment in the two types of threshold in two different ovariectomized, estrogen-treated rabbits, identified by circular and square symbols, are illustrated in Fig. 8. The figure also contains data on estrous behavior and the EEG afterreaction to copulation and to vaginal stimulation. The two types of thresholds in a given rabbit (e.g., the "square" one) parallel each other, and, correlated with the briefly lowered thresholds, the animal mated and revealed EEG afterreactions to this and to vaginal stimulation. The latter activities ceased as the thresholds became secondarily elevated. The "circular" rabbits showed an unusually prolonged lowering of thresholds following progesterone, and the duration of estrous behavioral and EEG afterreaction data remained consistent with this prolonged lowering.

The two thresholds are to a certain extent antagonistic to each other, one related to behavioral arousal, the other to sleeplike depression. The "hyperaroused" EEG condition cannot be evoked in a noisy room or under other behaviorally arousing conditions. When EEG "hyperarousal" has been achieved, the threshold of inducing behavioral arousal is temporarily highly elevated.

Where it has been possible to separate the two curves, e.g., elevate one threshold while lowering the other, it would appear that the reticular formation arousal threshold is more closely related to estrous behavior, while the EEG afterreaction threshold seems to relate to pituitary activation. For example, treatment for several days with large doses of estrogen raises the EEG afterreaction threshold and elevates the threshold of pituitary activation, while the reticular formation threshold remains low and the rabbit remains "hot." Testosterone elevates the EEG afterreaction threshold and blocks ovulation, while it is still consistent with a low reticular formation threshold and estrous behavior.

The ulterior significance or meaning of the EEG "hyperarousal" afterreaction is an intriguing question. It has certain characteristics of a psychomotor seizure, and it should perhaps be diagnosed as such. At first it was thought that the afterreaction might represent an EEG correlate of neurogenic activation of the hypophysis. A serious objection to this concept was the relative lateness of the appearance of the after-reaction to coitus, under conditions at which a blocking agent must be injected within a minute to prevent the release of pituitary ovulating hormone. The time relationships were such as to suggest that the phenomenon was more closely related to the actual release of ovulating

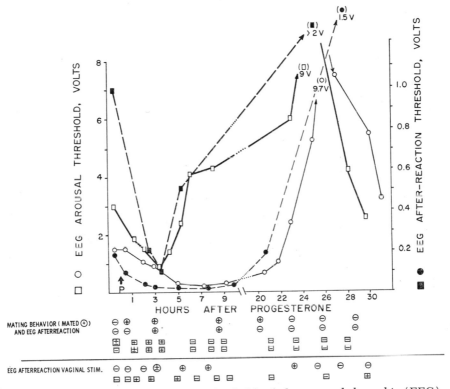

Fig. 8. Effects of progesterone on thresholds of electroencephalographic (EEG) arousal on stimulating the reticular formation and EEG afterreaction on stimulating the hypothalamus (ventromedial nucleus). The rabbits were ovariectomized and estrogen-treated. Square and circular symbols represent two different rabbits. For further explanation, see text.

hormone or its action back on the nervous system. Confirmation of the latter hypothesis has come from the evocation of the phenomenon with ovulation-inducing dosages of human chorionic gonadotropin, equine gonadotropin, and purified luteinizing hormone but not with other anterior lobe hormones. Recently oxytocin has been observed to evoke the afterreaction, an interesting finding in view of the observation that coitus induces the release of oxytocin. Perhaps the phenomenon represents the result of a feed-back system to shut off further neural activation of the hypophysis.

VI. Summary and Interpretation

Certain differential "centers" of nervous integration or control of reproductive behavior and pituitary gonadotropic secretion have been revealed in the hypothalamus by electrical stimulation, lesioning, and recording techniques. The expression of activity in these hypothalamic centers appears to be modified by influences from the rhinencephalon and the brain stem reticular formation. Certain stimulation thresholds within these areas are seen to be altered dramatically by the "feedback" of ovarian steroids and perhaps by pituitary hormones. The widespread and apparently generalized nature of the threshold changes suggests that the hormones exert broad spheres of influence within the nervous system rather than localized effects on isolated centers. Specific changes in the activity of a center might result from the generalized threshold changes: low threshold levels of the latter type may foster or permit "center" activities which would be inhibited at elevated generalized thresholds. Both the facilitatory and the inhibitory actions of ovarian steroids on ovulation may be attributable to the influence of these hormones on thresholds in the nervous system.

References

1. Adey, W. R., Merrillees, N. C. R., and Sunderland, S., *Brain* **79**, 414 (1956).
2. Adey, W. R., Sunderland, S., and Dunlop, C. W., *Electroencephalog. and Clin. Neurophysiol.* **9**, 309 (1957).
3. Anderson, E., Bates, R. W., Hawthorne, E., Haymaker, W., Knowlton, K., Rioch, D. M., Spence, W. T., and Wilson, H., *Recent Progr. in Hormone Research* **13**, 21 (1957).
4. Bard, P., *Research Publs. Assoc. Research Nervous Mental Disease* **20**, 551 (1940).
5. Barraclough, C. A., and Sawyer, C. H., *Endocrinology* **57**, 329 (1955).
6. Barraclough, C. A., and Sawyer, C. H., *Endocrinology* **61**, 341 (1957).
7. Benoit, J., and Assenmacher, I., *J. physiol. (Paris)* **47**, 427 (1955).
8. Brooks, C. M., *Am. J. Physiol.* **120**, 544 (1937).
9. Brooks, C. M., *Am. J. Physiol.* **121**, 157 (1938).
10. Bunn, J. P., and Everett, J. W., *Proc. Soc. Exptl. Biol. Med.* **96**, 369 (1957).
11. Bustamente, M., *Arch. Psychiat. Nervenkrankh.* **115**, 419 (1942).
12. Christian, C. D., Markee, S. J., and Markee, J. E., *Anat. Record* **121**, 275 (1955).
13. Critchlow, B. V., *Anat. Record* **127**, 283 (1957).
14. Critchlow, B. V., *Endocrinology* **63**, 596 (1958).
15. Dell, P., *in* "The Reticular Formation of the Brain" (H. H. Jasper, L. D. Proctor, R. S. Knighton, W. C. Noshay, R. T. Costello, eds.), p. 365. Little, Brown, Boston, Massachusetts, 1958.

16. Dempsey, E. W., and Rioch, D. M., *J. Neurophysiol.* **2**, 9 (1939).
17. Dempsey, E. W., and Searles, H. F., *Endocrinology* **32**, 119 (1943).
18. Dey, F. L., *Endocrinology* **33**, 75 (1943).
19. Everett, J. W., *Endocrinology* **27**, 681 (1940).
20. Everett, J. W., *Ciba Colloquia Endocrinol.* **4**, 167 (1952).
21. Faure, J., *J. physiol. (Paris)* **48**, 529 (1956).
22. Faure, J., *Rev. neurol.* **95**, 490 (1956).
23. Fisher, C., Magoun, H. W., and Ranson, S. W., *Am. J. Obstet. Gynecol.* **36**, 1 (1938).
24. French, J. D., *J. Neurosurg.* **15**, 97 (1958).
25. Gastaut, H., *J. physiol. (Paris)* **44**, 431 (1952).
26. Green, J. D., *in* "Hypothalamic-Hypophysial Interrelationships" (W. S. Fields, R. Guillemin, C. A. Carton, eds.), p. 3, C. C Thomas, Springfield, Illinois, 1956.
27. Greep, R. O., and Barrnett, R. J., *Endocrinology* **49**, 172 (1951).
28. Greer, M. A., *Endocrinology* **53**, 380 (1953).
29. Hansel, W., and Trimberger, G. W., *J. Animal Sci.* **10**, 719 (1951).
30. Harris, G. W., *Proc. Roy. Soc.* **B122**, 374 (1937).
31. Harris, G. W., *J. Physiol. (London)* **107**, 418 (1948).
32. Harris, G. W., *J. Physiol. (London)* **111**, 347 (1950).
33. Haterius, H. O., and Derbyshire, A. J., *Am. J. Physiol.* **119**, 329 (1937).
34. Heape, W., *Proc. Roy. Soc.* **B76**, 260 (1905).
34a. Hillarp, N. Å., *Acta Endocrinol.* **2**, 11 (1949).
35. Hohlweg, W., and Junkmann, K., *Klin. Wochschr.* **11**, 321 (1932).
36. Jacobsohn, D., *Acta Endocrinol.* **17**, 187 (1954).
37. Kawakami, M., and Sawyer, C. H., *Physiologist* **1**, 48 (1957).
38. Kawakami, M., and Sawyer, C. H., *Federation Proc.* **17**, 83 (1958).
39. Koikegami, H., Yamada, T., and Usui, K., *Folia Psychiat. Neurol. Japon.* **8**, 7 (1954).
40. Kurotsu, T., Kurachi, K., and Ban, T., *Med. J. Osaka Univ.* **2**, 1 (1950).
41. Laqueur, G. L., McCann, S. M., Schreiner, L. H., Rosemberg, E., Rioch, D. M., and Anderson, E., *Endocrinology* **57**, 44 (1955).
42. Markee, J. E., Sawyer, C. H., and Hollinshead, W. H., *Endocrinology* **38**, 345 (1946).
43. Marshall, F. H. A., and Verney, E. B., *J. Physiol. (London)* **86**, 327 (1936).
44. Moore, C. R., and Price, D., *Am. J. Anat.* **50**, 13 (1932).
45. Moruzzi, G., and Magoun, H. W., *Electroencephalog. and Clin. Neurophysiol.* **1**, 455 (1949).
46. Nauta, W. J. H., *J. Comp. Neurol.* **104**, 247 (1956).
47. Nowakowski, H., *Acta Neuroveget. (Vienna)* **1**, 13 (1950).
48. Papez, J. W., *A.M.A. Arch. Neurol. Psychiat.* **38**, 725 (1937).
49. Porter, R. W., Cavanaugh, E. B., Critchlow, B. V., and Sawyer, C. H., *Am. J. Physiol.* **189**, 145 (1957).
50. Pribram, K. H., and Kruger, L., *Ann. N.Y. Acad. Sci.* **58**, 109 (1954).
51. Rinaldi, F., and Himwich, H. E., *A.M.A. Arch. Neurol. Psychiat.* **73**, 396 (1955).
52. Robison, B. L., and Sawyer, C. H., *Physiologist* **1**, 72 (1957).
53. Saul, G. D., and Sawyer, C. H., *Federation Proc.* **16**, 112 (1957).
54. Sawyer, C. H., *Federation Proc.* **11**, 138 (1952).

55. Sawyer, C. H., *Anat. Record* **124**, 358 (1956).
56. Sawyer, C. H., *in* "Physiological Triggers" (T. H. Bullock, ed.), p. 164. American Physiological Society, Washington, D.C., 1957.
57. Sawyer, C. H., *in* "The Reticular Formation of the Brain" (H. H. Jasper, L. D. Proctor, R. S. Knighton, W. C. Noshay, and R. T. Costello, eds.), p. 223. Little, Brown, Boston, Massachusetts, 1958.
58. Sawyer, C. H., *in* "Handbook of Neurophysiology" (H. W. Magoun, V. E. Hall, J. Field, eds.), American Physiological Society, Washington, D.C., in press, 1958.
59. Sawyer, C. H., Critchlow, B. V., and Barraclough, C. A., *Endocrinology* **57**, 345 (1955).
60. Sawyer, C. H., and Everett, J. W., *Proc. Soc. Exptl. Biol. Med.* **83**, 820 (1953).
61. Sawyer, C. H., Markee, J. E., and Everett, J. W., *J. Exptl. Zool.* **113**, 659 (1950).
62. Sawyer, C. H., Markee, J. E., and Townsend, B. F., *Endocrinology* **44**, 18 (1949).
63. Shealy, C. N., and Peele, T. L., *J. Neurophysiol.* **20**, 125 (1957).
64. Smith, P. E., and Engle, E. T., *Am. J. Anat.* **40**, 159 (1927).
65. Spatz, H., Diepen, R., and Gaupp, V., *Klin. Wochschr.* **26**, 127 (1948).
66. Westman, A., and Jacobsohn, D., *Acta Obstet. Gynecol. Scand.* **20**, 392 (1940).
67. Whitelaw, M. J., *J. Clin. Endocrinol. and Metabolism* **16**, 972 (1956).
68. Zarrow, M. X., and Bastian, J. W., *Proc. Soc. Exptl. Biol. Med.* **84**, 457 (1953).

Discussion

CHAIRMAN: C. G. HARTMAN

G. PINCUS: I was very much interested in the latter part of your talk in which you described the effects of progesterone. First of all, when you say that progesterone lowers the threshold during the first few hours after administration to the rabbit, and then later raises the threshold, I would like to know whether this is actually reflected in mating behavior of the animal. If so, I am a little puzzled because a rabbit is one of the easiest animals in the world to mate. I have seen rabbits mate readily under the influence of large doses of progesterone.

Secondly, I should like to know whether the progesterone effect is altered by the dosage of progesterone which you administer. Dr. Chang and I published some years ago data indicating that the length of time during which ovulation following copulation is inhibited appears to be proportionate to the dosage of progesterone. In other words, with a low dosage this would be a matter of perhaps just a few days; with a larger dosage it might extend into a matter of weeks, so that the dosage relationship is extremely interesting.

Finally, I would like to know something about the effect of exogenous estrogen on the thresholds when given either in combination with progesterone or administered alone.

C. H. SAWYER: Let's see if I can remember the questions in the sequence in which you asked them. For the first few hours following progesterone treatment the animal is very highly estrous, about as "hot" a rabbit as can be found, but by the next day it has cooled off so completely that it will not mate. With weak dosages of progesterone (2 mg. subcutaneously), by the end of the second day the effects are beginning to wear off and the rabbits recover to the point where they will mate.

With larger dosages the effect of blockade lasts much longer. Actually the classical effect of progesterone is one of blockade rather than facilitation. It was only because of the facilitatory effect of progesterone on ovulation in the rat that we started looking for such a facilitation in the rabbit. A few animals will mate after progesterone treatment, but they do not ovulate in response to this mating. Estrogen alone will gradually lower the threshold of these systems, but in the castrate ovariectomized female the dosages of estrogen we have used will often not bring the animal into estrous behavior. It requires progesterone to do this under those conditions. Larger dosages or more prolonged treatment with estrogen will bring the animal into heat without progesterone, but these larger dosages of estrogen, which facilitate estrous behavior, inhibit the pituitary, and they do raise the threshold of this rhinencephalic system.

G. PINCUS: How does this effect work? Just what do the steroids do? Do you have any hypothesis as to the mechanism of their action?

C. H. SAWYER: This question is getting one stage beyond the data. We thought that we were showing what they did to a certain extent by demonstrating that they definitely altered electrical thresholds in the nervous system. Furthermore, I might say that they can work directly on the nervous system. You may remember that Kent some ten years ago induced estrus in the hamster by injecting progesterone in the lateral ventricle of the brain. In our first experiments, which I didn't have time to discuss here, in acute animals we used intraventricular injections of progesterone, and they also lowered the threshold in this general manner for a short time after injection. The rise in threshold followed, but in acute experiments we were not sure that this wasn't due to deterioration of the physical condition of the animals. We did not trust the results and this led to the use of chronically implanted animals which could be kept for months and the same experiment repeated over and over again.

A. E. RAKOFF: I would like to mention, along the clinical line also, some studies which we have been doing on patients who have developed amenorrhea following an acute psychogenic trauma. These patients developed a number of different hormonal excretion patterns. The most common pattern which we have seen in these patients has been inhibition of follicle-stimulating hormone (FSH) and, of course, secondary inhibition of ovarian function. There are a number of other patterns, but this is the commonest pattern. The thing that has interested us in these patients is the inability of these patients to respond to gonadotropic stimulation. Another pattern which we have seen in a fewer number of patients has been the production of a, shall we say, menopausal type of syndrome following acute psychogenic trauma in which high FSH appears with absence of estrogen and progesterone. Still another pattern which one sees in some patients with psychogenic amenorrhea has been a sort of persistent estrous state. This usually occurs in women in whom the psychogenic trauma has been less acute—usually with environmental changes—where small amounts of FSH are secreted over a long period of time with estrogen and progesterone secretion. These patients will sometimes respond with ovulation to large amounts of corticotropin.

Finally, still another pattern has been seen in the patients who developed amenorrhea following emotional disturbance. This occurs most typically in a patient with pseudocyesis syndrome, where one gets estrogen and progesterone produced continuously in large amounts. I wonder if these different patterns can be correlated with some of the studies which you have demonstrated.

One other point that I would like to raise, also from a clinical standpoint, with regard to the observations that you have made has been the peculiar aberrations of smell which some women get in association with ovarian dysfunction. Occasionally we see a menopausal patient in whom one of her chief complaints is peculiar sensations of smell. We also see this occasionally in some younger women with menstrual disturbance.

C. H. SAWYER: These remarks are very interesting. In connection with the perception of odors, a French worker, Le Magnen, has shown that both in patients and in rats there is a differential sensitivity which can be demonstrated following estrogen treatment. Using musk and other odors he could show a remarkable difference in the threshold of perception of these odors. Apparently, the change is quite fantastic. This phenomenon might be simply an effect on thresholds in the olfactory rhinencephalic system in general.

The other observations on stimulatory and inhibitory mechanisms can only be subjects for hypotheses. It would appear that these are balanced mechanisms, some stimulatory and others inhibitory, and that one can activate a stimulatory mechanism by irritating it or stimulating it or by blocking or knocking out inhibitory effects and vice versa. What I am doing is restating that these conditions may result from differential stimulation or inhibition within the brain. I suspect that many of the—this is just a hunch—rhinencephalic areas may be fundamentally inhibitory. We have been checking them only for the loss of stimulatory effects from these lesions. From the experiments conducted so far, we cannot say whether the rabbit mates or ovulates more readily in the absence of these rhinencephalic pathways. I suspect that this may be the case. It is quite likely in view of the hypersexual phenomena following amygdaloid lesions. I should mention that there have been several reports of men becoming hypersexual after traumatic or surgical damage of the amygdala.

The Nervous System — Follicular Ripening, Ovulation, and Estrous Behavior

G. W. Harris

Department of Neuroendocrinology, Institute of Psychiatry, Maudsley Hospital, British Postgraduate Medical Federation, London University, London, England

The act of ovulation forms a link in the chain of events essential for the continuance of the species. At least three major processes are involved, or closely associated, with ovulation. These are (a) the ripening of a follicle, (b) the rupture of a follicle and discharge of an ovum, and (c) the synchronization of the behavioral response of the organism, so that at about the time of ovulation the female is receptive to the male and fertilization of the ovum is successfully achieved.

These three processes are related to the hypothalamus. The first two, the ripening of the follicle and the rupture of the follicle, are regulated by the gonadotropic secretion of the anterior pituitary gland which is under the control of the hypothalamus. The latter—the estrous behavior pattern of the female mammal—appears to be evoked by a sufficient concentration of ovarian hormones in the blood acting on some neural mechanism in the posterior hypothalamus. The data relevant to these functions will be considered in turn.

I. The Ripening of Ovarian Follicles

In many cyclically breeding animals the ripening of a follicle marks the start of the breeding season and also the start of each estrous cycle within the breeding season. Some twenty years ago, F. H. A. Marshall suggested that changes in environmental conditions, such as those of lighting, temperature, humidity, food supply, and so on, played a decisive role in timing the onset of the breeding season. He expressed his view of the physiological mechanisms involved by saying that since many of these "exteroceptive factors" seemed to act primarily on the nervous system, the nervous system and pituitary gland probably acted as liaison organs between the external environment on the one hand, and the ovaries and reproductive organs on the other. The sequence of events may then be represented: external environment → central nervous system → anterior pituitary gland (adenohypophysis)→ follicle-stimulating hormone in blood (FSH) → follicle maturation in ovary and estrogen secretion → activation of accessory organs of reproduction and estrous behavior.

The over-all effects of environmental and central neural factors over reproductive processes may be seen in an animal in which the above sequence has been interrupted at some point. This is most easily achieved by disconnecting the pituitary gland from the central nervous system—by cutting the pituitary stalk and placing some impervious barrier between the brain and gland or by transplanting the gland from its normal situation to a distant site in the body. A number of workers have studied the reproductive processes after dividing the pituitary stalk and placing a plate of waxed paper, polythene, or some other impenetrable material between the cut ends. Such studies have been made on the rat (45), rabbit (34), ferret (24, 25, 78, 79), bird (13, 75), and human (30, 62), and the general finding is that cessation of sexual cycles and atrophy of the reproductive organs follow such surgical procedures. It should be mentioned that the results of Thomson and Zuckerman (79) are not in agreement with those of the other workers. However, the above conclusion is strongly supported by the results derived from studies of pituitary transplants. Many workers have grafted anterior pituitary tissue into the eye, spleen, kidney, or other sites remote from the sella turcica and investigated the potentiality of this tissue to maintain gonadotropic secretion and ovarian activity. Apart from a few workers, whose results are open to doubt on the grounds that their "hypophysectomized" animals were incompletely operated, the general conclusion has been reached that such transplanted tissue secretes no detectable amounts of follicle-stimulating hormone (FSH) or luteinizing hormone (LH) but may still liberate lactogenic or luteotropic hormone (LTH). This work has been recently reviewed (26, 46), and reference may be made to these accounts for more detailed discussion. For the present purpose, the position may be summarized by saying that if the connections between the central nervous system and the pituitary gland are severed and steps taken to prevent regeneration of these connections, then follicular ripening in the ovary ceases.

In the past few years information regarding the part played by the hypothalamus in regulating FSH secretion has accrued from studies made on ferrets and rats by Donovan and van der Werff ten Bosch in the Department of Neuroendocrinology, Maudsley Hospital. The sexual season of the female ferret normally extends, in England, from March to September. The factors governing the increased secretion of FSH in the spring have been subjected to much study and, under laboratory conditions, it is clear that the duration and intensity of light plays an important role in this respect. Exposure of female ferrets to increased illumination during the winter months can rapidly bring them into full reproductive activity. Since Donovan and Harris (25) had shown the importance of the pituitary stalk in the control of FSH release in the ferret, it was thought that nerve fibers, passing from the optic chiasma or tract toward the median eminence of the tuber cinereum, might form a link in the mechanism underlying this light response in the ferret. Accordingly Donovan and van der Werff ten Bosch (27, 28, 81), using a stereotaxic machine, placed electrolytic lesions just behind the optic chiasma in anestrous ferrets. The animals were operated in January and placed in a wooden hut lit by daylight supplemented by electric light from 9:00 A.M. to 5:00 P.M. The plan of the experiment was to see whether the lesions, by interrupting the supposed neural path, delayed the onset of estrus the following spring. It was surprising therefore to observe the reverse effect: that the lesions were associated with accelerated estrus. Out of twenty animals so operated, nine came into heat within 3–4 weeks of placement of the lesions; that was at a time when thirteen other animals, subjected to sham operation, remained anestrous (Fig. 1). Four animals with lesions (two estrous and 2 anestrous) were killed in February. Naked-eye examination of the base of the brain showed that in the estrous animals the lesions were situated basally and just posterior to the optic chiasma. One anestrous animal had a more unilateral lesion, and in the other the lesion was not visible on the surface of the brain. The two estrous ferrets had been mated previous to death, with a testosterone-primed male, and one of them had ovulated. The results of this experiment are clear cut but the physiological basis underlying them is more obscure. Herbert and Zuckerman (55), in a preliminary communication, have recently advanced data indicating the possibility of a nonspecific effect of cerebral trauma. However, Donovan and van der Werff ten Bosch have, up to the present time, placed lesions in the anterior hypothalamus of twenty-seven ferrets of which eleven have developed estrus in winter, when thirty-two control animals (with lesions in other sites in the brain, or sham-operated) were all anestrous. At first it seemed possible that the lesions might be exerting a stimulating effect through pressure on surrounding structures. In parallel studies Donovan

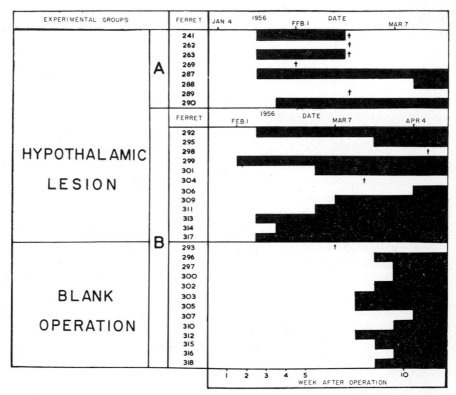

FIG. 1.   Diagram illustrating the time of onset of estrus in ferrets in which a lesion was placed in the anterior hypothalamus, and in blank-operated control animals. From Donovan and van der Werff ten Bosch, unpublished.

and van der Werff ten Bosch (28) found that prolonged periods (up to 12 weeks) of electrical stimulation of the anterior hypothalamus, by means of implanted electrodes, did not evoke estrus in the female ferret. In view of this finding it would seem that the lesion is exerting its effects by damage to some neural structure rather than by a stimulating action. In this case the most likely explanation is that the lesion has destroyed some nervous mechanism which normally inhibits the release of FSH.

   Lesions in the anterior hypothalamus, especially the paraventricular region, have been known for some years to abolish the estrous cycles of rhythmically ovulating forms and to result in a state of permanent estrus. Dey *et al.* (23) and Dey (22) noted the presence of permanent estrus, associated with hypertrophied genitalia and ovaries containing ripe follicles but no corpora lutea, in guinea pigs with such lesions. Later workers (9, 41, 57) have made similar observations on the rat. Anterior hypothalamic lesions then, may convert either the anestrous female ferret or the regularly cyclic female guinea pig or rat into a state of constant estrus. There is thus a superficial resemblance between the two phenomena. However in the case of the ferret, the animal is converted from a state of reproductive quiescence to one of apparently full activity, whereas in the guinea pig or rat the conversion is from one type of active state to another. Whatever is the final explanation, at the present time the situation in the ferret may be regarded as a release effect on FSH secretion, and in the guinea pig and rat as a blockading action on the rhythmic release of LH. A closer analogy with the results of hypothalamic lesions on ferrets may be drawn from the clinical cases in which precocious puberty occurs in young children in association with a hypothalamic tumor. [For recent reviews in this field, see Weinberger and Grant (82), Bauer (10), and Jolly (59).] The full changes of puberty may occur in these children before they reach the age of 2 years. Since the hypothalamic tumors are often small and localized, and do not impinge upon the pituitary, it has been suggested (82) that they bring about their effects by damaging some neural structure which normally inhibits the release of pituitary gonadotropin. In both the ferrets and these cases of pubertas praecox, the hypothalamic lesion results then in the transformation of a quiescent state, anestrous or prepubertal, to that of an active reproductive condition.

In view of such considerations as the above, Donovan and van der Werff ten Bosch studied the effect of anterior hypothalamic lesions on the reproductive organs of immature animals. It was found that young ferrets born in the months of June and July developed estrus the following January (about two months early) if a bilateral lesion was placed in the anterior hypothalamus when they were 5–6 months old (Donovan and van der Werff ten Bosch, personal communication). The same workers carried out a more detailed study in immature rats (29, 81). Anterior hypothalamic lesions were placed in nine 14–15-day-old female Lister rats and blank operations carried out on another eight. The animals were examined regularly and the day of opening of the vaginal orifice (which is an index of the occurrence of puberty in the rat) recorded. It was found that two lesioned rats reached puberty at 30 days of age and another four at 33 days of age. The vaginal orifice of one sham-operated animal also opened at 33 days. In a group of twenty-six normal animals only one had reached puberty at 33 days, while the average age for puberty was found to be 41 days (S.D. ± 3.7). The experimental animals were killed at 34–35 days of age, and examination of the reproductive tract showed that ovulation had occurred in five of the lesioned animals and in only one control operated animal. A further study, by the same two workers, using a different strain of (albino) rats, has substantiated these results. Again sexual maturation was advanced significantly in a group of twenty-four animals with lesions in the anterior hypothalamus, as compared with fifteen blank-operated controls or with animals with lesions in the posterior hypothalamus. In this latter study the animals that showed precocious puberty were kept alive and their estrous cycles followed by the vaginal smear technique. It was observed that they fell into two categories. One group showed regular cycles, mated, became pregnant, and underwent normal parturition and lactation; whilst the other group exhibited constant estrus and failed to become pregnant. In view of this, it was pointed out that the constant estrus seen by several workers in adult rats with anterior hypothalamic lesions, and the precocious puberty exhibited by these young rats, may not be related to identical mechanisms. It should be mentioned that Dr. E. M. Bogdanove (personal communication) has also obtained an advancement of puberty in the rat after placing lesions in the anterior hypothalamus.

Several points on the above experiments and results require comment. The fact that puberty may be advanced in the rat by about a week by anterior hypothalamic lesions seems in a general way to be a similar phenomenon to the precocious puberty observed in clinical cases in association with a hypothalamic tumor. In the human, though, puberty is in many cases advanced to a greater degree than that seen in the experimental animal. This is especially so in those cases in which a developmental abnormality (a hamartoma) is found in the hypothalamic region, when puberty may occur as early as 1 to 2 years of age. It may be argued that a hamartoma represents a lesion originating during fetal life and that experimental lesions placed during the same period might give similar results. So far as is known this experiment has not been tried. A further difference between the clinical and experimental results lies in the site of the lesion. In the human the tumor is often located in the posterior part of the tuber cinereum or in the region of the mammillary bodies (82), whereas the effective site in the rat seems to be in the chiasmal region. Since pituitary stalk section or pituitary transplantation results in a greatly reduced FSH release, and since a localized lesion in the anterior hypothalamus results in secretion of FSH at a time when it would otherwise not occur, it is necessary to suppose that the hypothalamus exerts a dual effect on the pituitary release of FSH, one excitatory and the other inhibitory. The lesions which result in early estrus or puberty may be supposed to damage the inhibitory mechanism, thus resulting in a release effect on the pituitary. If the pituitary stalk acts as a "final common path" between the central nervous system and pituitary and endocrine system (47), this view would be in keeping with many other examples well known in neurophysiology. The effect of spinal influences on anterior horn cells may be quoted as an analogy, in that an upper motor neurone lesion results in increased muscle tone whereas division of the final common path itself results in loss of all activity in the denervated muscles.

II. The Rupture of Ovarian Follicles

In generally accepted terms of pituitary hormone secretion, the process of ovulation seems to require for its initiation a sudden increase in the secretion of luteinizing hormone (LH) against a background of FSH secretion. This pattern of pituitary secretion, with resultant ovulation, occurs spontaneously in many mammals, but in some forms (most birds, the rabbit, ferret, cat, ground squirrel, short-tailed shrew, and mink) is triggered by a sensory stimulus, usually supplied by the presence of the male and coitus.

Experimental work on the nervous processes involved in the mechanism of LH release and ovulation has usually taken one of two forms: (a) the investigation of procedures calculated to result in ovulation in those forms normally requiring some external stimulus, and (b) the investigation of procedures calculated to blockade ovulation in those forms normally ovulating spontaneously. In the former group, the experimental animal of choice has often been the rabbit. Heape (54) first reported that ovulation in the rabbit normally occurs some 10 hours after coitus. Early experiments showed that this response was not due to absorption of semen from the female genital tract, and further work demonstrated that such ovulation could occur in transplanted ovaries (1, 35) and that hypophysectomy performed within an hour of coitus prevented any subsequent ovulation (31). The hypothesis then became current that coitus excited some nervous reflex which evoked discharge of pituitary gonadotropic hormone and so follicular rupture. The study of Marshall and Verney (66) gave support for this view. They found that diffuse electrical shocks applied to the head or lumbar spinal cord in the rabbit resulted in ovulation. Since the hypothalamus is the part of the central nervous system in most direct anatomical connection with the pituitary gland, it was decided, at Marshall's suggestion, to apply localized electrical stimuli to various regions of this basal area of the brain to see if it was possible to stimulate some part of the reflex path normally activated by coitus. In these early experiments (42), stimulation was performed with the aid of a stereotaxic machine in rabbits anesthetized with ether. The circuit, frequency of stimulation, and pulse wave form was similar to that used by Hess (56). It was found that stimulation in the posterior hypothalamus, median eminence, or anterior pituitary gland itself, might result in ovulation or the formation of hemorrhagic and cystic follicles. Similar results were reported by Haterius and Derbyshire (53). Some nine years later the problem was reinvestigated by two groups of workers who both reached the somewhat surprising conclusion that, whereas electrical stimulation of the hypothalamus evoked ovulation in the rabbit, stimulation of the pituitary gland itself failed to do so. Markee *et al.* (65), working on animals anesthetized with ether, stimulated the pituitary by a pharyngeal or temporal approach and the hypothalamus through the superior orbital fissure. They found that stimulation of the pituitary did not result in ovulation unless there were signs of spread of the stimulus, whereas stimulation of the hypothalamus at a lower voltage resulted in ovulation in three out of four animals. Harris (44) used the remote-control method for stimulation. This technique consists of implanting a coil subcutaneously in an animal, with electrodes soldered to the ends of the coil and their tips implanted in the site to be stimulated. After recovery from the initial operation, stimulation may be performed by placing the animal, and contained coil, in an electromagnetic field and so inducing the required voltage. The main advantages of this procedure are that the unanesthetized animal may be used and that the experiment may be repeated several times in the same animal. Using this method the effects of stimulating different areas in the hypothalamus and hypophysis for varying periods of time were investigated, and it was found that stimuli applied to the anterior part of the median eminence for as short a period as 3 minutes might be followed by a full ovulatory response, whereas similar stimuli applied to the anterior pituitary gland itself for periods up to $7\frac{1}{2}$ hours were not followed by any ovarian response. It was also observed that stimulation of the posterolateral part of the median eminence was effective in evoking ovulation. The evidence, then, indicated that some part of a nervous reflex path, normally excited by coitus, traversed the hypothalamus to stimulate, in some manner, the release of luteinizing hormone from the adenohypophysis.

The method by which the stimulus is transmitted from the hypothalamus to the anterior pituitary gland has received much attention, and the following facts seem pertinent. First, the pituitary stalk seems to be the anatomical structure involved, since section of the stalk with steps taken to prevent regeneration, or pituitary transplantation to a distant site, results in ovarian atrophy. Secondly, the pituitary stalk contains two prominent structures linking the hypothalamus and gland. The hypothalamo-hypophyseal nerve tract passes from the hypothalamus to the gland, to end, very largely, in the neural lobe. Once cut, this tract does not regenerate. The hypophyseal portal vessels carry blood from capillaries in the median eminence of the tuber cinereum to the sinusoids of the pars distalis. It has been established that a blood supply derived from these vessels exerts a profound effect on anterior pituitary activity, and the hypothesis put forward that the hypothalamus maintains and regulates anterior pituitary activity by means of a neurohumoral mechanism acting through this vascular system (see 46). The evidence relating to this view is summarized below.

(a)   The paucity or lack of a nerve supply to the pars distalis. There is evidence that the anterior pituitary is *not* regulated by a secretomotor nerve supply, since the majority of workers find few or no nerve fibers in the gland (38, 72, 84). This question has recently been discussed in detail (26, 46).

(b)   The hypophyseal portal vessels form a very constant link between the tuber cinereum and the anterior pituitary in all vertebrates from amphibians to man (38, 69, 70, 85). Analogous vessels are found also in cyclostomes and fishes. These vessels have been observed, microscopically, to drain blood from the median eminence and conduct it to the anterior pituitary in amphibians, rats, dogs, and mice (37, 39, 58, 80, 86). From the anatomical point of view these vessels form the only direct and constant system linking the central nervous system and adenohypophysis.

(c)   Electrical stimulation of the hypothalamus and hypophysis. As described above, electrical stimulation of the hypothalamus has been found by two different groups of workers to excite release of luteinizing hormone and ovulation in the rabbit, whereas direct stimulation of the pars distalis is ineffective in this respect. [Similar findings have been reported in studies made on the secretion of adrenocorticotropic and thyrotropic hormones (20, 50, 51).] Such a finding indicates that the effect of hypothalamic stimulation is not transmitted to the anterior pituitary by a direct nerve supply, for, if such were the case, discharge of anterior pituitary hormones should follow stimulation of any nerve fibers present in the gland. Direct stimulation of the neural lobe causes release of posterior pituitary hormones, as does stimulation of the hypothalamus (43).

(d)   Section of the pituitary stalk. Simple section of the pituitary stalk is followed by varied effects on reproductive functions, ranging from loss of estrous cycles and gonadal atrophy to normal sexual functions. Section of the stalk, or vessels of the stalk, with the placement of an impermeable barrier between the cut ends, has been found to lead constantly to loss of reproductive activity in the rat (45), ferret (25, see however, 79), rabbit (34), bird (13, 75), and human (62, Eckles and Ehni, personal communication; McCullagh and Norman, personal communication). In experiments in which reproductive activity returned following *simple* stalk section, it was observed that regeneration of the hypophyseal portal vessels had occurred across the site of the cut, thus re-establishing a path from the tuber cinereum to the anterior pituitary gland [rat (45), ferret (25), rabbit (34)]. It may be said then, that complete and permanent section of the pituitary stalk leads to an atrophic condition of the reproductive system. If, however, vascular regeneration occurs across the site of the section, normal gonadotropic secretion may be resumed. The fact that loss of a hypophyseal portal blood supply to the pars distalis results in loss of function of the gland may be explained in several ways. Barrnett and Greep (8, 40) suggested that stalk section leads to ischemic necrosis and loss of sufficient anterior pituitary tissue to account for the consequent hypopituitary state. That this is not so is demonstrated by the fact that studies on partially hypophysectomized animals have shown that only 30% of the volume of the normal pars distalis maintains apparently normal function and that 10% maintains some ovarian, thyroidal, and adrenal cortical activity [rat (76), dog (36), rabbit (17)]. This data, taken in conjunction with the fact that after stalk section 70–95% of normal anterior pituitary tissue is well vascularized and maintained [duck (13), ferret (25), rabbit (18)], shows that loss of anterior pituitary activity after stalk section is not due to ischemic necrosis and glandular atrophy. The mechanism by which the hypophyseal portal vessels maintain and regulate anterior pituitary secretion of gonadotropic hormone is uncertain. It seems most reasonable, at the present time, to assume that some hormonal substance(s), liberated by nerve endings in the median eminence, is transported by these vessels to the pars distalis to activate or inhibit the cells of the gland.

(e)   Pituitary transplantation. The conclusive proof of the importance of the portal vessels for pituitary function has come from the study of pituitary transplants. Numerous workers have shown that anterior pituitary tissue transplanted to a site remote from the hypothalamus in hypophysectomized animals fails to maintain the reproductive organs. Critical review of the few accounts reporting different findings reveals that in most of these there is reason to doubt the completeness of the original hypophysectomy. When it became apparent, from experiments on pituitary stalk section, that a blood supply derived from the hypophyseal portal system was of paramount importance to anterior pituitary function, it was decided (48) to compare the effects of pituitary transplants placed outside the sella turcica, but in the subarachnoid space under the hypothalamus, with those in the subarachnoid space under the temporal lobe of the brain. The former transplants were found to become revascularized by the portal system of vessels and to maintain normal gonadotropic functions (as shown by regular estrous cycles, pregnancy, parturition, and milk secretion), whereas the latter resulted in gonadal atrophy.

The precise and clear-cut experiments of Nikitovitch-Winer and Everett (68) have recently confirmed and extended the above results. These workers hypophysectomized female rats and transplanted the pars distalis to the kidney capsule. No estrous cycles were observed in these animals. The grafts were then removed from the kidney capsule, and, by the transtemporal route, placed either under the median eminence of the tuber cinereum or under the temporal lobe of the cerebral hemisphere. It was found that the animals with transplants under the median eminence, in which the tissue was mainly vascularized by the hypophyseal portal vessels, regained normal reproductive function as shown by cyclic estrous changes, pregnancy, and microscopically normal ovaries, uteri, and vaginas. On the other hand the animals with transplants under the temporal lobe of the brain remained anestrous during life and were found to possess completely atrophic reproductive organs. Nikitovitch-Winer and Everett conclude: "This experiment furnishes strong additional evidence that to function normally the pars distalis must receive some humoral stimulus from the hypothalamus by way of the hypophysial portal vessels."

In the above sections, examples have been described illustrating the control exerted by the hypothalamus via the hypophyseal portal vessels over the anterior pituitary secretion of FSH and LH. The relationship between the central nervous and endocrine systems is one of reciprocity. Just as the nervous system maintains and regulates endocrine function, so do the hormones react back on the nervous system to modify its activity and affect thereby the behavioral reactions of the organism. For example, the ovarian hormones exert actions on the central nervous sys-

tem, so that the behavior of the female mammal changes from aggression
to reception at precisely the appropriate time in the sexual cycle, related
to the time of ovulation, for successful fertilization to occur. The central
nervous system which mediates these behavioral changes must be looked
upon as a target organ for the ovarian hormones, and the overt behavior
of the animal may be taken as an indication of the response of the central
mechanism to hormonal stimulation.

III. The Action of Gonadal Hormones on the Central Nervous System and Behavior

There is little clear evidence regarding the factors controlling sexual
activity in primates. It has been known from times of antiquity that
castration before puberty reduces or abolishes adult sexual behavior.
In the adult the position is less clear. Ford and Beach (33), who summarize the data regarding ovariectomy in primates, state that the ovariectomized adult female chimpanzee shows few signs of desire for inter-
course, but that ovariectomized women may show as much erotic behavior after, as before, operation. These same authors also state that
castration of male primates often produces no diminution in the capacity
to mate or (in men) to experience orgasm. From the fact that removal
of the gonads from the adult human does not necessarily result in
diminished sexual activity, it may be suggested that learning from experience plays a dominant role in regulating this in man, and that
conclusions drawn from laboratory experiments should be regarded
cautiously in regard to their clinical application. Whilst this is undoubtedly true, it is likely that the basic (? diencephalic) mechanisms
concerned with reproductive behavior are the same in both subprimate
and primate forms, and that when sufficient data have accumulated regarding these mechanisms in experimental animals, useful application
of this information may be made in medical practice. In the discussion
which follows, attention is given to studies on the sexual behavior of
subprimate female mammals.

Various possible ways by which an increase in the concentration of
ovarian hormones in the blood may result in estrous behavior have been
postulated (11). The two most likely views are that estrogens activate
peripheral receptor mechanisms, and thus the sensory input to the central
nervous system, or act directly on some integrative function of the central
nervous system itself. The former view is generally held to be unlikely
on the grounds that removal of, or denervation of, the genital organs
and tracts do not inhibit estrous behavior or diminish sexual aggression
(2, 4, 16, 73). The evidence indicates that estrogens exert a direct action

on some neural mechanism in the brain, which then integrates lower spinal and brain stem reflexes into a complex behavioral pattern.

The site of such an integrative region has been investigated in several ways. The behavioral responses of ovariectomized animals primed with estrogen, or of animals in natural estrus, have been studied after making transection at different levels through the cerebrospinal axis and after making localized lesions in various parts of the brain. More recently, studies of the effects of locally applied estrogens to various sites in the brain in ovariectomized animals, of the ability of different neural sites to concentrate radioactive estrogens, and of changes in electrical activity in the hypothalamus to mechanical stimulation of the genitalia, have yielded data relating to this problem. The results of such studies will be briefly summarized.

A. The Spinal and Decerebrate Animal

Although the autonomic aspects of coitus (erection and ejaculation) may be obtained in the spinal animal, no movements (involving skeletal muscles) that resemble those observed during coitus, have been seen. Dempsey and Rioch (21) and Bromiley and Bard (14) studied chronic spinal guinea pigs and cats, before and after treatment with ovarian hormones. In neither case was any sign of normal estrous behavior observed in the spinal preparation. Similar results were obtained by the same workers on decerebrate animals. Maes (63) suggested that the failure to observe sexual reflexes in decerebrate preparations was due to the muscular rigidity of the animals. However Bromiley and Bard (14) point out that this rigidity was not sufficient to abolish other (nonsexual) reflex responses. It appears then that an area in the upper midbrain or above is involved.

B. The Decorticate Animal

Many studies have shown that removal of the cerebral cortex does not prevent the occurrence of normal estrous behavior [cats (3, 5, 6, 7), guinea pigs (21), rabbits (16), rats (19)]. The rhinencephalon and parts of the striatum were also removed in some of these studies. In acute experiments on guinea pigs, Dempsey and Rioch (21) found that a transection through the brain, passing from the rostral end of the mammillary body did not abolish estrous reflexes, but that if the mammillary bodies were included all such responses were abolished. Attention then became focused on the upper midbrain and hypothalamus.

C. Hypothalamic Lesions and Estrous Behavior

Magoun and Bard (64) reported that in some cases relatively large lesions in the hypothalamus of cats abolished the normal behavioral responses otherwise elicited by large doses of estradiol benzoate. Brookhart *et al.* (15) found that hypothalamic lesions in guinea pigs might prevent the behavioral estrous response previously elicitable in the same animals by treatment with estrogen and progesterone. Symonds (77) records a loss of libido and potency following injuries to the floor of the third ventricle in man. Sawyer and Robison (74) have briefly reported on their findings that lesions of the posterior hypothalamus in female rabbits, or of the anterior hypothalamus in female cats, result in loss of sexual behavior. The difficulty in interpretation of this type of study lies in the fact that hypothalamic lesions may result in profound general disturbances that in themselves could possibly affect patterns of overt behavior.

D. Localized Application of Estrogens to the Central Nervous System

A local effect of hormones on different sites in the central nervous system has been demonstrated on a few occasions. Kollros (61) and Weiss and Rossetti (83) demonstrated a local effect of thyroxine on the maturation of nerve cells and reflex responses in the tadpole. Somewhat similar studies of behavioral changes induced by local application of sex hormones to the brain have been made. Kent and Liberman (60) showed that introduction of progesterone into the lateral ventricle of estrone-primed hamsters resulted in psychic estrus. The doses of progesterone used were insufficient to produce effects when administered subcutaneously. Fisher (32) also reported acute behavioral effects in male rats when solutions of sex hormones were injected into the hypothalamus.

In an attempt to investigate the part played by the hypothalamus in the neurological mechanism underlying sexual behavior, Harris (unpublished observations) implanted minute fragments of various stilbestrol esters in different regions of the hypothalamus of ovariectomized rabbits. The fatty acid esters of stilbestrol are waxy substances that melt on heating. In these experiments the tip of a fine platinum wire was dipped in a molten ester so that a thin film of the ester covered the end of the wire. This was then implanted in the brain by a stereotaxic technique. When the animals were killed some weeks later, the wire was removed from the brain and the film of ester found to be still adherent. The rate of absorption of the stilbestrol can be controlled by varying the surface area of the implanted fragment and by varying the ester used. The rate of absorption varies inversely with the length of the fatty acid side chain. Although some of the implanted rabbits showed mating behavior when placed with the male, it was found that ovariectomized rabbits without implants would occasionally accept the male, so that no conclusion could be drawn from these experiments. Beach (12) has also noted that ovariectomized rabbits may accept the male, and this fact places the female rabbit in an exceptional position amongst the subprimate female mammals. The study was therefore repeated on the female cat (see 52). In the first part of the investigation (67) the appearance of the vaginal smear of the normal cat was compared with the behavior pattern at different stages of the estrous cycle. It was found that the smear was invariably cornified at the time of the first mating in a cycle. In confirmation of earlier work by Bard (5), it was found that the estrous behavioral response of the female cat disappears after ovariectomy. In one hundred animals studied for periods up to six months after ovariectomy, all signs of an estrous response disappeared within 24 hours of operation and did not reappear. *Systemic* (subcutaneous) administration of varying doses of estradiol or stilbestrol dipropionate to spayed cats was found to induce vaginal cornification and mating behavior in a predictable manner. At a low dose level (3–12 µg. stilbestrol dipropionate per day) the latent period to mating exceeded 7 days and a fully cornified vaginal smear always preceded the mating response. At doses of less than 3 µg. per day, no mating occurred, although in some cats the vaginal smear showed persistent cornification. With this basis of information, the second part of the investigation was undertaken (49). This was designed to compare the effects of implants of stilbestrol esters in the hypothalamus and other sites in the brain and subcutaneously on both the behavioral responses and on the reproductive tract (including the vaginal smear) of ovariectomized cats. It seemed from the data presented above that if mating behavior was elicited by the locally applied stilbestrol ester in the absence of estrous changes in the pelvic reproductive organs, then there would be good grounds for ascribing the behavioral changes to a local action of the stilbestrol in the central nervous system. The responses of sixty spayed female cats have been studied. Preliminary experiments showed that the butyrate ester had a rate of absorption that was suitable for the purpose and that the posterior hypothalamus appeared to be an effective site. Where possible littermate pairs bred in the laboratory, spayed for the same duration, treated in exactly the same way with regard to mating tests, diet, conditions of illumination, and day of operation, were used for control purposes. The following results were obtained:

Subcutaneous implants. Mating does not occur in animals carrying a single subcutaneous implant of the order of 1.0 mg. of stilbestrol dibutyrate fused on a needle tip. With multiple subcutaneous implants mating was observed, in association with estrous changes in the reproductive organs.

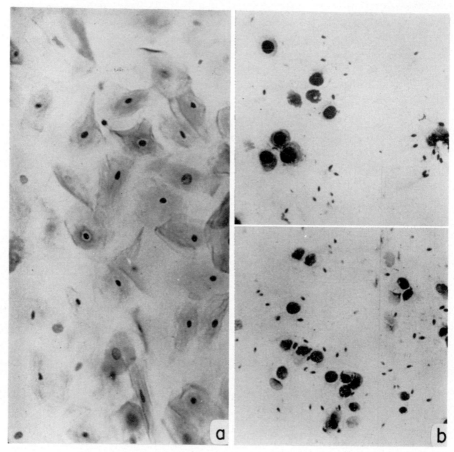

FIG. 2.   Vaginal smears of two cats.   a.   Typical estrous smear with cornified cells. Magnification: × 320.   b.   Anestrous smear of cat bearing a stilbestrol dibutyrate implant in the posterior hypothalamus. The smear was taken shortly after mating had occurred. Note the small dark nuclei of the sperm heads. Magnification: ×365. From Harris and Michael, unpublished.

Posterior hypothalamic implants.   Table I shows the behavioral effects produced by stilbestrol dibutyrate implants in the posterior hypothalamus; full mating resulted in thirteen of the seventeen animals studied. Nine out of the thirteen responsive animals had reproductive tracts in-

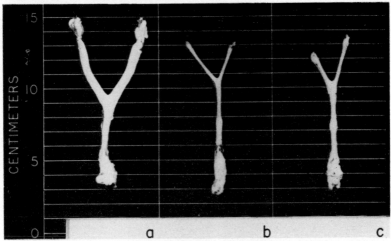

FIG. 3. Photographs of the genital tract of three cats and their behavioral response to estrogen implants at different sites. a. Normal female cat killed during its first estrous period; mating. Body weight, 2800 gm.; genital tract weight, 6.5 gm. b. Female cat (spayed at 14 weeks) that had a stilbestrol dibutyrate implant (0.1 mg.) in the posterior hypothalamus for 78 days. This animal had been mating for the last 36 days previous to killing. Body weight, 2500 gm.; genital tract weight, 2.4 gm. c. Female cat (spayed at 21 weeks) that had a stilbestrol dibutyrate implant (0.1 mg.) in the cerebellum for 67 days. This animal persistently refused the male. Body weight, 2870 gm., genital tract weight, 2.8 gm. From Harris and Michael, unpublished.

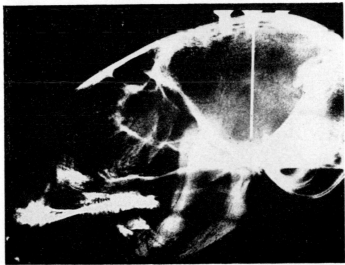

FIG. 4. Lateral X-ray photograph of the skull of a cat with implanted needle bearing stilbestrol. The screws, to which the needle is fixed with dental cement, are visible in the vault of the skull. Magnification: ×2. From Harris and Michael, unpublished.

distinguishable from those of anestrous control animals (as shown by
vaginal smears, total genital tract weight and endometrial development)
(see Figs. 2 and 3). Figures 4–6 demonstrate the technique and an effective implant site in the mammillary region in the posterior hypothalamus.

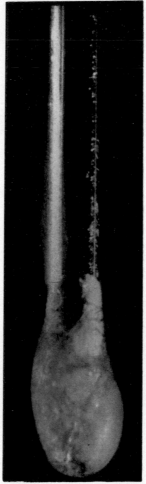

FIG. 5. Photomicrograph of a steel needle bearing a coating of stilbestrol
dibutyrate on the tip. Magnification: ×18. From Harris and Michael, unpublished.

Implants in other neural sites. Table II shows the behavioral effects
observed in nineteen animals with implants in the cerebellum, preoptic
region, white matter of the frontal lobe, head of the caudate nucleus,
thalamus, and amygdaloid nucleus. In only one animal was mating

observed, and in this cat histological study of the brain showed the implant (intended for the cerebellum) was misplaced and situated in the cisterna magna.

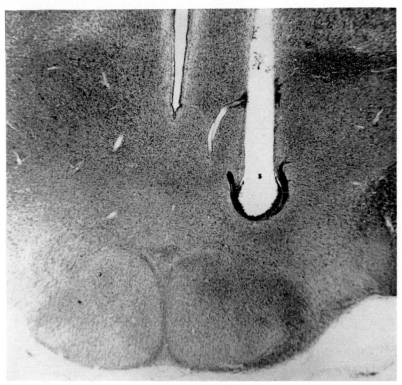

FIG. 6.   Photomicrograph of a transverse section of the hypothalamus of a cat. Note the site of the implant just dorsal to the mammillary bodies. 100 μ thick; Weigert's hematoxylin. Magnification: ×13. From Harris and Michael, unpublished.

These results show then that stilbestrol dibutyrate implants in the posterior hypothalamus can evoke mating behavior in the spayed cat, in the absence of any effects on the reproductive organs. It is reasonable to conclude that this is due to a local effect on some neural mechanisms existing in this region.

E.   CONCENTRATION OF RADIOACTIVE ESTROGENS IN NEURAL STRUCTURES

With the possibility in mind that a hormone may become locally concentrated in a neural structure upon which it exerts a specific effect, Glascock and Harris (unpublished, see 46) studied the localization of tritiated hexestrol in the brain of ovariectomized rabbits. No concentration of this substance was found in different parts of the brain, or pituitary gland, but equally no concentration was found in such structures as the mammary gland and endometrium, upon which hexestrol is known to exert an effect. The method of assay used in this investigation was to excise a measured weight of the structure under investigation and to estimate, by a counter technique, the radioactivity of the sample. This may account for the difference in these results and those of J. B. Trunnell (Anderson Hospital, University of Texas), who has studied (personal

TABLE I

EFFECT UPON BEHAVIOR PRODUCED BY STILBESTROL DIBUTYRATE IMPLANTS IN THE POSTERIOR HYPOTHALAMUS

| Cat | Weight of implant (mg.) | Duration (days) | | Result |
		To mating	Of mating	
31	0.22	4	3	Mating
32	0.19	7	55	occurred
33	0.05	9	41	in each
34	0.40	14	62	case
35	0.25	14	15	(cats
36	0.10	41	36	31 to 43).
37	0.40	42	34	
38	0.80	54	26	
39	0.15	63	4	
40	0.15	75	1	
41	0.11	106	3	
42	0.13	15	1	
43	0.23	14	3	
44	0.11	121		No mating
45	0.075	115		No mating
46	0.13	136		No mating
47	0.185	90		No mating

communication) the localization of systemically administered C^{14}-labeled estradiol in the brain of mice, by autoradiography. This latter worker found the radioactive estrogen became concentrated in an area of the midbrain somewhat caudal to the mammillary bodies, in the ventral part of the midbrain.

F. ELECTRICAL ACTIVITY OF THE HYPOTHALAMUS WITH GENITAL STIMULATION

Porter et al. (71) investigated the electrical changes in the hypothalamic and septal regions of anesthetized and curarized cats when glass-rod stimulation of the vagina was applied. A reproducible electroencephalographic pattern in the anterior and lateral hypothalamus around the medial forebrain bundle was recorded in response to this stimulus during estrus (natural or artificial), though not in anestrus. This electrical change may be correlated with one, or both, of two responses. Artificial stimulation of the vagina of the cat is known to result in nervous reflex release of ovulating hormone from the adenohypophysis and is also

TABLE II

BEHAVIORAL EFFECT OF STILBESTROL DIBUTYRATE IMPLANTS AT DIFFERENT INTRACRANIAL SITES

Site	Cat	Weight of implant (mg.)	Duration (days)	Result
Cerebellar hemisphere	12	0.10	67	No mating
	13	0.10	58	No mating
	14	0.16	126	No mating
	15	0.20	50	No mating
	16	0.21	90	No mating
	17	0.22	54	No mating
	18	0.32	75	No mating
	19	0.20	30	Mating
Preoptic region	20	0.25	28	No mating
	21	0.26	57	No mating
	22	0.30	47 (died)	No mating
	23	0.285	65	No mating
Frontal white matter	24	0.21	30	No mating
Head of caudate nucleus	25	0.235	62	No mating
	26	0.220	32	No mating
D M nucleus of thalamus	27	0.16	70	No mating
	28	0.214	62	No mating
Amygdaloid complex	29	0.20	69	No mating
	30	0.30	50	No mating

known to result in various aspects of sexual behavior (the afterreaction) normally associated with coitus in the male. It is possible, or even probable, that the neural mechanisms for both these phenomena are closely linked, and on this basis the data of the above workers may be presented as relating to a neural focus of sexual behavior.

IV. Summary

The possibility exists that there is in the hypothalamus a nervous mechanism which integrates brain stem and spinal reflexes into the pattern of behavior normally concerned with mating in the female cat.

Such an integrating mechanism would appear to be sensitized by a certain threshold concentration of estrogen in the circulating blood. Under these conditions various sensory stimuli (visual, olfactory, tactile), normally derived from the presence of an acceptable male, play upon this integrating area and so result in the stereotyped pattern of overt behavior typical of the female cat when mating.

If the above thesis is true, then there would be a dual relationship between the hypothalamic region of the brain and the endocrine system. First, the hypothalamus, through the control it exerts over the pituitary gland, exerts a major effect over much endocrine activity. And secondly, the hormones derived from the more peripherally situated endocrine glands, would in turn "feed back" onto the hypothalamus (and other areas of the brain) to influence central nervous activity and so behavior. From the point of view of ovulation and fertilization, processes of major importance to the survival of the species, the hypothalamic-endocrine relationships seem of basic significance.

References

1. Asdell, S. A., Studies in the physiology of lactation. Dissertation, Cambridge University, England (1926).
2. Ball, J., *J. Comp. Psychol.* **18**, 419 (1934).
3. Bard, P., *Psychol. Rev.* **41**, 424 (1934).
4. Bard, P., *Am. J. Physiol.* **113**, P5 (1935).
5. Bard, P., *Am. J. Physiol.* **116**, 4 (1936).
6. Bard, P., *Research Publs. Assoc. Research Nervous Mental Disease* **19**, 190 (1939).
7. Bard, P., and Rioch, D. M., *Bull. Johns Hopkins Hosp.* **60**, 73 (1937).
8. Barrnett, R. J., and Greep, R. O., *Endocrinology* **49**, 337 (1951).
9. Barrnett, R. J., and Mayer, J., *Anat. Record* **118**, 374 (1954).
10. Bauer, H. G., *J. Clin. Endocrinol.* **14**, 13 (1954).
11. Beach, F. A., "Hormones and Behavior." Hoeber, New York, 1948.
12. Beach, F. A., *Ciba Colloquia Endocrinol.* **3**, 59 (1952).
13. Benoit, J., and Assenmacher, I., *Arch. anat. microscop. et morphol. exptl.* **42**, 334 (1953).
14. Bromiley, R. B., and Bard, P. (1940). Cited by P. Bard, *Research Publs. Assoc. Research Nervous Mental Disease* **20**, 551 (1940).
15. Brookhart, J. M., Dey, F. L., and Ranson, S. W., *Proc. Soc. Exptl. Biol. Med.* **44**, 61 (1940).
16. Brooks, C. M., *Am. J. Physiol.* **120**, 544 (1937).
17. Campbell, H. J., Submitted to *J. Physiol. (London)* (1958).
18. Campbell, H. J., and Harris, G. W., *J. Physiol. (London)* **136**, 333 (1957).
19. Davis, C. D., *Am. J. Physiol.* **127**, 374 (1939).
20. de Groot, J., and Harris, G. W., *J. Physiol. (London)* **111**, 335 (1950).
21. Dempsey, E. W., and Rioch, D. M., *J. Neurophysiol.* **2**, 9 (1939).
22. Dey, F. L., *Endocrinology* **33**, 75 (1943).

23. Dey, F. L., Fisher, C., Berry, C. M., and Ranson, S. W., *Am. J. Physiol.* **129**, 39 (1940).
24. Donovan, B. T., and Harris, G. W., *Nature* **174**, 503 (1954).
25. Donovan, B. T., and Harris, G. W., *J. Physiol.* (*London*) **131**, 102 (1956).
26. Donovan, B. T., and Harris, G. W., *in* "Marshall's Physiology of Reproduction" (A. S. Parkes, ed.), Vol. 1, Chapter 10.3. Part 2. Longmans, Green, New York, 1958. In press.
27. Donovan, B. T., and van der Werff ten Bosch, J. J., *J. Physiol.* (*London*) **132**, 57P (1956).
28. Donovan, B. T., and van der Werff ten Bosch, J. J., *Proc. Intern. Congr. on Animal Reproduction, 3rd Congr., Cambridge* **1**, 75 (1956).
29. Donovan, B. T., and van der Werff ten Bosch, J. J., *Nature* **178**, 745 (1956).
30. Dugger, G. See discussion of paper by B. S. Ray and O. H. Pearson, *Ann. Surg.* **144**, 394 (1956).
31. Fee, A. R., and Parkes, A. S., *J. Physiol.* (*London*) **67**, 383 (1929).
32. Fisher, A. E., *Science* **124**, 228 (1956).
33. Ford, C. S., and Beach, F. A., "Patterns of Sexual Behavior." Eyre & Spottiswoode, London, 1952.
34. Fortier, C., Harris, G. W., and McDonald, I. R., *J. Physiol.* (*London*) **136**, 344 (1957).
35. Friedman, M. H., *Am. J. Physiol.* **89**, 438 (1929).
36. Ganong, W. F., and Hume, D. M., *Endocrinology* **59**, 293 (1956).
37. Green, J. D., *Anat. Record* **99**, 21 (1947).
38. Green, J. D., *Am. J. Anat.* **88**, 225 (1951).
39. Green, J. D., and Harris, G. W., *J. Physiol.* (*London*) **108**, 359 (1949).
40. Greep, R. O., and Barnett, R. J., *Endocrinology* **49**, 172 (1951).
41. Greer, M. A., *Endocrinology* **53**, 380 (1953).
42. Harris, G. W., *Proc. Roy. Soc.* **B122**, 374 (1937).
43. Harris, G. W., *Phil. Trans. Roy. Soc. London* **B232**, 385 (1947).
44. Harris, G. W., *J. Physiol.* (*London*) **107**, 418 (1948).
45. Harris, G. W., *J. Physiol.* (*London*) **111**, 347 (1950).
46. Harris, G. W., "Neural Control of the Pituitary Gland." Arnold, London, 1955.
47. Harris, G. W., *Bull. Johns Hopkins Hosp.* **97**, 358 (1955).
48. Harris, G. W., and Jacobsohn, D., *Proc. Roy. Soc.* **B139**, 263 (1952).
49. Harris, G. W., and Michael, R. P., *J. Physiol.* (*London*) **142**, 26P (1958).
50. Harris, G. W., and Woods, J. W., *Ciba Colloquia Endocrinol.* **10**, 3 (1957).
51. Harris, G. W., and Woods, J. W., *J. Physiol.* (*London*) **143**, 246 (1958).
52. Harris, G. W., Michael, R. P., and Scott, P. P., *Ciba Foundation Colloquium on Neurological Basis of Behaviour*, page 236 (1958).
53. Haterius, H. O., and Derbyshire, A. J., *Am. J. Physiol.* **119**, 329 (1937).
54. Heape, W., *Proc. Roy. Soc.* **B76**, 260 (1905).
55. Herbert, J., and Zuckerman, S., *Nature* **180**, 547 (1957).
56. Hess, W. R., "Beitrage zur Physiologie des Hirnstammes." Georg Thieme, Leipzig, 1932.
57. Hillarp, N. Å., *Acta Endocrinol.* **2**, 11 (1949).
58. Houssay, B. A., Biasotti, A., and Sammartino, R., *Compt. rend. soc. biol.* **120**, 725 (1935).
59. Jolly, H., "Sexual Precocity." Blackwell, Oxford, 1955.
60. Kent, G. C., and Liberman, M. J., *Endocrinology* **45**, 29 (1949).

61. Kollros, J. J., *Physiol. Zoöl.* **16**, 269 (1943).
62. McCullagh, E. P., Clamen, M., and Gardner, W. J., *J. Clin. Endocrinol.* **17**, 1277 (1957).
63. Maes, J. P., *Nature* **144**, 598 (1939).
64. Magoun, H. W., and Bard, P. (1940). Quoted by P. Bard, *Research Publs. Assoc. Research Nervous Mental Disease* **20**, 551 (1940).
65. Markee, J. E., Sawyer, C. H., and Hollinshead, W. H., *Endocrinology* **38**, 345 (1946).
66. Marshall, F. H. A., and Verney, E. B., *J. Physiol. (London)* **86**, 327 (1936).
67. Michael, R. P., and Scott, P. P., *J. Physiol. (London)* **138**, 46P (1957).
68. Nikitovitch-Winer, M., and Everett, J. W., *Nature* **180**, 1434 (1957).
69. Popa, G. T., and Fielding, U., *J. Anat.* **65**, 88 (1930).
70. Popa, G. T., and Fielding, U., *J. Anat.* **67**, 227 (1933).
71. Porter, R. W., Cavanaugh, E. B., Critchlow, B. V., and Sawyer, C. H., *Am. J. Physiol.* **189**, 145 (1957).
72. Rasmussen, A. T., *Endocrinology* **23**, 263 (1938).
73. Root, W. S., and Bard, P., *Am. J. Physiol.* **119**, 392 (1937).
74. Sawyer, C. H., and Robison, B. A., *J. Clin. Endocrinol. and Metabolism* **16**, 914 (1956).
75. Shirley, H. V., and Nalbandov, A. V., *Endocrinology* **58**, 694 (1956).
76. Smith, P. E., *Anat. Record* **191**, 207 (1932).
77. Symonds, C. P., *in* "Injuries of the Brain, Skull and Spinal Cord" (S. Brock, ed.), pp. 65-103. Williams & Wilkins, Baltimore, Maryland, 1943.
78. Thomson, A. P. D., and Zuckerman, S., *Nature* **171**, 970 (1953).
79. Thomson, A. P. D., and Zuckerman, S., *Proc. Roy. Soc.* **B142**, 437 (1954).
80. Török, B., *Acta Morphol. Acad. Sci. Hung.* **4**, 83 (1954).
81. van der Werff ten Bosch, J. J., and Donovan, B. T., *Acta Physiol. et Pharmacol. Neerl.* **5**, 491 (1957).
82. Weinberger, L. M., and Grant, F. C., *A.M.A. Arch. Internal Med.* **67**, 762 (1941).
83. Weiss, P., and Rossetti, F., *Science* **113**, 476 (1951).
84. Wingstrand, K. G., "The Structure and Development of the Avian Pituitary," p. 316. C. W. K. Gleerup, Lund, Sweden, 1951.
85. Wislocki, G. B., and King, L. S., *Am. J. Anat.* **58**, 421 (1936).
86. Worthington, W. C., *Bull. Johns Hopkins Hosp.* **97**, 343 (1955).

Discussion

CHAIRMAN: C. G. HARTMAN

S. J. FOLLEY: I should like to ask Professor Harris if he has done any experiments or has anything to say about experiments with tritio-hexestrol, with which I believe he was associated. Tritium-labeling gives, of course, much higher specific activities than labeling with C^{14}. Has he anything to say about localization of tritium-labeled hexestrol in the brain?

G. W. HARRIS: The possible localization of systemically administered hexestrol in the brain of the rabbit was studied in collaboration with Dr. R. F. Glascock of Shinfield, near Reading, who has developed a beautiful technique for preparing and also for assaying tritiated hexestrol. The experiments were performed in rabbits, the procedure being as follows. Ovariectomized rabbits were tested with the male to see whether these particular females showed any signs of sexual behavior after removal of the ovaries. This is necessary when using the rabbit since this animal is exceptional amongst subprimate mammals in that the spayed female will occasionally receive the male. In our experiments a series of spayed females that uniformly refused the male were used; they were then injected with 15 μg. of labeled hexestrol. When these animals responded to the mating test they were killed and dissected. Various regions of the brain, pituitary gland, mammary gland, endometrium, and other organs were pooled, dried, and assayed for radioactivity. No difference in radioactive content was found between any parts of the nervous system and what may be regarded as inert tissue, such as muscle, etc. The only tissue or body fluid that contained any concentration of tritiated hexestrol was the bile, which might have been expected from what was known regarding the excretion of estrogens. The difficulty with this type of work, however, is that when small pieces of the central nervous system are cut out as little blocks, any nuclear group which might have concentrated radioactive material may be so diluted with surrounding tissue that a localized concentration of radioactive material could be missed. I think the method of using autoradiography, at least as a screening procedure, gets around this difficulty. This would appear to be true, for example, in the case of studies concerning radioactive thyroxine and triiodothyronine. Taurog and associates failed to observe an uptake of I^{131}-labeled thyroxine or triiodothyronine by the paraventricular nucleus of the hypothalamus, although they found a concentration of radioactivity in similar masses of pituitary tissue dissected out and measured with a scintillation counter [A. Taurog, G. W. Harris, W. Tong, I. L. Chaikoff, *Endocrinology* **59**, 34 (1956)]. On the other hand, D. Ford and J. Gross [*Endocrinology* **62**, 416 (1958)] detected the uptake of these hormones in the paraventricular nucleus using an autoradiographic technique.

I. ROTHCHILD: I have two questions. The first relates to the experiments you described in which lesions in the anterior hypothalamus were associated with early estrus in ferrets and is also related to the phenomenon of sexual precocity in children with hamartomas in the hypothalamic area. Would permanently implanted electrodes in this area that could be used for stimulation lead to the opposite effect—namely, the delay of the onset of estrus in the ferret? This might be expected if this area were actually one that was either directly inhibitory of folliculotropic hormone secretion, or if it were part of a pathway involved in such inhibition.

The second question is: Is this area the same or close to the hypothetical area in the central nervous system that responds to estrogens in the mediation of the feed-back control of folliculotropin secretion? If this were so, have you any evidence, or has anybody else any evidence that animals with lesions like those you described in the ferret do not respond by showing a diminution of gonadotropin secretion when they are given estrogens? In other words, do animals with such lesions also lack this inhibitory feed-back mechanism?

G. W. HARRIS: With regard to the first question, I am afraid I have no answer. The effect of stimulating the anterior hypothalamus to see if any delay in the onset of estrus occurs, is obviously a very interesting experiment to carry out. Donovan and van der Werff ten Bosch stimulated the hypothalamic region of ferrets for up to 12 weeks. This experiment was, however, performed during the winter months, the animals being investigated mainly to see whether estrus would be induced. It would have been interesting to carry the stimulation period on through the spring to see if in these animals the normal onset of estrus was delayed.

With regard to your second question, again I can't give a dogmatic answer. I think the data that young rats, in which precocious puberty has been brought about by hypothalamic lesions, may show regular estrous cycles, mate, and become pregnant, would indicate a possible separation of the two regions you mention. However, I suppose it is also possible that the neural site upon which the feedback of estrogens occurs, is the same as that involved in these experiments on precocious puberty and that the available data could be explained by only a partial destruction of the effective neural mechanism.

S. SEGAL: In describing the gonadotropin-inhibiting region in the neural system, you have shown us that the destruction by lesion of this region can result in precocious puberty or, in the case of adults, in constant estrus. You then were able to show by citing your own experiments with Jacobsohn and the Nikitovitch-Winer and Everett experiments that the portal system is important for the transport of a neurohumor. But these experiments are concerned with stimulatory mechanisms. Do you feel that the inhibitory region also involves a specific neurohumor?

Concerning the steroid feed-back mechanism, in establishing the feed-back mechanism activity at the level of the neural system, do you disallow the possibility that there may also be an action on the hypophysis itself, perhaps influencing its threshold in responding to hypothalamic stimulation? If one does make this disallowal, then it would be necessary to conclude that the neural system is responsible for the morphologic changes in the pituitary following estrogen treatment, for example.

G. W. HARRIS: My own views would be as follows: I think there can be little doubt that the portal system of vessels is highly significant with regard to anterior pituitary activity. The details of the mechanism involved are not certain. The most probable view seems to be that some neurohumoral mechanism is involved, i.e., that nerve fibers in the hypothalamus liberate some specific humoral agents into the portal vessels, which then carry these agents to the pituitary gland where they exert a direct action on anterior pituitary cells. This view of course raises many questions, such as—How many humoral transmitters must be supposed in order to regulate the various hormonal activities of the anterior pituitary, and in view of a likely inhibitory mechanism of the hypothalamus over pituitary secretion, are separate agents to be supposed involved in this mechanism? I don't know how profitable it is to discuss such questions in our present state of ignorance. I would, however, like to make one or two comments. First, it is uncertain how many hormones the anterior pituitary manufactures. One knows that there are six or more purified extracts that the biochemists can present to the physiologists, but whether these represent the hormones—that is, the molecules that are actually liberated from the gland cells into the blood stream—is a different matter, and I don't think that problem is precisely solved. However, assuming that there are four or five hormones, and assuming that the hypothalamus may influence their secretion in both an excitatory and an inhibitory manner, there are again many possibilities with regard to the way in which these hypothetical humoral agents might be involved. For example, there might be a tonic release of such an agent from the hypothalamus, the amount of which could be either excited or depressed with a resultant excitation or inhibition of pituitary secretion of a particular hormone. It is certainly possible to make all sorts of hypotheses at the present moment, but whether they bear any resemblance to what actually occurs, is a different matter.

Your second question was with regard to the feed-back mechanism—whether the target organ hormones act at a hypothalamic or pituitary level. This is a question that has come very much to the fore with regard to the feedback of the thyroid hormone, and I think there are a few more data in respect to this hormone than with regard to the feedback of the gonadal hormones. The evidence at the moment seems to indicate that the thyroid hormone can act at both a hypothalamic and pituitary site. For example, section of the pituitary stalk, although decreasing thyroid activity, does not abolish the feed-back inhibitory effect of thyroxine. Similarly, transplantation of the pituitary to the anterior chamber of the eye does not abolish the inhibitory effect of thyroxine on thyroid activity. These data indicate that an *increase* in the blood content of thyroid hormone produced by the administration of *exogenous* thyroxine, may act directly on the pituitary gland. On the other hand, a *reduced* content of *endogenous* thyroid hormone in the blood seems to exert its effect on the secretion of TSH by an action on the hypothalamus. The data for this statement lie in the fact that anterior hypothalamic lesions abolish the goitrogenic action of propylthiouracil, and abolish compensatory hypertrophy in the remaining part of the gland after hemithyroidectomy. At the moment, therefore, it seems that the feedback mechanism may be exerted at both a hypothalamic and anterior pituitary site, and my own guess would be that in the normal animal the more sensitive receptor mechanism would be located in the hypothalamus rather than in the pituitary gland itself.

S. GELFANT: I would like to raise a point regarding the local application of stilbestrol to the hypothalamus. Although all of the concentrations of stilbestrol used had an effect on the hypothalamus and produced a behavioral change, none of the concentrations used had any effect on the uterus. Is it possible that the effect on the hypothalamus is due to injury produced by implanting the needle rather than to the stilbestrol? Did you implant the needle alone as a control?

G. W. HARRIS: The control experiments that were performed used mainly the insertion of the needle coated with stilbestrol esterified with the higher members of the fatty acid series. It is known that the rate of absorption of stilbestrol is slowed if it is combined with the higher fatty acids, and in our experiments no behavioral or other effects were observed from these implants. I might mention that the sequence of changes observed using systemic administration of estrogens in small doses (0.3 µg. per day) is as follows: First, the development of the uterus and vagina (to the stage of full vaginal cornification) and then secondly, development of estrous behavior. The processes occur in that order. It then becomes more convincing that the fully developed behavioral changes observed after hypothalamic implants of stilbestrol butyrate, which occur in the absence of any change in the reproductive organs, are *not* due to systemic absorption of the implant.

P. L. PERLMAN: I would like to ask a technical question with regard to stilbestrol. Stilbestrol is a synthetic material, a stilbene derivative, and not at all closely related to a steroid in structure. It is an estrogen in the sense that it causes the type of responses characteristic of steroid estrogens. What has been your experience with steroid estrogens? Does estriol differ from estradiol, and does that differ from estrone?

G. W. HARRIS: We have studied the effects of estradiol in comparison with those of the stilbestrol series and have seen no qualitative differences in the behavioral responses obtained. I am speaking now of the effects observed after systemic administration.

G. PINCUS: I noticed in your localization studies with stilbestrol esters that there was a fairly long latent period before their effect was evidenced. Would this latent period be shortened by the administration of progesterone, in view of Dr. Sawyer's remarks; and does this long latent period indicate the possibility, not of a direct neural effect, but perhaps of an indirect one via some pituitary mechanism. In other words, what would happen in a hypophysectomized cat subjected to stilbestrol?

Finally, I would like to make a remark about localization, which unfortunately has to be very incomplete. The localization of steroids in the brain depends a good deal on the blood-brain barrier. I know yet of no unequivocal demonstration that the steroids pass the blood-brain barrier. The few attempts made in our laboratories indicate that perhaps some metabolite or lower molecular weight fragmentation product might enter the brain, in which case the question of localization would depend very largely on the substance you use, and the hexestrol may be out of the picture because it does not fragment to what is wanted.

G. W. HARRIS: First, with regard to the latent period of the behavioral response. This did vary and in some cases as you say, was quite long. The explanation of this is not clear, but it is possible that some of the implants were a little remote from the sensitive cells and that diffusion of the stilbestrol ester had to occur before any result was seen. We have no data at the moment as to how far these implants do effectively diffuse. The Radiochemical Centre in Amersham, England, is now preparing radioactive stilbestrol. We plan to implant this material and then study the diffusion of the compound by an autoradiographic technique. This might give some data regarding the neuronal cells groups affected in this experiment.

Your second question concerned some possible indirect effect via the pituitary. That, of course, is possible, but it is difficult to visualize the pituitary playing any direct part in regulating the sexual behavior of these ovariectomized cats. One could suppose that the stilbestrol implant elicits release of some pituitary hormone and that this feeds back directly on to the brain. However, under normal circumstances, the pituitary gland does not come into the picture, since I believe it is possible to get hypophysectomized animals to mate if they are given estrogen. Isn't that true?

As for the localization of the pick-up and the crossing of the blood-brain barrier by steroids, the only evidence I can quote on that point is the data of Dr. J. B. Trunnell of the Anderson Hospital, University of Texas. Dr. Trunnell found that radioactivity localized in a small area in the ventral part of the upper midbrain after systemic administration of labeled estrogen to mice. This site would be just posterior to that found active in our present work. It is possible that in Trunnell's experiments, so far as I know, the localized radioactivity represented only a fragment of the estradiol molecule. I do not know whether the radioactivity picked up has been identified as the intact estradiol molecule.

C. G. HARTMAN: Dr. Pincus, do I understand that you implied that this steroid had to enter the cell as sugar has to enter the cell under the influence of insulin to have its action? Is that what you meant?

G. PINCUS: I think that there is evidence of direct action of steroids on cells. For example, inunction of estrogen into the mammary gland or local application of estrogen to the vagina will undoubtedly cause hypertrophy. I don't think there is any question that the blood-brain barrier is a big problem, and it may be that there somehow one has to have a different type of substance, a metabolite of the steroid rather than the steroid itself. I don't know whether Dr. Bloch would like to say something about what he has observed.

E. BLOCH: Our observations can be summarized quite briefly. We injected into rats 4-C^{14}-testosterone and 4-C^{14}-cortisol, respectively, and analyzed the cerebrospinal fluid for the presence of radioactivity and radioactive steroids. After a series of purification steps, using the isotope dilution technique, we found no radioactivity associated with any of the added steroid zones, as based primarily on chromatographic localization and some crystallizations.

I think it would be very interesting and very important to be able to correlate your findings with *in vivo* production of estrogens and progesterone and their passage into the brain.

By what means did Dr. Trunnell administer his radioactive estradiol?

G. W. HARRIS: Dr. Trunnell gave C^{14}-labeled estradiol by a systemic route.

The point that Dr. Pincus raised was one that occurred to Dr. Glascock and myself, quite strongly, after we had failed to find any localized radioactivity in the brains of our ovariectomized rabbits injected with tritiated hexestrol. It seems difficult to explain the behavioral effects produced by estrogens unless they cross the blood-brain barrier and come into contact with the nerve cells of the central nervous system. On the other hand, there may be little reason to expect a concentration of estrogen at any site at which it acts. It might be that certain nerve cells are more sensitive to a particular concentration of estrogen than other nerve cells, but not necessarily accumulate the hormone.

A. E. RAKOFF: Dr. Harris has shown us very nicely the two distinct areas in the brain for precocious puberty and constant estrus production and also has indicated the cases reported in the literature of precocious puberty in the human following certain intercranial lesions.

I would like to record a case of persistent ovarian function due to an intracranial lesion in the human. This was a 17-year-old girl, who apparently went into a normal pubescence and menarche and then developed a secondary amenorrhea. Her vaginal smears showed persistent cornification, and gonadotropin was present in her urine. Further study of the girl revealed that she had a chronic hydrocephalus. A subsequent attempt to correct this was unsuccessful. When the girl came to post mortem, she was found to have polycystic ovaries. As is unfortunately the style nowadays, pathologists reported these ovaries as Stein-Leventhal ovaries. Actually they were simply polycystic ovaries with signs of constant estrogen production and constant gonadotropic stimulation.

C. H. SAWYER: I think the point that Dr. Harris made a few moments ago, about the diffusion of stilbestrol, may be important as far as its site of action is concerned. I would suggest that perhaps the delay that Dr. Pincus inquired about represents the time for diffusion of the stilbestrol placed in the posterior hypothalamus to reach the behavioral center in the anterior hypothalamus. I notice that Dr. Harris' one point in the anterior hypothalamus as such was positive. I suspect that Harris and Michaels were influenced by Bard, as Bard was by Dempsey and Rioch, in placing the behavioral center in the posterior hypothalamus.

I don't think that stimulation data, either chemical or electrical, are as good from a localizing point of view as are recording data or lesion data. So I would still hold for a behavioral center in a different site from the gonadotropic center in the cat hypothalamus. Bard raised this point several years ago and proposed that because the two centers existed in the hypothalamus it did not necessarily mean that they were "cerebral bedfellows." Our work with Robison, described earlier this morning, suggests that they are not "cerebral bedfellows."

G. W. HARRIS: I am not quite sure what you mean about the anterior hypothalamus being positive from our data. The slides I showed summarized the evidence we had collected about a year ago. Since then we have done more animals and we have not seen the response if the implant is in the anterior hypothalamus.

Dr. Sawyer raises the point as to the validity of stimulation data, either electrical or chemical, as compared with recording or lesion data. I should like to mention my own views on this point, since I think they are rather different from those he holds. Recording data I think are often difficult of interpretation in terms of physiological significance because of the circumstances under which the recordings are made. Data obtained from the anesthetized or curarized, or decorticate or thalamic preparation can hardly be translated directly into terms of the normal intact animal, especially when one is considering the mechanism underlying patterns of overt behavior. In considering the reliability of stimulation versus lesion data, in a confined area of the central nervous system such as the hypothalamus, I think the following points are of importance. First, many autonomic and visceral functions are represented in the hypothalamus. Stimulation or damage to this region, then, could theoretically influence endocrine activity in many ways. Secondly, the situation depends very much on whether one is studying a positive or negative response. If one is studying a positive response, that is, a state of increased function in an organ such as the ovary, whether produced by a lesion or stimulation, one is on much safer ground than if studying a negative response. This is because so many nonspecific stimuli, that may be called stressful or noxious, tend to produce loss of ovarian function. The effect of psychological trauma as seen in concentration camps in causing amenorrhea, and the effect of dietary insufficiency resulting in a state of pseudohypophysectomy in the rat or in anorexia nervosa in women, come to mind. To translate this into practical terms, I believe that when one is dealing with experimental interference in such a small confined region of the central nervous system as the hypothalamus, which is related to so many bodily functions, it is more significant to produce—for example—(1) release of luteinizing hormone and ovulation in the rabbit by stimulation, than it would be to block the process by placing a lesion, (2) to produce active sexual behavior by local chemical stimulation, than to abolish it by means of a lesion, or (3) to evoke precocious puberty by a lesion than it would be to retard puberty by stimulation. The reliability of data derived from either stimulation or lesioning experiments depends on the characteristics of the response under consideration, and especially on the effects of "nonspecific" stimuli in exciting or inhibiting the response.

S. SEGAL: In Dr. Rakoff's comments he indicated that you have demonstrated a clear separation between the inhibitory centers concerned with constant estrus and precocious puberty. I would just like to make certain that you feel strongly about this—that you actually do interpret your observations in this manner.

I think about this because it is possible, by the administration of small doses of various steroids at birth to newborn female rats, to elicit a constant estrous response when the animals eventually reach sexual maturity and also to elicit precocious puberty. These animals show vaginal openings about 5–7 days earlier than normal.

C. G. HARTMAN: While you are answering Dr. Segal's point, will you consider Dr. Leathem's sterilization of the newborn rat, for life, with a single injection of testosterone.

G. W. HARRIS: I certainly know the results Dr. Segal and Dr. Hartman have mentioned and am very interested in them.

The sort of picture that seems to be developing is that between birth and puberty some part of the central nervous system, such as the hypothalamus, is undergoing maturation, and that this maturation is under the influence of the low-level secretion from the gonads that is occurring throughout this time. If one upsets seriously the blood concentration of the steroids between birth and puberty, then in some way this mtauration of the central nervous system is prevented or changed. Such a view was indicated by the old and beautiful experiments of C. A. Pfeiffer [*Am. J. Anat.* **58**, 195 (1936)]. Pfeiffer interpreted his results as indicating that a sexual differentiation of anterior pituitary tissue occurs between birth and puberty. However, more recent experiments dealing with anterior pituitary transplants have shown that this tissue remains sexually undifferentiated and plastic. It is likely that Pfeiffer's results were due to sexual differentiation of some central nervous mechanism.

The question as to the identity or otherwise of the neural mechanism underlying the constant estrous response and precocious puberty must, I think, be left for further experiments. Drs. Donovan and van der Werff ten Bosch have found that anterior hypothalamic lesions placed in immature animals may result in precocious puberty followed by the development of normal rhythm cycles. This would, I think, indicate that different mechanisms may be involved, but other explanations may be valid.

H. KUPPERMAN: In answer to some of the other data on this point about precocious estrus and maturity, the statement that you made that there may be a low gonadal threshold level which perhaps keeps the hypothalamus stimulating it, perhaps is very true.

A number of years ago we showed that if we gave a gonadotropic hormone, by injection, to rabbits so that we actually build up an antihormone against this gonadotropic complex, and then injected this into newborn rats for 10 days—from day 1 to day 11—and then stopped, these animals became precocious. By day 20 or 25 they were cycling and showed normal estrous cycles.

The explanation was rather a diffuse one. The ovaries of an immature animal that received the antihormone were considerably smaller than the ovaries of the immature control littermates that had not received any hormone, indicating that there may be even at that young age some pituitary control of ovarian activity. The pituitary glands of these animals, interestingly enough, on the day of the last injection showed an increased degree of ovulating ability, and we theorized that when the injections were discontinued, then this hyperactivity of the pituitary gland or what-have-you took over and precipitated precocious sexual maturity.

There is one other point I would like to make, if I may. This is about the use of estrogens for the induction of ovulation in the human. The procedure which we have used has been to inject a conjugated estrogen intravenously in a dose of 20 mg. in a patient in whom we feel sure there is no evidence of thyroid or adreno-cortical abnormality. We believe we have been successful in inducing ovulation in these patients, as evidenced by various criteria and the fact that pregnancy has occurred in patients who have been sterile for an average of four or five years.

I. ROTHCHILD: I would like to make a brief remark about the question of the central nervous system (CNS) involvement in the secretion of pituitary hormones, generally. The question has been touched on this morning, but was argued for a fair amount at the recent Cold Spring Harbor Symposium. This is whether the feed-back mechanism of pituitary hormone regulation is an either/or business. If gonado-tropic hormone regulation is by means of a feed-back mechanism, does it absolutely have to work through the central nervous system or does it absolutely have to work on the pituitary gland? This question, put this way, it seems to me, is perhaps a wrong way of looking at it. There is no reason why a particular pituitary trophin cannot be subjected to influences from both directions—that is, from target-organ hormones acting directly on the pituitary, as well as from action through some CNS mechanism that would have the same effect on the secretion of hormones from the pituitary gland.

It seems to me that what we need is a viewpoint on the whole question of the role of the CNS in the control of the pituitary hormone secretion. Several things are involved in arriving at this viewpoint. It is not just the question of the feed-back, which is the operation of an *inhibitory* effect on pituitary hormone secretion. There is also the very obvious phenomenon of the *stimulation* of secretion of pituitary hormones by means of steroid hormones. The best example of this is the induction of LH release by means of progesterone. There is a great deal of evidence that progesterone exerts this effect only through a central nervous system area.

You presented evidence this morning for the possible separation between two areas in the brain, one of which may be the one that responds to estrogens by inhibiting gonadotropin secretion, but the other may be one that exerts, by direct nervous influence, an inhibitory effect on FSH secretion. There may be such a direct nervous mechanism that functions to inhibit LTH secretion, so that when the pituitary is removed and transported to the kidney, it secretes LTH indefinitely. Everett offered this as a possible explanation for his results, and it may be the correct one. I wish there were some way of tying all these apparently, but not necessarily, conflicting facts about the way the nervous system affects the pituitary system into a cohesive theory.

G. W. HARRIS: I would just like to say I agree with most of the things you said.

Estrogen Excretion in Normal and Abnormal Menstrual Cycles

J. B. Brown

Clinical Endocrinology Research Unit (Medical Research Council), University of
Edinburgh, Edinburgh, Scotland

The present study is concerned with the estimation of urinary estrogen excretion during (a) normal ovulatory menstrual cycles, and (b) anovulatory menstrual cycles. This work was done in collaboration with Professor R. J. Kellar and Dr. C. D. Matthew of the Department of Gynecology and Obstetrics, University of Edinburgh. (c) In addition, the peaks of estrogen excretion which occur during ovulatory menstrual cycles are correlated with changes in gonadotropin and pregnanediol output and the rise in basal temperature. This work was done in collaboration with my colleagues Dr. A. Klopper and Dr. J. A. Loraine.

I. Methods

Estrogens were estimated by the method of Brown (1). This measures urinary estriol, estrone, and estradiol-17β, but not the more recently discovered estrogens. The reliability of this method has been reviewed by Brown and associates (4). All the evidence available indicates that, except in rare and usually predictable circumstances, the method gives reliable estimates of each of the three estrogens at levels down to approximately 3 µg. per 24-hour specimen of urine.

Oral temperatures were recorded each morning on awakening.

Pregnanediol was estimated by the method of Klopper *et al.* (8).

Gonadotropins were extracted from urine by the method of Loraine and Brown (9). The main steps in this method are adsorption on kaolin, elution from kaolin, acetone precipitation, and purification of the crude

kaolin acetone powders by treatment with tricalcium phosphate. Bioassays were done by the uterine weight test in intact immature mice and
sometimes also by the ventral prostatic weight test in hypophysectomized
immature rats. Results were calculated in terms of a standard prepared
from the urine of menopausal and postmenopausal women (HMG-20A)
and were expressed as "HMG units" per 24 hours.

Eight women were studied in the preliminary investigation of the
normal ovulatory menstrual cycle. All were healthy and none had any
history of menstrual abnormalities. Morning basal temperatures were
recorded in each case.

Proven anovulatory menstrual cycles were found in four women
who were being investigated for irregular bleeding or sterility. Each
subject was studied over a period of time which included at least two
phases of bleeding. Endometrial biopsies were performed, usually at the
onset of bleeding, to test for the occurrence of ovulation. Also, in some
cases, urinary pregnanediol was estimated at crucial times to test for the
presence of a functioning corpus luteum.

Nine women were studied in the investigation involving parallel
estimations of urinary estrogens, pregnanediol, and gonadotropins during
ovulatory menstrual cycles. Seven of these were healthy women, normally
active. The remaining two were patients in hospital suffering from
carcinoma of the breast. There was no history of menstrual abnormalities in any of the subjects investigated.

Complete urine samples were collected daily without preservative and
were stored at 4°C. while awaiting assay.

II. Results

A.   NORMAL OVULATORY MENSTRUAL CYCLES

The results of the preliminary investigation have already been fully
reported (2). Examples are shown in Fig. 1–3.

It will be noted that the amounts of the three estrogens excreted
generally rise and fall together. The estradiol levels are almost always
about one-half of the corresponding estrone levels. The estriol levels
may be approximately equal to the estrone levels (Fig. 2) or greater
than the estrone levels (Figs. 1 and 3). The amounts excreted are smallest
during the first week of the cycle and then rise to a well-defined peak
at about mid-cycle. The amounts then decrease and usually rise again
to a second maximum during the luteal phase of the cycle and then decrease once more before the onset of menstruation. This decrease usually
continues for several days into the next menstrual cycle.

The mid-cycle peak occurs about the same time as the rise in basal temperature and is presumably related to ovulation. Several features characterize this peak.

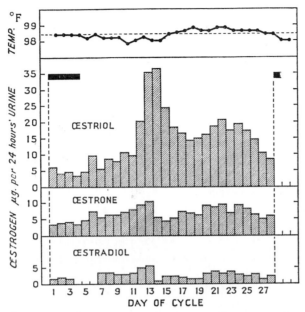

FIG. 1. Subject 1: aged 36; para, 3. This figure and Figs. 2–5 show the amounts of estriol, estrone, and estradiol excreted per 24 hours and also the variations in basal temperature; menstrual period indicated by solid horizontal bar. From Brown (2).

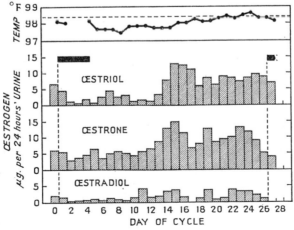

FIG. 2. Subject 5: aged 17; nullipara. From Brown (2).

1. The peak is shown by all three estrogens.

2. The rise to the peak is usually gradual and the fall after the peak is often abrupt.

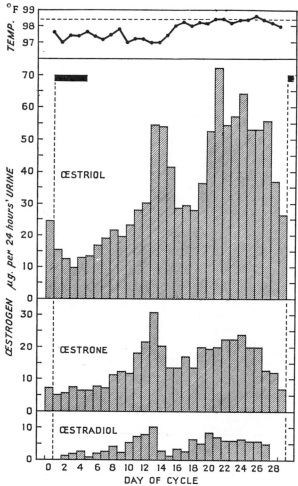

Fig. 3.   Subject 6: aged 32; para. 2. From Brown (2).

3. The interval of time between the peak and the onset of menstruation is usually about 14 days.

4. The rise and fall of the estriol level tends to lag behind those of the estrone and estradiol levels. For instance, in Fig. 1, the peak of estrone and estradiol excretion occurred on the 13th day of the cycle, while that of estriol excretion occurred on the 14th day. This sequence

is the same as that observed after the intramuscular injection of estrone or estradiol-17β (3), and should be expected if estrone and/or estradiol-17β were the hormones secreted by the ovary at this time.

The second rise and fall in estrogen excretion are probably due to estrogen produced by a growing and then regressing corpus luteum.

Figures 2 and 3 were selected from the series to illustrate the extreme ranges of excretion values encountered.

B. ANOVULATORY MENSTRUAL CYCLES

The results obtained from two of the subjects having anovulatory cycles are shown in Figs. 4 and 5. During the period studied, case 4 showed no evidence of ovulation, while case 5 had an anovulatory menstrual cycle followed by an ovulatory one. The other two subjects also had both ovulatory and anovulatory cycles during the periods studied and their urinary estrogen excretion resembled that of case 5 in pattern and amount.

During the anovulatory menstrual cycles, the urinary estrogen levels remained remarkably constant. There was no rise resembling the mid-cycle peak of an ovulatory menstrual cycle nor a fall prior to menstruation. The amounts excreted were maintained at approximately 20 μg. of total estrogen per 24 hours. These amounts are some two to three times greater than those found after the menopause or in younger women suffering from complete amenorrhea. They are also within the range found at the onset of menstruation during an ovulatory menstrual cycle. It seems that these amounts of urinary estrogens reflect threshold levels of estrogen in the body which are sufficient to stimulate growth of the endometrium. Since menstrual bleeding can also occur at these levels, the endometrium becomes unstable as it builds up. It therefore breaks down from time to time resulting in anovulatory bleeding from a pro-liferative-phase endometrium. Unlike normal menstruation, this type of bleeding occurs without the withdrawal of the estrogen (and progesterone) stimulus. These conditions appear to be analogous to those produced experimentally by Zuckerman and others, who found that uterine bleeding will occur periodically in oophorectomized monkeys and women maintained on a constant threshold dose of estrogen (10).

In case 5, the third period of bleeding shown was from a secretory-phase endometrium. It can therefore be concluded that this terminated an ovulatory cycle. The urinary estrogen excretion pattern showed the characteristic "ovulation" peak followed by a luteal maximum. Bleeding began 13 days after the peak. An interesting feature, also observed in the other cases where an ovulatory cycle followed a period of anovulatory bleeding, was that the peak occurred immediately after the bleeding without any intervening proliferative phase.

The subjects shown in Figs. 4 and 5 are selected examples taken from a series comprising more than 80 cases who were complaining of menstrual abnormalities and in whom urinary estrogen levels have been correlated with clinical and surgical findings [Brown, Kellar, and Matthew; in press (6)]. During this study, it was found that ovulation was invariably associated with a rise and fall in the amounts of the three estrogens excreted in the urine. This peak had all the characteristics

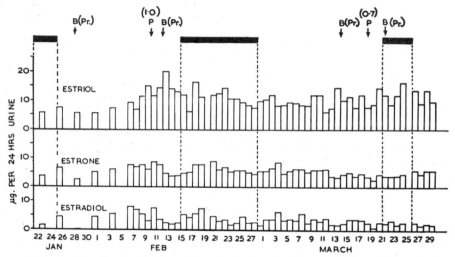

Fig. 4. Case 4: aged 19; nullipara; dysfunctional uterine hemorrhage. From Brown, Kellar, and Matthew (6).

of the mid-cycle peak of the normal ovulatory menstrual cycle. The interval of time between the estrogen peak and the beginning of the previous menstrual period varied from 4 months to 5 days; between the estrogen peak and the onset of the next menstrual period the time interval varied from 8 to 16 days. However, very occasionally the luteal-phase rise and fall in urinary estrogens could not be demonstrated, although all the other evidence indicated that a functioning corpus luteum was present.

C. Time Relationship between the Estrogen Peak and Ovulation

There are good reasons for believing that the estrogen peak and ovulation are closely related. In an attempt to determine the relationship in time between the two, parallel determinations have been made of urinary estrogen, pregnanediol, and gonadotropin output and of basal temperature during ovulatory menstrual cycles. Figures 6 and 7 show examples of the results obtained (5).

A definite rise in gonadotropin excretion ranging from 13 to 40 HMG units per 24 hours was observed at approximately mid-cycle in seven of the nine cases studied. In two individuals this rise was absent although

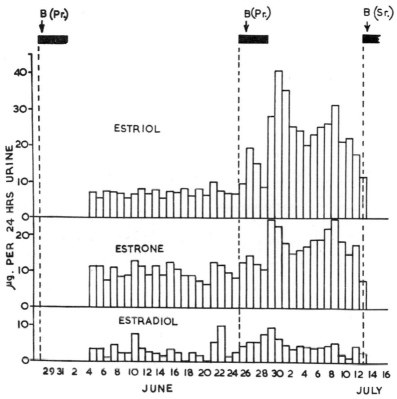

Fig. 5. Case 5: aged 26; nullipara; irregular periods. From Brown, Kellar, and Matthew (6).

all the other evidence available indicated that ovulation had occurred. In five of the seven cases, the increased output of gonadotropins was confined to a single pooled sample collected over 48 hours; in the remaining two, the peak was more diffuse, being spread over 6 and 9 days. In none of the subjects studied did the gonadotropin peak precede the estrogen peak. In four, the peak of estrone and estradiol excretion occurred during the first 24 hours of the 48-hour period during which the gonadotropin peak occurred (e.g., see Fig. 6). In the other three, the gonadotropin peak occurred 2–4 days after the estrogen peak (e.g., see Fig. 7).

The amounts of pregnanediol excreted were similar to those previously reported by Klopper (5). It is generally believed that the midcycle rises in pregnanediol excretion and in basal temperature are due to progesterone secreted by the newly formed corpus luteum and that they occur soon after ovulation. In this series, the rise in pregnanediol

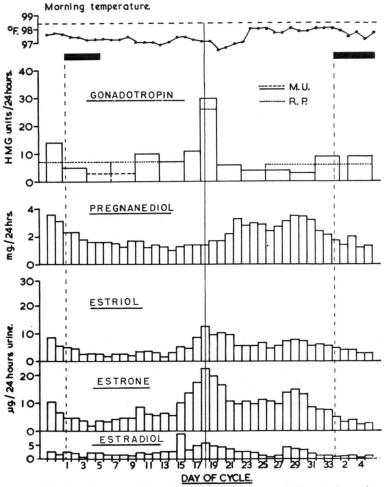

Fig. 6.   Miss E. B.: aged 27; nullipara. This figure and Fig. 7 show the daily excretion of gonadotropin, pregnanediol, estriol, estrone, and estradiol and also the variations in basal temperature. Gonadotropin assays: ———, results by the mouse uterus test; – – – –, results by the mouse uterus test in which the reading was actually less than the figure shown; . . . ., results by the hypophysectomized rat prostate test. The vertical line indicates the day of the mid-cycle peak of excretion of estrone and estradiol. The solid horizontal bar indicates the menstrual period. From Brown, Klopper, and Loraine (5).

coincided approximately with the rise in basal temperature. These rises always occurred after the estrogen peak, the time interval ranging from 1 to 4 days. In two subjects the rise in pregnanediol output occurred before the gonadotropin peak.

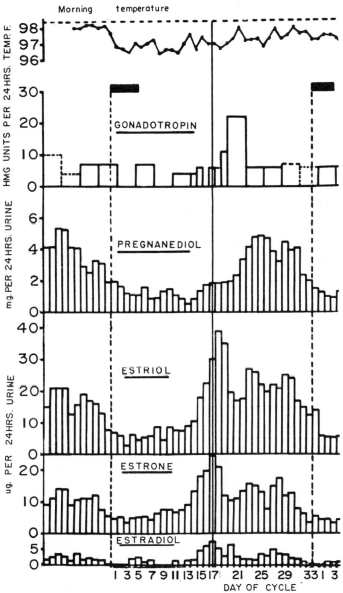

FIG. 7. Mrs. M. R.: aged 41; para 2; mammary carcinoma. From Brown, Klopper, and Loraine (5).

The time from the estrogen peak to the onset of menstrual bleeding varied in different subjects from 11 to 16 days, with a mean figure of 13.9 ± 1.6* days. The corresponding intervals dated from the gonadotropin peak, the increase in urinary pregnanediol excretion and the rise in basal temperature were respectively 13.2 ± 1.7,* 11.7 ± 2.1,* and 11.2 ± 2.5* days. The estrogen peak is therefore the earliest indication of ovulation.

III. Summary

The urinary excretion of estriol, estrone, and estradiol has been estimated during normal ovulatory menstrual cycles and during anovulatory menstrual cycles with the following results.

1. During ovulatory menstrual cycles, at least one and usually two peaks of estrogen excretion were observed. One was highly characteristic and occurred at about mid-cycle; the other was often less well defined and occurred during the luteal phase. Menstruation began about 14 days after the mid-cycle peak as the levels were decreasing after the luteal-phase peak.

2. During anovulatory menstrual cycles, the estrogen levels remained more or less constant at approximately 20 μg. total estrogen per 24-hour urine. There was no indication of an estrogen peak or a decrease in levels before the onset of menstruation.

An estrogen peak with the characteristics of the mid-cycle peak of the ovulatory menstrual cycle seems always to be associated with ovulation. In attempting to determine the relationship in time between this estrogen peak and ovulation it was found that:

1. The estrogen peak occurred 1–4 days before the rise in basal temperature and the luteal-phase increase in urinary pregnanediol.

2. The estrogen peak either coincided with the mid-cycle peak in urinary gonadotropin or preceded it by an interval of up to 4 days. In none of the nine women studied did the gonadotropin peak precede the estrogen peak. In two cases the gonadotropin peak was absent, although all the evidence available indicated that ovulation had taken place.

The evidence presented here suggests that the estrogen peak is the earliest and one of the most reliable indications of ovulation.

Acknowledgments

I wish to emphasize that much of the work reported here has been done in collaboration with Professor R. J. Kellar and Dr. G. D. Matthew of the Department of Obstetrics and Gynecology, the University of Edinburgh, and Drs. A. I. Klopper and J. A. Loraine of the Clinical Endocrinology Research Unit. I am indebted to

---

* Standard deviation.

them for their permission to report some yet unpublished studies. I also wish to thank Professor G. F. Marrian, F.R.S., for his interest in this work. The skilled technical assistance of the following is greatly appreciated: Mr. and Mrs. H. A. F. Blair, Miss M. K. Burnett, Miss M. R. Gillon, Miss M. A. Mackay, Miss W. McGillivray, and Mrs. Mary Ramsey.

References

1. Brown, J. B., *Biochem. J.* **60**, 185 (1955).
2. Brown, J. B., *Lancet* i, 320 (1955).
3. Brown, J. B., *J. Endocrinol.* **16**, 202 (1957).
4. Brown, J. B., Bulbrook, R. D., and Greenwood, F. C., *J. Endocrinol.* **16**, 41 (1957).
5. Brown, J. B., Klopper, A., and Loraine, J. A., *J. Endocrinol.* **17**, 401 (1958).
6. Brown, J. B., Kellar, R. J., and Matthew, G. D., *J. Obstet. Gynaecol. Brit. Empire* (1959) in press.
7. Klopper, A., *J. Obstet. Gynaecol. Brit. Empire* **64**, 504 (1957).
8. Klopper, A., Michie, E. A., and Brown, J. B., *J. Endocrinol.* **12**, 209 (1955).
9. Loraine, J. A., and Brown, J. B., *J. Clin. Endocrinol. and Metabolism* **16**, 1180 (1956).
10. Zuckerman, S., *Lancet* i, 1031 (1949).

Discussion

CHAIRMAN: J. ROCK

H. HELLER: With what "efficiency" are estradiol, estrone, and estriol excreted by the kidney after intravenous injection? What is the time course of the excretion and what percentage of the injected dose appears in the urine?

J. B. BROWN: Approximately 25% of an intramuscularly (I.M.) injected dose of estradiol or estrone can be accounted for as estradiol, estrone, and estriol excreted in the urine. The urinary levels of estradiol and estrone are maximal on the day of the injection and fall to base-line levels in 2–4 days. Estriol excretion is usually maximal on the day after the injection and takes up to a week to return to normal.

H. HELLER: You say about 25%. What I really wanted to know is the degree of scatter round this average value. For example, is it 10–40% or is it 25 ± 5%?

J. B. BROWN: According to our figures the recoveries vary from about 16 to 35%.

H. HELLER: Have you ever done any renal function studies in your abnormal cases? Do you know whether changes in renal function (owing, for instance, to a change in body temperature) influence hormone excretion?

J. B. BROWN: We have not made a detailed study of the relationship between estrogen excretion and renal function. However, from the cases we have done, it appears that gross renal damage is necessary before the clearance of estrogen is affected. There is certainly no indication that the fluctuations in estrogen excretion reported here are due to changes in renal function.

M. L. TAYMOR: Dr. Brown, I was particularly interested in the case in which the patient had a long period of amenorrhea and then had a rather sharp peak of estrogen simulating an ovulatory cycle. Do you have many more cases like that? The reason I ask the question is that those of us who do clinical infertility work often see these cases with infrequent ovulation. When we follow the cervical mucus changes, which we think are dependent upon the estrogen secretion at this time, we often see these changes long before actual ovulation. In addition, I have seen cases where the cervical mucus seems to get to a point where one would think you are getting close to ovulation and then it regresses again. It would be interesting to know if estrogen rises and falls in such cases. In such cases perhaps estrogen rise would not be an indicator of incipient ovulation.

J. B. BROWN: It would be very interesting to correlate the changes in cervical mucus, such as you describe, with urinary estrogen excretion. This has not yet been done. However, a certain amount of information is available concerning the relationship between urinary estrogen levels and the state of the endometrium. The endometrium is atrophic when the urinary excretion has been less than about 5 µg. total estrogen per 24 hours for some time; it proliferates when the excretion exceeds about 14 µg. per 24 hour urine. In between these figures, the grading of the endometrium depends very much on the individual. During a period of amenorrhea, it is possible for the urinary estrogen levels to rise and fall within this range without a semblance of a sharp ovulation peak and without ovulation occurring. I think this would be the explanation of your findings.

G. PINCUS: The luteal-phase changes you described, which are very consistent and which have been observed even by those of us who have used bioassays as well as chemical methods, may or may not be influenced by progesterone. You may remember that Smith and Smith at one time thought that progesterone might be a responsible agent for the estriol output increase. Have you tested this possibility by the administration of progesterone to see what effect it had on estrogen excretion?

J. B. BROWN: Yes, we have administered estradiol I.M. to women during the luteal phase, during the follicular phase, and along with progesterone. We could find no evidence that progesterone influences in any way the amounts of estrone, estradiol, and estriol recovered in the urine.

G. PINCUS: I noted that on some of your charts the absolute values through a cycle were quite different in different patients. I wondered whether you had correlated the total daily estrogen excretion with the vaginal cytology pattern throughout a cycle. I think that this may be of importance because apparently individual estrogen values don't mean very much. It is what they do from day to day since they may vary so much in different cycles. Did you study any vaginal smears in these cycles?

J. B. BROWN: We did not do vaginal smears in this series. However, workers in London, using the same estrogen method, have compared vaginal cytology with urinary estrogen levels. They obtained a good correlation between the two, providing they allowed for a certain delay in the response of the vaginal smears to a change in estrogen levels.

A. E. RAKOFF: In other words the vaginal cytology smear would give essentially the same picture as the daily urinary excretion pattern irrespective of the difference in the total value excreted by different patients.

J. B. BROWN: That is probably correct. How feasible would it be to obtain quantitative data relating the two?

A. E. RAKOFF: Well, I would think the vaginal cytology picture would probably depend a whole lot on the responsiveness of the individual patient. Some patients might show a full cornification response to less estrogen than another patient. The other point that interested me was the fact that the gonadotropin peak occurred later than the estrogen peak and you then, therefore, intimated that the peak of the estrogen level was not due to gonadotropin, but you did not say what you thought the cause of the peak of estrogen was.

J. B. BROWN: I had hoped that someone else at this meeting might have some ideas on this point.

J. ROCK: Dr. Brown brought out another point that interested me very much, and that is that he does not show that anovulatory bleeding is due to estrogen withdrawal as far as excretion here is concerned. I wonder if anybody knows what causes intermenstrual bleeding. I would like so much to know what makes the endometrium bleed. It is so easy to say that the tissue is built up by these trophic hormones and then the level drops down and the tissue cannot support itself and, therefore, the vascular system breaks down; but I wish somebody would tell me how.

Mid-cycle Changes in Urinary Gonadotropin Excretion*

JANET W. MCARTHUR

Department of Gynecology of the Harvard Medical School and the Gynecological Service of the Massachusetts General Hospital (Vincent Memorial Hospital), Boston, Massachusetts

The last quarter century has seen many significant advances in our knowledge concerning the gonadotropic hormones. The site of origin of the placental and pituitary gonadotropins, uncertain for a number of years after their detection in human body fluids, has been established beyond question. Two separate gonadotropic principles, follicle-stimulating hormone (FSH) and luteinizing (or interstitial cell-stimulating) hormone (LH or ICSH) have been isolated in highly purified form from the pituitary glands of sheep and swine, and a wealth of information has been accumulated concerning their biological characteristics. Evidence has been obtained that a third pituitary gonadotropic principle, luteotropic hormone† (LTH), is necessary for corpus luteum function in the rat.

Moreover, by a series of deductions from these data, a logical explanation of the events of the human menstrual cycle has been evolved. One such schema is illustrated in Fig. 1. As a result of stimulation by FSH, ovarian follicles which have reached the antrum stage are thought to grow and, at the point in the cycle when LH begins to be released by the pituitary, to secrete estrogen. The rising level of estrogen in some manner conditions the release of additional LH with resultant ovulation and corpus luteum formation. By extrapolation from the rat to man, it

---

* The original data to be presented in this paper were obtained in collaboration with Dr. Francis M. Ingersoll, of the Harvard Medical School, and Dr. Jane Worcester, of the Department of Biostatistics of the Harvard School of Public Health.

† Luteotropin is thought to be identical with the luteotropic hormone, prolactin.

is postulated in this particular schema that LTH maintains the corpus luteum and causes it to secrete estrogen and progesterone.

Plausible though such schemata are, their validation at the primate level has proved exceedingly difficult. The insensitivity of presently available methods of assaying LTH in body fluids is such that unequivocal evidence to indicate the presence of LTH in the urine during the luteal phase of the cycle has not yet been adduced. Moreover, attempts to

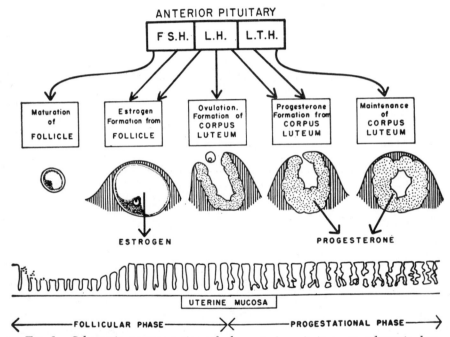

Fig. 1. Schematic representation of the anterior pituitary gonadotropic hormones and their relation to ovarian and uterine changes during the human menstrual cycle. (Courtesy of *Principles of Internal Medicine*, 3rd ed., edited by T. R. Harrison *et al.*, 1958, Blakiston Div., McGraw-Hill Co.)

prolong the life of the corpus luteum in the monkey and human being by means of injections of luteotropic hormone have met with failure.

If we turn to the events of the cycle which precede the luteal phase, the situation is somewhat more satisfactory. Follicular growth, though not ovulation, has been induced in the monkey and man by the injection of pituitary gonadotropic preparations. Gonadotropic activity is now demonstrable in the urine of the adult woman and, with difficulty, in that of the monkey. At first it proved impossible to detect the presence of gonadotropic hormone in human urine during any phase of the menstrual cycle. The paper which Zondek (53) published in 1930 announcing the discovery of prolan A in the urine of postmenopausal and castrate women also records a series of negative findings in women tested during the years of reproductive maturity. For some time thereafter, attempts by other workers (2, 22) were no more successful. Eventually, however, positive responses were obtained. Occasional subjects were found to excrete detectable amounts of gonadotropin during mid-cycle (16, 25, 26) or just prior to menstruation (25, 26, 44) by the use of such indices as histological changes in the ovaries of mice and vaginal cornification in the rat. Employing the latter criterion Venning and Browne (49), for example, were able to demonstrate the presence of gonadotropin during mid-cycle in only four of ten subjects studied. However, they secured information of physiological importance concerning the timing of events related to ovulation. Subsequent investigators employing improved methods of extraction and such biological criteria as rat ovarian and uterine weight and mouse uterine weight (all of which are thought to reflect the combined action of FSH and ICSH) have secured positive responses on virtually every day of the menstrual cycle.

Attempts to increase the specificity of bioassay by effecting a prior chemical separation of the hormonally active substances, present in very low concentration in body fluids, have so far met with failure (23, 39, 46). This, and other (30–32) negative evidence has led a growing number of investigators to postulate that the original characterization of FSH and ICSH from pituitary tissue constituted a chemical artifact and that, in reality, the pituitary secretes but one gonadotropic hormone.

Pending the characterization from body fluids of a homogeneous substance or substances possessing follicle-stimulating and luteinizing properties, an alternative approach is to attempt a biological, in lieu of a chemical, partition by the employment of response criteria thought to be relatively specific for one or other of the two hormones. Efforts were made by a number of investigators to utilize the known effects of pituitary ICSH upon the interstitial tissue of the hypophysectomized male and female rat for the detection of ICSH apart from FSH. However, only fragmentary and conflicting results were obtained (13, 17, 24, 45, 47, 48) because extracts prepared by precipitation with organic solvents or by ultrafiltration proved toxic to hypophysectomized animals in doses too small to elicit consistent physiologic effects. When, in 1952, we (34) found that urine purified by the technique of kaolin adsorption, as modified by Bradbury et al. (5), could be tolerated by hypophysectomized rats in doses sufficient to elicit graded physiological responses, the way appeared open to utilize this approach in the study of the human menstrual cycle. According to traditional dualistic theory, the mid-portion of the cycle constitutes the period when a preovulatory increase in ICSH over FSH secretion might be anticipated. Therefore, it seemed of interest to determine whether, in fact, any difference in the urinary excretion of these hormones could be detected during mid-cycle, using ventral prostate weight as an indicator of ICSH and testis weight as an indicator of FSH effect.

Greep and his co-workers (19) have shown that biologically pure FSH induces a selective growth of the seminiferous tubules of the hypophysectomized rat and causes them to produce spermatozoa. ICSH, on the other hand, acts upon the Leydig cells of the testis, which it stimulates to produce androgenic hormone. The androgenic hormone, in turn, stimulates the growth of the accessory sexual organs, the penis, seminal vesicles, and prostate. The ventral lobe of the prostate gland was found to be a sensitive and relatively specific* indicator of ICSH effect (18), its weight not being influenced by the simultaneous administration of biologically pure FSH (15, 40, 41).

Admittedly, testis weight is a less specific indicator of FSH effect. Pituitary ICSH maintains the testis weight of hypophysectomized male rats when administered for periods of 15 days, beginning on the day of hypophysectomy (42). If, however, ICSH is administered after atrophy has been allowed to overtake the testes, its capacity to increase testis weight is slight. Repair of interstitial atrophy occurs, but the tubules exhibit minimal enlargement unaccompanied by differentiation of the germinal epithelium (40). In Table I are summarized the alterations in testis weight induced by graded doses of pituitary ICSH administered according to a procedure almost identical with that employed in the present study. Under these conditions, a dose of ICSH which constituted a maximal stimulus to ventral prostate growth increased testis weight by only 60%. Since testis weight approximates 550 mg. in intact rats of this age, the capacity for potential increase is in the vicinity of 400%. The effects of FSH and ICSH upon the testis appear to be additive, rather than synergistic, in character (15) (Table II). Therefore, although testis weight leaves much to be desired as an indicator of FSH effect, its qualified use appears justifiable.

---

* In certain strains of rats, growth hormone and prolactin appear to potentiate the action of ICSH or of androgen in some manner (33). However, the difficulty of detecting the presence of either growth hormone or prolactin in human urine is such as to suggest that the concentrations in which they are excreted must be exceedingly low. Their capacity to influence ventral prostate growth under the actual conditions of urinary gonadotropin assay is doubtful.

The data to be presented are drawn from a larger study (36), which dealt with the pattern of urinary FSH and ICSH excretion throughout the menstrual cycle.

TABLE I

THE EFFECTS OF PITUITARY ICSH UPON THE GENITALIA OF HYPOPHYSECTOMIZED MALE RATS[a]

Dose (micrograms of nitrogen)	Number of rats	Mean weights		
		Body (gm.)	Testes (gm.)	Ventral prostate (mg.)
0	8	48.5	130.7	8.49
1	9	52.4	142.0	11.01
2	6	49.3	160.8	16.97
10	5	44.9	209.6	34.58

[a] The animals were hypophysectomized at an age of 21 days. Two days later subcutaneous injections of ICSH were begun and continued for a total of 4 days. Necropsy was performed 24 hours later. From Shedlovsky, T., Rothen, A., Greep, R. O., van Dyke, H. B., and Chow, B. F., *Science* **92**, 178 (1940).

TABLE II

THE EFFECTS OF PITUITARY FSH AND ICSH UPON THE GENITALIA OF HYPOPHYSECTOMIZED MALE RATS[a]

Dose (micrograms of nitrogen)		Number of rats	Mean weights	
FSH	ICSH		Testes (mg.)	Ventral prostate (mg.)
0	0	4	116.1	6.86
20	0	4	187.9	7.89
0	4	6	128.4	10.02
20	4	5	187.4	11.36
30	0	4	204.4	7.25
0	5	4	124.7	13.77
30	5	5	212.8	11.87

[a] The hormones were combined *in vitro* and administered under the same experimental conditions as described in Table I. From Greep *et al.* (18).

I. Methods and Materials

The subjects were thirteen healthy volunteers, who were followed throughout a total of seventeen cycles. Their urine was collected in serial 24-hour specimens and concentrated by means of kaolin adsorption. Creatinine determinations were performed as a check against gross errors of collection. The equivalent of 6 hours of urine was administered to each of three hypophysectomized immature male rats, according to a method previously described (35). The animals were injected twice daily for 4 days, beginning on the third day after hypophysectomy, and killed on the day following the last injections.

Spot determinations of urinary pregnanediol content were made during the luteal phase of the cycle and the basal body temperature was recorded daily. The limitations of indirect indices of ovulation are recognized. However, it seems reasonable to presume that these cycles were ovulatory in character, inasmuch as pregnanediol appeared in the urine and a mid-cycle shift in basal body temperature occurred in every instance.

Since ovulation is a climactic event* whose timing is variable, it seemed essential to reduce the pooling of specimens to a minimum. Therefore, despite its limitations, a single-dose assay of individual specimens was preferred over a multiple-dose assay of pooled specimens. Prior to statistical analysis, the data were converted to logarithmic form.

II. Results and Discussion

A. Individual Patterns

The most striking feature of the individual patterns, and the only one which occurred uniformly, was a period of peak FSH and ICSH excretion during mid-cycle. The number of consecutive "days of maximal excretion"† at this time varied from one to four. In this respect and, indeed, in their over-all configuration, the individual curves bear a strong resemblance to many obtained by investigators who determined the level of urinary gonadotropin excretion by techniques employing rat ovarian histology (12), rat uterine and ovarian (3, 8–11, 21, 27, 37, 38, 52) weight, and mouse uterine weight (4, 29, 50, 51).

The magnitude of the mid-cycle increase cannot be inferred from these data, which provide a purely qualitative description of the excre-

* The rate of gonadotropin release in the rabbit has been studied (14) by noting the effect upon ovulation of hypophysectomy performed at intervals after mating. In this species, the preovulatory discharge of gonadotropin occurs in a sharp burst, as shown by the fact that ovulation is prevented only if the pituitary is removed less than 1 hour after coitus. The insensitivity of currently available methods of assay precludes determination of the concomitant changes in the gonadotropin titer of body fluids. However, if gonadotropin release in spontaneously ovulating species occurs at a comparable rate, the undesirability of even 24 hours' pooling of urine specimens is apparent.

† These have been arbitrarily defined as the days on which the testicular and prostatic responses exceeded the geometric mean of a given cycle by more than twice the standard error, calculated from the standard deviation of the organ weights of the control animals. Such differences may be regarded as statistically significant (p = 0.025).

tion patterns. However, the results of an earlier study (35) suggest that during mid-cycle the rate of ICSH excretion increases by two- to four-fold over that characteristic of the follicular and luteal phases. Albert (1) has recently analyzed his own and others' data obtained by the rat ovarian weight, mouse uterine weight, and hypophysectomized rat prostate methods and has found somewhat smaller relative increases during mid-cycle. To what extent the differences are a function of the methods employed, the use of a standard preparation in some cases and not in others, and the factor of pooling cannot be ascertained at present.

During five of the seventeen cycles the rate of excretion of FSH and ICSH was clearly on the increase before the day of minimum basal body temperature; in the remainder, the ascending limbs of the excretion curves and the luteal temperature rise tended to parallel one another. This close temporal relation between the peak period of gonadotropin excretion and the thermal shift is in agreement with such meager data as are available for comparison. Lloyd *et al.* (28) observed a rise in gonadotropin excretion just prior to the shift in basal body temperature in one normal subject. D'Amour (9) included records of basal body temperature and gonadotropin excretion among a variety of indices employed to determine the time of ovulation in five subjects. The incidence of abnormal cycles appears to have been unusually high in his study. However, in seven of the fifteen cycles during which both indices were utilized, close conjunction is apparent between a peak in gonadotropin excretion and the luteal rise in basal body temperature.

If a substantial increase in gonadotropin stimulation is a necessary condition for the occurrence of ovulation, the time relations between parameters suggest that ovulation more often follows than precedes the thermal nadir. Such an inference is in harmony with the limited clinical data which have been recorded. During eighteen laparotomies timed to coincide with a substantial rise in temperature, Buxton and Engle (7) found corpora lutea whose estimated age varied from 18 to 72 hours in twelve instances; in six, ovulation had not yet occurred. In six women whom Greulich and associates (20) subjected to laparotomy before the basal body temperature had risen, ovulation had not yet taken place; in fifteen operated upon when the temperature was either approaching, or had attained, the luteal plateau, ovulation was found to have occurred in every instance.

B. COMPOSITE PATTERNS

Composite patterns for FSH and ICSH excretion during mid-cycle were obtained by averaging each individual's day-by-day variation from the geometric mean of her own cycle in relation to an independently

derived variable, the basal body temperature. The day on which the basal
body temperature reached its lowest reading during the cycle was taken
as the mid-point* and designated as day 0. Days preceding the day of
minimum temperature became days −1, −2, etc. and those following
+1, +2, etc. The results are depicted in Fig. 2. In appraising their
significance, it should be borne in mind that the greater the departure

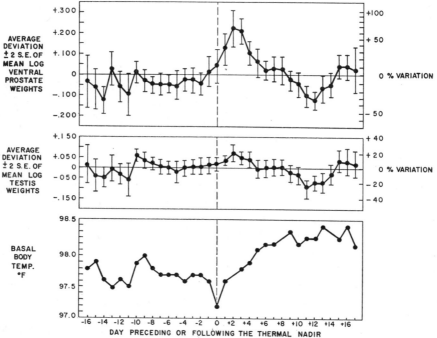

Fig. 2.   The average deviations from the mean log ventral prostatic and mean
log testicular weight of each cycle grouped in relation to the day of minimum basal
body temperature, together with limits indicating twice their standard error. Departures of composite values from the base line which exceed twice their standard
error are regarded as statistically significant ($p < 0.05$).

from the mid-point in either direction, the smaller the number of cycles
summated and the more variable the result.

It will be noted that: (a) a progressive increase in the excretion of
both FSH and ICSH began as early as day −2, but failed to achieve
statistical significance until the day after the thermal nadir, (b) the

---

* In cycles where no one minimum temperature was observed, the day on
which there was recorded the last low temperature before the sustained rise was
regarded as the day of minimum temperature.

level of excretion of both hormones remained significantly above the base line for a total of 4 days, and then gradually declined, and (c) the FSH and ICSH excretion curves tended to parallel one another closely.

Composite curves with which these data may be compared have been obtained by Buchholz (6) through a process of biological, rather than

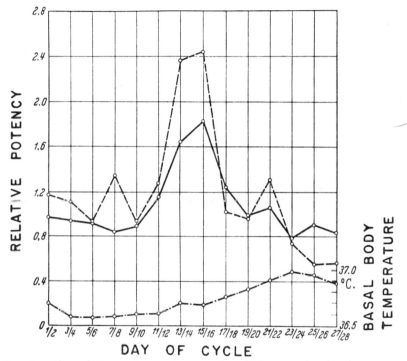

FIG. 3. The relative potency of successive 48-hour pools of urine compared with a laboratory standard by means of the mouse uterine weight method (o— — — —o) and the hypophysectomized rat ventral prostate weight method (o————o). From Buchholz, R., Z. *exper. Medizin* **128**, No. 3, 219 (1957). Springer-Verlag, Berlin, Göttingen and Heidelberg.

mathematical, summation. He combined the urine specimens collected by seventeen normal women throughout the menstrual cycle into serial 48-hour pools and assayed them for ICSH and "total gonadotropin" by the rat prostate and mouse uterine weight methods, respectively. In the timing and duration of the mid-cycle peak, the two biologically summated curves (Fig. 3) are strikingly similar to one another and to the mathematically summated curves derived in this study. The potency of the pool for days 15 + 16, the period of maximal excretion, assayed 2.44

times that of the standard by the mouse uterine weight method as against 1.83 by the rat prostate weight method. However, since there was virtually complete overlapping of the 95% confidence limits throughout, the two curves are regarded as indistinguishable from one another.

C.   QUANTITATIVE RELATIONS BETWEEN FSH AND ICSH EXCRETION

Whether proportionality as well as parallelism obtained between the FSH and ICSH excretion curves secured in this study was of considerable theoretical interest. Presumably, if a single gonadotropin or a constant mixture of gonadotropins were secreted throughout the menstrual cycle, the changes in prostate and testis weight would maintain a comparatively fixed relation to one another; if, on the other hand, two or more gonadotropins were secreted in varying proportions, this fact might be perceptible from alterations in the ratio of prostate to testis weight.

Accordingly, the quantitative relations between the day-to-day variations in testis and prostate weight were examined by computing regression equations expressing logarithmically the change in prostate weight per unit of change in testis weight. Manifestly, biological as well as statistical considerations must be taken into account in the interpretation of data obtained with unfractionated extracts. Slopes indicating a preponderance of ICSH might be expected to be reduced below their true value by the presence of FSH; slopes indicating a preponderance of FSH might be expected to be increased by the presence of ICSH.

The day-to-day variation in the coefficient* expressing the regression of ventral prostate on testis weight for the data, grouped in accordance with the thermal nadir, are depicted in Fig. 4. It will be noted that during mid-cycle, on days 0, +1, and +2, the slopes significantly exceeded the cycle mean. These slopes approximate values derived from data recorded by investigators who have employed the hypophysectomized male rat for the assay of pituitary ICSH preparations; at all other times, they are statistically indistinguishable from the mean trend for the cycle and approach the values derived from the assay of unfractionated pituitary gonadotropic extracts (36).

In suggesting that during mid-cycle there may be a change in the ratio of ICSH to FSH, and a relative increase in ICSH, the data are in agreement with the findings of Simpson et al. (43). These investigators

---

* The standard error of each coefficient was also computed and the squares of these standard errors were averaged, using as weights the number of cycles entering into the calculation of each coefficient. Regression coefficients differing by more than twice this average S.E.$_b$ from the mean trend are regarded as statistically significant ($p < 0.05$).

sacrificed monkeys on different days of the menstrual cycle and determined the gonadotropic potency of their pituitary glands, using follicle stimulation and interstitial cell repair in the ovaries of the hypophysectomized female rat as criteria of FSH and ICSH effect, respectively. Both FSH and ICSH were noted to attain maximal levels in mid-cycle, but ICSH appeared to increase relatively more.

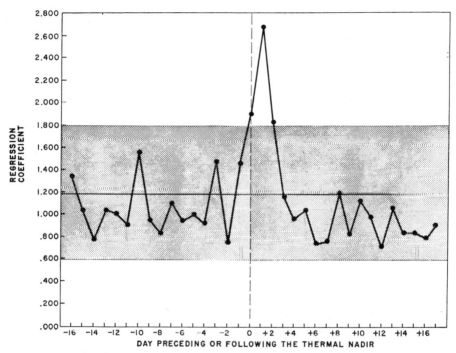

FIG. 4.   The day-to-day variation in the coefficient expressing the regression of ventral prostate on testis weight for the data grouped in relation to the day of minimum basal body temperature. The shaded area represents twice the average standard error about the mean trend. Departures from the mean by more than twice the average standard error are regarded as statistically significant ($p < 0.05$).

III. Comment

This study has been undertaken in an effort to shed light upon the difficult problem of the unity or multiplicity of the pituitary gonadotropic hormones. Changes in various biological parameters have been examined during the mid-portion of the human menstrual cycle, the period when a preovulatory increase in ICSH over FSH secretion might be predicted by the dualistic theory. A number of assumptions, which may or may not be entirely valid, have been made concerning the speci-

ficity of the indices employed and their dose-response characteristics. For
this reason, the results admit of more than one interpretation. However,
they suggest that during mid-cycle the excretion of ICSH increases more
than that of FSH, and hence that there are at least two pituitary gonadotropins which exist as separate entities.

Acknowledgments

These studies were supported, in part, by grants from the Barbara C. Willcox
Fund, the Milton Fund, the Commonwealth Fund of New York and research
grant A-364, National Institutes of Health, United States Public Health Service.

References

1. Albert, A., *Fertility and Sterility*, in press.
2. Albright, F., Halsted, J. A., and Cloney, E., *New Engl. J. Med.* **212**, 192 (1935).
3. Bagby, B. B., Jr., *J. Lab. Clin. Med.* **25**, 687 (1940).
4. Borth, R., Lunenfeld, B., and de Watteville, H., *Fertility and Sterility* **8**, 233 (1957).
5. Bradbury, J. T., Brown, E. S., and Brown, W. E., *Proc. Soc. Exptl. Biol. Med.* **71**, 228 (1949).
6. Buchholz, R., *Z. ges. exptl. Med.* **128**, 219 (1957).
7. Buxton, C. L., and Engle, E. T., *Am. J. Obstet. Gynecol.* **60**, 539 (1950).
8. D'Amour, F. E., *Am. J. Obstet. Gynecol.* **40**, 958 (1940).
9. D'Amour, F. E., *J. Clin. Endocrinol.* **3**, 41 (1943).
10. D'Amour, F. E., Funk, D., and Liverman, H., *Am. J. Obstet. Gynecol.* **37**, 940 (1939).
11. D'Amour, F. E., and Woods, L., *J. Clin. Endocrinol.* **1**, 433 (1941).
12. Drips, D. G., and Osterberg, A. E., *Endocrinology* **23**, 703 (1938).
13. Evans, H. M., and Gorbman, A., *Proc. Soc. Exptl. Biol. Med.* **49**, 674 (1942).
14. Fee, A. R., and Parkes, A. S., *J. Physiol.* **67**, 383 (1929).
15. Fraenkel-Conrat, H., Li, C. H., Simpson, M. E., and Evans, H. M., *Proc. Soc. Exptl. Biol. Med.* **48**, 723 (1941).
16. Frank, R. T., and Salmon, U. J., *Proc. Soc. Exptl. Biol. Med.* **32**, 1237 (1935).
17. Greep, R. O., and Jones, I. C., *Recent Progr. in Hormone Research* **5**, 197 (1950).
18. Greep, R. O., van Dyke, H. B., and Chow, B. F., *Proc. Soc. Exptl. Biol. Med.* **46**, 644 (1941).
19. Greep, R. O., van Dyke, H. B., and Chow, B. F., *Endocrinology* **30**, 635 (1942).
20. Greulich, W. W., Morris, E. S., and Black, M. E., *in* "Proceedings of the Conference on Problems of Human Fertility" (E. T. Engle, ed.), p. 37. National Committee on Maternal Health, Menasha, Wisconsin, 1943.
21. Heller, E. J., *J. Clin. Endocrinol.* **1**, 813 (1941).
22. Israel, S. L., and Mendell, T. H., *Endocrinology* **21**, 123 (1937).
23. Johnsen, S. G., *Acta Endocrinol.* **20**, 106 (1955).
24. Jones, G. E. S., and Bucher, N. L. R., *Endocrinology* **32**, 46 (1943).
25. Katzman, P. A., and Doisy, E. A., *Proc. Soc. Exptl. Biol. Med.* **30**, 1188 (1933).
26. Kurzrok, R., Kirkman, I. J., and Creelman, M., *Am. J. Obstet. Gynecol.* **28**, 319 (1934).

27. Levin, L., *Endocrinology* **28**, 378 (1941).
28. Lloyd, C. W., Morley, M., Morrow, K., Lobotsky, J., and Hughes, E. C., *J. Clin. Endocrinol.* **9**, 636 (1949).
29. Loraine, J. A., *Acta Endocrinol.* **31**, 75 (1957).
30. Loraine, J. A., and Brown, J. B., *Acta Endocrinol.* **17**, 250 (1954).
31. Loraine, J. A., and Brown, J. B., *J. Endocrinol.* **13**, i (1955).
32. Loraine, J. A., and Brown, J. B., *J. Clin. Endocrinol. and Metabolism* **16**, 1180 (1956).
33. Lostroh, A. J., Squire, P. G., and Li, C. H., *Endocrinology* **62**, 833 (1958).
34. McArthur, J. W., *Endocrinology* **50**, 304 (1952).
35. McArthur, J. W., Ingersoll, F. M., and Worcester, J., *J. Clin. Endocrinol. and Metabolism* **18**, 460 (1958).
36. McArthur, J. W., Worcester, J., and Ingersoll, F. M., *J. Clin. Endocrinol. and Metabolism* **18**, 1186 (1958).
37. Main, R. J., Cox, W., O'Neal, R., and Stoeckel, J., *J. Clin. Endocrinol.* **3**, 331 (1943).
38. Pedersen-Bjergaard, G., and Pedersen-Bjergaard, K., *Acta Endocrinol.* **1**, 263 (1948).
39. Rigas, D. A., Paulsen, C. A., and Heller, C. G., *Endocrinology* **62**, 738 (1958).
40. Simpson, M. E., Li, C. H., and Evans, H. M., *Endocrinology* **30**, 969 (1942).
41. Simpson, M. E., Li, C. H., and Evans, H. M., *Endocrinology* **30**, 977 (1942).
42. Simpson, M. E., Li, C. H., and Evans, H. M., *Endocrinology* **35**, 96 (1944).
43. Simpson, M. E., van Wagenen, G., and Carter, F., *Proc. Soc. Exptl. Biol. Med.* **91**, 6 (1956).
44. Smith, G. V. S., and Smith, O. W., *New Engl. J. Med.* **215**, 908 (1936).
45. Smith, P. E., Engle, E. T., and Tyndale, H. H., *Proc. Soc. Exptl. Biol. Med.* **31**, 745 (1933).
46. Stran, H. M., and Jones, G. E. S., *Bull. Johns Hopkins Hosp.* **95**, 162 (1954).
47. Tyndale, H. H., quoted by Engle, E. T., in "Sex and Internal Secretions" (E. A. Allen, ed.), 2nd ed. Williams & Wilkins, Baltimore, 1939.
48. Varney, R. F., Kenyon, A. T., and Koch, F. C., *J. Clin. Endocrinol.* **2**, 137 (1942).
49. Venning, E. H., and Browne, J. S. L., *Endocrinology* **21**, 711 (1937).
50. von Haam, E., and Rothermich, N. O., *Proc. Soc. Exptl. Biol. Med.* **44**, 369 (1940).
51. Werner, S. C., *J. Clin. Invest.* **20**, 21 (1941).
52. Woodward, F. R., and Main, R. J., *Virginia Med. Monthly* **68**, 530 (1941).
53. Zondek, B., *Klin. Wochschr.* **9**, 393 (1930).

Discussion

CHAIRMAN: J. ROCK

M. L. TAYMOR: We recently carried out ICSH assays in women who were undergoing laparotomy for other gynecological problems at the mid-cycle. I would like to confirm the finding of this peak of ICSH excretion. We certainly didn't go into the marvelous statistical analysis that was shown here. These patients were operated on what would be considered to be the 17th day of a 28-day cycle. This particular study utilized a method using two animals per level. The average of the ventral prostate weight is compared to a series of controls which weighed 9.4 mg. This was statistically significant to 1%.

The patients were operated on. In one patient a very early corpus luteum was obtained on the 17th day with proliferative endometrium putting ovulation approximately 24 hours before. In this particular patient, a peak of ICSH or LH excretion occurred approximately 48 hours before. In a group of six patients so studied, the peak of ICSH excretion occurred anywhere from zero to 48 hours before ovulation as dated by this method.

C. G. HARTMAN: I was a little disturbed about one point. The thinning of cervical mucus was the first of the three criteria of ovulation you have. Because the cervix is the most sensitive to estrogen, that would be the first effect as the estrogen rises. The rise in temperature comes 4 days later. Ovulation having occurred, it takes a couple of days for the progesterone, which is the cause of the rise in temperature in the cycle, to make its effects felt.

Now I may have misread your data, but it seems to me that your curve of greatest response is about in there and I would expect the greatest response to be before ovulation, if gonadotropin causes ovulation.

J. McARTHUR: In the excretion curves of the individual cycles, a rising trend in the excretion of FSH and ICSH can be seen to have begun several days before the day of minimum basal body temperature. Such levels in all likelihood acquire biological significance before they meet the rigid criterion of statistical significance. In the composite curve the same trends are evident, but they are diminished by the process of averaging.

I. ROTHCHILD: I have a comment I would like to make on one of the aspects of the curve that you have shown. I want to make sure first that I have interpreted them correctly. Is there actually a rise in the excretion of both FSH and LH starting about the middle of the luteal phase of the cycle and continuing up into the next cycle?

J. McARTHUR: Yes. There is a trend upward, which starts 3 days prior to the next menstrual period. In the composite cycle this trend approaches, but never quite attains, statistical significance.

I. ROTHCHILD: But it would appear as though the trend toward the mid-cycle rise, the peak that occurs at or about the time of ovulation, actually begins in the middle of the luteal phase of the preceding cycle?

J. McARTHUR: If you take a composite view of individual curves, it appears that there may be two peaks of gonadotropin excretion. There is one seen during menstruation itself which began earlier and which, in some individuals, reaches even higher levels than the true mid-cycle peak. But in many individuals this phenomenon was not observed at all, and when all these seventeen cycles are put together they tend to cancel one another out.

I. ROTHCHILD: I don't know whether it is worth while to make any comment, but maybe I can get you to make one, on whether you are willing to interpret this rise in excretion of gonadotropins that begins in the mid-luteal phase of the cycle, in terms of when the new cycle actually begins, or in terms of when follicular growth that leads to the next ovulation begins and how this is related to the death of the corpus luteum?

J. McARTHUR: I am afraid I would not hazard an interpretation of that, Dr. Rothchild.

Reproduction in Hot Environments

W. V. MACFARLANE, PAMELA R. PENNYCUIK,* N. T. M. YEATES,† AND
E. THRIFT‡

*Sir William MacGregor School of Physiology, University of Queensland,
Brisbane, Australia*

I. Introduction

Functionally a mammal is concerned first with survival as an individual: with growth, defense, and food gathering. Reproduction and continuance of the species are less emergent. In a temperate environment the organism is not likely to be under thermal stress, and if nutrition is adequate, both growth and reproduction are optimal. In fringe environments of habitable range of altitudes, temperatures, or humid-

---

* Present address: Zoology Department, Duke University, Durham, North Carolina.

† Present address: Department of Animal Husbandry, University of New England, Armidale, New South Wales, Australia.

‡ Present address: General Hospital, Toowoomba, Queensland, Australia.

ities, functional strain usually shows as deficient reproduction earlier than failure of individual maintenance or survival. There are of course races or strains of mammals that are genetically and physiologically capable of breeding and persisting in extreme temperatures. About 500 million humans live in the tropics. In India or Indonesia, for instance, they are too fecund for the economic and social matrix. There is a large postnatal wastage in those areas, but the prenatal efficiency of reproduction is unknown.

Temperate zone animals, even if adapted over generations, are measurably under strain in hot environments. In the tropical regions of Australia effective human conception, for instance, is reduced during the hot season. There are traditions (2) that white women suffer more abortions, particularly after several generations in the tropics, and have more unexplained amenorrhea than those in temperate regions. But it is not easy to obtain accurate data on this type of reproductive efficiency. As alternative approaches, field and laboratory studies of the possible effects of heat on tropical Merino ewes, and on partly adapted and heat-acclimatized rats were examined.

II. Human Reproduction

A. Seasonality of Conception

There is seasonal fluctuation with a summer minimum in apparent conception of man in the tropics of Australia, where there is an almost pure European population of temperate zone origin. Mills (7, 8) reported a similar summer minimum in the conception rate of the population of the southern United States. The monthly births occurring in Australia inland or along the coast at latitudes ranging from 44° to 10°S. were related to the annual mean birth rate (expressed as 1000). The conception time was taken to be nine calendar months prior to birth. These vital statistics relate to the years 1927–1936 and 1937–1946, inclusive. The war years' pattern did not differ apparently from that in the earlier decade.

In the tropical inland population there was 22% less apparent conception in midsummer than in midwinter (Fig. 1). The hottest period of the year occurs during two months prior to midsummer in this region, then the monsoonal rain provides cloud and relative coolness through autumn. On the coast the summer minimum of conception (14% below the winter maximum) is later by about two months than it is in the dry inland. The highest thermal stress is brought about during the humidity of later summer in this zone. In populations living further from the equator the winter peak of conception slowly disappears. This is more evident on the coast than inland, where a hot continental effect persists down to latitude 35°S. In the cold climate of Tasmania there is a reversal of the tropical pattern, with a winter minimum 24% lower than the summer conception rate.

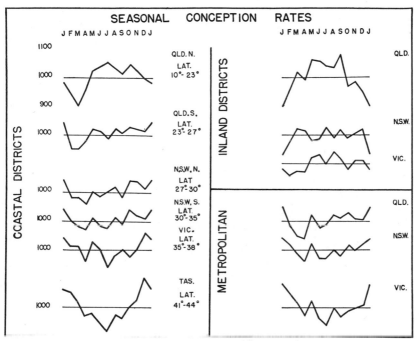

Fig. 1. The mean annual conception rate of European Australians for twenty years is used as a base line of 1000 to which the mean monthly conceptions are related. There was depression of conception in the hot periods of the year north of about 30°S. latitude. In the cold temperate latitudes there was winter reduction of conception. The continental climate inland showed a midsummer reduction in conception, but this was delayed one or two months on the coast where humid heat occurs in late summer.

These human fluctuations of reproduction with season may in time be eliminated as air-conditioning spreads. But the statistics presented measured over-all reproductive function during a period when relatively inefficient heat protection was provided for these tropical people.

B. Latitude and Conception Rates

A secondary check on the apparent effect of heat was made by comparing the seasonal reproductive trends in similar towns of different latitude as well as by comparing the annual birth rates of similar towns with different temperature ranges in Queensland (Table I).

W. V. MACFARLANE ET AL.

TABLE I

Comparison of Seasonal Reproductive Trends in Similar Towns of Different Latitudes[a]

Town	Lat. (°S)	Mean summer temp. °C. (°F.)	Mean winter temp. °C. (°F.)	Mean population (8 years)	Average conceptions Summer[b]	Winter[c]	P
Townsville	19°	27.2 (81)	20.6 (69)	34280	1438	1548	<0.001
Rockhampton	23°	27.2 (81)	17.2 (63)	36950	1488	1608	<0.001
Toowoomba	27°	21.7 (71)	11.1 (52)	34250	1554	1527	N.S.

[a] In towns of nearly equal population, but with different latitudes and climates, there was a significant difference over eight years between summer and winter conception rates when there was a hot summer. When the summer and winter temperatures were more nearly in the comfort zone, there was no difference between seasons.

[b] December, January, and February.

[c] June, July, and August.

The pairs of towns illustrated have very nearly the same number of inhabitants and social structure. There is little seasonal change in conception in the lower latitude (and higher altitude) towns. There are, however, significant differences between summer and winter conceptions in the tropical towns. Similarly there is a significant difference between annual gross birth rates in the tropical and subtropical towns of Queensland (Table II).

Athough birth weights were about 120 gm. lower in Cairns (latitude 15°S.) than in Brisbane (27°S.), this difference is not significant. Other factors than thermal load undoubtedly enter in determining population behavior. Economic developments, religious customs, and levels of education influence reproduction. The data presented probably represent an underlying effect of heat, yet in man it is almost impossible to prove a causal relation between environmental temperature and the changes of reproduction. The correlation may be translated more readily into cause and effect by the study of more manageable animals than man.

III. Tropical Sheep

The Merino sheep originated in the dry mountains of Andalusia and it survives well in both cold and hot environments. Yet in tropical Australia these sheep (which produce some of the world's best wool) rarely produce a lamb crop equal to 50% of the ewes mated. Other types of sheep, such as the Romney Marsh, developed in England and are limited to the cooler coastal zone in Australia, yet they are readily disturbed by thermal stress.

A. Environment and Reproduction

Part of the tropical reproductive inefficiency is due to male infertility caused by direct effects of heat in the scrotum and testis (5) or to epididymitis (9). The stimulus to rutting is normally the decreasing photoperiod of autumn (12), but in spring and summer, rams are less active because day length is increasing. Amongst Merinos, however, estrous cycles occur in ewes throughout the year, with autumn maxima and spring minima determined by light and regardless of temperature; while rams will mate to some extent during all seasons. The low reproduction rate is thus the product of many factors associated with heat and light, while nutrition is involved in an ill-defined fashion.

B. Dwarfism of Lambs in the Heat

It was observed in the field (9) that tropical ewes, pregnant during the hot season produced undersized lambs that were often too small or

TABLE II

COMPARISON OF ANNUAL BIRTH RATES IN SIMILAR TOWNS WITH DIFFERENT TEMPERATURE RANGES[a]

Town	Lat. (°S)	Mean summer temp. °C. (°F.)	Mean winter temp. °C. (°F.)	Mean population (8 years)	Birth rate/1000	P
Townsville	19°	27.2 (81)	20.6 (69)	34280	20.8	
Toowoomba	27°	21.7 (71)	11.1 (52)	34250	22.5	<0.001
Charters Towers	20°	27.7 (82)	18.3 (65)	7800	17.1 (21.1[b])	
Stanthorpe	28°	20.6 (69)	8.3 (47)	7560	25.9	<0.001

[a] Pairs of towns in Queensland, Australia, on different latitudes (but with similar populations) show a significant reduction of the eight-year sample of birth rates in the hotter environment. Mean temperatures were taken at 9 A.M. in a screen and averaged for each month.

[b] When corrected for a transient population of school children the difference from Stanthorpe is still significant.

weak to feed. Similar observations were made by Bonsma (1) on calves in Africa. Laboratory studies on sheep exposed to high temperature during pregnancy made it clear that light and food supply were not important factors in the syndrome. Heating the mother caused dwarfing of the lambs and dwarfing was proportional to the duration of heating and the thermal load. Romney Marsh sheep are much less tolerant to heat than Merinos. It was possible to reduce the size of Romney lambs to two-thirds normal (13) by three months' heat (7 hours a day) at 41°C. (Table III). For Merinos, five months at 44°C. was necessary to produce a similar change (14, 15). A hot room temperature of 44°C. dry bulb, 37°C. wet bulb, without sun radiation produced the same

TABLE III

DECREASES IN NUMBER AND SIZE OF LAMBS BORN TO ROMNEY MARSH EWES EXPOSED TO HEAT DURING PREGNANCY[a]

	Months of exposure to 41°C.[b] during pregnancy			
	0	Last 1½	Last 3	5
Number of ewes	8	6	6	6
Ewes failing to lamb	0	1	3	5
Lambs born	8	6	4	1
Average weight of lambs (kg.)	4.22	3.59	3.04	3.07

[a] Note that decrease in the number and size of lambs was proportional to the duration of heating.

[b] Dry bulb 41°C., wet bulb 31°C.

TABLE IV

COMBINED EFFECTS OF FOOD INTAKE AND EXPOSURE TO HEAT IN PREGNANT MERINO EWES[a]

	Series I		Series II		Series III	
Number of Merino ewes	10	10	6	6	8	10
Plane of nutrition	High	High	Low	Low	High	High
Max. air temp. (°C.)	26°	41°[b]	26°	44°[c]	26°	44°[c]
Duration, months	5	4	5	4	5	5
Ewes failing to lamb	0	0	0	2	0	0
Av. wt. of lambs (kg.)	3.83	3.71	3.13	1.81	4.17	3.34

[a] Merinos exposed to heat during pregnancy were little affected by 41°C. unless food intake was reduced. At 44°C. there was a 20% reduction in size of lamb. Dwarfed lambs appeared, however, and there were some apparent resorptions when poor nutrition was combined with heat. Low levels of nutrition did not cause dwarfing, but only lack of fat, when the ewes were in a cool environment. The differences between heated and cool lamb weights in Series II and III are significant ($P < 0.01$).

[b] Dry bulb 41°, wet bulb 33°C., 7 hours per day.

[c] Dry bulb 44°, wet bulb 37°C.

amount of respiratory cooling activity in Merinos as an air temperature of 41°C. in the field, where the sun's radiation doubled the thermal load. The size of lambs was significantly ($P < 0.001$) reduced by this severe heating (Table IV) whereas 41°C. in the hot room failed to have significant effect. When nutrition was reduced there was, in a cool environment, no decrease in stature of lambs, although there was some fall of weight. A combination of low nutrient plane with heat, induced dwarf lambs in which the adrenals were relatively enlarged and the bones were small (15). The mechanism by which heat produces the dwarfing is obscure—placental defect, reduced blood supply, pituitary insufficiency, or adrenal steroid excess are possibilities. Adrenal steroid and ACTH injected into the mother failed, however, to reduce the size of lambs in unheated ewes. Growth hormone may underlie the poor intrauterine growth.

IV. Wistar Albino Rats

Since human experiments are difficult in the field of reproduction and numbers of sheep cannot easily be studied in hot rooms, rats were employed in efforts to analyze the reproductive strain imposed by heat. Some experiments of a similar type were undertaken by Sundstroem (11) in California thirty years ago.

An inbred Wistar strain of albino rats was used. The strain had lived over twenty years on 27°S. latitude. Experiments fell into three groups: (a) comparison of the course of reproduction in female rats suddenly exposed to 32–35°C., with rats living at 20–28°C.; (b) comparison of heat-acclimatized and unacclimatized female fecundity; (c) comparison of a strain of rats living continuously at 32–35°C. during two to three generations, with rats at room temperature. Groups of twelve or more were used, except in the later generations at 32–35°C., where there were seven rats in a group.

A. Acute Heating of Pregnant Rats

Litter size was reduced to less than half by exposing pregnant females to 35°C. between the 6th and 12th days of gestation. Fetal resorption demonstrated by laparotomy was the main cause of fetal loss (6). Since protein, vitamin, and endocrine disturbance can cause fetal resorption in rodents these factors were adjusted. Some sparing of fetal resorption took place on increasing the protein and vitamin status of the diet, or on injecting thyroxine or progesterone (Table V). But three to four times the control resorption rate persisted in all groups of acutely heated rats (6).

TABLE V

EFFECTS OF PROGESTERONE ACCLIMATIZATION AND ACCLIMATIZATION PLUS
CORTISONE ON FETAL RESORPTION IN HEATED RATS[a]

	Temperature (°C.)	Number of mothers	Fetuses lost per mother	Resorptions Implants	% P[b]
Stock controls	22–28°	88	0.6	7	
Acute heat	34–36°	23	4.3	58	<0.001
Progesterone 0.1–1.0 mg./48 hr.	35°	25	2.6	32	<0.001
Acclimatized 2–4 weeks	35°	25	0.6	8	0.6
Acclimatized + 2 mg./100 gm./day cortisone	35°	8	4.1	60	<0.001

[a] Wistar strain rats fed on stock cubes were examined for resorption by laparotomy. When acutely heated to about 35°C. resorption of 58% of implants occurred. Mothers acclimatized 2–4 weeks resorbed few fetuses, but cortisone induced a reversion to a high resorption rate.

[b] Comparison of stock rats at room temperature with experimental groups.

B. ACCLIMATIZATION AND FETAL RESORPTION

Female adult rats were exposed for 14–79 days to 32–35°C., mated, and replaced in the heat. There was then no significant difference in resorption rate between control and heated rats, though acclimatization for periods beyond 28 days tended to increase resorption a little.

The sparing effect of acclimatization suggested that the placenta and fetus were destroyed during the process of acclimatization, which is normally associated with vascular adjustment and adrenal cortical activity. Injection of 2 mg. per 100 gm. cortisone acetate into cool rats caused 22% resorption, while the same dose of cortisone in heated acclimatized females, induced 60% of fetal loss. These findings suggested that the acute phase of acclimatization of rats to heat might be associated with the release of sufficient hydrocortisone-like steroids to induce resorption.

Other changes occurred, however, in acclimatized animals. There was a significant reduction in ovulation (as estimated from corpora lutea present at the sixteenth day of pregnancy) in acclimatized rats. In addition there was greater loss at the stage of implantation than in cool rats. These changes were studied more intensively in rats maintained during several generations in a hot environment.

C. STRAIN OF RATS LIVING AT 32–35°C.

By adequate protein and vitamin feeding, and by mating at first in a cool environment, a strain of Wistar rats was established at 32–35°C. Rats eat less in the heat and, since vitamin deficiency is a potent factor in fetal resorption (4, 10), increased quantities of vitamins were given. There may be increased need for the B group in the heat. Supplements of vitamins A and E and the B group (probably pyridoxine was the most important B vitamin) increased the growth rate of heated rats and improved reproduction, but the vitamins did not restore reproductive function to the level of controls.

To test the possibility that low food intake was responsible for poor growth and reproduction, groups of ten rats were fed on the same low nutrient plane at 20–25° and 34°C. Restricted food intake in the cool environment resulted in rats weighing 99.2 ± 10 gm. at 20 weeks, compared with 138.9 ± 8.9 gm. for rats living on the same amount of food at 34°C. Later generations continued to take smaller quantities of food than rats kept at room temperature but attained greater weights at 20 weeks (Table VI). The poor growth of heated rats was not primarily due, therefore, to food deficiency, nor to malnutrition, although vitamin E assisted growth in the heat.

Many rats did not survive the adaptive period, but the naturally selected colony differed functionally from the animals at room temperature from which it originated. The heated rats grew more slowly, ate less, drank more, moved less, and had shorter hair than the control groups. There were also reduced extracellular and increased intracellular fluid spaces.

The effects of heat on the various stages of reproduction from mating to weaning of the young may be compared in cool and hot rats on the same vitamin supplements.

1. Mating

Each male rat was caged 24 hours with a female in estrus. On successive nights twelve different females were offered. At room temperatures (18°–26°C.) males reared in a cool environment served 81.9% of possible estrous females and there were 65.3% of pregnancies. Males reared at 32–35°C. and mated at that temperature served 51.4% of cycles and 34.7% of females became pregnant. The heated males undertook 30.5% fewer services than room temperature males with equal opportunities (Table VI).

TABLE VI

REPRODUCTIVE EFFICIENCY OF A RACE OF ALBINO RATS REARED IN THE HEAT FOR THREE GENERATIONS[a]

	Rats at room temperature	No supplements 1st gen.	Generations at 32°–35°C. Supplements		
			1st Gen.	2nd Gen.	3rd Gen.
Weight of females at 20 weeks	156.7 ± 20	118.5 ± 8	131.5 ± 12	137.0 ± 6	139.1 ± 15
% Mated at 1st estrous cycle[b]	57%	—	34.6%	—	42.9%
Corpora lutea per ovulation	9.1 ± 1.0	7.4 ± 2.5	7.7 ± 1.3	8.6 ± 0.5	7.0 ± 0.5
Implants	8.4 ± 1.2	4.7 ± 1.9	5.3 ± 1.8	8.0 ± 1.3	5.7 ± 1.4
Viable 16-day fetuses	8.3 ± 1.2	1.2 ± 1.2	4.5 ± 2.0	7.2 ± 1.5	5.6 ± 1.2
Viable young	8.1 ± 1.3	0	2.2 ± 2.1	6.2 ± 1.6	5.0 ± 1.2
Gestation period (days)	22.1 ± 0.5	24.6 ± 1.7	23.6 ± 0.6	22.8 ± 0.7	22.8 ± 0.6

[a] All rats except those indicated were fed supplements of vitamins A, B group, and E and choline. There was a general reproductive dysfunction in the first generation of heat-reared animals, with some recovery in the second generation, and some regression in the third generation.
[b] Males and females were reared in hot or cool environments and mated at the temperature at which they were reared.

2. Estrus and Ovulation

In the absence of vitamin supplements in the heat, some females came into estrus only on the 5th to 8th day. There were more long cycles in heated than amongst unheated females. Corpora lutea were used as indices of ovulation, although occasional ovulations may occur with little visible luteal transformation. There was no consistent influence of diet on corpus luteum formation. But the first generation in the heat formed, on the average, one less corpus luteum per mating than rats at room temperature. Subsequent generations maintained this reduced ovulation, which was statistically significant ($P < 0.01$).

3. Implantation

The preparation of the endometrium for implantation is a hormone-controlled event which appears to be disturbed by sojourn in a hot environment. Three fewer implantations took place, on the average, in the first generation heated females than in rats kept at room temperature. This loss did not occur in the second generation, but recurred in the third generation of heated animals.

4. Fetal Survival and Resorption

Resorption of fetuses takes place between the 8th and 14th day of pregnancy, but mostly about the 10th day. Retroplacental hemorrhage and placental necrosis are the earliest signs of this process, and in some cases vascular occlusions take place in the uterus. Fetal necrosis and resorption take place in 2–3 days, leaving a visible uterine scar.

In the absence of vitamin supplements, heated rats resorbed 74% of implants but supplemented first generation females lost only 14% of implants in the heat. The second and third generation rats lost 10% and 2% of conceptuses, respectively, at this stage.

The evidence indicates that uteroplacental function was improved both by supplements to the diet (probably pyridoxine is important) and by long-term acclimatization taking place over generations.

5. Duration of Pregnancy

At room temperature, pregnancy lasted 22.1 days. Heating, without vitamin additions, prolonged the period of gestation to 24.6 days. Some shortening of gestation was produced by giving vitamins A and E to the first heated generation of mothers. In the second and third generations an average of 22.8 days was found for the duration of pregnancy when vitamins were added to the diet.

6. Viable Young

When pregnancy was prolonged, fewer viable young appeared. Heated females (first generation) littered 96% of the fetuses present at 16 days, when pregnancy lasted 22 days. But 25-day pregnancies resulted in live birth of only 12.5% of the fetuses present at 16 days. There was progressive decrease of survival as the pregnancy failed to terminate, with an average of 28% more fetal deaths for each day of prolongation beyond 22 days. There was no sex differential in survival.

Fetal mortality after inspection of the uterus by laparotomy at the sixteenth day was 100% in heated rats without supplements. Survivals increased when supplements were given.

7. Postnatal Development

Estimation of lactation was difficult. But it was observed that heated mothers were indifferent to their young and often ate them. For this reason it was necessary to have parturition take place in a cool environment, and the first two postnatal days were spent at room temperature. This allowed survival of the first and second generation young while they adapted to milk feeding.

Room temperature mothers showed an increase of weight during lactation and heat-reared animals, lactating at room temperature, exaggerated this effect. When lactation took place in the heat, maternal weight fell until the time of weaning. This could be correlated with adrenal function and water status, since adrenalectomized rats (3) also fail to gain weight during lactation.

There was no significant difference of birth weights between heated and unheated rats. Since the average number of rats per litter was smaller in heated animals, this could mean an increased relative weight at 32–35°C. This would be expected in the first generation where many of the young were postmature by 1–5 days. The growth in weight of the young after birth was significantly ($P < 0.01$) slower among heated animals than in those at room temperature. At room temperature the average weaning weight was 29.5 ± 4.3 gm. while first generation rats reached 26.7 ± 4.3 gm. and the second generation 25.2 ± 6.6 gm. at weaning.

During the postnatal period the heated mother, under nutritional strain also, behaves less adequately toward her young. She may eat them or neglect them. She loses weight, even when given supplements, and her young grow more slowly in weight than young rats at room temperature.

Pituitary and adrenal hormones may combine with behavior changes to cause these defects.

8. *Endocrine Glands*

The weights of pituitary, thyroid, adrenal glands, and gonads were measured in control and chronically heated races. There was significant reduction in the weight per 100 gm. body weight of ovary and adrenal glands among the heated females. The glands were not atrophic; but reduced activity probably resulted from the reduction in mass.

The observations on heated rats could, as a first approximation, be interpreted to be the product of hypopituitarism. This would account for the poor growth rate of the rats in the heat, the small ovaries and adrenals, their irregular and reduced ovulation, poor luteal response, placental dysfunction, and their prolonged gestation. The sluggish behavior and short hair could be associated with low levels of thyroid activity. The intracellular increase of water and relative frailty of the heated rats may be linked with the small adrenal glands, and failure to gain weight during lactation could be the result of relative adrenal cortical deficiency. There are almost certainly, however, other factors than the anterior pituitary and its associated glands involved in the functions of such a strain of animals. The cellular and genetic bases of the adaptation require further examination. It remains to be determined, also, whether the changes induced during several generations in the heat are reversed at once or are genetically maintained.

V. Conclusions and Summary

Europeans in the Australian tropics conceive less frequently in summer than in winter. This cannot easily be explained, but reduced ovulation and fetal resorption may contribute, as well as any behavioral changes in mating.

Among sheep exposed to heat there are notable racial differences in reproduction. There is more apparent fetal resorption and dwarfing of the lamb at lower temperatures in the Romney Marsh breed derived from wet cold regions than in the Merino, which developed in a dry and hot climate. Dwarfing of lambs may be associated with adrenal steroid excess, but the endocrine complex underlying the condition remains obscure.

Pregnant white rats acutely exposed to heat in the first half of gestation respond by fetal resorption. Protein and vitamin or thyroxine and progesterone supplements prevent some of the resorption. Acclimatization of the mothers, however, leads to normal fetal survival during pregnancy in the heat. This sparing effect is readily reversed by cortisone. When rats were brought up at 35°C. over several generations, a race of rats was developed with slow growth and low reproductive potential. They present a hypopituitary type of syndrome with small ovaries and adrenals. All stages of reproduction from mating behavior and ovulation, to lactation and mothering are disturbed.

Some of the mechanisms analyzed in heated rats may be relevant to the economic and social problems associated with reproduction of the larger mammals in the tropics.

Acknowledgments

We are indebted to Mr. D. Solomon for the provision of statistics on births in Australia and to Dr. D. Spalding for his analysis of differences in conception rate between towns.

References

1. Bonsma, J. C., *J. Agr. Sci.* **39**, 204 (1949).
2. Castellani, A., and Chalmers, A. J., "Manual of Tropical Medicine," 2nd ed., p. 98. Woods, New York, 1913.
3. Cupps, P. T., *Endocrinology* **57**, 1 (1955).
4. Evans, H. M., and Simpson, M. E., *Endocrinology* **27**, 305 (1940).
5. Gunn, R. M. C., Sanders, R. N., and Granger, W., *Bull. Council Sci. Ind. Research No.* **148** (1942).
6. Macfarlane, W. V., Pennycuik, P. R., and Thrift, E., *J. Physiol.* (*London*) **135**, 451 (1957).
7. Mills, C. A., *Arch. Biochem.* **1**, 73 (1943).
8. Mills, C. A., and Senior, F. A., *A.M.A. Arch. Internal Med.* **46**, 921 (1930).
9. Moule, G. R., *Australian Vet. J.* **30**, 153 (1954).
10. Nelson, M. M., Emerson, G. A., and Evans, H. M., *Proc. Soc. Exptl. Biol. Med.* **45**, 157 (1940).
11. Sundstroem, E. S., *Univ. Calif.* (*Berkeley*) *Publs. in Physiol.* **1**, 103 (1930).
12. Yeates, N. T. M., *J. Agr. Sci.* **39**, 1 (1949).
13. Yeates, N. T. M., *J. Agr. Sci.* **43**, 199 (1953).
14. Yeates, N. T. M., *Australian J. Agr. Research* **7**, 435 (1956).
15. Yeates, N. T. M., *J. Agr. Sci.* in press (1958).

Discussion

CHAIRMAN: J. ROCK

J. STUCKI: You will recall that Nelson and Evans of California found that pregnant rats fed a protein- and pyridoxine-deficient diet failed in most cases to produce living young, but that the administration of exogenous progesterone to these deficient pregnant rats greatly increased their ability to produce living young. Have you found that progesterone increases the ability of your heated rats to produce living young?

W. V. MACFARLANE: All the heated rats that we are talking about have had vitamin supplements which are more than enough to compensate for any decreased food intake. We gave the acutely heated rats vitamins plus progesterone and rescued quite a lot of fetuses; but the second and third generation rats have not received progesterone although they received pyridoxine, vitamin E, and vitamin A. I think there is some other action of heat in addition to any action dependent on the vitamins and proteins, but it is uncertain whether progesterone plus vitamins would have rescued fetuses, especially since in the acutely heated rats the combination did not save more than 20% of the fetuses.

S. SEGAL: I would just like to comment on your last remark and point out that the tropics represent the area of the world with the most explosive population growth at the present time. I would also like to ask, just out of curiosity, really, if there is any relationship between this area of reduced reproduction rate among the sheep and the occurrence of the subterranean clover in Australia that is supposed to be estrogenic and to have an influence on fertility.

W. V. MACFARLANE: Yes. The human population is obviously pretty well adapted. It very reasonably doesn't stay out in the noonday sun like sheep. One sensible part of human organization is to get under cover, and that cuts down the heat input a great deal.

No, the subterranean clover does not grow anywhere near this tropical territory. It requires quite a good rainfall. The rainfall in the tropical sheep country is intermittent. It is heavy for two months and then dry, so sub-clover doesn't survive.

C. G. HARTMAN: Have you counted rams' sperms for seasonal changes in number? Fred McKenzie and V. Berliner [*Missouri Univ. Agr. Expt. Sta. Research Bull. No.* **265** (1937)] found fewer in the summer season. Dr. Robert Hotchkiss noted the same for men ("Fertility in Men," p. 147. Lippincott, Philadelphia, 1944). E. Huntington's "Season of Birth" (Wiley, New York, 1938) contains some data on relatively fewer conceptions in summer in Miami, Florida; no seasonal changes in Boston; while Charleston, South Carolina, was intermediate.

J. ROCK: I think it just as well we don't bring in all the factors that Dr. Hartman might mention as affecting seasonal conception frequencies.

The Effects of Increase or Decrease of Body Temperature or of Hypoxia on Ovulation and Pregnancy in the Rat

Luis Fernandez-Cano[*]

San Marcos University, Lima, Peru, and the Worcester Foundation for Experimental Biology, Shrewsbury, Massachusetts

I. Introduction

Various disturbances of reproduction have been described in mammals subjected to hot climate or high altitude. Castellani and Chalmers (6) have demonstrated a high rate of abortion and of dysmenorrhea in women in hot climates; Macfarlane *et al.* (15) described 30% reduction in human conception in the summer months as compared with the winter months in Australia; Sundstroem (31) and Macfarlane *et al.* (15) found high rates of fetus resorption in rats subjected to increased temperatures; Ogle (19) showed a reduction in litter size when mice were kept at 31–32°C.; and Chang (7) demonstrated the degeneration of rabbit fetuses after administration of pyrogen.

In regard to high altitude, there is historical evidence of its effect on reproduction in man and in animals, dating back to at least the Peruvian conquest and colonization by the Spaniards(16).

The historian Antonio de la Calancha wrote in his "Cronica" (9) that when the city of Potosi (14,000 ft. above sea level) was founded, there were 100,000 natives and 20,000 Spaniards seeking gold and riches. While the former went on reproducing with customary Indian fertility, the latter either did not succeed in having children or the children failed to survive. The birth of the first Spaniard did not take place until fifty-three years after the founding of the city and was attributed to a miracle performed by St. Nicholas of Tolentino.

---

[*] Now Research Fellow in Gynecology, Harvard University; Rock Reproductive Study Center at the Free Hospital for Women, Brookline, Massachusetts.

De la Calancha (9) described this episode as follows: "Francisco Flores, who is now secretary to the Royal High Court of Lima, did not succeed in raising a single child. He was a devotee of St. Nicholas and decided to dedicate his first child to his protection; trusting that the Saint would preserve the child even without taking it away from Potosi, he promised to name him after the Saint, who subsequently gave him a son. He was born on Christmas Eve in the year 1598. He gave it the name of Nicholas and raised him there, curing him miraculously of many sick spells caused not by the cold but by other deadly diseases.

"He who was this child, is now become a Doctor in this university and an Alderman on the Municipal council, known as Doctor Don Nicholas Flores, he was the first child of Spaniard parents to be born and survive in 53 years. This novelty so impressed the people that it was acclaimed a miracle and now everyone dedicated his child to Saint Nicholas and by naming it after him, the child would survive, so that in those times all those who were born were called Nicholas."

The animals were also affected in this change of environment, and one of the motives for transferring the capital of Peru from Jauja (11,500 ft. above sea level) to Lima (sea level) was precisely the fact of infertility of animals or the high mortality rate among newborn animals in the higher location. In the act for the founding of Lima (14), it is pointed out that there was at Jauja "the great disadvantage and lack felt by the citizens, who people this said city in that, neither there, nor in its surroundings, nor anywhere in the upland could pigs be raised, nor mares, nor fowls because of the great cold and sterility of the land and because we have seen by experience among the many mares that have dropped colts their offspring usually die, and finally because we could not ever secure wood to build our dwelling houses."

In contemporary literature, Monge (16) reported human infertility in several coastal couples during residence in the Andes, whereas they had reproduced before and did so again later when back at sea level. Cutting (8) reported that Dachshund and Dalmatian dogs did not reproduce in Lhasa, Tibet at an altitude of 10,000 ft. Dohan (10), Shettles (29), Altland (2), Sundstroem and Michaels (32), Monge and San Martin (18), San Martin and Atkins (24), and Monge and Mori-chavez (17) observed that continuous or intermittent changes of altitude induced disturbances in the reproductive functions evidenced as diminution of libido, prolonged diestrum, and trophic changes in the germinal epithelium. Ingalls et al. (13) reported increased resorption of fetuses in mice under chronic hypoxia.

The present study reports the effects of increased or decreased body temperature or of hypoxia on ovulation of the rat and also the effects of these conditions imposed at various times after fertilization on the subsequent development of embryos in normal and adrenalectomized rats.

II. Methods

Adult female rats of the Sprague-Dawley strain, weighing about 200–250 gm., were used. A thermostatically controlled oven at an average air temperature of $103° \pm 1°F.$ was used to effect increase of body temperature; an ordinary refrigerator at $26°F.$, decrease of body temperature. A large desiccator with a suction device to maintain barometric pressure at 410 cm. of mercury was used as a hypoxia chamber.

We observed the time interval between caging with the males and the occurrence of a successful fertile mating, which has been described by Slechta et al. (30) as an indication of inhibition of ovulation in rats. The method was applied as follows: (a) The animals were subjected to the experimental conditions for 5 hours daily for 2 consecutive days. (b) Then they were caged with adult males of proved fertility, six females and two males per cage. (c) The females were examined regularly for vaginal sperm. (d) When pregnancy was established, the females were sacrificed. The presumed length of pregnancy was determined by the time since the appearance of vaginal sperm, and checked by the crown-rump length of the normal embryos. (e) Control animals without treatment were similarly caged and subjected to the same regime as the experimental animals.

To study the effects of the experimental conditions on pregnancy of the rat, normal females were first caged with fertile males from 5 P.M. to 8:30 A.M. and then immediately examined for vaginal sperm. The day that vaginal sperm were observed was considered as day 0. Then on each of 2 consecutive days—either days 1 and 2, days 3 and 4, days 6 and 7, or days 10 and 11—the females were kept under the experimental conditions for 5 hours. A group of rats without treatment served as controls.

For the experiments with adrenalectomized animals, the surgery was performed according to the description of Dorfman (11) on the day before the start of treatment. Immediately after the adrenalectomy, the animals were treated with subcutaneous implantation of 10 mg. of DOCA (11-deoxycorticosterone acetate) in pellet form and were thereafter given normal saline (0.9% NaCl) to drink. The control animals were adrenalectomized at the same times as the experimental groups and received the same doses of DOCA and saline to drink but were not subjected to increase or decrease of body temperature or to hypoxia.

The animals were sacrificed on the 15th or 18th day after mating. In the adrenalectomized group, the adrenal region was examined to ascertain the complete removal of the adrenal in every case. The number of corpora lutea present in the ovary were counted under a stereoscopic microscope. Both uteri were cut open and examined, and the number of normal fetuses and number of placentas with degenerated embryos counted.

By comparing the number of corpora lutea with the total number of normal fetuses and placentas, the percentage of degeneration before implantation was deduced. By comparing the number of corpora lutea with the number of placentas showing embryo degeneration, the percentage of degeneration after implantation was calculated.

III. Results and Discussion

Figure 1 shows the rectal temperature when rats were kept in the oven or in the refrigerator for 5 hours. When the animals were subjected to an environmental temperature of 103° ± 1°F., body temperature increased from 99° ± 1°F. to 104° ± 1°F. in 1 hour's time and kept relatively steady for the next 4 hours. When the animals were kept in the refrigerator at 26°F., the body temperature decreased from 99° ± 1°F. to 94° ± 1°F. in 1 hour's time and continued to drop during the next 4 hours.

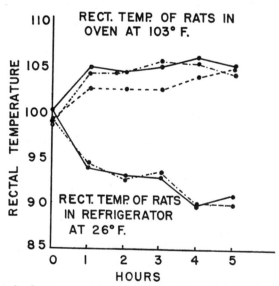

Fig. 1. Graph showing rectal temperature of rats kept in environmental temperatures of 103°F. and 26°F. From L. Fernandez-Cano, Effect of increase or decrease of body temperature and hypoxia on pregnancy in the rat. *Fertility and Sterility* **9**(5), 455-459 (1958).

Table I presents data on the time required for the establishment of pregnancy in the control animals and in those subjected to the experimental conditions for the 2 days immediately before caging. The interval between caging and successful mating is significantly increased in all the experimental groups; in each experimental condition the increase is approximately equivalent to three normal cycles. This seems to indicate inhibition of ovulation during this length of time.

TABLE I

THE EFFECT OF INCREASE OR DECREASE OF BODY TEMPERATURE OR OF HYPOXIA ON ESTABLISHMENT OF PREGNANCY IN THE RAT

Group	Number of animals	Average number of days between cohabitation and successful mating	P against control
Control	24	3.7 ± 3.4	—
High body temperature	30	14.1 ± 6.2	<0.001
Low body temperature	28	11.8 ± 8.0	<0.001
Hypoxia	28	12.7 ± 6.8	<0.001

As shown in Table II, each experimental condition—increased body temperature, decreased body temperature, and hypoxia—resulted in a significant increase in percentage degeneration of embryos, regardless of the days on which treatment occurred. However, the most pronounced effects on the embryos were observed with temperature changes *before* implantation and with hypoxia *after* implantation.

With increased body temperature there was 64% total degeneration when treatment occurred on days 1 and 2; 31%, when on days 3 and 4; and only 12%, when on days 10 and 11. Total degeneration in the control was 2.4%. With decreased body temperature there was 30% total degeneration when treatment occurred on days 1 and 2; 37%, when on days 3 and 4; and only 14.2%, when on days 10 and 11. The corresponding figures for the group subjected to low barometric pressure are 24.2% degeneration for treatment on days 1 and 2; 29.6%, when on days 3 and 4; and 68%, when on days 10 and 11.

Table III shows the effect of high or low body temperature or hypoxia on the pregnancy of adrenalectomized rats. There is no statistically significant difference between any adrenalectomized experimental group and the adrenalectomized controls. That the adrenalectomy per se does not increase the embryonic degeneration is shown by the absence of statistically significant differences between the adrenalectomized controls and the intact controls (0.93 and 1.60 vs. 0.2; $P > 0.05 < 0.1$). DOCA and saline *per os* increase the resistance of the adrenalectomized

TABLE II

THE EFFECT OF INCREASE OR DECREASE OF BODY TEMPERATURE OR OF HYPOXIA ON THE PREGNANCY OF NORMAL RATS

Group	Days of treatment	Number of animals	Total number of corpora lutea	Degeneration (%)			Degeneration (mean for each animal)	S.E.	P (against control)
				Before implantation	After implantation	Total			
Control	—	16	166	2.4	0	2.4	0.2	0.11	—
High body temperature	1 and 2	8	98	52.0	12.0	64.0	8.3	1.6	<0.01
	3 and 4	8	117	28.0	3.0	31.0	4.6	2.6	<0.01
	6 and 7	8	95	2.0	14.0	16.0	1.9	0.5	<0.01
	10 and 11	8	89	2.0	10.0	12.0	1.3	1.8	<0.01
Low body temperature	1 and 2	8	93	25.0	5.0	30.0	3.5	1.0	<0.01
	3 and 4	8	98	33.0	4.0	37.0	4.5	1.4	<0.01
	6 and 7	8	100	3.0	13.0	16.0	2.0	0.2	<0.01
	10 and 11	8	91	2.1	12.1	14.2	1.6	0.5	<0.01
Hypoxia	1 and 2	8	103	21.3	2.9	24.2	2.1	0.4	<0.01
	3 and 4	8	108	25.9	3.7	29.6	3.8	0.3	<0.01
	6 and 7	8	97	0	25.7	25.7	3.1	1.0	<0.01
	10 and 11	8	94	2.1	65.9	68.0	8.0	1.4	<0.01

TABLE III

The Effect of Increase or Decrease of Body Temperature or of Hypoxia on the Pregnancy of Normal Rats

Group[a]	Days of treatment	Number of animals	Total number of corpora lutea	Degeneration (%)			Degeneration (mean for each animal)	S.E.	P (against control)
				Before implantation	After implantation	Total			
Control I	—	12	147	2.9	3.7	6.6	0.93	0.36	—
High body temperature I	3 and 4	12	145	1.4	4.8	6.2	0.83	0.24	>0.8
Low body temperature I	3 and 4	12	132	5.2	5.2	10.4	1.16	0.34	>0.6
Hypoxia I	3 and 4	12	122	2.4	5.7	8.1	0.80	0.40	>0.8
Control II	—	12	133	0	6.0	6.0	1.60	0.60	—
High body temperature II	10 and 11	12	133	4.5	4.5	9.0	1.00	0.63	>0.5
Low body temperature II	10 and 11	12	126	2.3	11.9	14.2	1.50	0.57	∞
Hypoxia II	10 and 11	12	138	1.0	3.8	4.8	0.50	0.20	0.2

[a] I indicates adrenalectomy performed on day 2; these animals were sacrificed on day 15; II indicates adrenalectomy performed on day 9; these animals were sacrificed on day 18.

rats to stress conditions (12, 20) without being harmful to the embryos. When the adrenalectomy is postponed until the second day after mating, there is no interference with the formation of corpora lutea (4).

Shah (33) has shown that embryonic degeneration induced by high body temperature is due to the effect through the maternal environment rather than directly on the embryos; working on transplantation of early rabbit embryos, he found them normal when the temperature of only the donor rabbit was raised, whereas degeneration occurred when the temperature of only the recipient was raised.

The mechanism for the operation of this stress factor through the mother may well be the adaptation syndrome described by Selye (27) as a nonspecific reaction elicited by adverse environmental conditions. A feature of one phase of this syndrome is an increase of ACTH production with subsequent adrenal cortical hyperplasia together with an increase of cortical hormone secretion, as shown for high body temperature by Barlow et al. (3), for low body temperature by Seller (26), and for low barometric pressure by Pincus and Hoagland (22), San Martin et al. (25), Calderon (5), Aliaga (1), and others.

Comparison of our results in intact and in adrenalectomized rats points up a crucial role in a stress condition of the maternal adrenal gland on degeneration of embryos. It seems likely that the increased ACTH of stress conditions does not influence embryo degeneration directly but produces its effect by way of the adrenal gland, perhaps by increasing production of some of its hormones (cortisone, cortisol, corticosterone, etc.). Robson and Sharaf (23) have interrupted pregnancy in the rabbit and the mouse by the administration of either ACTH or cortisone. Degeneration of embryos followed administration of ACTH to intact rats, Velardo (34) found, but not to adrenalectomized ones.

It is also possible that in the present experiment the effect may be due to a shift of anterior pituitary hormonal production with an increase of ACTH and subsequent decrease of gonadotropic secretion (28) under stress conditions, since pituitary plays an important role in maintaining pregnancy in rats during the first 11 days (21). Our findings on inhibition of ovulation when rats were subjected to the experimental conditions tend to support this view.

It is still difficult to explain, on the basis of this general nonspecific stress-pituitary-adrenal reaction, the qualitative difference noted in the effect of temperature and hypoxia at different stages of pregnancy. This may depend on the quality of the stress stimulus, the critical stage of development of the embryo at the time of application of stress, and other maternal factors that may influence the development of the fetus.

IV. Summary

Experimental conditions of increase or decrease of body temperature or of hypoxia produced inhibition of ovulation in rats. When these same conditions were imposed on normal pregnant rats, there was a significant increase of embryonic degeneration, regardless of the time at which treatment occurred. However, the most pronounced effects on the embryos were observed with temperature changes before implantation and with hypoxia after implantation.

The same conditions do not increase significantly embryo degeneration in adrenalectomized pregnant rats.

The relationship between embryonic degeneration and adrenal-pituitary secretion under adverse conditions is discussed.

References

1. Aliaga, R., Thesis, Faculty of Medicine, San Marcos University, Lima, Peru, 1955.
2. Altland, P. D., *J. Exptl. Zool.* **110**, 1 (1949).
3. Barlow, G., Agersborg, H. P., Jr., and Keys, H. E., *Proc. Soc. Exptl. Biol. Med.* **93**, 280 (1956).
4. Burdick, H. O., Baird, J. A., and Rogers, R. T., *Endocrinology* **55**, 369 (1954).
5. Calderon, A., Thesis, Faculty of Medicine Veterinary Science, San Marcos University, Lima, Peru, 1955.
6. Castellani, A., and Chalmers, A. J., "Manual of Tropical Medicine," 3rd ed. Wood, New York, 1919.
7. Chang, M. C., *Federation Proc.* **16**, 21 (1957).
8. Cutting, S. C., *J. Am. Museum Nat. Hist.* **37** (1936).
9. de la Calancha, Antonio, "Cronica Moralizada de la Orden de San Agustin." Barcelona, 1639.
10. Dohan, F. C., *Proc. Soc. Exptl. Biol. Med.* **49**, 404 (1942).
11. Dorfman, R. I., *in* "Hormone Assay" (C. W. Emmens, ed.), p. 329. Academic Press, New York, 1950.
12. Houssay, B. A., *Rev. soc. arg. biol.* **21**, 316 (1945).
13. Ingalls, T. H., Curley, F. J., and Prindle, R. A., *New Engl. J. Med.* **247**, 758 (1952).
14. "Libros de Cabildos de Lima," Book I (1534–1539). Lima, Peru, 1935.
15. Macfarlane, W. V., Pennycuik, P. R., and Thrift, E., *J. Physiol.* **135**, 451 (1957).
16. Monge, C., "Acclimatization in the Andes." Johns Hopkins Press, Baltimore, 1948.
17. Monge, C., and Mori-chavez, P., *Anales fac. med. Univ. nacl. mayor San Marcos Lima* **28**, 15 (1945).
18. Monge, C., and San Martin, M., *Anales. fac. med. Univ. nacl. mayor San Marcos Lima* **25**, 58 (1942).
19. Ogle, C., *Am. J. Physiol.* **107**, 628 (1934).
20. Page, E. W., and Glendenning, M. B., *Proc. Soc. Exptl. Biol. Med.* **82**, 466 (1953).

21. Pencharz, R. I., and Long, J. A., *Science* **74**, 206 (1931).
22. Pincus, G., and Hoagland, H., *J. Aviation Med.* **14**, 173 (1943).
23. Robson, J. M., and Sharaf, A. A., *J. Physiol.* (*London*) **116**, 236 (1952).
24. San Martin, M., and Atkins, J., *Anales. fac. med. Univ. nacl. mayor San Marcos Lima* **25**, 41 (1942).
25. San Martin, M., Prato, J., and Fernandez-Cano, L., *Rev. San de Policia* **13**, 75 (1953).
26. Seller, E. A., *Rev. can. biol.* **16**, 175 (1957).
27. Selye, H., *J. Clin. Endocrinol.* **6**, 117 (1946).
28. Selye, H., and Heuser, G., eds., "Fifth Annual Report on Stress," p. 53. MD Publications, New York, 1956.
29. Shettles, L. B., *Federation Proc.* **6**, 200 (1947).
30. Slechta, R. F., Chang, M. C., and Pincus, G., *Fertility and Sterility* **5**, 282 (1954).
31. Sundstroem, E. S., *Physiol. Revs.* **7**, 320 (1927).
32. Sundstroem, E. S., and Michaels, G., *Mem. Univ. Calif.* **12** (1942).
33. Shah, M. K., *Nature* **177**, 1134 (1956).
34. Velardo, J. T., *Am. J. Physiol.* **191**, 319 (1957).

Discussion

CHAIRMAN: J. ROCK

G. PINCUS: In connection with these effects on the rat, it should be pointed out that the rat differs from the human in its steroidogenic capacity. The rat is a producer of small amounts of hydrocortisone, so that one of the questions that might very well be asked is: Is corticosterone a potent agent for inducing embryo degeneration? I wish I knew the answer. Perhaps someone here does.

L. FERNANDEZ-CANO: The corticosterone and cortisol ratios are about 20:1 in the rat. I did not determine in this experiment the excretion of steroid hormones, but that would be very useful in the interpretation of the result.

E. BLOCH: My question is addressed to both of the previous speakers. Does temperature or hypoxia have any effect on the sexual differentiation of the fetuses; in other words, does the sex index of the newborn differ from your control studies?

L. FERNANDEZ-CANO: I cannot answer this question because in this experiment which you saw, I killed the animals after 15 or 18 days.

S. SEGAL: It may be of interest to Dr. Bloch that while this may not have been observed in mammalian experiments with heat, in amphibian experiments heating the eggs immediately after fertilization will alter the sex ratio and cause, in fact, 100% development of male larvae if the treatment is severe enough and for a long period of time.

E. BLOCH: This was after fertilization?

S. SEGAL: Yes.

C. G. HARTMAN: According to Selye, there is the stress reaction of the adrenal which causes an increase of adrenal corticoids. Then, there comes a period of exhaustion so that there is no more output of corticoids.

L. FERNANDEZ-CANO: This is correct. When we studied the acclimatization of humans at high altitude, we found that after a little more than one year the urinary steroids came back to the level originally found at sea level.

C. G. HARTMAN: Have you looked at the adrenals after a rat has been in the ice box for 12 or 24 hours?

L. FERNANDEZ-CANO: I have not.

Initiation and Maintenance of Testicular Function

SHELDON J. SEGAL AND WARREN O. NELSON

Laboratory of the Population Council, The Rockefeller Institute, New York, New York

I. Introduction

In reviewing some aspects of testicular physiology, the late Earl Engle suggested this provocative chronologic sequence for the phases of man's life (2):

Fertilization	minutes
Implantation	hours
Embryonic development	weeks
Fetal life	months
Puberty	two to three years
Senescence	decades

Contributory events toward the organization and function of the male gonad may be recognized during each of these phases. To include in this generalization those early moments of life, indicated by the first two listings, one must adopt the traditional theory of the continuity of the germinal line. Recent evidence from the study of human embryos, which shall be reviewed presently, supports this concept of separation of soma and germ plasm. An illustration of the principle of germ cell separation is provided by an animal form quite low in the phylogenetic order (Fig. 1). In the small crustacean, *Tisbe furcata*, by the time of the sixth cleavage division, a cell at the vegetal pole has accumulated special cytoplasmic inclusions, and its mitotic rate has become slower than that of all other cells (Fig. 1, d). This cell and its descendants, distinguishable from the general somatic cells at this early stage, can be traced through subsequent ontogenesis; it gives origin to the germ plasm (Fig. 1, k).

II. Early Embryologic Events

The question of separation of germ plasm and soma in the human has been controversial for many decades. In 1870, Waldeyer introduced the term "germinal epithelium" to describe the specialized portion of the coelomic epithelium which serves as the gonadal ridge (8). His

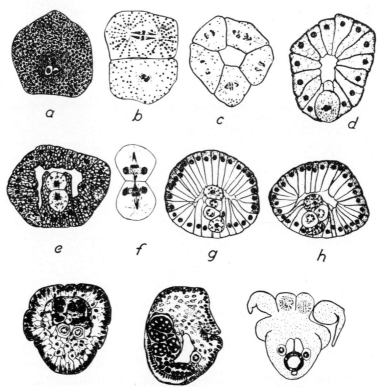

FIG. 1.   Separation of germ plasm and soma in the development of the crustacean, *Tisbe furcata* (11). Following the initial cleavages (a–c) a single large stem cell is present in the vegetal pole of the blastula (d). During gastrulation (e–h) division of this stem cell is unequal (f), resulting in two primordial germ cells, (g, center) and two endodermal cells. During differentiation of the larva (i–k) the two germ cells remain separate from the soma. This figure was kindly provided by E. Witschi.

observations led him to believe that germ cells proliferated from this somatic tissue. So uniformly was this supposition accepted in 1870 that Waldeyer's own recantation was virtually ignored in 1906 (9). In spite of the fact that the original proponent of the theory abandoned the embryologic concept of the "germinal epithelium," the term has persisted.

A. Germ Cell Migration

The origin of primordial germ cells of the human in the region of the yolk-sac endoderm and their migration by ameboid motion to the genital folds has been confirmed by several independent investigations. An admirable description of these events was published by Witschi (10), who studied several stages from the Carnegie collection of embryos. But these observations, employing usual histologic procedures, could not establish that the migrating primordial germ cells are the progenitors of the definitive germ cells of the primitive sex glands. The alternative possibility could still be proposed that the arrival of these migrating cells at the gonadal ridges *induces* the proliferation of the definitive germ cells from the local somatic epithelium. Final resolution of the question has been possible on the basis of the specificity of the alkaline phosphatase reaction exhibited by the germ cells (4). The migrating cells react specifically to this histochemical procedure during their migration from the endoderm, along the dorsal root of the mesentery, around the coelomic angles, and thence to the paired gonadal ridges (Fig. 2). No other cells of the coelomic epithelium show the alkaline phosphatase reaction. At a slightly later stage, when the definitive germ cells are characteristically distributed throughout the primitive gonad, the positive alkaline phosphatase reaction still prevails (Fig. 3). This indicates the continuity of the primordial germ cells and the definitive germ cells in man.

B. Organization of the Testes

During testicular development, at the completion of their migration, the germ cells distribute initially throughout both cortical and medullary rudiments of the indifferent gonad. As the medullary cords begin to organize during the second month of gestation, they incorporate those germ cells that have initially resided in the medulla. The majority of the gonia, however, originally locate in the embryonic cortex. These, along with their nurse cells, aggregate as cortical cords and cross the primitive albuginea (the primary gonad cavity) to become contiguous with the medullary cords. Condensation of cortical and medullary cords, representing the earliest specific stages of testicular development, can be recognized as early as 6 or 7 weeks of age. The testicular morphology becomes distinct about a week later when all the germ cells have departed from the coelomic epithelium and, crossing the albuginea, have been incorporated into the medulla. The cortex immediately becomes reduced to a single-layered epithelium covering the broad fibrous al-

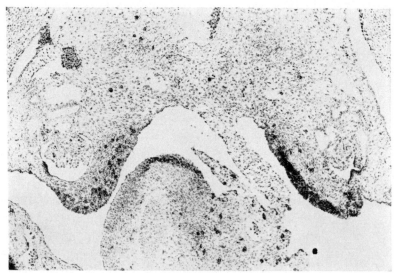

Fɪɢ. 2.   Cross section through gonadal region of 13-mm. human embryo prepared by the α-naphthyl alkaline phosphatase method. The germ cells are concentrated in the gonadal ridges; some can be seen in the mesenteric connective tissue. Magnification: ×97.5. This figure is from the original publication by McKay *et al.* (4) and was kindly provided by these authors.

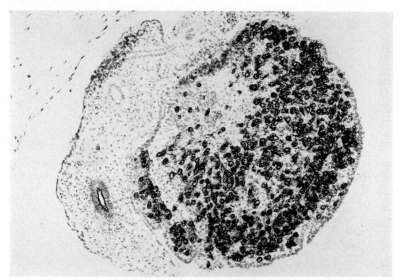

Fɪɢ. 3.   Cross section through gonad of a 35-mm. human female embryo. The germ cells are characteristically distributed throughout the gonad and still retain their positive reaction to α-naphthyl alkaline phosphatase. Magnification: ×135. This figure is from the original publication by McKay *et al.* (4) and was kindly provided by the authors.

buginea (Fig. 4). Into this region project the blood vessels, which give the testis its characteristic peripheral pattern of vascularization (Fig. 5).

In the development of the testis, the medullary component contributes to the medullary cords, the rete tubule connecting system, and, in addition, to the steroid-producing component of the male sex gland—the interstitial cells of Leydig.

C. Fetal Testicular Activity

Once organized in its characteristic morphologic form, the functional and developmental history of the testis is closely linked with its exposure to both endogenous and exogenous gonadotropic hormones. From the moment of its differentiation, the fetal testis is exposed to a significant quantity of chorionic gonadotropin. Although of trophoblastic origin, this hormone may be considered as an external stimulus to the fetus. Available evidence indicates that it enters the fetal system across the wall of the chorionic vesicle by seepage into the fetal fluids, rather than through the umbilical circulation. According to Bruner, the amount of chorionic gonadotropin in the fetal body as early as 11 weeks of age is physiologically significant (1). This assumption is supported by the morphologic stimulation of the interstitium of the fetal testes during late pregnancy and its post-partum regression. By the eighth fetal month, the Leydig cells show hypertrophy and secretory activity. Presumably these secretions contribute to initiating descent of the testes into the scrotum at this time (6). Soon after the fetus leaves its uterine environment, the Leydig cells regress and, in fact, are not identifiable for many years, until the approach of puberty.

III. Postnatal Development

During infancy the testicular cords have not yet formed lumina. They are small in diameter, containing undifferentiated, infantile sustentacular cells and spermatogonia. Reticular fibers are present in the intertubular spaces, but no distinct tunica propria has begun to organize (Fig. 6). The ensuing years of childhood and early adolescence proceed without the occurrence of maturation changes in the testes. The tubular diameters do not change significantly, but with increase in length, the tubules become moderately tortuous. Upon the initiation of hypophyseal gonadotropin production, several testicular phenomena herald the onset of puberty. The earliest phases are marked by the appearance of pale, fusiform cells in the interstitium. These interstitial cells gradually increase in number as sexual maturity becomes established. Although they do not achieve the characteristic morphology of adult interstitial cells for several years, they are functional and provide the source of androgen production through the puberal period. Apparently, differentiation of the intertubular connective tissue to form the tunica propria is related to this onset of androgen secretion. The tunica albuginea also undergoes maturation phenomena and thickening at the time of puberty. These

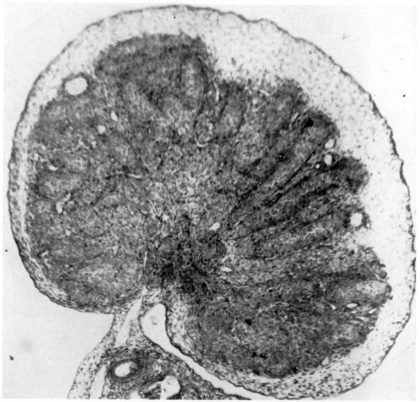

Fig. 4.   Cross section through the testis of human fetus of 56 mm., 11 weeks old. The embryonic cortex has been reduced to a thin epithelium covering the broad, fibrous albuginea. All germ cells have been incorporated into the medulla. Magnification: ×50.

events are now under study by Mancini, de la Balze, and their collaborators in Argentina (5).

The intratubular changes of puberty include the maturation of sustentacular cells and the initiation of spermatogenesis. Gamete production does not begin uniformly in all seminiferous tubules. Spermatogenic forms may appear in some tubules, while others retain their immature character for as long as several years. Even within a single

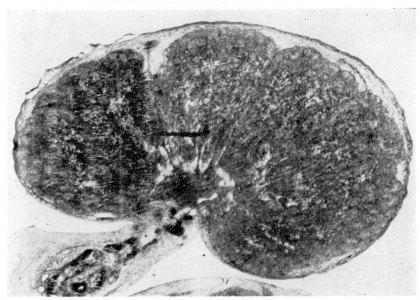

Fig. 5. Cross section through the testis of human embryo of 120 mm., 16 weeks of age. The albuginea has been reduced, and into this region have migrated the blood vessels, giving the testis its characteristic peripheral pattern of vascularization. Magnification: ×36.

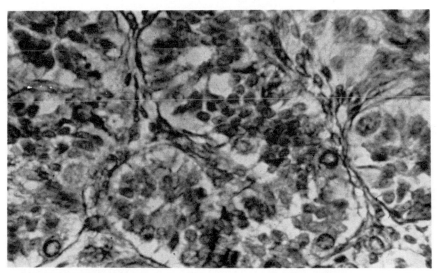

Fig. 6. Cross section through testis of 1-year-old infant. Nonpatent seminiferous cords with spermatogonia and undifferentiated sustentacular cells. Tunica propria is not yet organized.

tubule only patches of gametogenic activity may be observed during the
initial stages of sexual maturation (Fig. 7).

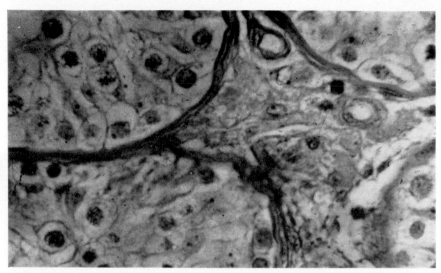

Fig. 7.   Testis of 13-year-old boy. Spermatogenesis occurs in patches within the
seminiferous tubules. Tunica propria has begun to organize from the intertubular
connective tissue. Interstitial cell development has become apparent.

By the completion of the puberal period, the male sex gland is fully
matured, and its dual function of gamete production and hormone
secretion may be maintained indefinitely (Fig. 8). It is now quite clear
that the hormonal function of the testis includes both androgen and
estrogen production. Testicular production of estrogen is undoubtedly
responsible for the presence of estrogenic substances in semen samples
of normal reproductive males (3).

IV. Testicular Function in Aging

With aging, there is a gradual increase in tubular fibrosis, but it
should not be generalized that this phenomenon corresponds to a gradual
loss of testicular function.

We shall consider now the question of maintenance of testicular
function with advancing age, presenting our observations concerning
this problem (7).* In this study we have analyzed various hormone
excretion levels of men, ranging to nearly 100 years of age, and have

---

* This work, in collaboration with Dr. Rubin Flocks, was carried out at Iowa
City with the cooperation of the Department of Urology.

determined average values of 17-ketosteroids, gonadotropins, and estrogens that can be correlated with chronologic age. But an analysis of this type shows that among a group of men within a particular age range, there exists a great variability in the quantity of each of these substances excreted per 24-hour urine sample. However, if the urinary hormone values are considered as a composite, representing an individual's hormone-excretion pattern, for most aging males, this pattern will fit one of several very distinct and characteristic types. Because a

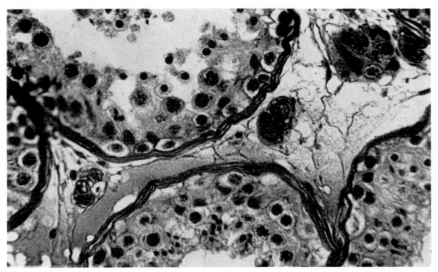

FIG. 8. Postpuberal testis from 18-year-old youth. This example represents the fully matured testis from all aspects, including intratubular, peritubular, and intertubular development.

testicular biopsy has been obtained from most individuals for whom the urinary hormone-excretion patterns were determined, it has been possible to correlate this hormonal index of testicular function with aging changes in the testis.

Figure 9 indicates the trend in the average 17-ketosteroid excretion with advancing decades of life. There is a gradual decline with aging until 60 years, but the value remains relatively constant thereafter. The normal range for young reproductive males is established as 6.0 mg. to 10.0 mg. per 24 hours. Until age 60, the average, though declining, remains in the normal range. Even among octogenarians, there are individuals with 17-ketosteroid values within the range for normal, young adults.

The percentage of cases with elevated gonadotropins increases slightly with aging; but increased gonadotropin excretion is not even generally characteristic of old age in the male. In the oldest age group, more than 50% of the cases have average excretion values (Fig. 10).

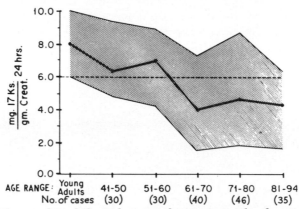

Fig. 9. The trend in daily 17-ketosteroid excretion with advancing decades of life. The shaded area delimits the upper and lower ranges obtained for each age group. Determinations of total 17-ketosteroids were carried out on three consecutive 24-hour urine samples from each subject, using the Zimmermann reaction following acid hydrolysis. Corrections for collecting-errors were based on creatinine determinations.

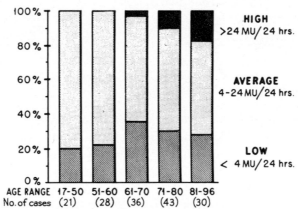

Fig. 10. Total gonadotropin excretion with advancing age. The light portion of each bar represents the percentage of total cases with normal excretion of gonadotropins per 24 hours (4–24 mouse units). The darkly stippled area of each bar indicates the percentage with elevated gonadotropins, and the lightly stippled region at the base shows the percentage of cases with low, actually nonassayable, gonadotropins. Total urinary gonadotropins were determined by biological assay following kaolin extraction of three consecutive 24-hour urine specimens from each subject. Assays were based on uterine weight increase in immature female mice.

As shown in Fig. 11, estrogen excretion values are at nonassayable levels in approximately 10% of the cases in the oldest age group, while elevated levels occur in almost 40%. The remaining 50% retain the average estrogen excretion values. Among the 180 cases studied in all age groups, only 22 failed to have assayable estrogens per 24-hour urine sample. The preferential retention of estrogen production by the aging testis, as indicated by these data, is emphasized by the composite hormone excretion values of the individual cases.

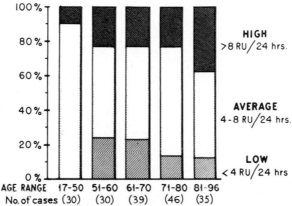

FIG. 11.   Estrogen excretion with advancing age. The light portion of each bar represents the percentage of total cases with normal excretion of estrogens per 24 hours (4–8 rat units). The darkly stippled area of each bar indicates the percentage with elevated estrogen levels and the lightly stippled region at the base shows the percentage of cases with low, actually nonassayable, estrogens. Urinary estrogens were assayed biologically using the phenolic fraction recovered after NaOH extraction of three consecutive 24-hour urine specimens from each subject. Assays were based on uterine weight increase in immature female rats.

In Table I are listed several aggregates of hormone assay values, each forming a distinct pattern. The designations assigned to these patterns are not proposed for literal interpretation, but they seem to apply, at least in a suggestive fashion, to the particular pattern described. A significant percentage of the cases (16%) have normal gonadotropin, 17-ketosteroid, and estrogen values. On the basis of hormone excretion pattern, they could not be distinguished from younger, normal reproductive males. By far the largest percentage of cases have a particular pattern characterized by at least normal estrogen excretion levels along with low 17-ketosteroids and nonelevated gonadotropin values. The high frequency (52%) with which this pattern appears shows that it, rather than any of the others, is the most characteristic of the aging individual. This pattern suggests a selective androgen loss by the aging testis, with a retention of estrogen production. For comparison, there is listed in the table a theoretical pattern that would be indicative of "selective estrogen loss." Cases to fit this category have not been observed.

TABLE I

DISTRIBUTION OF HORMONE EXCRETION PATTERNS AMONG 100 MEN, AGE 60–94

Hormone excretion pattern		Number of cases (%)
"Normal reproductive"		
Gonadotropins	4–24 M.U./24 hr.[a]	
17-KS	6–10 mg./24 hr.	16
Estrogens	4– 8 R.U./24 hr.[a]	
"The aging testis"		
Gonadotropins	Low or normal	
17-KS	Low	52
Estrogens	Normal or high	
"Male climacteric"		
Gonadotropins	High or normal	
17-KS	Low	10
Estrogens	Absent	
"Hypophyseal impairment"		
Gonadotropins	Absent	
17-KS	Low	5
Estrogens	Absent	
"Selective estrogen loss"		
Gonadotropins	Normal	
17-KS	Normal or high	0
Estrogens	Absent	

[a] M.U. = mouse units; R.U. = rat units.

Ten per cent of the cases have high or normal gonadotropin values with low 17-ketosteroids and absent, or nonassayable, estrogens. These cases, indicating general loss of steroid production by the gonads could, by analogy to the female, be referred to as the "male climacteric type," although the term is meant to imply nothing more than a description of the hormone excretion pattern. The remaining pattern that is representative of a definite group of individuals includes no measurable gonadotropins or estrogens and low 17-ketosteroids. This pattern suggests hypophyseal impairment with a cessation of gonadotropic hormone output.

Among the cases reviewed in this analysis, 17% are not readily categorized, but most of these would have to be discounted, for they proved to have been on hormone therapy which would have influenced the hormone-excretion pattern. The remaining few represent isolated instances of various inconsistent combinations of hormone-excretion values, probably explicable on the basis of method errors on our part. In Table II the observed hormone-excretion patterns and the distribution are again listed, and next to each a description is suggested for the expected testicular histology, based on the quantitative and qualitative character of the hormone-excretion pattern. In the last column is the observed distribution of testicular biopsies, evaluated according to spermatogenesis, fibrosis, and appearance of Leydig cells.

TABLE II

CORRELATION BETWEEN HORMONE-EXCRETION PATTERNS AND TESTICULAR HISTOLOGY

Hormone-excretion pattern (100 cases)	Per cent	Expected testicular histology (84 cases)	Per cent
"Normal reproductive"	16	Active spermatogenesis Slight-moderate fibrosis Functional Leydig cells	20
"The Aging Testis"	52	Poor-active spermatogenesis Progressing fibrosis Functional Leydig cells	52
"Male climacteric"	10	Poor-active spermatogenesis Progressing fibrosis Less active Leydig cells	4
"Hypophyseal impairment"	5	Poor spermatogenesis Severe to complete fibrosis Inactive Leydig cells	7

Twenty per cent of the biopsies show active spermatogenesis, slight to moderate fibrosis, and functional Leydig cells. With one exception, in this group with essentially normal testicular histology, each individual has the normal reproductive type of hormone-excretion pattern.

The largest percentage of biopsies show evidence of progressing fibrosis, poor to active spermatogenesis, and Leydig cells that are judged active by their histologic appearance. The great majority of individuals in this group have matching biopsies and hormone patterns. In the remaining two categories, the fit between testicular biopsy and hormone pattern is somewhat more erratic, so that for the entire series, a total of twelve biopsies do not correspond with the expected hormone patterns. On the whole, however, the series represents a good correlation between the aging changes in the testis and the hormonal patterns as an index of testicular function. Figures 12–15 illustrate testicular biopsies representative of each hormone-excretion pattern.

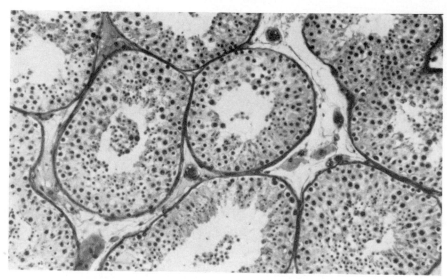

Fɪɢ. 12.   Testicular biopsy from a 67-year-old man with a normal reproductive type of hormone excretion pattern; gonadotropins, 17-ketosteroids, and estrogens all in the normal range. The biopsy shows no significant aging changes; spermatogenesis is active, Leydig cells are well differentiated. Magnification: ×60.

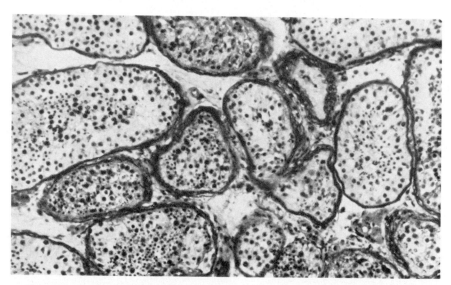

Fɪɢ. 13.   Testicular biopsy from a 73-year-old man with the "aging testis" type of hormone excretion pattern; normal gonadotropins, low 17-ketosteroids, normal estrogens. The tubules are mildly fibrosed, there is good spermatogenic activity, and Leydig cells are well differentiated. Magnification: ×60.

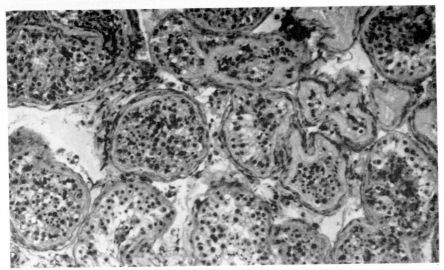

Fig. 14. Testicular biopsy from an 84-year-old man with the "male climacteric" type of hormone-excretion pattern; high gonadotropins, low 17-ketosteroids, and nonassayable estrogens. There is extensive sloughing of the germinal elements, progressive fibrosis. Leydig cells are infrequent and nonfunctional in appearance. Magnification: ×60.

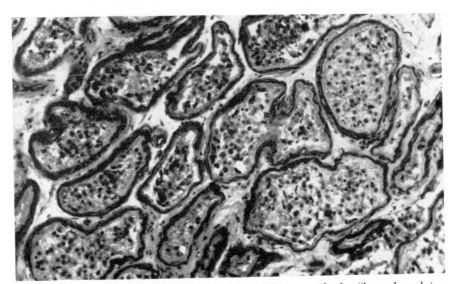

Fig. 15. Testicular biopsy from a 65-year-old man with the "hypophyseal impairment" type of hormone excretion pattern; low gonadotropins and 17-ketosteroids, nonassayable estrogens. No normal Leydig cells are present, fibrosis is severe, and there is extensive sloughing. Magnification: ×60.

From this study of testicular function of aging men, we conclude that in approximately 15% of the cases, the gonads and corresponding urinary hormone excretion are not unlike those of much younger men. About 10% suggest an aging change analogous to the climacteric female with maintenance of hypophyseal gonadotropin output, but with a regression of interstitial function of the testis. Five per cent show testicular atrophy that is most likely secondary to a functional impairment of the hypophysis.

However, in over 50% of the cases, and this therefore must be considered as the average situation, the aging gonad shows a retention of a functional interstitium. For the Leydig cells, the aging phenomenon appears to involve a distortion of the ratio of estrogen-androgen production with the estrogen function being retained preferentially. We believe that this is a characteristic feature of the aging testis and the hormone excretion pattern that develops with aging.

References

1. Bruner, J. A., *J. Clin. Endocrinol. and Metabolism* **11**, 360 (1951).
2. Engle, E. T., *Cold Spring Harbor Symposia Quant. Biol.* **10**, 35 (1942).
3. McCullagh, E. P., and Schaffenburg, C. A., *J. Clin. Endocrinol. and Metabolism* **11**, 1403 (1951).
4. McKay, D. G., Hertig, A. T., Adams, E. C., and Danzinger, L., *Anat. Record* **117**, 201 (1953).
5. Mancini, R. E., Arrillaga, F., Scarpa-Smith, C., Vilar, O., Andiada, J. A., Gurtman, A. I., and de la Balze, F. A., *J. Clin. Endocrinol. and Metabolism* in press (1959).
6. Nelson, W. O., *Recent Progr. in Hormone Research* **6**, 29 (1951).
7. Segal, S. J., Nelson, W. O., and Flocks, R. H., *Proc. 39th Annual Meeting Endocrine Soc., New York*, p. 38 (1957).
8. Waldeyer, W., "Eierstock und Ei." Leipzig, 1870.
9. Waldeyer, W., in "Handbuch der vergleichenden und experimentellen Entwicklungslehre der Wirbeltiere" (O. Hertwig, ed.), Vol. 1, p. 86. Fischer, Jena, 1906.
10. Witschi, E., *Contribs. Embryol. No.* **209**, *Carnegie Inst. Wash. Publ.* **32**, 63 (1948).
11. Witschi, E., "Development of Vertebrates." Saunders, Philadelphia, 1956.

Discussion

CHAIRMAN: W. O. NELSON

T. FORBES: A point relating to the embryology of the testis, so well reviewed by Dr. Segal, is the fact that at about the time the early germinal epithelium is proliferating medullary cords, which in the case of the male will eventually become seminiferous tubules, there is also proliferated from an anlage just medial to that of the gonad, epithelial cords which will form the adrenal cortex. At some stages it is hard to distinguish the dividing point between the gonadal and adrenal cortical anlagen. I think their early morphologic continuity is of some interest in view of the known androgenic activity of the adrenal cortex later on.

In addition, each gonad has a bisexual potency, a potency which is largely obliterated as sex differentiation goes on but which is never, somehow, quite extinguished. An example is the production of estrogen by the normal human testis.

P. Troen: I want to ask a question about the initiation of the changes of puberty. If I understood your data correctly, you indicated that the changes in the Leydig cells preceded those in the tubules, suggesting that ICSH (interstitial cell-stimulating hormone) secretion precedes FSH (follicle-stimulating hormone) secretion. I think others, notably Albert, have suggested that the reverse order takes place. I wonder whether you have any comment about that.

The second question is that in some of your slides of testicular biopsies in older men with apparently normal function there appeared to be changes suggesting sloughing in the seminiferous tubules. I wonder whether you had any sperm counts to go along with the other studies.

S. Segal: I shall answer your second question first. We did not have sperm counts on these individuals. As you well know, a certain amount of sloughing is present in all biopsies and I really do not believe that it was extensive in the particular ones that were shown. With regard to the changes at puberty, you have asked whether intratubular events precede interstitial activity. I believe that the clearest evidence is the differentiation of the tunica propria, which certainly occurs before the initiation of spermatogenesis. A distinct tunica propria is organized. Most likely this event is related to the beginning of androgen production, as de la Balze has proposed. I think this would indicate that there is some interstitial-cell production of androgens prior to spermatogenesis.

E. Bloch: Adding to what Dr. Forbes has said, it might be of some interest to note that the early fetal adrenal is primarily a weak androgen-producing gland. We have obtained evidence recently that the fetal zone of the fetal adrenal, as well as the definitive cortex, produces steroids. Both cell layers are capable of synthesizing dehydroepiandrosterone, Δ^4-androstene-3,17-dione, 11-hydroxy-Δ^4-androstene-3,17-dione, cortisol, and several unidentified steroids. In terms of acetate incorporation and ACTH responsivity, little difference was observed in our incubation studies.

I have two questions with respect to your very interesting paper. I was intrigued by Bruner's statement, namely that the amount of HCG (human chorionic gonadotropin) in the fetus is present in physiologically active amounts. I would like to know what the evidence for this is. And secondly, do you consider that the Leydig cell hypertrophy toward term is primarily due to fetal or to placental gonadotropin?

S. Segal: Dr. Bruner's data are from the study in which she assayed fetal, placental, and maternal tissues throughout the course of pregnancy. Her data indicate that by 11 weeks of age a dry powder prepared from fetal tissue contained 2 R.U. of gonadotropin per gram wet weight of fetal tissue. A 30-gm. embryo would contain approximately 60 R.U. of gonadotropins, for example. She interprets this quantity to be a physiologically active amount. Now, whether the interstitial-cell stimulation is the result of this chorionic gonadotropin or of fetal hypophyseal gonadotropin can be approached by inference. I think we can say that the chorionic gonadotropin is present in amounts that may be considered physiologically active, so there is no reason to believe that it would not be active. Gonadotropin production by the pituitary of the fetus may certainly be important as well. I think that observations on anencephalic fetuses would probably separate between these two possibilities. It is my impression that fetal interstitium stimulation is observed in these pituitaryless cases. Perhaps Dr. Nelson would confirm or deny this impression.

W. O. NELSON: There is very little that I can contribute beyond what Dr. Segal has said. It is, I think, very well established that the first evidence of puberty in the testis is the formation of the tubular tunica propria. In the absence of male sex hormone activity this structure never forms, as is the case in hypergonadotropic eunuchoids even in the fourth and fifth decades of life. When one sees evidence of the tunica propria being deposited in young boys, one can predict rather confidently that within the next year or so other evidences of puberty will be manifest. I think this does indeed represent activity of Leydig cells prior to evidences of spermatogenic activity. I think I can add nothing more regarding the relationship between Leydig cell hyperplasia prior to parturition and chorionic gonadotropin. It does, indeed, seem to be a manifestation of chorionic gonadotropin action, because Leydig cell hyperplasia very quickly disappears once the fetus leaves the mother's uterus.

C. G. HARTMAN: I wonder if you have utilized this precious material of a hundred men that submit to biopsy from a psychological standpoint, specifically the libido. The Steinach theory is dead. However, there are quite a number of men available that have been vasectomized and I wonder if you have any of the material there in order to determine exactly what happens in the human testis.

S. SEGAL: None of the men have been studied from the latter point of view so I am afraid I cannot contribute anything in that regard. With regard to the possible utilization of this data from a psychological point of view, we have included in the work-up of each case various questions that would relate to libido and general sexual activity. I think that the responses are completely unreliable and I certainly never want to use them in anything but parlor discussions to amuse and shock my guests.

S. ZUCKERMAN: I think that one of the more interesting and challenging issues which Dr. Segal's very lucid paper has revealed for the student of gametogenesis in the mammal is the difference between the behavior of the gonocyte which becomes the male, and that which becomes the female, germ cell. We all believe that the theory of the extragonadal origin of primordial germ cell applies to both sexes. We recognize, too, that there is doubt about the way the primordial gonocytes get into the area which becomes the definitive gonad. But we know that once in the genital ridge, the primordial germ cell becomes differentiated sexually and that this depends partly on where the primordial germ cell lodges. The gonocyte which ends up in the medulla becomes a male, and that in the cortex a female, germ cell. We know of cases where genetically female primordial cells become induced into spermatogonia and vice versa.

The question which kept recurring to me as you described the extraordinarily clearly defined changes of the male climacteric is: What is it that determines the difference from the point of view of senescence between the male and female germ cell? Why should the male germ cell continue to function so late in life when the female germ cell becomes a senescent unit almost before puberty. Are we dealing here with an issue which relates to the genetic constitution of the gonocyte or to some pituitary factor—you have definitely revealed changes which occur in the secretion of gonadotropin—or the site within the genital ridge in which the gonocytes lodge? The experimental question which occurred to me is this: What happens if you transplant a fragment of aged male testis into a young animal? Could an experiment of this kind help decide whether the spermatogonium or the pituitary had failed—

given, of course, that they did not fail togther? We all know that if you transplant a bit of ovary you do not get any recrudescence of oogenetic capacity.

S. SEGAL: I will attempt to sort out some of those very interesting points. You have asked, what is the basis for the difference in the longevity between the male and the female germ cell? I think that in other terminology that might be asking what is the cause for follicular atresia. You would be much more qualified to answer that question than I would, certainly. I think this is a basic difference between the male and female germ cell; there occurs continuously from the time of birth this process of intragonadal degradation of the female germ cell. In fact, our good friend, Dr. Jim Bradbury, once calculated that the event of ovulation is statistically insignificant because by far the overwhelming percentage of germ cells undergo atresia and, by comparison, the small number that eventually ovulate is statistically insignificant.

Continuing with the several interesting points you have raised, I do not believe that the hormonal environment is responsible for the difference in the ontogenic events of the male and female gonad. I believe that this interpretation implies a sort of Fountain-of-Youth approach that has been attempted over and over again, trying to modify the internal milieu by altering and controlling the hormonal balances. I don't believe that, in any experimental situation, either in the male or in the female, this has had any effect in prolonging the eventual history of the germ cells. As far as the histology of the gonad is concerned, these aging changes that we referred to today are most readily recognized in the human. Histologic changes in the testis of experimental animals are a little more difficult to define and certainly hormone-excretion patterns would be very difficult to establish.

W. O. NELSON: One point you made, Sir Solly, deserves further emphasis: This is, the reason why a germ cell becomes a male or a female germ cell. It does, indeed, seem to be decided by where primordial germ cells develop. There are many evidences of this in lower animals and even in the human being, where, as you know, in the case of the Klinefelter syndrome the germ cells presumed to be determined genetically to be ova become spermatogonia and even sperm.

G. PINCUS: I am interested in three points. Number one, it is my recollection that A. Albert's data (*Recent Progr. in Hormone Research* 12, 227, 1956) showed that on the average there is a rise and then a fall in gonadotropin excretion in the later ages; and I wonder if there were any correlations with your data or whether you thought his findings might have some special significance.

Secondly, in the case of steroid excretion we have pointed out that the decline in 17-ketosteroid excretion was attributable chiefly to the reduction in output of 11-deoxy-17-ketosteroids; whereas, the 11-oxyketosteroid output seemed to be maintained fairly well. One would thus be very much interested in the question as to whether the 11-oxyketosteroids had any function in maintaining the testis activity. I would like to know whether this has been specifically tested. I don't offhand recall it.

Thirdly, if you administer estrogen to experimental animals you can get types of tubules, at least, that look very much like those shown for aged men, and I wondered if you might not consider the so-called aging tubule as an estrogen-induced tubule.

S. SEGAL: We did not find cyclic gonadotropin activity that Albert reports. But I believe you are referring to his observations in the aging female. In the case of the male, there was just a gradual increase in a small percentage of the cases; nothing that one can consider a biphasic trend, certainly. I am sorry that we did not analyze 17-ketosteroids to separate between the classes of steroids you mention. The important thing that we had in mind was that of trying to find some parameter of testicular androgen production. Total 17-ketosteroid determination was, perhaps, not the best approach, but we are heartened by the correlation of our results with the study of H. Nowakowski (*Acta Endocrinol. Suppl.* **31**, 117-148, 1957) and, for that matter, with the results you, yourself, have reported. In Nowakowski's study of aging changes, he used fructose of the semen as a measure of androgen activity, and his curve, set up according to decades of life, fits very nicely with that which we proposed for 17-ketosteroid decline.

A final point you have raised was with regard to testicular fibrosis and the possible effect of estrogen. I can only accept your interpretation as being a likely possibility. I don't think it is definitely established that this is the case, however, because not only estrogen will cause this fibrosis. Tubular fibrosis may result from many things, including orchitis and gonadotropin suppression.

W. O. NELSON: I might add just a word to that point. The testicular changes that occur in animals receiving estrogen are, of course, a result of gonadotropin suppression. One rarely sees in animals the kind of progressive fibrosis that is present in aging man, but if estrogen or androgen is given in sufficient quantities to the human male, a very marked type of fibrosis does appear. This is not characteristic of estrogen only since androgen will do the same thing. In either case the suppression of gonadotropin certainly occurs and perhaps has quite a bit to do with the phenomenon.

C. W. LLOYD: About this matter of the male climacteric: I wonder if it could be a matter of the low estrogen level which produces the symptoms in the occasional male who has the same symptoms as women who have real hot flashes. In your grouping you classified as "male climacteric" only males who had really low estrogens. The rest of them had high estrogens. In my own experience we can control the flashes in the males very nicely with estrogen. Could it be then that in these folks there is some correlation between the estrogen level and the flashing? Did these men that you classify on an excretion basis as "male climacteric" have flashes?

S. SEGAL: I apologize for the use of a very bad term, "male climacteric," since it does connote a definite meaning to you who use it all the time in connection with the female. We in no way intended to draw an analogy from the over-all point of view, comparing the male and the female, but simply with regard to the pattern of hormone excretion. These individuals showed, as far as we know, none of the symptoms that would be analogous to the female climacteric. The use of the term was merely to give to one who is familiar with the general hormonal pattern of the climacteric female, an idea of the comparability of this pattern in a small percentage of aging males. In fact, I would interpret our results as in opposition to the usual concept of the "male climacteric.'

A. E. RAKOFF: There are several questions I would like to ask. Chorionic hormone reaches a peak during early pregnancy and then drops fairly rapidly to extremely low levels just before parturition. Have you been able to note any correlation at all between the appearance in number or size of Leydig cells during the early stage in pregnancy versus those just before parturition?

The second thing is that we know that at the time of puberty there is an incidence of gynecomastia in young males, that this may be as high as 10% or 20% of all boys going through puberty. Is there any correlation at all with the appearance of Leydig cells or is there an increase in estrogen output at this time? Do you believe that the Leydig cells are actually a source of estrogen as has been demonstrated, or is it possible that it may be from the Sertoli cells?

The last thing is, there has been some confusion or some differences of opinion as to the effect of chorionic gonadotropin on spermatogenesis. Do you have any views on that? Do you think it accelerates it, retards it, or has no effect upon spermatogenesis?

S. SEGAL: With regard to the effect of chorionic gonadotropin on the Leydig cells in the fetal testis, the first time that the Leydig cells become sensitive to or show stimulation during *in utero* development is during the sixth month, at the very earliest, and perhaps not until the seventh month. This is, apparently, the time when they become sensitive. By this time, of course, the initial peak of chorionic gonadotropin has long passed and there is a rather constant low level.

We believe that the appearance of gynecomastia at puberty is related to the function of the Leydig cells rather than the Sertoli cells. A type of evidence supporting this contention is the fact that in some pathologic conditions, the Klinefelter syndrome, for example, in which the testicular histology shows complete tubular hyalinization, but functional-appearing Leydig cells are present, estrogen-dependent gynecomastia can develop.

I would like to refer your third question to Dr. Nelson, who has worked on the problem.

W. O. NELSON: All I can do in this instance is recite our findings with Dr. William Maddock in a study that we made on the effects of chorionic gonadotropin in hypogonadotropic eunuchoids and in relatively normal men.

In the first case there was stimulation of tubular activity and in some instances at least partial spermatogenesis; whereas in the individual with established spermatogenesis, there tended to be spermatogenic damage. We presumed the latter occurred because of the increased output of androgens and estrogens which inhibited pituitary FSH and thus interfered with normal spermatogenesis. Beyond that I can give no suggestion. Chorionic gonadotropin certainly does appear to damage spermatogenesis in cases where the latter is established.

E. C. REIFENSTEIN: I would be interested in your comments concerning the role of the adrenal cortex in the aging of the testis. In particular, what are your views on the relationship of the adrenal cortex to the production of estrogen and to the maintenance of the estrogen level with aging, and on the effect of the relative excess of corticoids that develops with aging on the development of the fibrosis in the testis?

S. SEGAL: If you are asking about the adrenal production of estrogen, some of the older, unsophisticated data, before Dr. Brown's beautiful technique was developed, showed that following castration of the human male there still remained assayable levels of estrogen. Following adrenalectomy these disappeared completely. I think this indicates that estrogen production is a normal capacity of the human adrenal. We have no way, of course, of distinguishing between adrenal and testicular production of estrogen in these data.

With regard to corticoid influence on testicular fibrosis, I really don't know and would be glad to hear the opinions of others.

C. G. HARTMAN: Another way of reducing spermatogenesis is by cryptorchidism or the elevation of the temperature, by insulation, and by other means. How do you explain that? Do you put that on an endocrine basis?

S. SEGAL: No, I don't believe this is an endocrine effect. I think that heat causes a specific damage to the seminiferous epithelium. Dr. Nelson, who has done so much experimental work in this area, would perhaps elaborate more completely on your question.

W. O. NELSON: I don't know other than that in the case of animals who have evolved a scrotum, it appears necessary that the germ cells be the beneficiary of a somewhat lowered body temperature if they are to undergo their normal maturation changes. It is certainly not a hormonal mechanism, but apparently is a heat sensitivity—and a very delicate sensitivity at that.

S. ZUCKERMAN: Since experimental cryptorchidism has been referred to, may I refer back to a point that has already been raised—that the Sertoli cells or the interstitial cells of Leydig are responsible for the production of estrogen. Is it not possible that both might in different circumstances be responsible? There is considerable evidence to show that in conditions in which the seminiferous tubules involute, the interstitial cells may start hypertrophying. For example, in intersexual pigs you may find completely destroyed tubules and a testis which consists almost entirely of apparently healthy and swollen interstitial cells. There is evidence that these cells may in some circumstances produce estrogen.

Similarly in the case of certain testicular tumors there is suggestive evidence that the Sertoli cells are responsible for the production of estrogen. At the recent Long Island Conference we were shown pictures of the testis in certain lower forms in which interstitial elements were apparently absent. Yet it was plain that androgen was affecting the soma.

S. SEGAL: I would like to comment on the latter point first. Dr. Zuckerman is referring to a particular reptilian testis that we were shown at the Cold Spring Harbor Symposium. It was a testis biopsy or section, I can't remember which, showing closely packed seminiferous tubules with no intertubular space whatsoever. However, I believe that if some means were employed to reduce these seminiferous tubules by experimental cryptorchidism, estrogen treatment, or what have you, suddenly would appear the interstitial cells which, in the fully developed condition, are stretched so tautly around the tubules that they probably are not observable by normal resolution.

Do you believe, Dr. Zuckerman, if I may answer your first question with another question, that the granulosa cells in the female are responsible for estrogen production?

I think by way of homology, one would have to, since the granulosa cells and the Sertoli cells derive from a common origin, at least according to my interpretation of the embryologic events.

S. ZUCKERMAN: If you are asking me whether I believe as an act of faith, the answer is no.

There is clear evidence that the ovary can produce estrogen when all the granulosa cells have apparently been destroyed. What we don't know is just how polymorphic these cells are, what shapes they can take, and when they disappear. I agree with your interpretation of the reptilian testis which we were shown. I was merely trying to indicate that to derive conclusions about the cytological source of a particular hormone from histological pictures is a highly hazardous enterprise.

S. SEGAL: I couldn't concur more completely.

W. O. NELSON: One more question and I think we will have to close this session.

A. E. RAKOFF: I wonder whether sufficient attention has been given to the adrenal at puberty as a source of adrenal estrogens. I have in mind a youngster we saw with gynecomastia who had an estrogen excretion during puberty ranging about 440 mouse units which is about ten times our normal value. By the administration of cortisone we were about to get suppression of estrogen excretion to normal levels.

This continued for quite some time, and then the estrogen level gradually faded back to normal without cortisone therapy.

I think perhaps there may be in the male an adrenarche in which estrogen is produced in increased amounts for a given period of time.

S. SEGAL: I have no comment to make about that interesting situation. I don't believe that there is adequate study of the possible change in adrenal production of estrogen at that given moment of development.

W. O. NELSON: I might make one brief comment in that direction. It is an interesting observation that in the two extremes of the period of reproductive vigor in the male there tends to be manifestation of estrogenic activity, that is, at puberty and in older age. This may be, as Dr. Rakoff has suggested, an evidence of adrenal cortical activity, but I am inclined to think that it reflects an imbalance on the part of Leydig cell function as it shifts into and out of fully vigorous production of androgen.

S. SEGAL: I would like to express my gratitude to the discussants for their interesting comments and questions.

Fertilizing Capacity of Spermatozoa

M. C. CHANG

Worcester Foundation for Experimental Biology, Shrewsbury, Massachusetts

In 1946 I gave a paper on the fertilizing capacity of rabbit spermatozoa (12) at the conference on fertility in New York City under the auspices of the National Committee on Maternal Health. I am privileged once again to be invited to give a paper on the same subject at the conference on the endocrinology of reproduction in the Dedication Year of the State University of New York. It is the purpose of this paper to review what we have learned during the past twelve years, or rather, what I have done on this subject and what my points of view are on the problems of fertilizing capacity of mammalian spermatozoa. I shall therefore report some experimental results I have obtained during the past twelve years and, in the light of the contributions of contemporary workers, evaluate our understanding of the fertilizing capacity of spermatozoa.

I. Number of Spermatozoa in Relation to Fertilization

On this topic, let me quote our revered teacher and authority Dr. C. G. Hartman (42). He stated that "the prodigality of sperm production is a striking phenomenon. Thus in the reproductive lifetime of an average man he will discharge four hundred billion sperms or a billion for every ovum that leaves a woman's ovary. No satisfactory explanation of the phenomenon has been offered. Factors that have been suggested are: natural selection among sperms, some enzymes brought in for dissipation of corona cells of the ovum, cell exudates necessary for life of the sperms and for fertilization." Let me try to examine the biological and physiological significance of the number of spermatozoa in relation to fertilization.

A. Number of Spermatozoa Ejaculated at Copulation and Transported into the Site of Fertilization

In a study of the reaction of the uterus on spermatozoa (22), I have reported that a rabbit ejaculates on the average about 200 millions of spermatozoa at a time, but only about 2 million or 1% of an ejaculate get into the whole uteri about 12 hours after mating (Tables I and II). The distribution of spermatozoa in both uteri following natural mating is in agreement with the observations made by Braden (11), who obtained no more than 2 million spermatozoa in the whole uteri from the first to the twenty-eighth hour after mating (0.98–1.90 million). It is obvious that the cervix of the uterus acts as a barrier to prevent the entry of a large number of spermatozoa.

It was found further not only that a large number of sperm could not get into the uterus but that there is a physiological and biochemical mechanism in the uterus to evacuate and to disintegrate spermatozoa (separation of sperm tail from head). This was shown by counting and examining sperms at various times after the injection of a definite number of sperms into the uterus of live rabbits (22). As shown in Fig. 1, sperms disappeared and disintegrated completely within 48 hours. The phagocytosis of sperms in the rat and mouse uterus has been reported by Austin (4), and the disappearance of sperm in the uterus of rat within 12 hours has also been reported by Posalaky and Törö (61). It seems, therefore, that there is a severe physiological process in the uterus that either prevents the entry of unnecessary or weak spermatozoa or disintegrates the weak ones in a short time.

TABLE I

SPERM COUNTS OF A RABBIT EJACULATE[a]

Male rabbits	Ejaculates	Days after last ejaculation	Volume (ml.)	Concentrat. (millions/ml.)	Total Number (in millions)	Percentage of sperm heads
1	1	27	0.8	590	472	—
	2	8	1.1	580	638	3.7
	3[b]	2	1.15	320	368	1.6
	Average		1.01	496	492	2.6
2	1	7	0.95	285	270	3.5
	2	5	1.9	370	703	—
	3	2	0.67	80	54	2.0
	Average		1.17	245	342	2.7
3	1[c]	12	1.2	150	180	6.0
	2[c]	4	0.9	82	74	2.7
	3	2	0.4	125	50	0
	Average		0.83	119	101	2.9
4	1[b]	9	1.7	125	212	0
	2[b]	4	1.0	214	214	2.3
	3[b]	2	3.2	114	364	3
	Average		1.9	151	263	1.8
5	1[b]	12	1.5	365	547	15
	2	4	1.0	95	95	10
	3	2	0.6	115	69	14
	Average		1.0	192	237	13

[a] From Chang (22).
[b] Contamination with urine.
[c] Presence of gelatinous clot.

TABLE II

NUMBER OF SPERMATOZOA RECOVERED FROM THE UTERI OF A RABBIT AT VARIOUS TIMES ATER MATING[a]

Hours after mating	No. of rabbits	No. of sperm recovered (in millions)	
		Average	Range
2	2	0.6	0.38–0.81
4	3	1.28	0.64–3.0
6	2	0.98	0.52–1.45
12	7	1.74	0.04–4.2
16	3	1.75	0.54–2.6
24	2	0.32	0.24–0.4
48	2	0.06	0.00–0.12

[a] From Chang (22).

I have also counted the number of sperm recovered from the Fallopian tubes of rabbits following natural mating and following the artificial insemination of 20 million or 1 million sperms into the vagina (18). It was found that the number of sperm recovered from the tubes

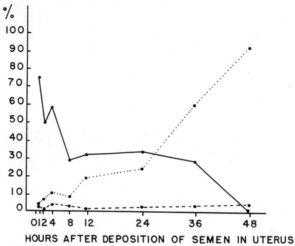

FIG. 1. Percentage of spermatozoa recovered from the uterus of live rabbits. Solid line: Recovery as compared with that from the excised uterus. Dotted line: Sperm heads in the uterus of live animals. Dashed line: Sperm heads in the excised uterus. From Chang (22).

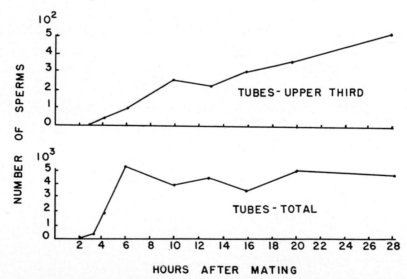

FIG. 2. Distribution of spermatozoa in the Fallopian tubes at various times after mating. From A. W. H. Braden, *Australian J. Biol. Sci.* 1953 (11).

was relatively constant, about 5000, whether 200 million or 20 million sperms were inseminated. When insemination was with 1 million sperms, the number recovered from the tubes was lower, but fertilized eggs were obtained (Table III). Since only 2 million out of 200 million sperms could get into the whole uteri and only 5000 sperms could be recovered from the Fallopian tubes it appears that only 0.25% of uterine

TABLE III

NUMBER OF SPERMATOZOA RECOVERED FROM THE FALLOPIAN TUBES OF RABBITS[a]

Rabbit no.	No. sperms inseminated (in millions)	No. sperms recovered from tubes	Fertilized eggs observed	Hours between insemination and examination
1	Naturally mated	1,950	All fertilized	24
2	Naturally mated	10,500	All fertilized	24
3	Naturally mated	11,670	All fertilized	24
4	Naturally mated	750	All fertilized	24
5	Naturally mated	720	All fertilized	29
Averages:	200 approx.	5,120		
6	25	18,400	All fertilized	24
7	25	1,700	None fertilized	24
8	21	5,830	All fertilized	18
9	21	2,920	All fertilized	18
10	12	8,100	All fertilized	34
11	22	1,930	All fertilized	24
Averages:	21	6,480		
12	0.63	490	All fertilized	24
13	0.63	350	8 of 12 fertilized	24
14	1.80	No sperm recovered	All fertilized	24
15	1.80	No sperm recovered	None fertilized	24
16	1.20	No sperm recovered	All fertilized	24
Averages:	1.21	88		

[a] From Chang (18).

sperms, or only 0.0025% of ejaculated sperms, could have reached the site of fertilization. Braden (11) has carefully examined the number of sperms present in the Fallopian tubes of rabbits from 2 to 28 hours after one or two matings. Figure 2 presents the average number of sperms present in the Fallopian tubes of six rabbits in Braden's report. From these results it seems that the uterine-tubal junction also acts as a barrier to prevent a large number of spermatozoa from reaching the site of fertilization.

B. Fertilization of Eggs by Vanguards of Spermatozoa

Considering the fact that very small numbers of sperms are present in the Fallopian tubes, it appears that eggs are not necessarily fertilized by sperm swarms as suggested by Hammond (40), and they may quite well be fertilized by vanguards of spermatozoa. Data to demonstrate this possibility were acquired by counting the number of sperm on the zona pellucida of fertilized and unfertilized eggs following artificial inseminations; the data are presented in Table IV. It appears that although most of the fertilized eggs (92%) had extra sperm on their zona

TABLE IV

NUMBER OF SPERMS ON THE ZONA PELLUCIDA OF FERTILIZED AND UNFERTILIZED RABBIT EGGS

	Total eggs	Eggs with 1-100 extra sperms on zona	Eggs without extra sperms on zona
Fertilized	398	367 (92.2%)	31 (7.8%)
Unfertilized	416	54 (13%)	362 (87%)

pellucida at the time, or after the entry, of fertilizing sperm, there are a few eggs (7.8%) which might have been fertilized by a single vanguard sperm without other sperm around. Although most of the unfertilized eggs (87%) had no sperm on their zona, a few of them (13%) did have sperm on their zona but failed to be fertilized. This shows that it is not necessary that the sperm swarm effect fertilization but that a single sperm may do so. Further, it is the physiological integrity of an individual sperm that plays an important role in fertilization rather than a large number of sperms around the eggs. Certainly, a large number of sperms around the eggs would increase the probability of the presence of more physiologically functional sperms capable of penetrating the egg.

In this connection it should be mentioned here that although hundreds of millions of sperms are present in an ejaculate, a minimal effective number of sperms to insure fertilization is only about 1% of this number. For example, a rabbit ejaculate contains about 200 million sperm but 1 million would be enough to insure the fertilization of 10 eggs shed each time (cf. 12). A bull ejaculate contains about 5000 million sperms which can be diluted to 100 or 320 for the practice of artificial insemination (65, 73). Human beings ejaculate on the average about 500 million sperms, but it has been reported that a human ejaculate containing 20 million is not necessarily sterile (44, 49). This is another strong point to illustrate that a large number of sperm are not needed to assure fertilization. Even if a large number of sperms were inseminated, either they would be prevented from reaching the site of fertilization or would disappear and disintegrate in the uterus.

C. ENZYMES OF SPERM, HYALURONIDASE, AND SPERM CELL EXUDATES

About fifteen years ago, it was thought that a large number of sperms would reach the site of fertilization if a large number were ejaculated at mating and that a large number of sperm are needed for the dissipation of cumulus oöphorus and corona cells in order to facilitate the penetration of the fertilizing sperm into the egg. Although we know very little about the enzymes present in the sperm cells or the enzymatic reaction of sperm cells during the process of fertilization, the best-known, and extensively studied, sperm enzyme is hyaluronidase. It is definitely known that sperm cells of most mammalian species, perhaps with the exception of the dog (67), contain large amounts of hyaluronidase and that the follicular cells surrounding the ova can be dispersed by addition of hyaluronidase or of spermatozoa *in vitro*. Thus, it was thought that a large number of sperms are needed at the site of fertilization for the dispersal of follicular cells because the corona cells attached to the zona pellucida of each egg and the cumulus oophorus around a group of eggs are obvious barriers for the penetration of sperm. However, when we examine the situation *in vivo*, the position is quite different because (a) the number of sperm present in the Fallopian tube is too small to effect the complete dissolution of follicular cells: there are about 5000 sperms in rabbit tubes (18), but it requires 20,000/cc. to dissolve cumulus clot (59); (b) the presence of hyaluronidase would not disperse the corona cells of the rabbit egg and the denudation of rabbit egg requires a tubal factor (68); (c) addition of hyaluronidase into a minimal number of sperms would not increase the chance of fertilization (14); and (d) fertilization occurs before the dissociation of cumulus oöphorus and corona radiata (cf. 19). Although these facts do not preclude the possibility that hyaluronidase carried by an individual sperm would help it to pass through several heavy membranes surrounding the ovum, they do demonstrate that a large number of sperm are not necessary in order to have sufficient hyaluronidase for the fertilization of an egg.

The suggestion by Hartman (42) that the "cell exudates are necessary for life of sperm and fertilization" may be partially true, but their contributions may play a part only under certain adverse conditions. This was shown by artificial insemination of rabbits with a minimal effective number of sperms suspended in the seminal plasma of different species or in fructose Ringer solution containing rapidly killed (deep-frozen) sperm cells of different species. When females were inseminated with these sperm suspensions Chang (16) found that "the seminal plasma of human or rabbit had a beneficial effect while that of bull had an ill effect on the fertilizing capacity of rabbit sperm as compared with fructose Ringer. Fructose Ringer containing dead sperm of human, rabbit or bull was found as good or better media for the preservation of sperms as egg yolk; which indicates the presence of

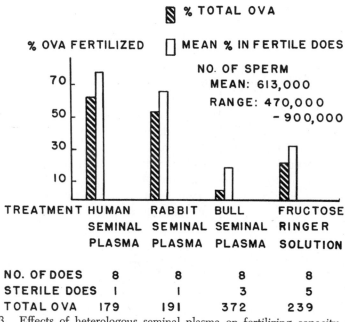

FIG. 3. Effects of heterologous seminal plasma on fertilizing capacity of rabbit spermatozoa stored for 1 hour before insemination. From Chang (16).

essential substances in the sperm cells for the maintenance of their fertilizing capacity" (cf. Figs. 3 and 4).

In this study the live sperms were kept with dead sperms *in vitro* for 1 hour before insemination. Under such an artificial condition the beneficial effect of the exudates of cells was revealed. However, considering the fact that at natural mating, sperms are ejaculated into the vagina and transported through a vast space of uterine lumen to the site of fertilization in a few minutes to a few hours, how far the cell exudates of one sperm could be of any use to the other sperm in the female tract within such a short time is hard to comprehend and also difficult to ascertain.

D.   Fertility in Relation to Number of Spermatozoa

Now let us examine the importance of a large number of sperms for fertilization from another angle. Dr. A. Walton (72) has illustrated the quantitative relationship between the number of spermatozoa at the site of fertilization and the possibility of fertilization as shown in Fig. 5. The curve *n*, represents the sperm distribution resulting from a

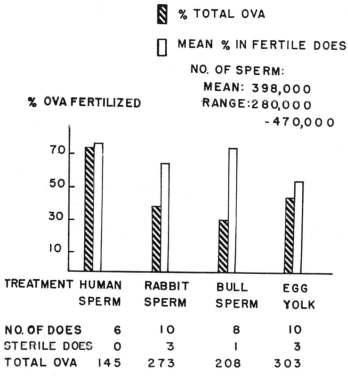

Fig. 4.   Effects of dead sperm of different species on fertilizing capacity of rabbit spermatozoa stored for 1 hour before insemination. From Chang (16).

normal ejaculation. The part of the curve above the minimum line represents the duration of the period of fertility. If ovulation occurs within this period, as at *A*, the eggs will be fertilized. If ovulation occurs later at *B* or *C* the eggs will not be fertilized and· sterility will result. Suppose only one-fourth of the normal number of spermatozoa are present as in the curve *n*/4, it will then be apparent that although some spermatozoa reach the Fallopian tubes, they are not in sufficient number to effect fertilization and the mating will be sterile. On the other hand, if the number of spermatozoa is twice the normal as in curve $2n$, twice the number of spermatozoa will be present throughout the whole period. The result will be an extension of the period of fertility. Hence, ovulation at time B will in this case be fertile, whereas it would be sterile if only the normal number of spermatozoa were present.

Theoretically the correlation between fertility and the number of sperms is well illustrated. But it assumes that (a) a large number of sperms would reach the site of fertilization if a large number of sperms were ejaculated into the vagina or into the uterus and (b) a sufficient number of sperms present in the tubes is necessary for fertilization.

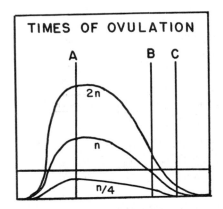

FIG. 5. Relationship between time of ovulation (A, B, C), distribution of sperm at Fallopian tube, and fertility. See text for details. The horizontal line represents the minimum for fertility. From A. Walton, *Folio Morphol.*, 1938 (72).

As discussed above, these two propositions are not necessarily true. However, let us see experimentally whether insemination with a large number of sperms plays a role when the time of ovulation is varied. Chang (26) inseminated rabbits with about 200 million or about 2 million spermatozoa 2, 4, and 28 hours before ovulation and found that the proportion of fertilized eggs was significantly increased when a large number of sperms was inseminated 28 hours before ovulation but was not significantly increased 2 and 4 hours before ovulation (Table V). This shows that when ovulation occurs later some sperms would survive longer, or more sperms would be reserved in the female tract, to fertilize the eggs if a large number of sperms were inseminated. When ovulation occurred earlier, the transportation and survival of sperms was neither prolonged nor shortened whether the number of sperms inseminated was small or large.

TABLE V

Probability of Fertilization in Relation to the Number of Sperms Inseminated at Various Times before Ovulation

Insemination (hours before ovulation)	No. of sperms inseminated (in millions)		Rabbit no.	Eggs recovered			Avg. no. of sperms on zona	
				Total	Fertilized	Fertilization (%)	Fertilized	Unfertilized
2	High	107	1	12	4	33	8	21
		120	2	10	10	100	17	0
		120	3	4	0	0		
		Total:		26	14	54		
	Low	0.99	4	10	10	100	—	3
		0.50	5	10	8	80	3	0
		0.50	6	12	5	42	0	—
		Total:		32	23	72		
4	High	179	7	8	8	100	27	
		119	8	6	6	100	—	
		Total:		14	14	100		
	Low	1.27	9	10	10	100	31	
		2.13	10	3	3	100	—	
		Total:		13	13	100		
28	High	179	11	10	8	80	30	16
		119	12	7	4	57	—	1
		107	13	15	11	73	2.6	—
		Total:		32	23	72		
	Low	2.13	14	10	0	0		0
		1.27	15	7	0	0		0
		0.99	16	16	0	0		0
		Total:		33	0	0		

E. Biological Significance of the Prodigality of Sperm Production

All the facts mentioned above illustrate that a large number of sperm is not required for fertilization. What, then, is the use of the millions of sperms produced by a male or ejaculated at copulation? Here I have to refer to my previous statement (12) that spermatozoa are a heterogeneous population—some are weak, some are strong, some are young, and some are old. This is due to the long distance and long time interval required from spermatogenesis to ejaculation and is also influenced by the frequency of ejaculation. Thus, the more sperm inseminated, the better is the chance to have strong sperms. I mention this again here to stress my point that a large number of sperms at ejaculation is a biological necessity rather than a physiological requirement. Physiologically, a large number of sperms produced in the whole lifetime of a male or at ejaculation is not required to fertilize the eggs. Their enzyme content, hyaluronidase, and their cell exudates are not necessary for the facilitation or for the survival of the fertilizing sperm to enter the egg. Then the only suggestion left to interpret the prodigality of sperm, as stated by Hartman (42), is the natural selection among sperms. However, I should like to put forward three other complementary suggestions: (a) More sperms would provide more strong sperms to endure the hardship in reaching the site of fertilization, and with more sperms there is a better chance to have strong ones. (b) A large number of sperms produced by a male provides a greater variation for the genetic transmission of the character, that is, for a greater variation in the recombination of genes. Suppose a man or a woman produces only a few germ cells, then the brothers and sisters would be more alike and their variations to adapt to a particular environment would be very limited. (c) A large number of sperms produced in higher animals may be a vestige of evolution, because a large number of germ cells produced in lower organisms is needed for a chance meeting of spermatozoa and egg in the environment.

II. Fertilizing Capacity of Spermatozoa as Affected by Environmental Conditions in Vitro

Since the publication of Professor Elie Ivanov's work in 1907 (43) the behavior of mammalian spermatozoa *in vitro* has been extensively investigated for the application of artificial insemination in animal breeding. Experimental study to elucidate the physiology of sperms *in vitro*, and in the genital tract of males and females with special reference to the problem of fertilization, however, is of great interest. Unless and until we have a better knowledge of the basic facts underlying the behavior of sperms *in vivo* and *in vitro,* practical or clinical application of our knowledge will be futile.

As I have mentioned (12), various approaches can be employed for the study of the physiology of sperms, such as sperm count, morphology, motility, metabolism (respiration and glycolysis), and viability of sperms, but it would be more direct and reliable to ascertain the actual fertilizing capacity of spermatozoa for the determination of the physiological integrity of sperms. I am not going into detail to review the vast literature on the physiology of mammalian spermatozoa *in vitro.* Detailed and comprehensive reviews can be found elsewhere: Hartman (42), Austin and Bishop (5), and Chang (23) for biological observations; Mann (50) for the biochemistry of semen; Anderson (1), Emmens and Blackshaw (36), and Salisbury (66) for artificial insemination; Bishop and Austin (7) for morphology of mammalian sperms; and Edwards and Sirlin (33) for labeling of mammalian spermatozoa. Here I shall comment only on some work I have done recently.

A. Effects of Dilution

The immobilization of mammalian spermatozoa when suspended in a large volume of physiological saline was used by Milovanov (53) as a test of resistance for the assessment of sperm quality. I have reported that the motility and fertilizing capacity of rabbit sperm are better when the same number of sperms are suspended in a small, rather than a large, volume of saline (12, 13). The better maintenance of the motility of sperms in a concentrated suspension has been confirmed by Emmens and Swyer (37) in the rabbit, by Blackshaw in the bull and ram (9), and a significantly higher conception rate in cows inseminated with a sperm suspension of 1:100 as compared with a sperm suspension of 1:300 was also reported by Willett (74). The protective function of seminal plasma for the maintenance of fertility and the beneficial effect of seminal plasma or of sperm cells of one species to another have been also reported (14, 16). The prevention of the escape of essential materials, perhaps an enzyme from the sperm cells, by addition of seminal plasma or of other substances was postulated (37), and the detoxication of heavy metals by chelating agents was also proposed (70). When dealing with the dilution effect and chemical changes associated with sperm senescence, Mann (50) stated that "it may be said at once that as yet, there is no perfect semen diluent, and the precise mechanism of 'dilution effect' still remains to be solved."

It should be mentioned here, however, that in the course of evolution the reproductive system has developed in such a fashion that each organ performs its function in accordance with the internal and external environmental and sequential conditions of the male and female of a particular species. For instance, spermatozoa may survive for 38 days in the cauda epididymis of a rabbit, but they survive only for 30 hours in the female tract (41). On the other hand, bat spermatozoa may be able to survive in the male tract as long as rabbit sperms in the male tract, but they may also survive for several months, from fall to spring, in the female tract (39, 52). Seminal plasma, the secretions of accessory glands, is mainly a vehicle for the transportation of sperms, and its function to maintain the activity of sperms is only for a very short time. Once semen is ejaculated it is mixed instantly with other secretions of the female tract; thus sperms are in a very diluted form in the female tract. Academically, the biochemistry of seminal plasma and the effect of dilution are of great interest for the understanding of the behavior of isolated cells, but practically its importance in clinical treatment of fertility and sterility is perhaps very little. Furthermore, one does not expect seminal plasma to be a good diluent for the prolongation of the life of sperm *in vitro*. To prolong the life span of sperms for artificial insemination, other media ought to be employed. The discovery of egg yolk for the preservation of sperms *in vitro* for a few days by Phillips and Lardy (58) and the discovery of dilution of semen with glycerol to keep sperms in a frozen condition for several months by Polge *et al.* (60) are of great importance in the application of artificial insemination.

B. Effect of Serum on Spermatozoa

Blood serum is considered an excellent nutritive and protective medium for the preservation and the growth of animal cells and tissue, and yet I have found that a spermicidal factor is present in fresh human, bovine, rabbit, guinea pig, and rat sera (15). Except in human serum, this factor kills the spermatozoa of its own species and the sperms of other species. It is unstable and thermolabile and can be destroyed by sodium citrate, trypsin, and snake venom and also can be used up by a definite number of sperms. When rabbit sperms were treated with various portions of fresh rabbit serum and inseminated to the females, fertilized eggs were obtained if all the sperms were not immobilized even though they were agglutinated. Since this factor has many characteristics similar to complement in immunology, it is considered to be a character of the antigen and antibody reaction. It may have no relation to the fertilizing capacity of sperm or to the process of fertilization under normal conditions, because the germ cells are well protected by specialized organs.

C. Sperm Agglutination

In this connection, I should like to bring up the subject of sperm agglutination. Agglutination, used in immunology, denotes the phenomenon that microorganisms or red cells will stick together in clumps when antibody is added. The mechanism of agglutination in immunology is believed to be due to the "divalent molecules of antibody, one end combined with one cell and the other end with another cell acting as links to hold the cells together" (10). The mechanism of agglutination of red cells in the presence of antibody may be quite different from agglutination of sperms which are highly motile. The importance of sperm agglutination in fertilization was put forward by Lillie (46), whose classical study of sea urchin eggs had shown that sea urchin sperms could be very active and would agglutinate in the presence of a substance from eggs, fertilizin. The reaction substances at fertilization in the marine species, for instance, the fertilizin of eggs and the antifertilizin of sperm, have been extensively investigated physiologically and biochemically (cf. 62, 64, 71). But the importance of fertilizin which induces the agglutination of sperm is still uncertain. From a layman's point of view, whether the removal or addition of fertilizin and antifertilizin would decrease or increase the fertilizability of egg and the fertilizing capacity of sperms should be a good test. From a recent review by Metz on marine organisms (51), it seems that, although fertilizin molecules of the egg combine with antifertilizin groups of sperm to effect the linkage between sperm and egg, experimental evidence is very conflicting as to the value of the effect of fertilizin and antifertilizin on the fertilizability of eggs and the fertilizing capacity of sperms.

In the mammalian species, it has been reported recently by Bishop and Tyler (8) that sperms would agglutinate in the presence of eggs and that this reaction was found to be predominantly species-specific in cross-tests between rabbit, mouse, bovine, and human sperms and rabbit, mouse, and bovine eggs. They stated that this agglutination reaction is attributed to the diffusion from the egg of a substance analogous to the fertilizins that have been demonstrated in lower animals.

Sperm agglutination is a very general phenomenon (23). Spontaneous head agglutination *in vitro* as a result of dilution with saline is shown notably by rat, mouse, and guinea pig sperms but occurs less readily with bull or ram spermatozoa (5). Bull sperm would agglutinate when semen is stored for some time undiluted or diluted with saline, and this was interpreted as due to inactivation of a sperm antiagglutinin produced in the prostate gland (47, 48). Although we do not know exactly whether sperms agglutinate in the female tract or at the site of fertilization, we do know that sperms recovered from the vagina, uterus, and Fallopian tube are invariably agglutinated when examined *in vitro*. According to Bishop and Tyler (8), "it would require correspondingly fewer sperm, than in the case of such animals as the sea urchin, to counteract the dissolved fertilizin and so permit unreacted spermatozoa to reach the surface of the egg." This implies that agglutinated sperms are incapable of fertilization. Since there is no clear-cut evidence to demonstrate that agglutinated sperms are incapable of fertilization (23), the real importance of sperm agglutination and the substances or condition to induce sperm agglutination in relation to fertilizing capacity of sperms and in relation to the process of mammalian fertilization is still obscure.

D.   Effects of Urine on Motility and Fertility of Rabbit Spermatozoa

It is generally believed that the secretions from Cowper's and Littré's glands of man at sexual excitement are for the neutralization of any residual urine in the urethra that might be harmful to spermatozoa at ejaculation. Then the harmful effect of urine on sperms must be very severe. In the rabbit, contamination of semen with urine was quite frequently observed when semen was collected with an artificial vagina, especially when the temperature of the artificial vagina was too high. Such a urine-contaminated semen sample has a yellowish color with yellowish white precipitates characteristic of the urine of rabbit, and the concentration and the motility of sperms are very poor. The motility and fertilizing capacity of rabbit sperms in semen contaminated with urine at ejaculation and in the normal semen diluted with various proportions of rabbit urine were investigated by Chang and Thorsteinsson (30). We found that the motility of sperms decreased and the concentration of reducing substances increased as the proportion of urine contamination increased, but the fertilizing capacity of sperms as determined by the percentage of ova fertilized and the transportation of sperms from the vagina to the Fallopian tubes as determined by the number of sperms on the zona pellucida of ova, were not disturbed even when sperms were suspended in 50% of urine. However, when normal rabbit semen was suspended in 75% of urine practically no sperm was motile and yet up to 30% of ova were fertilized. It seems, from this study, that although urine depresses the motility of sperms it is not so harmful to the fertility of sperms as is generally believed.

E. EFFECTS OF OSMOTIC PRESSURE AND HYDROGEN ION CONCENTRATION ON THE MOTILITY AND FERTILITY OF SPERMATOZOA

The osmotic pressure and the hydrogen ion concentration of semen has been determined in various species (cf. 1, 42, 50), and their effect on the motility of sperm has been also reported (34, 35), but very little work has been done on their effects on motility and fertility of mammalian spermatozoa. The motility and fertilizing capacity of rabbit sperms suspended in hyper- or hypotonic Krebs-Ringer solutions at normal pH value, in isotonic solution at higher or lower pH values, and in hyper- or hypotonic solution at higher or lower pH values were studied

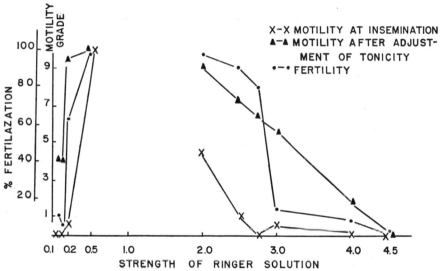

FIG. 6. Effect of hypertonic and hypotonic solutions on the motility and fertility of rabbit spermatozoa (31).

by Chang and Thorsteinsson (31). From Fig. 6, the following facts are obvious: (a) Sperms can withstand half the strength or twice the strength of Ringer solution without ill effect either on their motility or on their fertility at normal pH value. (b) Even in a solution of one-tenth the strength, or four times the strength of Ringer solution, the motility of sperm is very much depressed, and yet fertility is not completely abolished. (c) The motility of sperm drops much earlier than the fertility as the tonicity of solution changes from isotonic to hyper- or hypotonic. (d) The motility and fertility of sperm can perhaps withstand hypertonic solution better than hypotonic solutions. (e) A sharp drop of fertility occurs at a region from 1/5 R to 1/10 R in hypotonic solutions and at a region from 2¾ R to 3 R in hypertonic solutions. This shows that although the optimal osmotic pressure for the maintenance of fertility is not too narrow, critical points exist beyond which the fertility would be very much injured. (f) Finally it seems that the motility after adjustment of tonicity is a better reference to determine fertility than the motility at first appearance.

Figure 7 shows the results when sperms were suspended in isotonic solution at various pH values and inseminated to females. It is surpris-

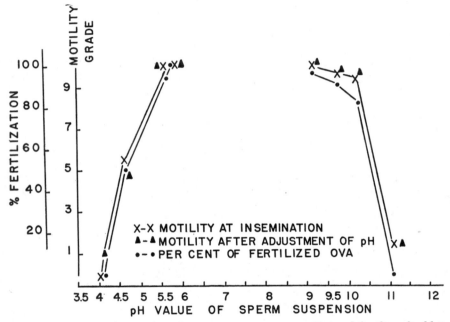

Fig. 7. Effect of pH value of sperm suspension on motility and fertility of rabbit spermatozoa (31).

ing to note that, as isolated cells, spermatozoa withstand a very wide range of pH changes. That is, from 5.57 to 10.94, there is no severe damage to either their motility or their fertility. Unlike the effect of osmotic pressures, the motility and fertility corresponded closely to each other at various pH values. A very sharp drop of motility and fertility occurred at 10.19 to 11.07 and at 5.57 to 4.10. This indicates that there is a very critical pH region at which the motility and fertility of sperm are abolished suddenly. This may be due to a blockage of functional groups of vital enzymes, the denaturation or precipitation of proteins at a particular pH.

When the tonicity and pH value were changed at the same time, it was found that in hypertonic or hypotonic solutions, the fertility of sperm is better at normal or at lower pH (5.51) than at a higher pH (9.54) and in isotonic solutions the fertility is better at higher pH (10.19) than at a lower pH (4.61). This may indicate that the ill effect of hyper- or hypotonicity and lower or higher pH value on the fertility of sperm may function independently at certain ranges, but these two factors may also function concurrently at other ranges.

III. Physiology of Spermatozoa in the Female Tract

Although mammalian spermatozoa have to spend various lengths of time in the female tract before performing their ultimate function of fertilization, our understanding of the physiology of sperms in the female tract is very limited. It is known that mammalian sperms survive much longer in the male tract than in the female tracts, and that the vagina is the most unfavorable place while the cervical canal is the most favorable place for the survival of sperm (cf. 27). The morphology, the metabolism, and the physiology of sperms in the different parts of the female tracts however have not been systematically and extensively investigated. Here I shall report some of my published and unpublished work on the physiology of sperms in the female tract.

A. FERTILIZING CAPACITY OF SPERM DEPOSITED INTO THE FALLOPIAN TUBES

From the biological point of view, it is a striking phenomenon that in the natural sequence of mammalian fertilization it is the spermatozoa that wait for the arrival of eggs, not the eggs that wait for the arrival of sperm. The time of waiting may vary from 6 hours in the rabbit to 24–30 hours in the ferret, sheep, and cattle, and up to perhaps several months in the bat. As it is known that the transportation of sperms from the vagina to the upper part of the tube is very rapid and that the number of sperms present at the site of fertilization is very small, this time interval is therefore not necessary for the transport and accumulation of large number of sperms to ensure fertilization. There may be other biological reasons to account for this time interval which spermatozoa spend in the female tract. In order to determine first whether rabbit spermatozoa may fertilize the eggs when they first encounter them, or whether they have to spend a certain length of time in the Fallopian tube before they are capable of fertilization, I deposited, by surgical means, ejaculated or epididymal sperms into the Fallopian tubes where freshly shed eggs were present (17). To my surprise no egg was fertilized. However, when sperm was deposited into the Fallopian tubes a few hours before ovulation the proportion of fertilized ova increased as the time interval between deposition of sperm and the time of ovulation increased (Table VI). From Table VI it is evident that ejaculated or epididymal sperms cannot penetrate the eggs unless they have spent 6 hours in the tube. As it has been shown that the fertilizability of rabbit eggs lasts for about 6–8 hours after ovulation (40, 20), it would seem that lack of fertilization from tubal insemination 4 hours before ovulation (or later) was due to the loss of fertilizability of the eggs before the development of fertilizing capacity of sperm occurred in the female tract.

TABLE VI

FERTILIZING CAPACITY OF RABBIT SPERMATOZOA DEPOSITED INTO THE FALLOPIAN TUBES AT VARIOUS INTERVALS[a]

	Deposition [hours before (+) or after (−) ovulation]	No. of rabbits	Ovulation points	Ova recovered	
				Total	Per cent fertilized
Tubal:	−2	5	58	40	0
	−1	2	14	10	0
	+2	5	42	31	0
	+4	5	39	34	6
	+6	4	49	41	78
	+8	5	50	47	55
Controls (mating):	−2	2	20	14	43
	+2	1	13	13	100
Controls (uterine sperm):	−2	2	20	15	13
	+2	2	13	12	75

[a] From Chang (17).

This phenomenon has also been observed by deposition of sperms, under operational procedure, into the periovarian sac of rats or into the Fallopian tubes of rabbits (2) and termed "capacitation of sperm" by Austin (3). He further ruled out the possibility that the effects observed may have been due to the operative procedure employed, because a delay between the arrival of the sperms at the site of fertilization and the penetration of the eggs in intact rats was observed when coitus occurred after ovulation (3). Noyes (56) has also found, by insemination into the uterus, that rat uterine sperms penetrated eggs after a shorter time than did epididymal spermatozoa. The capacitation of sperm in the female tract probably occurs also in the cow because

Trimberger and Davis (69) reported that the best rates of conception were obtained in the cows inseminated more than 6 hours, but less than 24 hours before ovulation. In the hamster, it has been estimated by Chang and Sheaffer (28) that it may require about 2–4 hours for the sperms to develop their fertilizing capacity in the female tract.

B. Capacitation of Sperm in the Uterus

In an earlier paper (17) I have reported that fertilization is possible if the deposited spermatozoa were not freshly ejaculated but recovered from the uterus of another rabbit. This indicates that the capacitation of sperm can be achieved not only in the Fallopian tube but also in the uterus. In order to determine further the time required to develop the fertilizing capacity in the uterus, I recovered rabbit sperms from the uterus at various times after mating and then deposited them into the tubes of another rabbit that had ovulated recently (21). The results are presented in Table VII, which shows that as in the case of Fallopian tube it requires about 6 hours for the sperm to develop their fertilizing capacity in the uterus. By comparison of the proportion of fertilized eggs obtained when 4- or 6-hour uterine sperms were deposited into the tubes of rabbits 2 hours before or after ovulation, it was shown that spermatozoa can be partially capacitated in the uterus and then completed in the Fallopian tubes. By counting the number of sperms on the zona pellucida of the fertilized and unfertilized eggs it seems that the failure of fertilization in the deposition of freshly ejaculated, epididymal, or 2–4 hour uterine sperm is mainly due to the failure of spermatozoa to penetrate into the zona pellucida, because all the unfertilized eggs had 1–30 or more sperms on the surface of the zona but not one penetrated into the perivitelline space. It seems that the mechanism of the capacitation of sperm is to render spermatozoa capable of penetrating through the mucoproteins of the zona pellucida.

C. Morphology of Capacitated Spermatozoa

After the finding that ejaculated rabbit sperm required a certain length of time in the female tract to develop their fertilizing capacity, Slechta and I (29) tried to find whether there is any morphological difference between ejaculated and uterine sperm. Since the acrosome (or gelea capitis) attached to the anterior end of sperm head was frequently absent in the spermatozoa treated with serum (15) and since no acrosome was seen in the sperms in the perivitelline space or on the zona pellucida of fertilized eggs, we thought that the detachment of the acrosome might be a morphological change of sperm after the capacitation in the female tract. However, when we counted the number of sperms without acrosomes after staining with Giemsa stain we could not find any significant difference between rabbit spermatozoa freshly ejaculated and those recovered from the uterus. As the acrosome is more

TABLE VII

DEVELOPMENT OF FERTILIZING CAPACITY OF RABBIT SPERMATOZOA IN THE UTERUS[a]

Sperm deposited	No. of rabbits	No. of sperm deposited into each tube (range)	Ova recovered		Percentage of fertilized ova
			Total	Fertilized	
Uterine (hours between mating and recovery):					
2	7	30,000–46,000	73	0	0
4	8	20,000–198,000	86	0	0
6	8	40,000–116,000	69	26	38
12	11	20,000–180,000	117	63	54
16	5	27,000–630,000	65	50	77
24	5	25,000–57,000	55	31	56
Epididymal (fresh, centrifuged)	5	80,000–1,400,000	52	0	0
Ejaculated (fresh, centrifuged)	8	630,000–8,800,000	107	0	0
In various solutions for different times	17	15,000–1,230,000	274	0	0
Incubated or stored in uterine fluid, endometrium, or in excised uterus	12	154,000–1,640,000	139	2?	0

[a] From Chang (21).

obvious in guinea pig sperm, we also counted the number of sperms without acrosomes in sperms recovered from the epididymis or from the uterus of guinea pigs. Again we could not find a significant difference.

Recently Austin and Bishop (6) reported that modification and loss of acrosomes have been observed in living spermatozoa of hamster, guinea pig and Libyan jird recovered in the Fallopian tubes and in the cumulus oöphorus. They considered that the removal of the acrosome may be the morphological mechanism of capacitation of sperms in the female tract. Since they stated that removal of the acrosome probably occurs at the surface of the zona pellucida, and since we could not find detachment of the acrosome in the uterine sperms, the detachment of the acrosome is probably only part of the process of capacitation.

Slechta and I (29) have also studied the difference between ejaculated and uterine sperm by means of histochemical techniques, such as acid and alkaline phosphatase, glycogen, lipids, calcium, DNA, and RNA methods: We could not find any difference between ejaculated sperms and sperms recovered from the uterus by ordinary visual examination. However, Thornsteinsson and I (32) employed the microspectrophotometric method, and found unexpectedly that there is a significant increase of DNA as shown by Feulgen reaction in the sperm recovered from Fallopian tubes or from the uterus as compared with ejaculated rabbit sperms. Since capacitation of sperm in the female tract is not expected to involve DNA, which is believed to be a compound for genetic transmission, the higher content of DNA in the capacitated sperm may be due to a change in the cytoplasmic membrane, because it can be stained with dyes of the Sudan series and is a sharp test for proteins and a Feulgen reaction (45). If capacitated sperms are studied microspectrophotometrically after being stained with histochemical methods, one may expect to have more revealing results.

D. DECAPACITATION OF SPERMATOZOA BY SEMINAL PLASMA

While ejaculated sperms have to spend a few hours in the female tract to develop their fertilizing capacity, it was found that capacitated sperms can be rendered incapable of fertilizing if treated with seminal plasma for half an hour (24). Table VIII shows that treatment of capacitated rabbit sperms with 10–20% of rabbit seminal plasma causes them to lose their fertilizing capacity, while treatment of capacitated rabbit sperms with bull seminal plasma has a more harmful effect than human seminal plasma. Since the capacitation is not simply a process of elimination of seminal plasma by the female tract (17), and since seminal plasma of different species and rabbit serum (26) can decapacitate rabbit sperms, the decapacitation of sperm is probably due to certain substances present in the seminal plasma or in the serum, which may adhere to the sperms and cause them to be unable to fertilize the eggs. This view is also supported by the fact that the decapacitated rabbit sperms can be recapacitated again to be able to

TABLE VIII

DETRIMENTAL EFFECTS OF SEMINAL PLASMA ON THE FERTILIZING CAPACITY OF RABBIT UTERINE SPERM[a]

Concentration of different seminal plasma (%)	No. of rabbits	No. of uterine sperm deposited (range)	Left tube, experimental			Right tube, control		
			Total ova	Fert. ova	Fertilization (%)	Total ova	Fert. ova	Fertilization (%)
Rabbit plasma:								
Undiluted	4 + 3[b]	73,000–275,000	23	0	0	41	24	59
20	8	19,000–220,000	33	1	3	32	19	59
10	8	52,000–208,000	36	2	6	26	17	65
5	7 + 3[b]	15,000–139,000	38	0	0	47	25	53
2	6	3,000–255,000	36	18	50	31	26	84
Bull plasma: 2	6	12,000–55,000	18	1	6	22	14	64
Human plasma: 5	6	29,000–55,000	22	6	27	18	14	78
Rabbit plasma: 5% or 10% deposited 6 hr. before ovulation	8	55,000–303,000	29	17	59	35	23	66

[a] From Chang (24).
[b] Received uterine sperm obtained by insemination of epididymal sperm.

fertilize the eggs if deposited into the tubes 6 hours before ovulation (24).

E. CAPACITATION OF SPERMATOZOA IN THE UTERUS OF ANIMALS AT DIFFERENT REPRODUCTIVE PHASES OR UNDER DIFFERENT HORMONE TREATMENTS

In order to determine whether capacitation of sperm in the female tract is related to the endocrine activity of the females (25), rabbit semen was injected into the uterus of estrous or pseudopregnant rabbits and into the uterus of these animals treated with gonadotropin, estrogen, or progesterone. Twelve hours later, the sperms were recovered and deposited into the Fallopian tubes of another rabbit that had recently ovulated. When the eggs were examined 24 hours after the deposition of uterine sperm into the tubes, as shown in Table IX, it was found that capacitation was not achieved in the uterus of pseudopregnant rabbits or in the uterus of estrous rabbits treated with progesterone and that gonadotropin or estrogen treatment of pseudopregnant rabbits did not improve their ability to capacitate spermatozoa. It seems, therefore, that the progestational activity of the endometrium under the influence of the corpus luteum or progesterone inhibits sperm capacitation.

In order to determine whether estrogen plays a part in the capacitation of sperm in the uterus, immature and ovariectomized rabbits treated with gonadotropin, estrogen, or progesterone were used to incubate ejaculated sperms. The results of this study are presented in Table X, which shows that capacitation can be achieved in the immature or ovariectomized rabbit and that treatment with gonadotropin or estrogen gives no significant enhancement of the capacitation of sperms in the uterus. However, with progesterone treatment, the capacitation could not be significantly accomplished. This demonstrates that capacitation is probably a general reaction and is independent of estrogen action upon the uterus. Even without estrogen, the influence of progesterone in inhibiting the capacitation of sperms in the uterus is revealed.

As it is known that the uterus is more susceptible to infection at the luteal phase than at the follicular phase (63), and that semen contains a large number of bacteria (38), it was thought that the inhibition of capacitation in the pseudopregnant uterus might be due to a microbial reaction. When ejaculated semen mixed with strong antibiotics or epididymal sperms without the contamination of bacteria were incubated in the pseudopregnant uterus, capacitation was not achieved (Table XI). It appears, therefore, that the inhibition of capacitation in the pseudo-

TABLE IX

Capacitation of Sperm in the Uterus of Pseudopregnant and Estrous Rabbits[a]

Semen injected into the uterus	No. of rabbits injected with semen	No. of rabbits deposited with sperm[b]	Sperm quality		No. of ova examined		
			Avg. no. and range deposited (millions)	Motility grade	Total	Fertilized	Fertilization (%)
6–14 days' pseudo-pregnant rabbits							
No treatment	6	5B + 10 U	3.81 (0.27–7.0)	2 (1–3)	84	1 + 1 ?	2.4
Gonadotropin-treated	3	10 U	3.93 (1.8–6.2)	1.8 (1–3)	47	0	0
Estrogen-treated	3	10 U	6.42 (0.04–12.5)	1.8 (0–3)	58	0	0
Estrous rabbits							
No treatment	6	5B + 12 U	0.21 (0.02–1.2)	2.7 (1–3)	95	60	63
Progesterone-treated	5	9 U	1.43 (0.14–2.4)	3 (3)	47	1	2.1

[a] From Chang (25).
[b] 5B denotes that sperm samples subjected to the same treatment were deposited into both tubes of five animals. 10 U denotes that sperm samples subjected to the same treatment were deposited into one tube of ten animals and sperm samples treated differently were deposited into the other tube.

TABLE X

CAPACITATION OF SPERM IN THE UTERUS OF IMMATURE AND OVARIECTOMIZED RABBITS[a]

Semen injected into the uterus	No. of rabbits injected with semen	No. of rabbits deposited with sperm[b]	Sperm quality		No. of ova examined		
			Avg. no. and range of sperm deposited (millions)	Motility grade	Total	Fertilized	Fertilization (%)
Immature rabbits							
No treatment	3	3	0.15 (0.06–0.29)	2.7 (2–3)	32	11	34
Treated with estrogen	3	3	0.189 (0.16–0.22)	3 (3)	32	17	53
Treated with gonadotropin	3	6	0.098 (0.075–0.14)	3 (3)	32	22	69
Treated with progesterone	3	6	0.89 (0.63–1.12)	3 (3)	32	1	3.1
Ovariectomized rabbits							
No treatment	4	11	0.24 (0.11–0.45)	2.5 (2–3)	41	15	37
Treated with estrogen	4	11	0.98 (0.35–1.5)	3 (3)	48	16	33
Treated with gonadotropin	5	9	0.58 (0.25–1.1)	2.9 (2–3)	42	11	26
Treated with progesterone	5	10	1.09 (0.26–1.9)	2.6 (1–3)	36	3	8.4

[a] From Chang (25).
[b] Sperm samples subjected to the same treatment were deposited into one tube of each animal and sperm samples of different treatment were deposited into the other tube.

TABLE XI

Capacitation of Sperm in the Uterus or in the Fallopian Tubes under Various Conditions[a]

Sperm injected into	No. of rabbits injected with sperm	No. of rabbits deposited with sperm[b]	Sperm quality		No. of ova examined		
			Avg. and range of sperm deposited (millions)	Motility grade	Total	Fertilized	Fertilization (%)
Uterus of estrous rabbits							
No treatment of semen	3	6	0.15 (0.017–0.35)	2.8 (2–3)	31	18	58
Treatment of semen with penicillin	3	7	0.21 (0.07–0.35)	2.7 (2–3)	36	20	56
Uterus of pseudopregnant rabbits							
Semen treated with penicillin and streptomycin	5	11	1.75 (0.2–4.72)	2.4 (2–3)	52	4	7.7
Epididymal sperm used	4	10	0.75 (0.04–1.88)	2.7 (2–3)	42	4	9.5
Uterus of 1-day pseudopregnant rabbits	2	4	0.15 (0.02–0.29)	2 (2)	29	7	24
Uterus of 19-days pseudopregnant rabbits	2	5	0.23 (0.15–0.32)	3 (3)	23	9	39
Tubes of 7–9 days pseudopregnant rabbits	2	7	0.09	2 (2)	45	23	51
Tubes of estrous rabbits	2	5	0.12 (0.07–0.29)	1.2 (1–2)	27	20	74

[a] From Chang (25).
[b] Sperm samples of the same treatment were deposited into one tube of each rabbit and sperm samples of different treatment were deposited into the other tube.

pregnant uterus is not due to an effect of infection but to the progestational reaction of the endometrium. It was shown further that the inhibition of capacitation in the pseudopregnant uterus occurred only at the height of progestational activity because after incubation of sperm in the uterus of 1-day or 19-day pseudopregnant rabbits capacitation was accomplished (Table XI).

It is known that following the administration of gonadotropin to induce ovulation, the fertility of the pseudopregnant rabbit is practically nil although 60% of fertilized eggs are obtained when insemination is performed via the uterus instead of via the vagina (54, 55). Since capacitation of sperm cannot be achieved in the pseudopregnant uterus, as mentioned before, the capacitation of sperm must be accomplished in the Fallopian tubes of pseudopregnant rabbits, or fertilization cannot occur. When ejaculated semen was injected into the Fallopian tubes of pseudopregnant rabbits for 12 hours as shown in Table XI, capacitation of sperm did occur. This shows that, so far as capacitation of sperm is concerned, the Fallopian tube is not affected, but the uterus is affected, by the presence of the corpus luteum or by progesterone.

Recently Noyes et al. (57) reported that capacitation of rabbit sperm can be achieved in the isolated bladder and isolated colon of male or female animals, the anterior chamber of the eye, in the glandula vesicularis of the male, and the uteri and Fallopian tubes of ovariectomized rabbits, and they concluded that the site of capacitation of sperms is not specific. They succeeded further in capacitating sperm in vitro by incubation of sperm in the excised uterus at 37°C. or by suspension of sperm in strips of endometrium at room temperature. I have tried many times to capacitate sperm in various solutions or in various extracts of female organs in vitro without success. Since I used whole semen in my experiment and they used centrifuged sperm in their experiment and since capacitation cannot be achieved in the presence of red cells or dead sperm as they observed, my unsuccessful attempt to capacitate sperm in vitro may be due mainly to the involvement of seminal plasma and other serological factors.

IV. Summary

Recent experimental investigations, mainly by the present author, on the fertilizing capacity of rabbit spermatozoa are reviewed. It is known that, of hundreds of millions of spermatozoa which are ejaculated into the vagina at copulation, only a few thousand reach the site of fertilization. More than 99% of ejaculated spermatozoa will be either prevented from reaching the site of fertilization by the cervix and the tubal-uterine junction, or evacuated and disintegrated by the uterus. Since about 1%

of spermatozoa in an ejaculate is enough to ensure fertilization by artificial insemination, and since very few sperms are present at the site of fertilization, the eggs may be fertilized by vanguards of spermatozoa rather than by a sperm swarm. Physiologically, a large number of sperms are not needed either to reach the site of fertilization, or to maintain their survival, or to facilitate penetration of the egg by the fertilizing sperm. Biologically, the probability of fertilization is higher if a large number of sperms are inseminated because a large number of sperms will contain more strong ones capable of survival in the female tract, especially if ovulation is late. The prodigality of sperm production by the male is probably to achieve greater variation in the recombination of genes.

Fertilizing capacity of sperm as affected by various treatments *in vitro* is discussed. Although seminal plasma, the secretions of accessory glands, has a beneficial effect for the maintenance of motility and fertility of sperm under adverse conditions, its function in normal mating is as a vehicle for the transportation of sperms and as a medium for the maintenance of a higher activity of sperm for a very short time. The spermicidal factor present in the blood serum of various species and sperm agglutination under various circumstances may have no relation to the fertilizing capacity of sperm or to the process of fertilization, because the germ cells are well protected by specialized organs. Although urine was found to depress the motility of spermatozoa it is not so harmful to the fertility of sperm as is commonly believed. As isolated cells, spermatozoa can withstand a very wide range of osmotic pressure changes, from $\frac{1}{4}$ to $2\frac{3}{4}$ the strength of Ringer solution without ill effect on their fertility, but with depressing effect on their motility. They can also withstand a very wide range of pH changes, from 5.6 to 10.94, without striking ill effects on their motility and fertility. This is probably due to their high evolutionary adaptability to survive *in vitro*, as in the lower organisms, or to perform their function from one individual to another as in the higher animals.

The discussion of the physiology of sperm in the female tract is mainly based on recent investigation of the capacitation of sperm in the female tract. Capacitation is probably a general feature in mammalian fertilization because ejaculated spermatozoa cannot fertilize when they first encounter the eggs, and require a certain length of time either in the uterus or in the Fallopian tubes to develop their fertilizing capacity. The capacitation of sperm can be partially achieved in the uterus and then completed in the Fallopian tubes. The capacitated sperms can be decapacitated by treatment with seminal plasma or with serum, but can be recapacitated if they remain longer in the female tract. Capacitation can be achieved in the uterus of the immature or ovariectomized rabbits, and it is independent of gonadotropic or estrogenic stimulation. It cannot be achieved in the uterus of pseudopregnant rabbits or of estrous rabbits treated with progesterone. In contrast, it can be achieved in the Fallopian tubes of pseudopregnant rabbits. The site of capacitation is not specific, and capacitation can be achieved *in vitro*. Although there may be morphological differences between capacitated and ejaculated spermatozoa, such as the absence of the acrosome or the increase of Feulgen stain in the capacitated sperm, the real physiological mechanism of capacitation is still obscure.

References

1. Anderson, J., "The Semen of Animals and Its Use for Artificial Insemination," I. A. B., Edinburgh, 1947.
2. Austin, C. R., *Australian J. Sci. Research* [Ser. B] **4**, 581 (1951).
3. Austin, C. R., *Nature* **170**, 326 (1952).
4. Austin, C. R., *J. Endocrinol.* **14**, 335 (1957).
5. Austin, C. R., and Bishop, M. W. H., *in* "The Beginnings of Embryonic Development" (A. Tyler, R. C. von Borstel, and C. B. Metz, eds.), p. 71. American Association for the Advancement of Science, Washington, D. C., 1957.
6. Austin, C. R., and Bishop, M. W. H., *Nature* **181**, 851 (1958).
7. Bishop, M. W. H., and Austin, C. R., *Endeavour* **16**, 137 (1957).
8. Bishop, D. W., and Tyler, A., *J. Exptl. Zool.* **132**, 575 (1956).
9. Blackshaw, A. W., *J. Gen. Physiol.* **36**, 449 (1953).
10. Boyd, W. C., "Fundamentals of Immunology," 3rd rev. ed. Interscience, New York, 1956.
11. Braden, A. W. H., *Australian J. Biol. Sci.* **6**, 693 (1953).
12. Chang, M. C., *in* "The Problem of Fertility" (E. Engle, ed.), p. 169. Princeton Univ. Press, Princeton, New Jersey, 1946.
13. Chang, M. C., *Science* **104**, 361 (1946).
14. Chang, M. C., *Proc. Soc. Exptl. Biol. Med.* **66**, 51 (1947).
15. Chang, M. C., *J. Gen. Physiol.* **30**, 321 (1947).
16. Chang, M. C., *Proc. Soc. Exptl. Biol. Med.* **70**, 32 (1949).
17. Chang, M. C., *Nature* **168**, 697 (1951).
18. Chang, M. C., *Ann. ostet. e ginecol.* **2**, 918 (1951).
19. Chang, M. C., *Ann. N. Y. Acad. Sci.* **52**, 1192 (1951).
20. Chang, M. C., *J. Exptl. Zool.* **121**, 351 (1952).
21. Chang, M. C., *Nature* **175**, 1036 (1955).
22. Chang, M. C., *Ann. ostet. e ginecol.* **4**, 74 (1956).
23. Chang, M. C., *in* "The Beginnings of Embryonic Development" (A. Tyler, R. C. von Borstel, and C. B. Metz, eds.), p. 109, American Association for the Advancement of Science, Washington, D. C., 1957.
24. Chang, M. C., *Nature* **179**, 248 (1957).
25. Chang, M. C., *Endocrinol.* **63**, 691 (1958).
26. Chang, M. C., unpublished.
27. Chang, M. C., and Pincus, G., *Physiol. Revs.* **31**, 1 (1951).

28. Chang, M. C., and Sheaffer, D., *J. Heredity* **48**, 107 (1957).
29. Chang, M. C., and Slechta, R. F., unpublished.
30. Chang, M. C., and Thorsteinsson, T., *Fertility and Sterility* **9**, 231 (1958).
31. Chang, M. C., and Thorsteinsson, T., *Fertility and Sterility* **9**, 510 (1958).
32. Chang, M. C., and Thorsteinsson, T., unpublished.
33. Edwards, R. G., and Sirlin, J. L., *Endeavour* **17**, 42 (1958).
34. Emmens, C. W., *J. Physiol.* (*London*) **106**, 471 (1947).
35. Emmens, C. W., *J. Physiol.* (*London*) **107**, 129 (1948).
36. Emmens, C. W., and Blackshaw, A. W., *Physiol. Revs.* **36**, 277 (1956).
37. Emmens, C. W., and Swyer, G. I. M., *Nature* **160**, 718 (1947).
38. Gunsalus, I. G., Salisbury, G. W., and Willett, E. L., *J. Dairy Sci.* **24**, 911 (1941).
39. Guthrie, M. J., *J. Mammal.* **14**, 199 (1933).
40. Hammond, J., *J. Exptl. Biol.* **11**, 140 (1934).
41. Hammond, J., and Asdell, S. A., *Brit. J. Exptl. Biol.* **11**, 155 (1926).
42. Hartman, C. G., *in* "Sex and Internal Secretions" (E. Allen, ed.), p. 630. 2nd ed. Williams & Wilkins, Baltimore, 1939.
43. Ivanov, E. I., *Arch. sci. biol.* (*St. Petersbourg*) **12**, 377 (1907).
44. Jackson, M. H., and Harvey, G., *Nature* **162**, 67 (1948).
45. Knaysi, G., *J. Bacteriol.* **51**, 113 (1946).
46. Lillie, F. R., "Problems of Fertilization." University of Chicago Press, Chicago, 1919.
47. Lindahl, P. E., and Kihlström, J. E., *Rept. Intern. Congr. Physiol. Pathol. Animal Reproduction and Artificial Insemination, 2nd Congr. Copenhagen July* **1**, 70 (1952).
48. Lindahl, P. E., and Kihlström, J. E., *Nature* **174**, 600 (1954).
49. MacLeod, J., Gold, R. Z., and McLane, C. M., *Fertility and Sterility* **6**, 112 (1955).
50. Mann, T., "The Biochemistry of Semen." Methuen, London, 1954.
51. Metz, C. B., *in* "The Beginnings of Embryonic Development" (A. Tyler, R. C. von Borstel, and C. B. Metz, eds.), p. 23. American Association for the Advancement of Science, Washington, D. C., 1957.
52. Miller, R. E., *J. Morphol.* **64**, 267 (1939).
53. Milovanov, V. K., "Osnovy iskusstvennogo osemenenija" ("Principles of artificial insemination"). State Publishing House, Moscow-Leningrad, 1934.
54. Murphree, R. L., Black, W. G., Otto, G., and Casida, L. E., *Endocrinol.* **49**, 474 (1951).
55. Murphree, R. L., Warwick, E. J., Casida, L. E., and McShan, W. H., *Endocrinol.* **41**, 308 (1947).
56. Noyes, R. W., *Western J. Surg. Obstet. Gynecol.* **61**, 342 (1953).
57. Noyes, R. W., Walton, A., and Adams, C. E., *Nature* **181**, 1209 (1958).
58. Phillips, P. H., and Lardy, H. A., *J. Dairy Sci.* **23**, 399 (1940).
59. Pincus, G., and Enzmann, E. V., *J. Exptl. Zool.* **73**, 195 (1936).
60. Polge, C., Smith, A. U., and Parkes, A. S., *Nature* **164**, 666 (1949).
61. Posalaky, Z., and Törö, I., *Acta Biol. Acad. Sci. Hung.* **8**, 1 (1957).
62. Rothschild, Lord, "Fertilization." Methuen, London, 1956.
63. Rowson, L. E. A., Lamming, G. E., and Fry, R. M., *Vet. Record* **65**, 335 (1953).
64. Runnström, J., *Advances in Enzymol.* **9**, 241 (1949).
65. Salisbury, G. W., *J. Dairy Sci.* **29**, 695 (1946).
66. Salisbury, G. W., *Animal Breeding Abstr.* **25**, 111 (1957).

67. Swyer, G. I. M., *Biochem. J.* **41**, 409 (1947).
68. Swyer, G. I. M., *Nature* **159**, 873 (1947).
69. Trimberger, G. W., and Davis, H. P., *Neb. Agr. Expt. Sta. Research Bull.* **129**, 1 (1943).
70. Tyler, A., *Biol. Bull.* **104**, 224 (1953).
71. Tyler, A., *in* "Analysis of Development" (B. Willier, P. A. Weiss, and V. Hamburger, eds.), p. 170. Saunders, Philadelphia, 1955.
72. Walton, A., *Folio Morphol.* **8**, 1 (1938).
73. Willett, E. L., *J. Dairy Sci.* **33**, 43 (1950).
74. Willett, E. L., *J. Dairy Sci.* **36**, 1182 (1953).

Discussion

CHAIRMAN: W. O. NELSON

S. ZUCKERMAN: May I be informed on a question of fact? From one of the earlier tables which you showed us, it appeared that 87% of 362 unfertilized ova had no extra sperms in the zona. Did these unfertilized eggs all show polar bodies?

M. C. CHANG: They had only first polar bodies; not the second. That is why I showed the other slides to distinguish between the first polar body and the second polar body. There is a morphological difference between them. By the presence of the second polar body, not the fragmentation of the first polar body, you can determine whether the egg is really fertilized or not. Unless you see the second polar body, you are not sure the egg is fertilized even though there may be some fragments in the egg.

P. PERLMAN: I have two questions which I would like to ask. What in your estimation is the function and the control of the tubo-uterine junction? There apparently is a junction. What controls it? I have no idea but I think it is important in the distribution of sperm to the tract. That is the first question.

The second one is the problem of the biochemical individuality of the sperm of a given species. In some experiments we did several years ago with Dr. Leonard, we tried to add heterologous sperm to the rat uterus and observe its transport into the oviducts. I think you will recall that no sperm of the foreign species were transmitted. We mixed the foreign species with the rat sperm and the rat sperm got through but the other species did not.

So I think there is something peculiar to the biochemical nature of the sperm which is a factor in the selection of the transport of the sperm. I wish you would enlighten us on that a little bit.

M. C. CHANG: About the tubular junction, it must be controlled by the endocrine system.

About the transportation of eggs, my feeling is that progesterone may play a part. Why should it take about 4 days for the egg to get into the uterus, both in mice and cows? The development of the corpus luteum may play a part in the transportation of the egg from the tube to the uterus. Whether or not sperm transport is also controlled by endocrine factors, I don't know. It may be controlled by the endocrine system. Anyhow, because so small a number of sperm get there, it may not be very important.

About your second question as to the different species—some kind of morphological, physiological, or serological reaction may be involved. In some species, sperms do get through the tube of a different species. I put chinchilla sperm into the rabbit uterus. They get into the Fallopian tube all right. But in some species, as in your work, the sperms don't get through. There may be some physiological or immunological reaction to prevent or to destroy the foreign sperm.

But in another respect, as I showed you on one of the slides, if you suspend rabbit sperm among the dead sperms of a human and a bull, there is a beneficial effect on the rabbit sperm and they will survive longer.

R. H. BOWMAN: In regard to the uterine capacitation of spermatozoa which you observed in rabbits prior to ovulation I would just like to mention results I observed a few years ago in the rat. If I waited until ovulation had occurred, before the animals were bred, spermatozoa would almost without fail enter the ova. In the rat it appears then that a preovulatory capacitation of spermatozoa in the uterus is not necessary.

M. C. CHANG: Yes. I think that capacitation is a very general phenomenon. In the rats, Dr. Austin and Dr. Noyes demonstrated that. In the cow this is probably true because with artificial insemination 24 hours before ovulation, the conception rate is higher. In the hamster, I have estimated that the hamster sperms have to wait about 2–4 hours to be able to fertilize the egg. About your results—you have to realize that the rat eggs can be fertilized for about 10 hours after ovulation. So there is plenty of time for the sperm to be capacitated in the female tract.

S. ZUCKERMAN: I wonder if I may ask another question. Among the many points you have made, you have expounded two central propositions.

The first is that there is a higher chance of fertilization if more than one sperm comes into contact with an ovum. There seems to be a very distinct difference in the proportion of eggs fertilized depending on the number of sperms seen in the zona.

Your second proposition concerns the time that the sperm has to remain in the female genital tract before it is "capacitated."

Is it certain that the second of these two propositions implies a change in the sperm as opposed to something that is happening in the ovary? You do not know the exact moment ovulation and fertilization take place; that is something you cannot tell. Is it not possible that the capacitation phenomenon is something that is happening in the ovum, preliminary to fertilization and cleavage, in the same way as the numbers of sperm that make contact with the ovum are also a factor in the processes initiating cleavage?

I, myself, do not believe that polar bodies by themselves represent a proper indication of cleavage and fertilization. When you accelerate the senescence of an ovary by means of X-irradiation, the incidence of polar bodies, and also in some cases cleavage, goes up.

To go back to my first point—I am wondering whether you couldn't relate your second proposition to the first by supposing that the ovum has to be in contact with the sperm for a number of hours before cleavage occurs?

M. C. CHANG: As to your first question about the large number of sperms around the egg. What I would stress is that obviously the larger number of sperm around the egg will give a higher chance to have a physiologically functional sperm penetrate the egg. But, on the other hand, with a large number of sperm around the egg, as I showed on the slide, the egg may be not fertilized because there is not a physiologically functional one to penetrate it.

As to your second point, about the capacitation of the sperm, you think it may be something that happened to the egg. That is a possibility. We will have to study it.

After all, the sperm had to meet the egg to fertilize the egg rather than just stay around in the uterus. The capacitation of sperm in the uterus or in the Fallopian tubes is a fact which demonstrates that the sperm has to spend some time in the female tract before it can penetrate the egg. As to what the egg did to the sperm and what the sperm did to the egg, we are completely in the dark.

About your point on the polar body, I am talking about the rabbit, and about the second polar body which has morphological entity. It is shed only after fertilization. But in the hamster, the second polar body is shed frequently without fertilization. You could find many fragments in the egg which look like polar bodies after you ill-treat the eggs but they are not second polar bodies. Some are fragments of first polar body. Some are fragments of cytoplasm without chromatin.

W. O. NELSON: I am sorry we will have to terminate a discussion that well might continue profitably the rest of the day. If the opportunity presents itself, I know all of us would like to resume the discussion of Dr. Chang's paper.

Hypothalamic Influences on Sperm Transport in the Male and Female Genital Tract

B. A. Cross

Sub-Department of Veterinary Anatomy, University of Cambridge, Cambridge, England

I. Introduction

According to modern views the motility of spermatozoa is of critical importance only for the penetration of the ovum at fertilization. The long journey from the seminiferous tubule to the ampulla of the Fallopian tube is probably effected at all stages by contractile mechanisms in the male and female genital tracts. Undoubtedly much of this contractile activity is independent of central nervous control; but there is reason to suppose that transportation of sperms is assisted by central nervous mechanisms set in motion by the sexual stimulation attending coitus. The hypothalamus may influence these processes in two ways: by autonomic pathways to the reproductive organs, especially via the sympatheticoadrenal system, and by its control of the secretion of oxytocin from the neurohypophysis (5) (see Fig. 1).

II. Sperm Transport in the Female

A. Chronic Uterine Fistula Experiments

The various mechanisms whereby sperms gain entry to the uterus at coitus have recently been discussed in detail by Hartman (13). In many species sperms reach the upper portions of the uterus and even the Fallopian tube within minutes of coitus. Such rapid transport can only be the result of mechanical propulsion, and it is reasonable to conclude that the movements of the uterus itself are chiefly responsible.

In the rabbit Reynolds (19) noted an augmentation of uterine motility following coitus, and Harris (12) suggested that reflex activation of the neurohypophysis with release of oxytocin might be an important factor in the transportation of sperm in this species. In attempts to test this hypothesis the writer made bilateral uterine fistulas in a series of rabbits. The ovarian end of the two uteri were incised, and the flaps so formed were sutured to the openings in the abdominal wall, leaving intact the rest of the genital tract including the ovaries. Uterine motility was recorded kymographically in conscious animals with the help of small balloons inserted through the fistulas. The amount of spontaneous activity in the uteri was very variable, and some difficulty was experienced through artifacts on the kymograph tracings produced by the movements of the rabbits. Nevertheless, in estrous subjects a clear augmentation of frequency and amplitude of uterine contractions was elicited by intravenous injection of Pitocin in doses of 20–200 mU. (milliunits). By contrast, injection of 5–20 µg. adrenaline (epinephrine) produced initially intensified contractions followed by a temporary diminution of spontaneous activity (4). In two experiments a uterine record was obtained during mating. An increase in uterine activity was seen, but this did not resemble the typical oxytocin effect. It compared better with the response to adrenaline and to some forms of movement artifact and lacked the persisting rhythmic character of the response to oxytocin.

In other mating tests attempts were made to recover sperms from the fistulas at various intervals during the 30 minutes after coitus. A drop of saline was introduced by means of a pipette, sucked in and out several times, and then examined microscopically. No sperms were found in the uterine samples, though they were very abundant in samples obtained from the vagina by the same technique. Intravenous injection of 50 or 100 mU. Pitocin just after mating did not result in the appearance of sperms at the fistula within 30 minutes of coitus.

B. Acute Experiments on Uterine Motility *in Vivo*

In view of the difficulties encountered with the fistula technique, it was decided to study in more detail the mechanisms controlling uterine motility in the rabbit in acute preparations (6). At a preliminary operation the ovaries were removed through small incisions in the two flanks, and a tablet of hexestrol was implanted subcutaneously to induce a relatively constant state of estrogenization of the uteri. One week later the animals were anesthetized with Nembutal, and a balloon was placed in the uterus via the cervix exposed by a small incision in the distal end of the vagina. Intravenous doses of Pitocin, much smaller than the estimated physiological output of oxytocin during suckling (4), were effective in augmenting uterine contractions. The threshold dose was 1–5 mU. Endogenous hormone discharged by electrical stimulation of the supraoptic or paraventricular nuclei in the hypothalamus or of their efferent connections to the neural lobe of the pituitary gland produced similar effects on the uterus. The latter were not affected by spinal anesthesia or section of the spinal cord in the mid-thoracic region. However, spontaneous uterine motility was not dependent on neuro-hypophyseal secretion, for it persisted for as long as 7 hours after decerebration and removal of the pituitary gland.

Electrical stimulation of the lateral or posterior areas of the hypothalamus also induced characteristic effects on the uterus, together with signs of sympathetic activity (pupil dilatation and exophthalmos). In this case the response closely paralleled that produced by injection of 1–5 µg. adrenaline, i.e., an initial contractile response followed by inhibition of spontaneous uterine motility. If a test dose of oxytocin were injected 10–30 seconds after hypothalamic stimulation or after injection of adrenaline, the oxytocic response of the uterus was partially or completely inhibited. Both these effects of stimulation of the sympathetic centers of the hypothalamus were abolished by spinal anesthesia or mid-thoracic cord section. Uterine contractions resembling those produced by central sympathetic stimulations or injection of adrenaline or nor-adrenaline, but unlike the response to oxytocin, could occur as a spinal reflex response to dilatation of the vagina. This response was abolished by spinal anesthesia but unaffected by spinal section at the mid-thoracic level.

These experiments revealed at least three possible mechanisms of uterine activation, any or all of which could be operative during mating, i.e., a spinal reflex initiated by vaginal stimulation, and hypothalamic influences mediated by sympathetic outflows or neurohypophyseal secretion.

C. Effect of Neurohypophyseal Destruction

If reflex secretion of oxytocin from the neurohypophysis is an important mechanism in transportation of sperms after coitus, one might expect that destruction of the neurohypophysis would reduce the chances of conception. Cross and Harris (8) reported an observation bearing on this point. A rabbit with a lesion placed in the median eminence was mated a month after operation. It became pregnant and delivered a litter. In the subsequent lactation a failure of milk ejection was observed and histological examination of the hypothalamus and pituitary gland post mortem showed that the neurohypophysis was atrophic.

In further experiments, the writer performed surgical section of the pituitary stalk in 33 rats [unpublished experiments cited by Cross and Harris (8)]. Daily vaginal smears were taken and the urine outputs were measured for evidence of diabetes insipidus. Eighteen animals exhibited only a mild polyuria with daily outputs of up to 50 ml. All these rats were mated when placed with fertile males, and all became pregnant. The subsequent lactational performance, however, indicated that secretion of oxytocin (probably from median eminence tissue) was still possible in this group. The remaining fifteen animals developed a severe diabetes with urine outputs of up to 200 ml. daily, indicating a total destruction of neurohypophyseal tissue. Only six of these animals were mated, but all six became pregnant. None reared litters. Apparently the absence of a functional neurohypophysis was not incompatible with conception.

D. COMMENT

It is perhaps unfortunate that the rabbit was chosen for most of the experiments described above, for some conflict of evidence exists on the rate of transportation of sperms in the female tract of this species. Krehbiel and Carstens (15) demonstrated that radio-opaque fluid could be transported from the vagina to the uterotubal junction within a few seconds, if the vulva was manually stimulated. However, Braden (2) counted the sperms in different portions of the tract at various intervals after coitus and found that no sperms had penetrated the Fallopian tube by 3 hours, and only 38 sperms (mean from six rabbits) had reached the distal third of the tube by 4 hours. Furthermore, Adams (1) showed that if the proximal segment of the Fallopian tube were ligated 2 hours after copulation, no fertilized eggs could be recovered later from the tube; but if ligation were delayed 4 hours, most of the eggs recovered had been fertilized. Greenwald (11) has reported similar findings. We may infer, therefore, that any mechanism operating to convey sperms to the oviduct within seconds or minutes of coitus can have little influence on fertility in this species.

The work of Vandemark and his colleagues on the cow [for summary see Vandemark and Hays (22)] is suggestive of reflex activation of the neurohypophysis by mating stimuli as an integral factor in the rapid transportation of sperms to the Fallopian tube. The evidence has been discussed by Cross (4) and Fitzpatrick (9). In this species it is claimed that injection of 15 U. of oxytocin within 5 minutes of artificial insemination increases the conception rate. However, Hays and Vandemark (14) found that injection of 2 mg. adrenaline just before insemination also increases the conception rate. From the evidence so far available it would seem that the functional significance of the neurohypophysis and the sympatheticoadrenal system in sperm transport in the female requires further clarification (see Fig. 1).

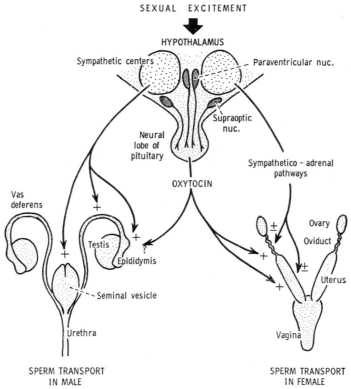

FIG. 1. Diagram showing possible hypothalamic influences on sperm transport in the male and female rabbit; + and — indicate excitatory and inhibitory effects on contractile activity.

III. Sperm Transport in the Male

A. CONTRACTILE MECHANISMS OF THE TESTIS

Various mechanisms have been proposed for the transportation of sperms through the long tortuous passages of the testis and epididymis. They include a continuous *vis a tergo* provided by the release of new sperm, passive conveyance in the secretions of the seminiferous

tubules, cilial action in the ductuli efferenti, and propulsion by the contractile activity of the smooth muscle encircling the epididymal tubules
(17, 21).

To study possible effects of hypothalamic excitation on sperm transport in the testis and epididymis, a simple technique was adopted which
allowed direct microscopic visualization of the male organs in rabbits
anesthetized with Nembutal. The abdominal wall was incised in the
midline and one or both testes pushed through the inguinal canal into
the abdomen. A small plastic cylinder was placed over the testes, and
other viscera were excluded from it. Then the abdominal wound was
closed tightly around the cylinder with Michel clips, and the chamber
thus formed was filled with saline and topped with a layer of mineral
oil. Observations were made with a low-power binocular microscope.

In the first experiment intravenous injection of 200 mU. Pitocin appeared to start rhythmic contractile movements of the testis. The contractions were seen as a gradual lessening of the space, separating the
straight veins passing from the convexity to the epididymal border of the
organ. Each contraction wave was followed by relaxation with the
vessels moving further apart. The whole cycle was repeated at a rate
of three per minute. However, in subsequent experiments the contractions appeared spontaneously within a few minutes of placing the testes
in the chamber. Though in several instances injection of Pitocin seemed
to accelerate the contractions, a clear stimulant action could not be
established on account of spontaneous fluctuations in contractile activity
(0–5 contractions per minute).

If the tunics were incised, the coiled masses of seminiferous tubules
were seen to be carried along by the movements of the overlying albuginea. They did not exhibit contractions of their own—a finding consistent with the absence of smooth muscle in their walls. Further study
revealed that the two sides of the testis performed their contractions al-
ternately; a contraction of one side was associated with an expansion and
increasing convexity of the opposite surface. When the organ was enclosed in a plethysmograph, it was found that the rhythmic contractions
produced no change in the volume of the testis as a whole. It seems
likely that the contractions would have the effect of massaging the seminiferous tubules and facilitating passage of sperms toward the efferent
ducts. That the contractions were not an artifact due to the unnatural
environment was evidenced by the fact that comparable activity could
be observed in the scrotal site, if the skin of the scrotum were incised to
expose the tunica vaginalis testis.

Electrical stimulation of the neurohypophysis produced no significant change in the testicular contractions. Intravenous injection of large doses of adrenaline (20 µg.) elicited a pronounced vasoconstriction and suppressed the testis contractions for 3–4 minutes. Plethysmograph experiments showed that as little as 0.5 µg. adrenaline induced a vasoconstriction of the organ which was maximal (0.7% reduction in testis volume) in 1 minute and had disappeared in 3 minutes. Injection of 1 µg. adrenaline produced a maximal reduction in testis volume amounting to 1.5% while 10 µg. adrenaline gave a reduction of 2.3%. Electrical stimulation of the sympathetic centers of the hypothalamus produced similar effects on the testis.

B.   Contractile Mechanisms of the Epididymis

The tunics covering the epididymis were in general less active than those of the testis. Occasionally contractile activity was seen, the chief effect of which was to swivel the head of the epididymis over the subjacent region of the testis where the efferent ducts emerge. These "head-nodding" movements occurred spontaneously and were apparently unaffected by injection of oxytocin or adrenaline.

The epididymal tubules exhibited clearly visible contractions of both pendular and peristaltic type. They were more marked in the body than in the head of the epididymis. In one experiment a segment of tubule from the body was nicked with fine-tipped scissors; tiny jets of epididymal fluid were ejected into the saline of the chamber with each peristaltic contraction. This process was observed for 40 minutes and the jets of fluid occurred approximately six times per minute over this period. There can be little doubt, therefore, that the contractile activity of the tubules in this region contribute to the transport of sperms. In the tail of the epididymis the tubules of smaller caliber showed little peristaltic activity, but they sometimes made segmentation contractions. No convincing evidence was obtained that injection of oxytocin or adrenaline or stimulation of the hypothalamus influenced the motility of the epididymal tubules, with the following exception. The larger tubules of the tail, i.e., those proceeding to the vas deferens, usually responded to intravenous doses of 1–5 µg. adrenaline by undergoing a rapid and extensive contraction (see below).

C.   Emission of Semen

Seminal emission is effected by the contraction of smooth muscle in the male accessory organs, innervated through predominantly sympathetic motor pathways (16, 20). Though the basic reflex mechanism requires only spinal connections, it seemed likely that higher nervous centers might participate in emission during the sexual excitement associated with coitus. Experiments were made, therefore, to investigate the effect on seminal emission of stimulation of the hypothalamus and neurohypophysis in the rabbit (7).

When the vas deferens was cannulated close to its origin with narrow-bore polyethylene tubing containing saline, stimulation of the sympathetic zone of the hypothalamus caused a marked contraction of the larger tubules in the tail of the epididymis. The saline in the cannula after this contraction was found on microscopic examination to be densely packed with spermatozoa. Such hypothalamic stimuli regularly elicited contractions of the tail of the epididymis and also of the vas deferens and the seminal vesicle.* Intravenous injection of 1–5 μg. adrenaline produced similar effects, as did stimulation of the posterior mesenteric ganglion or hypogastric nerve. That both direct nervous pathways (sympathetic) and adrenomedullary secretion were involved in the response to stimulation of the hypothalamus was shown by further experiments in which the response of the seminal vesicle was recorded kymographically. This organ displayed a diphasic response consisting of a quick initial contraction (latency < 5 seconds) which was abolished by section of the hypogastric nerves, and a second slower contractile response (latency < 55 seconds) which was abolished by adrenalectomy.

No effect on the male accessory organs was detected following electrical stimulation of the neurohypophysis or injection of 20 mU. Pitressin or 50–100 mU. Pitocin.

D. COMMENT

These experiments have added some fresh evidence on the nature of the contractile mechanisms which may contribute to the transportation of sperms from the seminiferous tubules to the tail of the epididymis. However, they have indicated no special role for oxytocin or sympatheticoadrenal activity in these processes. If oxytocin is discharged from the neurohypophysis at coitus in the male, it is difficult to see what function it serves in the conveyance of sperms to the tail of the epididymis or in the emission of semen into the urethra. In this connection it is of interest that Glover (10), working with rams, found no significant increase in the rate of transportation of sperms to the vas deferens in animals mated three times a day compared with those mated only once a week. Present evidence suggests that transportation of sperms along the epididymal tubules is a continuous process, the tail of the epididymis serving as a dissolution center for unused sperms (17, 18).

---

* The "seminal vesicle" of the rabbit is a median bilobed sac comprising the fused glandulae vesiculares and seminales derived from the paired Wolffian ducts.

The efficiency of seminal emission, on the other hand, does seem to be affected by the degree of sexual arousal (cf. 7). It has been shown in the rabbit that emotional arousal may lead to an activation of central sympathetic outflows (3). Quite possibly during mating the sympathetic centers of the hypothalamus play a part in augmenting the contractile response of the accessory organs mediated by spinal reflex mechanisms.

IV. Conclusion

It is clear that pathways emanating from the hypothalamus are potentially capable of exerting profound effects on the contractile activity of both male and female genital tracts (Fig. 1). Whether these mechanisms operate in the intact animal to influence the efficiency of sperm transport has not been unequivocally demonstrated. Moreover, there is no evidence that destruction of the neurohypophysis or interruption of the sympathetic pathways from the hypothalamus to the genital organs affect sperm transport in the male or female animal. The relationship of these two systems to fertility, therefore, remains problematical.

References

1. Adams, C. E., J. Endocrinol. **13**, 296 (1956).
2. Braden, A. W. H., Australian J. Biol. Sci. **6**, 693 (1953).
3. Cross, B. A., J. Endocrinol. **12**, 29 (1955).
4. Cross, B. A., Brit. Med. Bull. **11**, 151 (1955).
5. Cross, B. A., Proc. Intern. Congr. on Animal Reproduction, 3rd Congr., Cambridge (1956).
6. Cross, B. A., J. Endocrinol. **16**, 237 (1958).
7. Cross, B. A., and Glover, T. D., J. Endocrinol. **16**, 385 (1958).
8. Cross, B. A., and Harris, G. W., J. Endocrinol. **8**, 148 (1952).
9. Fitzpatrick, R. J., in "The Neurohypophysis" (H. Heller, ed.), p. 203. Academic Press, New York, 1957.
10. Glover, T. D., in "Studies on Fertility" (R. G. Harrison, ed.), Vol. 7. Blackwell, Oxford, 1955.
11. Greenwald, G. S., Science **124**, 586 (1956).
12. Harris, G. W., Phil. Trans. Roy. Soc. London **B232**, 385 (1947).
13. Hartman, C. G., Fertility and Sterility **8**, 403 (1957).
14. Hays, R. L., and Vandemark, N. L., J. Dairy Sci. **36**, 587 (1953).
15. Krehbiel, R. H., and Carstens, S. H. P., Am. J. Physiol. **125**, 571 (1939).
16. Langley, J. N., and Anderson, H. K., J. Physiol. **19**, 122 (1895).
17. Macmillan, E. W., in "Studies on Fertility" (R. G. Harrison, ed.), Vol. 6. Blackwell, Oxford, 1954.
18. Macmillan, E. W., and Harrison, R. G., in "Studies on Fertility" (R. G. Harrison, ed.), Vol. 7. Blackwell, Oxford, 1955.
19. Reynolds, S. R. M., Am. J. Physiol. **92**, 420 (1930).
20. Semans, J. H., and Langworthy, O. R., J. Urol. **40**, 836 (1938).

21.   Toothill, M. C., and Young, W. C., *Anat. Record* **50**, 95 (1931).
22.   Vandemark, N. L., and Hays, R. L., *Fertility and Sterility* **5**, 131 (1954).

Discussion

CHAIRMAN: W. O. NELSON

C. G. HARTMAN: I note that in Cambridge also, the more you know the less you believe.

Nature has a large margin of safety. Note, for example, that a rat can get along, though not too well, without an adrenal. Philip Smith long ago showed that the totally hypophysectomized pregnant rat can deliver its young at term; yet we would hardly infer from this that oxytocin has no relation to parturition.

As to the uterotubal junction, this labyrinthal passage constitutes a hurdle to the ascent of sperms and the descent of the egg. It has long been known to be under endocrine influence. Thus in studying uterotubal insufflation in the rabbit organs, we thought we might produce an endocrinologically uniform animal by first estrogenizing it [J. Stavorski and C. G. Hartman, *Obstet. and Gynecol.*, **11**, 622 (1958)]. This proved to be a mistake, for the uterotubal junction became so resistant that the uterus could not endure sufficiently high pressure to open the junction. Progesterone injected into such an animal enabled us to proceed with the experiment. In the normal cycle, the growing follicle theoretically puts out enough progesterone to relax the uterotubal junction sufficiently to let sperms pass slowly into the tube [cf. A. W. H. Braden, *Australian J. Biol. Sci.* **6**, 693 (1953)].

May I emphasize a fact well known to you, that the physiology and pharmacology of the epididymis is still an area incognita. Study in this area would be immediately rewarding. I have in my possession a film by Muraturi of Ferrara, Italy, showing the activity of the epididymal tubules. This is an excellent method of recording also.

S. ASDELL: I think that we can throw some light upon the function of the oviduct and perhaps of the uterotubal junction. During the last few years, we have been studying that and find, as Dr. Hartman says, that there are several mechanisms that nature does provide for protection.

The sperm, once they have got through the uterotubal junction, have the help of the circular, but not the longitudinal, muscle. The pendular and segmenting mechanism carries them up in very short order.

Secondly, the secretions of the oviduct wall discharge into the body cavity and not into the uterus at that particular time.

Thirdly, of course, there is the possibility of swimming up through the oviduct.

In regard to the transport of the eggs, they also come down by this segmenting and pendular movement and then stop. They get down very quickly to a point about 2 cm. above the uterotubal junction, and then they stop. At that point the muscle is thick and it is very inert, and there are no cilia below that point.

The function of the cilia above the point is to keep the eggs from going up the wrong way. Sometimes they do slip up, but they come down again fairly quickly.

The release from that particular point takes about 3 days and the eggs have to wait until the uterotubal junction is sufficiently open, until the amount of pressure needed to get things through it is small. By that time there is an accumulation of secretion sufficiently great that it is able to carry the eggs down through that particular junction.

What actually holds the uterotubal junction we are not quite sure. We believe it is edema. Histological evidence seems to show that it is an estrogen-induced edema. As Dr. Pincus showed many years ago, eggs can be tube-locked by injection of estrogens, and when we do that it prolongs the edema.

We have tried progesterone on several occasions and we were unable to hasten the transit of the eggs through the uterotubal junction. We have to wait until the estrogen influence has sufficiently worn off.

We have tried hastening that by injecting Diamox and many of the other anti-edema drugs that we could possibly find and failed in all cases to hasten passage of the eggs.

G. S. GREENWALD: We have recently performed some experiments on the rabbit similar to those reported by Dr. Asdell. There is an extremely rapid transport of the ovum through the upper half of the Fallopian tube. Two hours after ovulation, the egg has passed through the upper 8 cm. of the tube; the ovum then spends the remaining 3 days rather sluggishly moving down through the remaining portions. We have never recovered any ova at all from the segment directly adjacent to the uterotubal junction, which indicates that transport through this last segment must be extremely rapid.

This rapid movement through the initial segment of the tube probably is due to ciliary activity. Westman and his co-workers have recently published a paper based on stroboscopic recordings of the ciliary activity of the Fallopian tube. After estrogen administration, cilia move rather slowly in comparison to movement after progesterone administration. With the initial release of progesterone following coitus, there is probably an acceleration in ciliary activity which accounts for this extremely rapid initial movement through the upper segment of the tube.

In this connection it is interesting to recall some of Dr. Corner's observations. He pointed out that probably one of the essential functions performed by the delay of transport of the ova into the uterus, is to enable the uterus to prepare for the entry of the ova, transforming the environment due to stimulation of progesterone.

Extragonadal Factors in Reproduction*

JAMES H. LEATHEM

Bureau of Biological Research, Rutgers University, New Brunswick, New Jersey

Adequate nutrition and the factors which influence the availability of and metabolism of nutritive substances markedly influence the functional integrity of the reproductive system. Thus, the effect of inanition on maturation and fecundity by acute and chronic starvation and by caloric restriction is well known (15, 68, 88). In man, acute starvation may decrease urinary 17-ketosteroid and androgen levels as much as 50% (59). Prolonged starvation influences all cellular elements of the human testis with the abolishment of spermatogenesis following the loss of Leydig cell function (88). Similarly in the adult female, ovarian atrophy with an associated disruption of cycles follows underfeeding (74, 87).

Specific food elements such as proteins must also be considered in reproductive physiology. The protein composition of the body is in a constant state of change, with some proteins continuously being broken down and others being resynthesized. Thus, tissue protein breakdown and dietary proteins contribute to a common metabolic pool of nitrogen from which amino acids are withdrawn for rebuilding tissue protein and for the formation of new protein for growth. Dietary protein level will,

---

* These investigations were supported by research grants A-462 and A-4451 of the National Institutes of Health, United States Public Health Service, and by a grant from E. R. Squibb & Sons.

therefore, influence the metabolic pool of nitrogen in the presence or absence of adequate calories. Tissue protein synthesis may be restricted by dietary protein quality as a reflection of amino acid pattern. Furthermore, hormones which clearly influence protein metabolism might also alter the nitrogen pool. Since the tissues of the body do not contribute uniformly to the metabolic pool of nitrogen, one tissue may be maintained at the expense of another. Therefore, nutritional requirements during rapid growth of the body or during pregnancy will differ from those of a normal adult.

I. Male Reproductive System and Protein Nutrition

A. Testis and Diet

A delay in sexual maturation of the male can be induced by restricting food intake (16, 47, 54). Loss of Leydig cell function occurs before a cessation of spermatogenesis (52, 72) and is evident by the atrophy of the accessory sexual organs and by a cessation in secretion (41, 54, 58). Evidence of a tubular effect becomes apparent by the lack of motile sperm (63), and tubular morphology reveals a cessation of spermatogenesis (46, 50). Restriction of food intake to half normal in maturing bull-calves had a marked delaying effect on the onset of seminal vesicle secretion and a lesser delaying effect on spermatogenesis (14).

Maturation of testes and accessory sex organs is prevented in immature rats and mice by feeding a protein-free diet for 15–30 days after the time of weaning (25). After a month, the 400-mg. testes will have decreased to 140 mg. in rats fed a 0% casein diet but will have increased to 1694 and 1747 mg. in rats fed 20% and 65% casein, respectively (Table I). The testis, histochemically, revealed a decrease in tubular

TABLE I
Effect of Diet on the Immature Male Rat Reproductive Organs

Casein % × 30 days	Number of rats	Testis weight (mg.)	Seminal vesicles (mg.)
65	10	1747	65.4
20	10	1694	88.7
6	16	825	16.0
3	12	380	8.0
0	10	140	7.1

ribonucleic acid (RNA) and an increase in lipid, following protein depletion. A diet containing 6% casein permitted the formation of spermatozoa in some animals (24). When the 6% casein diet was fed for 30 days to immature rats, 50% of the animals exhibited some spermatozoa; in addition, testis weight increased slightly and seminal vesicle weight doubled but body weight was not improved (25). Testis weight gain in immature male rats and the biochemical composition of the immature testis is influenced by the nutritive value of the protein fed. The testes of immature rats fed 20% casein contained 85% water, 10.5% protein, 4.5% lipid and detectable glycogen (83). Proteins of lower nutritive value permitted some testis weight increase, but testis protein concentration decreased; per cent water increased, but lipid and glycogen remained unchanged (83) (Table II).

TABLE II

NUTRITIONAL EFFECTS ON IMMATURE RAT TESTIS COMPOSITION[a]

| | | Final body | Testis | | |
Diet	Number of rats	weight (gm.)	Weight (gm.)	Protein (% dry)	Fat (%)	Glycogen (%)
20% Casein	7	128	1468	72.3	30.4	0.11
20% Wheat gluten	8	82	1017	64.6	34.0	0.18
20% Peanut flour	8	81	1257	66.1	28.8	0.11
20% Gelatin	5	53	210	—	—	0.10
5% Casein	5	61	684	62.4	29.2	0.26
Fox chow	8	115	1515	70.3	30.3	0.15
Initial control	7	61	273	72.7	30.1	0.19

[a] From R. C. Wolf and J. H. Leathem (83).

If the diet is varied so that caloric intake per gram is reduced to half while retaining the dietary casein level at 20%, immature rat testes growth is prevented, unlike the effect obtained with this level of protein in the presence of adequate calories. Furthermore, the caloric restriction may increase testis glycogen.

The variation in protein quality is a reflection of amino acid pattern, and specific amino acid deficiencies cause testis atrophy (70). Furthermore, testicular damage follows ethionine administration (30).

The reproductive organs of the adult are more resistant to change imposed by diet than are those of the immature animal. Protein anabolic levels are higher in the tissues of young growing animals and the body is more dependent upon dietary protein level and quality for maintenance of the metabolic nitrogen pool. On the other hand, body protein reserves in adult rats permit internal shifts of nitrogen to the metabolic pool and to tissues when dietary sources are reduced or endocrine imbalances are imposed. Thus, Mann and Walton (43) found that 23 weeks of underfeeding produced little change in sperm density and motility in mature animals but seminal vesicle function was reduced. Removing protein from the diet for 30 days did not affect adult rat testis weight in the presence or absence of adequate calories. It was found that a prolonged protein depletion was required before the testis was markedly altered. Testis weight averaged 1429 mg. in 25 adult rats after 90 days of protein-free feeding as compared with 3001 mg. for normal adult rats. Testis atrophy was by no means uniform during the depletion period but total testis nitrogen decreased and the seminal vesicles were atrophic (36).

The rat testis consists of approximately 85% water and 15% solids. Testis solids of adult rats are 65–70% protein (1, 2) and approximately 30% lipid (39). A protein-free diet when fed for 30 days will not alter the testis water but may or may not decrease nitrogen concentration; the latter is usually negated when comparison is made with pair-fed controls. Subjecting the rat to a 7-day fast did not decrease testis nitrogen (1). However extending a protein depletion period to two months will decrease total testis nitrogen (36).

B. HYPOPHYSIS AND DIET

Inanition studies have shown that the primary cause of gonadal hypofunction during malnutrition is the diminished level of circulating hypophyseal gonadotropins. Because of the similarity to changes following hypophysectomy, this endocrine response to inanition has been referred to as "pseudohypophysectomy." Nevertheless, experiments designed to determine the hypophyseal gonadotropin content in starvation are not conclusive. Gonadotropin content of the hypophysis, as measured by the implantation method, was either reduced (47, 81) or unchanged in chronically starved rats (45). Anterior pituitary extracts of the hypophyses from chronically starved rats have also been reported as having a gonadotropin potency equivalent to normal (49) or to be greater than normal (65, 78). An increase in gonadotropin content was evident when hormone content was related to milligrams of tissue (42). Thus, the hormone release mechanism may fail in starvation, and eventually the hypophysis reflects minimal gonadotropin production.

Dietary protein levels of 15% and 30% did not influence hypophyseal gonadotropin content, whereas diets containing 80% to 90% casein caused an increase in hypophyseal gonadotropin (77, 80). However, protein depletion is also reported as increasing the follicle-stimulating hormone content of the adult rat (73). The influence of diet on hypophyseal gonadotropins must be considered for both the immature and mature state. Hypophyseal damage may result from severe restriction at puberty; continued hypophyseal hypofunction has been observed despite correction of the nutritional deficiency state (67, 79).

When anterior pituitary glands of 60-gm. male rats were administered to immature female recipients, ovarian weight increased from 13.0 mg. to 37.3 mg. After feeding 20% casein or fox chow ad libitum for 14 days, the hypophyses of male rats contained almost twice as much gonadotropin per milligram of tissue as did the hypophyses of the initial controls. However, if protein was removed from the diet for 14 days, pituitary gonadotropin content actually decreased below the level of controls. When the protein depletion period was extended for another 10 days, hypophyseal gonadotropin potency was not measurable, indicating that further hormone loss was incurred.

Hypophyseal gonadotropin content decreased in adult male rats fed a protein-free diet, but the decrease may or may not be significant in a 30-day period. Extension of the protein depletion for 50 and 90 days resulted in a significant lowering of hypophyseal gonadotropin levels. The reproductive system of the donor animal revealed a decrease in seminal vesicle weight suggesting that the hypophyseal change was related to luteinizing hormone. Nevertheless, an increase in follicle-stimulating hormone may occur in the initial stages of protein depletion (73) and thus active spermatogenesis is continued.

Despite chronic underfeeding, administration of chorionic gonadotropin increased the weight and activity of the reproductive organs (54). Nevertheless, response of the reproductive tissues to gonadotropin could be related to the nutritive value of the protein (84) although a response was obtained in animals fed a protein-free diet. In the mouse, the response to pregnant mare serum gonadotropin was reduced if the period of protein depletion was extended from 10 to 20 days (36) (Table III).

TABLE III

INFLUENCE OF DIET AND PREGNANT MARE SERUM (PMS) ON TESTES AND SEMINAL VESICLE OF IMMATURE MALE MICE[a]

Diet (% protein × days fed)	PMS (I.U.)	Stage of spermatogenesis				Seminal vesicles (mg.)
		1°	2°	Spermatids	Sperm	
0% × 10	0		1	4	1	2.7
0% × 10	3		4	3	0	4.5
0% × 20	0	1	5	0	0	2.7
0% × 20	3		5	2	0	3.5

[a] From V. J. DeFeo and J. H. Leathem, unpublished.

Administration of 0.1 mg. of stilbestrol for 20 days to adult male rats eliminated detectable hypophyseal gonadotropins. Feeding 18% casein during the postinjection period permitted a rapid return of gonadotropin content, whereas a protein-free diet markedly hindered the recovery of hypophyseal gonadotropins. The gonadotropin content of the pituitary correlated well with the recovery of the reproductive system, indicating that gonadotropin production was subnormal on protein-free feeding (36).

C. RECOVERY OF FUNCTION

Reproductive irregularities or infertility at an adult age might be a reflection of prepuberal disturbances. These disturbances may be induced by abnormal nutrition or by hormonal activity during the period of seminiferous tubule development. However, the withholding of testis maturation by inanition did not prevent a rapid growth and maturation on refeeding (6, 61). Furthermore, no evidence of a permanent testis damage due to protein-free regimes was noted in immature mice or rats. Refeeding adequate levels of dietary casein resulted in a stimulation of spermatogenesis and a secretion of androgen (25).

The potential for reproductive system recovery from nutritional inadequacies invoked in adult animals can involve a study of the accessory organs only. Using semen content of fructose and citric acid as an accurate reflection of seminal vesicle function, Mann and Walton (43) observed a recovery to normal during the refeeding of previously underfed animals. In adult rats, the subnormal seminal vesicle weight of protein-deprived rats is quickly returned to normal by feeding a diet containing casein (36).

A study of the testis requirements for proteins in adults can indirectly be studied by initially inducing testis atrophy with estrogen. Spermatogenesis and androgen secretion return to normal during the postinjection period, but little attention has been given to the nutritional requirements during this period. Administration of 0.1 mg. of stilbestrol daily for 20 days to adult male rats is an effective dose (36). Testis weight decreased, spermatogenesis was abolished, and testis water and protein concentration were significantly reduced. Cessation of hormone administration was followed by a rapid return of testicular function toward normal when 18% casein was fed. Within 10 days, 50% of the rats exhibited spermatozoa, and full recovery was observed in 30 days. Return of testicular function was correlated with a recovery of protein and water concentrations of the tissue. Androgen production by the testis permitted a marked stimulation of the seminal vesicles. However, if the adult rats were fed a protein-free diet during the postinjection period recovery was markedly impaired. Proteins of different nutritional value have been studied during the post-stilbestrol period. A 20-day postinjection period was chosen because recovery of spermatogenesis was noted in 65% of rats fed 18% casein diet ad libitum, as well as a doubling of testis weight; in contrast a protein-free diet prevented recovery of the testis.

Adult male rats were fed 18% casein and injected with 0.1 mg. of stilbestrol daily for 20 days. During the postinjection period, three proteins, lactalbumin, wheat gluten, and gelatin, were fed at the 18% level and in each instance the return of testis weight was compared with pair-fed controls fed 18% casein. The 18% lactalbumin and wheat gluten diets were essentially the equivalent of an 18% casein diet pair-fed for 20 days in permitting testis and seminal vesicle weight recovery. A diet containing 18% gelatin, as the protein source, was clearly inadequate for recovery of the reproductive system. However, some testis weight enhancement was obtained with gelatin although body weight did not increase (Table IV). Sterility may be caused by feeding maize or gelatin, initially evident by a reduction in motility and concentration of spermatozoa and an increase in abnormal spermatozoa (12).

TABLE IV

INFLUENCE OF VARIOUS PROTEINS ON THE POST-STILBESTROL RECOVERY OF ADULT RAT TESTIS WEIGHT

Recovery diet	Recovery period	Body weight gain (gm.)	Testis weight (mg.)
18% Casein	0	—	842
18% Wheat gluten	20	75	2064
18% Casein	20	62	1891
18% Lactalbumin	20	117	2055
18% Casein	20	99	2038
18% Gelatin	20	1	1208
18% Casein	20	71	1796

D. DIET AND RESPONSE TO ANDROGEN

Athough the accessory reproductive organs do respond to direct stimulation of an androgen despite inadequate food intake, the response may or may not be normal (20, 21, 58). To restudy the seminal vesicle responsiveness in relationship to protein nutrition, immature male rats were used. At 22 days of age, a single injection of 0.25 mg. of testosterone propionate increased seminal vesicle weight from 9.2 mg. to 27.3 mg. in 72 hours. If the animals were fed a protein-free diet for 13 days with androgen administration on day 10, seminal vesicle weight increased from 7.8 mg. to 16.3 mg., attesting to the subnormal responsiveness.

The maintenance of testis weight and spermatogenic activity with testosterone propionate in hypophysectomized adult male rats is well known. However, the influence of a protein-free diet on the androgen potential for testis maintenance has not been considered. Adult male rats were hypophysectomized and injected daily for 25 days with 0.25 mg. of testosterone propionate. Testis function was completely maintained when stock diet was fed. However, hypophysectomized rats injected with androgen but fed a protein-free diet exhibited a testis weight of 1885 mg. and a slightly subnormal spermatogenic activity. Testis protein was reduced from 66.1% in normal rats to 62.8% in the protein-depleted hypophysectomized rat. These data would suggest that influences of inanition on the testis are not entirely mediated through hypophyseal gonadotropin changes (Table V).

TABLE V

INFLUENCE OF HYPOPHYSECTOMY, TESTOSTERONE PROPIONATE (T.P.) (0.25 MG.) AND A PROTEIN-FREE DIET ON THE RAT TESTIS OVER 25 DAYS

Treatment	Testis weight (mg.)	Sperm	H_2O (%)	Testis protein (%)	Protein (gm.) total	Seminal vesicles (mg.)
None	2600	+++	86.0	66.1	0.24	689
Hypox. + T. P.	1885	++	85.7	62.8	0.17	1999
Hypox.	730	0	83.2	60.6	0.05	221

II.   Female Reproductive System and Protein Nutrition

Ovarian maturation and function are known to be inhibited by inanition. This inhibition is characterized by a state of anestrus and by a decrease in the number of ovarian vesicular follicles (23, 26, 27). However, the ovarian changes induced by inanition may be reversed by refeeding, with a resultant return of reproductive capacity (6, 69).

Availability of dietary protein has an important influence on the female reproductive system. In the immature animal, ovarian maturation was prevented by feeding a protein-free diet. However, in experiments involving the opposite extreme in which 90% protein diets were used, a retardation of ovarian growth was noted as well as a delay in the initiation of estrous cycles (76). The minimum amount of dietary protein which will support reproduction, lactation, and growth is 16.7% (19).

The prevention, by dietary restriction, of the maturation of the ovary may be associated with a decrease in circulating gonadotropin, but an ovarian response to administered gonadotropin is not prevented (54, 75). Nevertheless, a morphologic difference in ovarian response was observed in mice prefed varied levels of dietary protein for 10 days and injected with pregnant mare serum gonadotropin. The ovarian response to gonadotropin in mice fed 0% and 6% casein was follicular growth, whereas the ovarian response in mice fed 18% casein was mildly follicle-stimulating and strongly luteinizing. Furthermore, ovarian weight response was significantly less after 20 days of nonprotein feeding than after only 10 days of depletion (36).

In adult rats, estrous cycle irregularity or complete cessation of cycles followed the feeding of 3.5% to 5% levels of protein (24). Increasing protein in the diet permitted the return of cycles which became normal when 20–30% protein was fed (3). However, abnormally high levels of casein (80–90%) induced prolonged periods of constant estrus (76). The estrous cycle can also be interrupted by an incomplete protein source, such as wheat, which is specifically related to lysine deficiency (11). Specific amino acid deficiencies lead to cessation of estrus (82). A restudy of the influence of dietary protein level and protein quality

DIET AND ESTROUS CYCLES

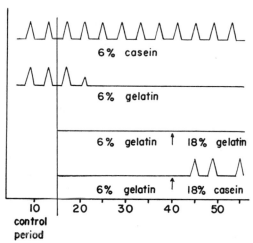

FIG. 1.   Influence of protein level and protein quality on the estrous cycles of adult rats.

was conducted using casein and gelatin as the protein sources. Adult female rats were examined for estrous cycle normality through three cycles, and these cycles continued in uninterrupted fashion in rats fed a 6% casein diet. Thus, a dietary protein level considered inadequate for reproduction was sufficient to sustain estrous cycles. Adult female rats placed on a 6% gelatin diet exhibited cyclic irregularity during the second cycle and a cessation of estrus thereafter; metestrous and diestrous vaginal smears were obtained for 40 consecutive days. Feeding 6% gelatin diets for 25 days to initially invoke anestrus in adult rats was followed by either 18% casein or 18% gelatin feeding; estrous cycles returned only when casein was fed (Fig. 1). While it is apparent that protein level and protein quality influence estrous cycles, a reduction in calories can negate the presence of an adequate protein level (40).

The anestrus imposed by protein-free feeding is accompanied by an ovarian weight decrease. Adult female rats fed a protein-free diet for 30 days exhibited ovaries weighing 22 mg. as compared with ovaries weighing 56 mg. in control rats. Ovarian glycogen, ascorbic acid and cholesterol were all influenced by the protein depletion.

The male on attaining adulthood is concerned with maintaining the body tissues built up during the growth period. However, the adult female body may be presented with the more formidable demands of pregnancy. In human females, even in the absence of pregnancy, it has been estimated that the replacement of menstrual losses may require the synthesis of tissue equivalent to 100% of her body weight (18). During 15 days of pregnancy, a rat may gain 50 gm. Since the fetuses and placentas are small, most of the weight gain is maternal, possibly as a reserve for rapid late-fetal growth. Restricting food intake or feeding a protein-free diet in the last trimester markedly influences maternal weight but does not alter fetal or placental weight (9). Hypophysectomy will alter fetal growth during the last half of pregnancy (31), and some of the biochemical changes appear to involve growth hormone (8).

The clinical indications that protein deficiency may play a role in the pathogenesis of the toxemia of pregnancy prompted further laboratory studies. Guilbert and Goss (24) had observed that adult rats fed a low-protein diet exhibited a reduction in fecundity as indicated by infertile matings and fetal loss. When rats were fed 5% casein and were mated, only 48% completed the pregnancy (13) and fluid retention was observed (71). Body weight gain was markedly restricted and fetal weight gain was subnormal as the result of a 5% protein feeding. Removing protein from the diet for 9–10 days from the time of mating resulted in 86–100% embryonic loss (55).

Pregnancy may be influenced by dietary protein level, but protein quality and caloric intake must also be considered. Preliminary studies have been conducted to explore some of these points. Food intake by normal rats in our colony, eating ad libitum, average 200 calories per kilogram of body weight per day. However, caloric intake increased markedly during pregnancy, so that a 200-calorie intake was restrictive. Nevertheless, if rats were placed on an 18% casein diet at the time of mating and were restricted to 200 calories per kilogram per day, implantation and pregnancy were normal (Table VI). Furthermore, 0% casein diets in our 250–280-gm. adult female rats did not prevent implantation as evidenced by autopsy on day 10. However, extending the protein-free feeding period to 20 days resulted in the loss of the embryos (Table VII). Nelson and Evans (55) observed a markedly adverse effect on protein depletion on pregnancy in 10 days. Our preliminary results may differ on the basis of our use of heavier animals with greater protein reserves and/or a different composition of the protein-free diets. It was apparent, however, that a protein-free diet was unable to continue pregnancy to term.

TABLE VI
NUTRITION AND PREGNANCY IN RATS

Diet[a] (% casein)	Number implantations day 10	Uterine weight (gm.)
18	9	1.88
18	7	2.83
6	14	4.13
6	10	1.51
0	11	1.90
0	11	2.46

[a] 200 Calories per kilogram per day.

TABLE VII
NUTRITION AND PREGNANCY IN RATS

Diet	Calories/kg. body weight	Fetuses (day 20)	
		Number	Average weight (gm.)
18% Casein	200	8	6.1
18% Casein	100	6	3.5
6% Casein	250	0	—
0% Casein	200	0	—
18% Gelatin	200	0	—
18% Gelatin	100	0	—

The influence of caloric intake on pregnancy was suggested by feeding an 18% casein diet at 100 calories per kilogram per day. Pregnancy was maintained, but fetal growth was retarded. Protein quality was also found to influence fetal survival; an 18% gelatin diet failed to maintain pregnancy. Despite the emphasis on dietary deficiencies and their effects upon fertility, one must also mention that overfeeding may also invoke infertility (5).

The deleterious effects of a protein-free diet on a pregnancy have been counteracted by administration of estrone and progesterone (56). Equally effective maintenance of pregnancy was obtained with the ovarian steroids in pyridoxine-deficient animals; less effective results were obtained with hypophyseal extracts, possibly implicating the ovarian response to stimulation (57). The influence of progesterone on maintenance of pregnancy was improved by supplementation of the 2% protein diet with methionine (4).

III.   Male Reproductive System and Thyroid

A.   HYPOTHYROIDISM

Secretions of the thyroid gland influence metabolic rate, appetite, absorption from the gut and may induce either a protein anabolic or protein catabolic effect (35). More specifically, thyroid hormones influence reproduction and fertility (44) and hormone action may include a direct effect upon the hypophyseal-gonadal axis or an indirect effect on the metabolic pool of nitrogen. Thus, an alteration in thyroid function may alter the nitrogen contributions made to the metabolic pool and the demands made upon the metabolic pool by other tissues so that the protein needs of the reproductive system are not met. In this vein, it is well known that body weight increase is retarded in hypothyroidism and the effect is more pronounced in the young animal. Similarly, the effect of hypothyroidism on the testis is more pronounced when induced before puberty, although the dog and possibly the guinea pig may not be markedly affected (85, 86).

In our experience, the feeding of 0.5% thiouracil in the diet of rats during pregnancy and continuing the drug through lactation has produced cretin offspring. At 40 days of age the cretins weighed 25 gm. and the normal controls weighed 97 gm.; testes weights were 112 mg. and 893 mg. respectively. The cretin testis contained spermatogonia and a few spermatocytes and was not secreting androgen.

The adult male reproductive system is less responsive than the immature to a decrease in thyroid function, just as the adult testis is less likely than the immature to reflect a change in protein nutrition. We have examined the adult rat testis 9–12 months after thyroidectomy and found no effect on testis weight or nitrogen content.

Administration of 0.1 mg. of stilbestrol for 20 days will induce testis atrophy and a negative nitrogen balance. Cessation of stilbestrol was followed by a marked retention of nitrogen and a rapid return of testis composition and function. If 0.5% thiouracil was added to the diet during the post-stilbestrol period, testis weight and composition of water, protein, and lipid recovered essentially as well as that of pair-fed controls. However, androgen production was somewhat subnormal, as recovery of seminal vesicle and ventral prostate weights were retarded (22).

In an attempt to relate protein nutrition and hypothyroidism we have performed two experiments. In one study, adult male rats were protein-depleted for 30 days which reduced testis protein concentration 7%.

Following the protein-free feeding period, half the animals were thyroidectomized and the recovery on an 18% casein diet compared with normal rats. After 20 days, testis protein returned to normal in both the hypothyroid and euthyroid rats (Table VIII). A similar type of study

TABLE VIII

INFLUENCE OF THYROIDECTOMY ON THE TESTES DURING PROTEIN REPLETION
IN ADULT RATS

	Normal rats	Normal rats	Thyroidecto-mized rats[a]	Normal rats
Dietary protein	18% × 30	0% × 30	0% × 30; 18% × 20	0% × 30; 18% × 20
Number of rats	10	10	10	9
Testis (mg.)	3190	3010	2870	2850
H₂O (%)	86.3	86.0	87.0	86.3
Protein (%)	73.5	66.1	71.5	71.1
Total protein (gm.)	0.32	0.29	0.26	0.28
Lipid (%)	31.9	31.5	30.5	29.5
Total lipid (gm.)	0.14	0.11	0.11	0.12

[a] Thyroidectomized on day 30 of protein-free feeding.

was conducted with immature male rats subjected to a 10-day period of protein-free feeding. Thereafter, a refeeding period of 14 days with 20% casein revealed that addition of 0.1% thiouracil to the diet somewhat retarded testis and seminal vesicle growth.

B.   HYPERTHYROIDISM

Stimulating and depressing effects on the gonad are known to follow thyroid hormone administration and one must consider hormone dosage, species, and age in evaluating the data (86). It seems certain, however, that a toxic level of thyroid hormone will impair the function of the male sex organs. It has been suggested that the action of thyroid hormone on reproduction may be due to general body emaciation (51). However, when adult rats were fed desiccated thyroid (0.2%; 1.0%) in either 18% or 78% casein diets no correlation could be observed between body weight loss and testis weight or testis protein composition (35). The testes were seemingly not influenced by the metabolic nitrogen changes which caused a loss in carcass nitrogen and an associated increase in kidney and heart nitrogen. In immature rats on adequate dietary protein (20% casein) the addition of 0.2% desiccated thyroid for 30 days resulted in a subnormal testis weight increase which was not negated by relating testis to body weight ratios (Table IX). Growth of seminal vesicles was completely prevented by hyperthyroidism. If the immature rats were fed 6% casein, testis weight increased 300 mg., but thyroid feeding resulted in a loss in testis weight, indicating a shift of tissue protein from the testes to the metabolic pool for other body uses.

TABLE IX
EFFECTS OF DIET AND THYROID (0.2%) ON IMMATURE RATS

Diet (casein) × 30 days	Testis weight (mg.)		Seminal vesicles (mg.)
	Actual	Relative	
20%	1694	1035	88
20% + Thyroid	1090	881	9
6%	825	1232	16
6% + Thyroid	245	650	7
0%	140	346	7
0% + Thyroid	95	261	6

Despite adverse effects of thyroid hormone on the testes, reports of no effect (10) and even increased gametogenic function in the rat have been published (64). Furthermore, thyroxine is known to stimulate spermatogenesis in the mouse, rabbit, and ram (44) and to be beneficial in normal guinea pigs (86). Cryptorchidism in the presence of hypothyroidism was aided by thyroxine treatment (33). Furthermore, Horn (25) has shown that 5-µg. doses of thyroxine aided testis spermatogenic recovery beyond that of nutrition alone in immature rats recovering from protein deprivation.

For many years thyroid hormones have been administered with success in many infertile couples with no demonstrable thyroid dysfunction (53), although the conversion of thyroxine to triiodothyronine may be hindered (34). Recent studies in subfertile and relatively fertile men have been conducted to estimate the effect of the thyroid hormones on testis function. Thyroxine was found to decrease the number of active cells in the semen and to reduce motility, whereas triiodothyronine increased the number of active spermatozoa and may potentially increase fertility (17, 62).

IV. Female Reproductive System and Thyroid

The importance of the delicate balance between thyroid secretions and bodily needs in establishing a "normal metabolism" is quickly made apparent by any prolonged hypo- or hyper-gland function. Excess thyroid hormone will induce ovarian atrophy with a resultant cessation of cycles. However, hyperthyroidism in the human female is not incompatible with pregnancy. Hypothyroidism has frequently been related to menstrual irregularities and infertility; thyroid therapy is recommended in these cases (48). In cases of anovulatory infertility related to subclinical hypometabolism, thyroid hormone will induce fertility (34). In the laboratory, normal guinea pigs treated with thyroxine respond by increasing the number of young born alive to levels above those of normal control animals (60).

In many species, reproduction occurs despite thyroidectomy but the fecundity may be subnormal (60). Hypothyroidism induced by anti-thyroid drugs has also been studied for an effect upon reproduction. Sulfaguanidine induced 95% sterility in the fourth generation of rats (66). In female rats, thiouracil feeding either effectively prevented pregnancy or favored abortion or resorption (7, 29). However, when the drug was started during pregnancy a cretin effect was obtained. Krohn and White (32) found that the number of young per litter was reduced by feeding thiouracil for 50 days to adult female rats with known breeding records. Our studies involved 21 female rats fed 0.5% thiouracil for 90–240 days. Mating with normal males resulted in 16 litters, 15 of which were weaned. The average litter size was subnormal for our colony and deaths during the lactation period further decreased litter size (Table X). Twenty-two days after birth is a rather established weaning time for rats, but weaning of cretin young at this age was followed by the death of 8 of 10 litters despite deletion of thiouracil. Cretins kept with the mother beyond the normal weaning time may suckle for 60–70 days but rarely exceed 25 gm. in body weight. The ovaries of the cretins when 40 days old were devoid of vesicular follicles and lacked lipid and cholesterol. Nevertheless, administration of pregnant mare serum gonadotropin revealed an ovarian capacity to respond. The ovarian response, however, was essentially follicular unlike the response of the normal rat's ovary which exhibited corpus luteum formation in addition to follicular growth.

TABLE X

REPRODUCTIVE CAPACITY OF THIOURACIL-FED RATS

Number of rats	Thiouracil feeding (days)[a]	Number of pregnancies	Average litter size	Average number weaned
12	0	11	8.2	7.1
9	90	8	4.8	3.2
8	180	5	3.2	2.4
4	240	3	5.3	4.3

[a] Thiouracil (0.5%) started at 30 days of age.

The relationship of hypothyroidism to ovarian function provides a clue to a possible origin of ovarian cysts, long known to be a common cause of infertility and associated reproductive disorders. Clinical cases of untreated myxedema exhibit ovarian cysts and rats made hypothyroid for eight months have a higher percentage of cystic ovaries than do euthyroid rats (28). Furthermore, chorionic gonadotropin, known to exert a luteinizing action, becomes a follicle stimulator in hypothyroid rats and favors the formation of cystic ovaries. Immature rats injected with 10 I.U. of chorionic gonadotropin for 20 days will rarely exhibit an ovarian weight of 100 mg. If thiouracil (0.5%) was fed for 30 days and chorionic gonadotropin administered during the last 20 days, ovarian weights ranged from 100 to 1000 mg. Spontaneous regression of ovarian weight and of cysts was rare when a single ovary weighed 200 mg. or more. The presence of ovarian cysts in the rat ovary did not preclude infertility but did reduce fertility when both ovaries were involved (38).

Established ovarian cysts resisted attempted correction by administration of 0.1% desiccated thyroid for periods up to six months. Furthermore, cyst formation was not necessarily prevented by doses of thyroxine or thyroglobulin which did prevent the thiouracil-induced goiter.

To gain further knowledge regarding the ovarian changes associated with ovarian cyst etiology, biochemical changes of the ovaries were explored. The data obtained have revealed that RNA and DNA synthesis was enhanced, lactic acid ovarian content increased despite a decrease in concentration, P^{32} uptake was enhanced during the formative stages of cysts, and the cystic ovary was characterized by a decrease in both free and total cholesterol (37). Chorionic gonadotropin administration to euthyroid animals will decrease esterified cholesterol in the ovary but does not influence free cholesterol. Using cholesterol as a guide toward corrective therapy, one ovary was removed at the end of the gonadotropin treatment period and the second ovary examined after 20 days of 0.1% desiccated thyroid feeding; ovarian cholesterol remained subnormal. Puncturing the cysts did not improve the chances for correcting ovarian composition (37).

The enhanced ovarian response to chorionic gonadotropin invoked by hypothyroidism has been studied in animals fed either a commercial laboratory chow (fox chow) or a purified diet containing 18–20% casein. When gelatin was substituted for casein or protein was deleted from the diet, the ovarian weight response to gonadotropin was reduced but ovarian cholesterol decrease was marked (Table XI). The addition of thiouracil to a protein-free or gelatin-containing diet permitted an enhanced ovarian response to gonadotropin. Esterified cholesterol was decreased more markedly in hypothyroid than in euthyroid rats and to the same concentration despite the varied diets. However, the decrease in free cholesterol which has been associated with ovarian cysts was not seen, on the average, when dietary protein was subnormal. Furthermore, free cholesterol was not detectable in the ovaries following 30 days of protein depletion.

TABLE XI

OVARIAN RESPONSE TO CHORIONIC GONADOTROPIN,[a] AS MODIFIED BY THIOURACIL AND DIET

Diet	Ovarian weight (mg.)	Cholesterol (%)	
		Total	Free
18% Casein	87	0.41	0.18
18% + Thiouracil	342	0.20	0.12
0%	59	0.47	0.23
0% + Thiouracil	133	0.22	0.15
18% Gelatin	59	0.66	0.22
18% + Thiouracil	186	0.26	0.18
Control	27.5	1.56	0.18

[a] Chorionic gonadotropin—10 I.U. + 20 days.

V. Conclusions

Normal functioning of the reproductive system is dependent upon adequate dietary protein. The nutritional quality of the protein fed as well as the protein proportion of the diet will influence the development and composition of the gonads. Hypophyseal gonadotropin content is definitely reduced by inadequate dietary protein, but the target end organs may also become less responsive.

Organs of the adult reproductive system do not contribute to the metabolic pool of nitrogen under circumstances of dietary deficiencies as readily as do other organs. Nevertheless during pregnancy the enhanced protein metabolic demands make the body more dependent upon diet; pregnancy may be terminated by a poor protein diet.

Functional integrity of the reproductive system is influenced by the thyroid gland and may be associated with delayed maturation, ovarian cyst formation, and adverse effects on pregnancy. Favorable corrective measures have been obtained with thyroid hormones even in circumstances in which a definite thyroid disorder was not evident.

References

1. Addis, T., Poo, L. J., and Lew, W., *J. Biol. Chem.* **115**, 111 (1936).
2. Aschkenasy, A., and Dray, F., *Compt. rend. soc. biol.* **146**, 44 (1953).
3. Aschkenasy-Lelu, P., and Aschkenasy, A., *Compt. rend. soc. biol.* **141**, 687 (1947).
4. Aschkenasy-Lelu, P., and Aschkenasy, A., *Arch. sci. physiol.* **11**, 125 (1957).
5. Asdell, S. A., *J. Dairy Sci.* **32**, 60 (1949).

6. Ball, Z. B., Barnes, R. A., and Visscher, M. B., *Am. J. Physiol.* **150**, 511 (1947).
7. Barker, S. B., *J. Endocrinol.* **6**, 137 (1949).
8. Blaton, G. H., Ryu, M. H., and McHenry, E. W., *Endocrinology* **57**, 748 (1955).
9. Campbell, R. M., and Kosterlitz, H. W., *J. Endocrinol.* **9**, 45 (1953).
10. Cohen, R. S., *Am. J. Anat.* **56**, 146 (1935).
11. Courrier, R., and Raynaud, R., *Compt. rend. soc. biol.* **109**, 881 (1932).
12. Cunningham, I. J., Hopkirk, C. S. M., and Cunningham, M. M., *New Zealand J. Sci. Technol.* **19**, 22 (1937).
13. Curtiss, C., *Metabolism, Clin. and Exptl.* **2**, 344 (1953).
14. Davis, D. V., Mann, T., and Rowson, L. E. A., *Proc. Roy. Soc.* **B147**, 332 (1957).
15. Ershoff, B. H., *Vitamins and Hormones* **10**, 79 (1952).
16. Escudero, P., Herraiz, M. L., and Mussmano, E., *Rev. assoc. arg. dietol.* **6**, 195 (1948).
17. Farris, E. J., and Colton, S. W., *J. Urol.* **79**, 863 (1958).
18. Flodin, N. W., *Agr. and Food Chem.* **1**, 222 (1953).
19. Goettsch, M., *Arch. Biochem.* **21**, 289 (1949).
20. Goldsmith, E. D., and Nigrelli, R. F., *Anat. Record* **106**, 197 (1950).
21. Grayhack, J. T., and Scott, W. W., *Endocrinology* **50**, 406 (1952).
22. Greenberg, C. M., Ph.D. Thesis, Rutgers University, New Brunswick, New Jersey (1955).
23. Guilbert, H. R., *J. Animal Sci.* **1**, 3 (1942).
24. Guilbert, H. R., and Goss, H., *J. Nutrition* **5**, 251 (1932).
25. Horn, E. H., *Endocrinology* **57**, 399 (1955).
26. Huseby, R., and Ball, Z. B., *Anat. Record* **92**, 135 (1945).
27. Jackson, C. M., *Am. J. Anat.* **21**, 321 (1917).
28. Janes, R. G., *Anat. Record* **90**, 93 (1944).
29. Jones, G. E. S., Delfs, E., and Foote, E. C., *Endocrinology* **38**, 337 (1946).
30. Kaufman, N., Klavins, J. V., and Kinney, T. D., *Am. J. Pathol.* **32**, 105 (1956).
31. Knobil, E., and Caton, W. L., *Endocrinology* **53**, 198 (1953).
32. Krohn, P. L., and White, H. C., *J. Endocrinol.* **6**, 375 (1949).
33. Krohn, P. L., and Zuckerman, S., *Ann. Rev. Physiol.* **15**, 429 (1953).
34. Kupperman, H. S., Epstein, J. A., Blatt, M. G. H., and Stone, A., cited by Morton (53).
35. Leathem, J. H., *in* "Protein Metabolism, Hormones and Growth" (W. H. Cole, ed.), pp. 17-27. Rutgers Univ. Press, New Brunswick, New Jersey, 1953.
36. Leathem, J. H., *Recent Progr. in Hormone Research* **14**, 141 (1958).
37. Leathem, J. H., *in* "Hormone Production in Endocrine Tumours" (G. E. W. Wolstenholme, ed.), Vol. 12. Little, Brown, Boston, 1958.
38. Leathem, J. H., *Anat. Record* **131**, 487 (1958).
39. Leathem, J. H., and Wolf, R. C., *Mem. Soc. Endocrinol.* **4**, 236 (1955).
40. Lee, Y. C. P., King, J. T., and Visscher, M. B., *Am. J. Physiol.* **168**, 391 (1952).
41. Lutwak-Mann, C., and Mann, T., *Nature* **165**, 556 (1950).
42. Maddock, W. O., and Heller, C. G., *Proc. Soc. Exptl. Biol. Med.* **66**, 595 (1947).
43. Mann, T., and Walton, A., *J. Agri. Sci.* **43**, 343 (1953).
44. Maqsood, M., *Biol. Revs. Cambridge Phil. Soc.* **27**, 281 (1952).
45. Marrian, G. F., and Parkes, A. S., *Proc. Roy. Soc.* **B105**, 248 (1929).
46. Mason, K. E., *Am. J. Anat.* **52**, 153 (1933).
47. Mason, K. E., and Wolfe, J. M., *Anat. Record* **45**, 232 (1930).

48. Means, J. H., "The Thyroid and Its Diseases," 2nd ed. Lippincott, Philadelphia, 1948.
49. Meites, J., and Reed, J. O., *Proc. Soc. Exptl. Biol. Med.* **70**, 513 (1949).
50. Menze, W., *Endokrinologie* **24**, 159 (1941).
51. Moore, C. R., *in* "Sex and Internal Secretions" (E. Allen, C. H. Danforth, and E. A. Doisy, eds.), 2nd ed. Williams & Wilkins, Baltimore, 1939.
52. Moore, C. R., and Samuels, L. T., *Am. J. Physiol.* **96**, 278 (1931).
53. Morton, J. H., *Intern. Record Med. & Gen. Practice Clins.* **171**, 63 (1958).
54. Mulinos, M. G., and Pomerantz, L., *Endocrinology* **29**, 267 (1941).
55. Nelson, M. M., and Evans, H. M., *J. Nutrition* **51**, 71 (1953).
56. Nelson, M. M., and Evans, H. M., *Endocrinology* **55**, 543 (1954).
57. Nelson, M. M., Lyons, W. R., and Evans, H. M., *Endocrinology* **52**, 585 (1953).
58. Pazos, R., and Huggins, C., *Endocrinology* **36**, 417 (1945).
59. Perloff, W. H., Lasche, E. M., Nodine, J. H., Schneeberg, N. G., and Vieillard, C. B., *J. Am. Med. Assoc.* **155**, 1307 (1954).
60. Peterson, R. R., Webster, R. C., Rayner, B., and Young, W. C., *Endocrinology* **51**, 504 (1952).
61. Quimby, F. M., *Endocrinology* **42**, 263 (1948).
62. Reed, D. C., Browning, W. H., and O'Donnell, H. F., *J. Urol.* **79**, 868, 1958.
63. Reid, J. T., *J. Am. Vet. Med. Assoc.* **114**, 158 (1949).
64. Richter, K. M., and Winter, C. A., *Am. J. Physiol.* **150**, 95 (1947).
65. Rinaldini, L. M., *J. Endocrinol.* **6**, 54 (1949).
66. Rogers, P. V., *Am. J. Physiol.* **169**, 111 (1952).
67. Samuels, L. T., "Nutrition and Hormones." C. C Thomas, Springfield, Illinois, 1948.
68. Samuels, L. T., *in* "Progress in Clinical Endocrinology" (S. Soskin, ed.), pp. 509-517. Grune & Stratton, New York, 1950.
69. Schultze, M. O., *J. Nutrition* **56**, 25 (1955).
70. Scott, E. B., *Am. J. Pathol.* **31**, 1111 (1955).
71. Shipley, R. A., Chudzik, E. B., Curtiss, C., and Price, J. W., *Metabolism Clin. and Exptl.* **2**, 344 (1953).
72. Skelton, F. R., *Proc. Soc. Exptl. Biol. Med.* **73**, 516 (1950).
73. Srebnick, H. H., and Nelson, M. M., *Anat. Record* **127**, 372 (1957).
74. Stephens, D. J., *J. Clin. Endocrinol.* **1**, 257 (1941).
75. Stephens, D. J., and Allen, W. M., *Endocrinology* **28**, 580 (1941).
76. Tuchmann-Duplessis, H., and Aschkenasy, P., *Compt. rend. soc. biol.* **141**, 689 (1947).
77. Tuchmann-Duplessis, H., and Aschkenasy, P., *Compt. rend. soc. biol.* **142**, 472 (1948).
78. Vanderlinde, R. E., and Westerfeld, W. W., *Endocrinology* **47**, 265 (1950).
79. Vollmer, E. P., *Nature* **151**, 698 (1943).
80. Weatherby, E. J., and Reece, R. P., *J. Dairy Sci.* **24**, 508 (1941).
81. Werner, S. C., *Proc. Soc. Exptl. Biol. Med.* **41**, 101 (1939).
82. White, F. R., and White, J., *J. Natl. Cancer Inst.* **2**, 449 (1942).
83. Wolf, R. C., and Leathem, J. H., *Endocrinology* **57**, 286 (1955).
84. Yamamoto, R. S., and Chow, B. F., *Federation Proc.* **9**, 250 (1950).
85. Young, W. C., and Peterson, R. R., *Endocrinology* **51**, 344 (1952).
86. Young, W. C., Rayner, B., Peterson, R. R., and Brown, M. M., *Endocrinology* **51**, 12 (1952).
87. Zimmer, R., Weill, J., and Dubois, M., *New Engl. J. Med.* **230**, 303 (1944).
88. Zubiran, S., and Gomez-Mont, F., *Vitamins and Hormones* **11**, 97 (1953).

Discussion

CHAIRMAN: E. C. HUGHES

F. M. HAAG: I would like to ask you about the first part of the paper in regard to proteins. Have you made any observations—not trying to lower the amounts of certain proteins, but to feed double or even higher amounts of such proteins in a diet?

My second question refers to the studies you have done concerning thyroid and spermatogenesis. Have you done anything in regard to sperm activity, that is, metabolic activity of the sperm in combination with the thyroid studies?

J. H. LEATHEM: With reference to the first question, yes, we have worked with levels of protein up to 78% and unlike some reported experiments on livestock, we have not seen deleterious effects. In fact, we have published two of these studies. I think you will influence protein efficiency but you do not interfere with maturation up to that level, nor do you interfere with adult functioning levels.

Tuchmann-Duplessis and Aschkenasy in France have reported that dietary levels of protein above 80% do have deleterious effects both in delaying maturation and also in upsetting reproduction itself.

We have done nothing over and above what we have reported here with thyroidectomy or thiouracil. Our interests were confined to long-standing hypothyroid states to discern whether the testis, in terms of its biochemical composition, would contribute to the body protein metabolic pool, rather than with attempts to mate these animals.

S. ASDELL: For obvious reasons, these problems of nutrition and reproduction have tremendous agricultural implications and there is a great deal of work.

I think, if I might summarize some of those, it might be useful. I would say that on the whole we have found that the higher the metabolic rate of a particular tissue, the higher priority it has for any feedstuffs and that it has the power of drawing on the tissues with a lower priority to keep itself going. It seems to me that when we give hormones to the adult animal, that confers a high priority upon the tissue by giving it this high metabolic rate.

We have been most impressed by the tremendous range that one can give to the nutrition of an animal without affecting reproduction. That is really a corollary of what I have been saying. The same thing, of course, is seen in the young animal, but here permanent damage results from gross underfeeding. I think it is because at that time with the absence of hormones there is a lower priority.

It has seemed to us too that, at any rate in the adult animal, one can never blame faulty nutrition for reproductive disorders unless the animal shows obvious physical signs of the deficiency.

J. H. LEATHEM: May I comment only to say thank you, Dr. Asdell. Nutrition is a broad subject and our interests have been focused fundamentally on the protein and on trying to make individuals cognizant of amino acid variabilities in the face of adequate minerals, calories, etc.—a point which I think in many instances has fallen by the wayside. I appreciate your comments very much.

S. L. LEONARD: I would like to ask: If you had punctured the cysts of the large, heavy ovaries you obtained with thiouracil treatment to let out all the fluid, what would be the weights of those ovaries? How would they compare with those of untreated animals not getting thiouracil? In other words, was this weight due entirely to this fluid and not due to other ovarian tissues—corpora lutea and the rest of the tissue?

J. H. LEATHEM: The average enhancement of weight without fluid is in the neighborhood of threefold. In other words, if we do remove the fluid, we still do have a highly statistically significant enhancement of weight. Furthermore, measures of ovarian cholesterol revealed very little cholesterol in cyst fluid. Thus, changes in ovarian cholesterol which characterize cystic ovaries relate essentially to the ovarian residue. We believe that the basic difficulty of cystic ovaries is in the residue and the follicles are only an expression of an abnormality. For example, if the animals are brought to the state of having cystic ovaries and if you remove one ovary for cholesterol estimation and then you operate the other ovary by puncturing all the cysts and cleaning it up as well as possible, you will find that over the next month—whether you put the animals on normal diets or feed them thyroid—the cholesterol composition of that ovary is as abnormal as it was to start with, which means to me that getting rid of the cystic follicles by the simple expedient of cyst expression does not get at the root of the disorder at all. The root of the disorder seems to me to be in the ovarian stroma, and until we find the hormonal balances that will correct it—and, incidentally, it is not thyroid that will do it—I do not think we can find a therapeutic correction for cysts.

S. GELFANT: In some of your earlier experiments you were using seminal vesicle weights as a measure of androgen release by the Leydig cells. I wonder if you checked this by examining the Leydig cells cytologically. The possibility exists that nutritional deficiencies affect a response of seminal vesicle rather than the production of androgen.

J. H. LEATHEM: If you subject an immature animal to a protein-deficient diet, the Leydig cells become atrophic. The nuclear chromatin cartwheel pattern that we describe for hypophysectomy is perfectly evident.

Secondarily, however, I do believe indeed that the seminal vesicle is influenced by protein deficiency. If this organ is forced to grow rapidly by being subjected to androgen stimulation, it must call upon the body's reserves for that growth to take place, and growth does not take place as well under malnutrition, in our experience at least, as it does when you are full-feeding.

Pazos and Huggins have suggested that the response of the dog prostate occurs perfectly well in a calorically deficient animal.

There are other experiments which do not concur with this finding, and Dr. Mann reports experiments which indicate that malnutrition does not permit a perfectly normal response.

S. ASDELL: I don't want to be misunderstood in my remarks because I was not criticizing your paper. I was really delighted with it. I think that every word you said bore out what our own agricultural experience has been.

There is one further question I would like to ask. That is: Have you had the opportunity of testing the follicular cystic fluid for estrogen?

J. H. LEATHEM: In answer to your first comment, I did not misinterpret it at all. In fact, it would have been your privilege to be insulting in an informal meeting.

In regard to the second comment—yes, we have aspirated the cyst fluid and estimated estrogen activity by removal of the lipid in the columnar epithelium of the mouse uterus which, in our experience, is a specific response. The content of estrogen here, runs something like 1 or 2 µg. per milliliter of fluid. I should suspect it is higher than normal.

We have run three checks for progesterone and obtained a positive response in two. We have tried the fluid for androgen and have failed in every instance. Our test method involved injecting the cystic fluid locally into a castrate rat seminal vesicle and looking for a histologic change. I am not sure this is the best method.

C. G. HARTMAN: In Dr. Adair's clinic in the Lying-in Hospital of the University of Chicago, Ruth M. Watts assayed the contents of hundreds of human ovarian cysts [R. M. Watts and F. L. Adair, *Cancer Research* **1**, 638 (1941)]. My recollection is that in only a small number of the cysts was any considerable amount of estrogen recoverable.

In the monkey, I have, in perhaps a dozen cases, encountered cysts of a type that interferes little with the normal processes of reproduction. I have palpated at frequent intervals a given cyst for some months, observing it to grow to the size of an English walnut, only to regress and permanently to disappear. I have aspirated cysts of hazelnut size and had them regress or refill. One cyst had a pressure-flattened functional corpus luteum in its wall. It is more than probable that such "benign," i.e., more or less harmless and evanescent cysts, occur also in women.

TABLE A

COMPARISONS OF SPEED OF SPERMATOZOA IN RESPONSE TO THERAPIES

Medication	Daily dose	Average speed of sperm (seconds per 1/20 mm.)	Change
	9 Subfertile men		
Control	—	1.3	—
L-Thyroxine	0.1 mg.	1.6	0.3 Seconds slower
	0.2 mg.	1.9	0.6 Seconds slower
Liothyronine	25 µg.	1.3	No change
	50 µg.	1.2	0.1 Second faster
	5 Relatively fertile men		
Control	—	1.2	—
L-Thyroxine	0.1 mg.	1.4	0.2 Seconds slower
	0.2 mg.	1.8	0.6 Seconds slower
Liothyronine	25 µg.	1.2	No change
	50 µg.	1.1	0.1 Second faster

E. J. FARRIS: This discussion relates some of the different ways in which L-thyroxine and liothyronine (Cytomel-3,5,3'-triiodothyronine) may affect the semen of subfertile and relatively fertile men.

Two groups of men with fertility problems were selected for this evaluation. Each man received at least two or more complete semen analyses before being included in this study. For each analysis semen was collected after the subject had been abstinent for at least 5 days.

The first group consisted of twenty-six men upon whom certain studies were accomplished. The results of these experiments appeared recently [E. J. Farris and S. W. Colton, *J. Urology* **79**, 863 (1958)]. A second study will be summarized briefly by my colleague, Dr. S. W. Colton. This deals chiefly with the practical application of the use of liothyronine.

The volume of the ejaculate was measured, and counts were made of the number and percentage of moving sperm (see E. J. Farris, "Human Fertility and Problems of the Male." Farris Institute for Parenthood Press, Palisades Park, New Jersey, 1950).

Normal progressive speed was considered to be an average time of 0.7 to 1.2 seconds for twenty-five sperm to travel 1/20 mm. (one square of an erythrocyte chamber). A patient with a total count of more than 185 million active sperm was classed as highly fertile, between 80 and 185 million relatively fertile, and fewer than 80 million subfertile. On the basis of these criteria, twenty-one men in the first group were classed as subfertile and five as relatively fertile.

TABLE B

OBSERVATIONS ON SEMEN OF 48 SUBFERTILE MEN TREATED WITH 5, 25, OR 50 µg. LIOTHYRONINE REGULATED ACCORDING TO RESPONSE

	Controls	Liothyronine
1. Experimental Conditions	(113)	(137)
2. Number of individuals	48	48
3. Volume of ejaculate (cc.)	3.95	4.30
4. Active and inactive sperm per cc. (millions)	41.85	51.11
5. Active sperm per cc. (millions)	13.55	18.23
6. Active and inactive sperm in total ejaculate (millions)	150.19	188.67
7. Active sperm in total ejaculate (absolute motility) (millions)	49.17	66.47
8. Percentage of active sperm (motility)	37.21	38.35
9. Speed (drive) of sperm (seconds)	1.11	1.08

TABLE C

OBSERVATIONS ON SEMEN OF EIGHTEEN RELATIVELY FERTILE MEN TREATED WITH 5, 25 OR 50 µg. LIOTHYRONINE REGULATED ACCORDING TO RESPONSE

	Controls	Liothyronine
1. Experimental conditions	(39)	(53)
2. Number of individuals	18	18
3. Volume of ejaculate (cc.)	4.35	4.33
4. Active and inactive sperm per cc. (millions)	80.96	87.73
5. Active sperm per cc. (millions)	28.97	30.47
6. Active and inactive sperm in total ejaculate (millions)	278.58	340.02
7. Active sperm in total ejaculate (absolute motility) (millions)	104.76	121.76
8. Percentage of active sperm (motility)	40.37	37.81
9. Speed (drive) of sperm (seconds)	1.02	0.95

L-thyroxine was given, 0.1 mg. daily for 2 weeks and 0.2 mg. daily for 4 weeks. At the end of 6 weeks medication was stopped. Semen analyses were made after 2, 4, and 6 weeks of medication, and 2, 6, and 10 weeks after medication was stopped.

Liothyronine therapy was started at a daily dose of 5 µg. and increased at 2-week intervals to 12.5 µg., 25 µg., and 50 µg. daily. After 2 weeks on each dosage semen analyses were made.

Five relatively fertile men and twenty-one subfertile men were treated in this evaluation of L-thyroxine and liothyronine (Cytomel). Semen analyses showed that the subfertile and relatively fertile men who received L-thyroxine had an average decrease in the percentage of active cells and a marked average decrease in the speed of the cells (Table A). After L-thyroxine therapy was discontinued, the sperm of half the subfertile men temporarily lost all forward movement. It took about 10 weeks before activity was recovered. Sperm of relatively fertile men also decreased in activity when L-thyroxine therapy was stopped, but recovered more rapidly.

Subfertile and relatively fertile men who received liothyronine therapy showed an average increase in the number of cells and in the percentage of active cells in the ejaculate. The speed of the cells was practically unchanged in the relatively fertile and subfertile men.

TABLE D

OBSERVATIONS ON PATIENT (H.S.F.) TREATED WITH LIOTHYRONINE

Experimental conditions[a]	Control		Liothyronine		
			5 µg.	25 µg.	25 µg.
	1	2	2 wks.	9 wks.	5 mos.[b]
Volume of ejaculate (cc.)	4.0	3.0	2.6	3.4	3.4
Active and inactive sperm per cc. (millions)	59.5	82.5	91.5	91.5	73.5
Active sperm per cc. (millions)	17.0	29.5	32.0	31.5	30.0
Active and inactive sperm in total ejaculate (millions)	288.0	247.5	237.9	311.0	249.9
Active sperm in total ejaculate (absolute motility) (millions)	68.0	88.5	83.2	107.1	102.0
Percentage of active sperm (motility)	28.5	35.7	30.5	34.4	40.8
Speed (drive) of sperm (seconds)	1.1	1.2	1.18	0.81	1.00
Percentage of oval forms	54.0	41.0	40.0	54.0	52.0

[a] The first emission was always preceded by five days of abstinence.

[b] Wife became pregnant after subject had been three months on 25 µg. liothyronine per day.

Seven of the subfertile men (35%) improved sufficiently to be reclassed as relatively fertile. Seven others improved to a lesser extent. Five showed no change, and one was consistently worse. Wives of five subfertile men became pregnant during the test of liothyronine therapy.

Comparison of the effects of L-thyroxine and liothyronine in equivalent doses (Table A) and in the same subfertile and relatively fertile men revealed that patients had a marked depression in the speed of spermatozoa when treated with L-thyroxine and either had no change or improved when treated with liothyronine. In this evaluation, L-thyroxine appeared to hinder the chances for conception while liothyronine may have enhanced them.

S. W. COLTON: In the second group under study, forty-eight men were classed as subfertile and eighteen as relatively fertile. In this group liothyronine was started at 5 or 12.5 µg. daily and then regulated according to the patient's response. A semen analysis was performed in each instance after 3 or more weeks of treatment. If improvement (absolute motility and speed) was observed, the dosage level was maintained. If there was no improvement, the dosage was increased. This procedure was followed throughout this study.

A comparison was made of the average values of the control counts and the average values during liothyronine treatment at all dosage levels. The maximum dosage was 50 μg., with three exceptions. Semen analyses showed that the subfertile and relatively fertile men who received liothyronine therapy had an increase in both the average active count per cubic centimeter and the average total active count. The improvement, as shown in Tables B and C, was more marked in the subfertile group. The average speed was also improved.

Sixteen of the subfertile men (33%) improved sufficiently to be reclassed as relatively fertile and one as highly fertile. Eleven others improved to a lesser extent. Fourteen showed no essential change, and six were consistently worse. Wives of ten of the subfertile and six of the relatively fertile men became pregnant during liothyronine therapy. In this group liothyronine appeared to have enhanced the chances for conception in the majority of instances (e.g., see case of patient H.S.F., Table D).

From these studies we conclude that male fertility may be improved by the conservative use of liothyronine, provided the patients are followed closely with accurate semen analyses and proper regulation of dosage. L-thyroxine, on the other hand, may have an adverse effect on male fertility.

[*Editor's Note*: Lack of time prevented discussion of the interesting data presented by Dr. Farris and Dr. Colton. In the editor's opinion, these data perhaps suggest modest improvement in some patients in association with the ingestion of liothyronine. However, spontaneous fluctuations in the various parameters of seminal function are often so great that the data would be more convincing if evidence of statistical significance of the differences could be shown.]

Endocrine Influences on Implantation

BENT G. BÖVING

Department of Embryology, Carnegie Institution of Washington, Baltimore, Maryland

I. Implantation Anatomy

Progesterone is required for implantation (2, 11), but implantation, like pregnancy itself, is not a single event but a sequence of integrated mechanisms. And, since, at least in the rabbit, there are perhaps half a dozen mechanisms, one must ask if and how progesterone affects each of them. For simplicity, they may be grouped as the *muscular* mechanisms which transport, then space, then immobilize the blastocysts with respect to the length of the uterus; the *adhesive* mechanisms which attach to the endometrium first the noncellular membranes of the blastocyst and then the trophoblast; and the *invasive* mechanisms by which the trophoblast penetrates the uterine epithelium.

A. Muscular Mechanisms

Briefly, the rabbit uterus scatters blastocysts at random until expansion of each blastocyst stimulates the uterus to mutual repulsion of adjacent blastocysts by propagated contractions that weaken with distance. Their propulsive effects cancel out when, and only when, blastocyst spacing is equal. Both the blastocyst expansion (11) and the decreased conductivity for propagated contractions (12) have been shown to be progesterone-dependent. Thus, progesterone regulation of blastocyst spacing is twofold.

After blastocysts have been spaced they continue to expand and soon become so large that they no longer can be propelled by the uterus. Thus, the progesterone-conditioned blastocyst expansion not only turns on the spacing mechanism but also turns it off (7, 9).

B. Adhesive Mechanisms

Attachment begins with an adhesion between the uterine epithelium and noncellular membranes covering the blastocyst (4). The envelope has sometimes been called zona pellucida, but it cannot be the same as the ovarian egg covering of that name, because it is a double rather than a single membrane and the volume is between one and two thousand times as great (5). The membrane present at the time of implantation consists of an outer layer, the gloiolemma, secreted by the uterus and an inner layer, the mucolemma or "albumen layer" secreted around the egg by the tube (8). Elaboration of the secretion within the tubal epithelium is estrogen-dependent; the release of the material into the tubal lumen is progesterone-dependent (18) and is inhibited by estrogen (17).

At nearly the time of membrane adhesion, the noncellular membranes are perforated near knobs (aggregates of trophoblastic syncytium) (5). The knobs, themselves, then become attached to antimesometrial uterine epithelium. The trophoblastic attachments are initially adhesive, but penetration of the epithelium follows promptly (10). It is probable that the same progesterone-regulated mechanism induces both adhesion and invasion (9), but it is most convenient to describe it by reasoning backward from invasions.

C. Invasive Mechanisms

The attachments are discrete and very localized. They may therefore serve as histological pointers to those regions where all requirements for attachment have been met. Conversely, regions without attachments must lack some essential factor.

Of trophoblastic factors, the knobs have been shown to be essential for invasion (5, 9, 25), but are probably not necessary for adhesion (10).

Uterine promotion of invasion has been attributed to many factors, of which a detailed evaluation is being prepared for publication (10).

1. *Physical Requirements for Attachment*

Suffice it to say here that contact between blastocyst and epithelium is, of course, necessary; but attachment is not influenced by the finer contours of the epithelium. From epithelial depressions ("gland openings"), attachments are located an average of $176 \pm 14\mu$ S.E., and this is not significantly different from that expected for random invasion ($160 \pm 11\mu$ S.E.).

2. *Chemical Requirements for Attachment*

Chemical factors which promote invasion may be looked for anatomically at: sites of production, sites of storage or sites of transfer.

a. Sites of production. The above relationship between invasions and gland openings suggests that sites of production are not involved.

b. Sites of storage. Invasion toward endometrial depots of some invasion-promoting substance is also unlikely during the antimesometrial invasion. Depots in the submucosa seem unlikely because invasions typically do not invade it deeply but spread instead in the plane of the epithelium. It must also be questioned if and how the blastocyst could detect something statically stored on the opposite side of the epithelium. Depots in the epithelium seem unlikely because invasion is polarized; it progresses from lumen to base, but after penetrating the epithelium and touching the base of deeper epithelium it does not invade it in reverse. The change of invasion contours with time is also inconsistent with static depots.

c. Sites of transfer. Invasion promotion at a site of chemical transfer is likely from a pair of general considerations. The occasional occurrence of ectopic implantation suggests that no uniquely uterine factor is essential to implantation, but its infrequent occurrence suggests that some generally available factor may be particularly plentiful or accessible in the uterus. Stimulation of invasion at sites of chemical transfer is specifically suggested by the impression that the antimesometrial invasions tend to be associated with blood vessels.

A site of transfer was defined more precisely as uterine epithelium accessible to trophoblast and having a blood vessel at its base. It was then ascertained ($P < 0.001$) that invasions in a specimen 7 days *post coitum* were much closer ($15 \pm 3\mu$ S.E.) to such sites than would have occurred by chance ($38 \pm 1\mu$ S.E.). Actually, over half of the invasions were centered on a vessel with an error less than about 5μ. Moreover, the width of invasions that had penetrated the epithelium ($16 \pm 2\mu$ S.E.) was not significantly different from the extent of contact between vessel and epithelium ($18 \pm 2\mu$ S.E.), which is, by definition, the width of the transfer site. These quantities were confirmed by a reconstruction and map of the same material which adds the negative information that, with

FIG. 1. This map is a view from the center of a blastocyst looking through the trophoblast and uterine epithelium as if they were transparent except where there is a trophoblast knob (white). The portions of the knob which have adhered to the epithelium are enclosed within a bold line; the portions which have completely penetrated the epithelium are shown by horizontal hatching. The vessels at the base of the epithelium are shown by stipple shading that suggests tubular contours. Gland openings are indicated by toothed lines.

Invasions are randomly related to gland openings, but it is evident that complete penetrations have occurred only over vessels and with an accuracy consistent with that estimated statistically. A small, separate, adhesion (circle, top center) is as accurately located as attachments that have penetrated; this suggests that the "aim" of attachments for vessels is accomplished at the time of adhesion. The figure is about 1/17 of the entire material measured and mapped.

certain reservations, there is no invasion where there is no vessel (Fig. 1). Thus, antimesometrial rabbit trophoblast invasion in a specimen 7 days *post coitum* was associated in both location and width with uterine epithelium that had a vessel at its base and may be said to require that anatomical complex (3, 10).

It was next ascertained that the mean distance between vessels at invasions ($105 \pm 7\mu$ S.E.) was not significantly less than the mean distance between vessels generally ($99 \pm 3\mu$ S.E.). Consequently, the proximity of invasions and vessels cannot be attributed to vascular peculiarities near the sites of invasion (e.g., new vessels, vasodilatation, hypervascularity, increased tortuosity, etc.). It was concluded that each trophoblastic attachment had been "aimed" at a site of chemical transfer (3, 10).

II. Chemical Inferences from Anatomy

A. Transfer Site Demonstrated Experimentally

The definition of the site of chemical transfer introduced above logically depends on the demonstration of precipitates that were restricted to uterine epithelial cells that overlay a vessel and were adjacent to a blastocyst (Fig. 2). Such precipitates were formed when anesthetized

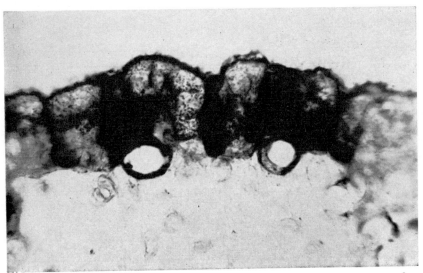

Fig. 2. The distribution of precipitates shows that at 7 days *post coitum* chemical exchange across the uterine epithelium is channeled through those cells that have a capillary at their base. Magnification: ×680.

pregnant rabbits were perfused with silver nitrate solution (0.5 to 5%) after flushing away blood by a chloride-free solution (10% sucrose or 0.1 to 1% sodium nitrite) (details are given on page 217).

B. Transfer Channeled by Uterine Epithelium

At 8 days *post coitum*, similar procedures gave a diffuse precipitate of silver. Since trophoblast attachments at 8 days *post coitum* spread much more widely than at 7 days, there is agreement in time as well as in three dimensions for the conclusion that trophoblast attachment depends on a chemical transfer between blastocyst and maternal circulation. Moreover, since intercellular membranes of the uterine epithelium disappear synchronously with the change in pathway of chemical exchange, the early channeling of transfer and the consequent precise "aim" of trophoblast for vessels may be attributed to them (6, 9).

C. Direction of Transfer

It was originally intended only that the silver perfusions should show the path by which a freely diffusible substance (presumably including the invasion stimulator) would pass from the maternal circulation to the uterine lumen. However, the occurrence of heavy silver precipitates in

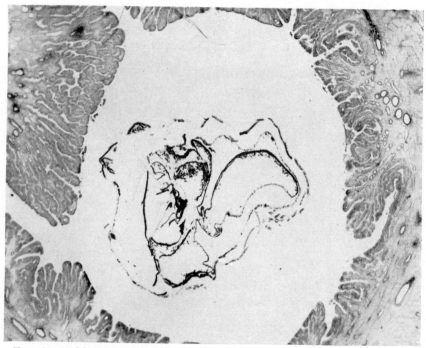

Fig. 3. A blastocyst at 6 days *post coitum* acquired dense precipitates from silver nitrate perfusion, whereas the epithelium, although stained by silver, had but few and fairly light precipitates at this early stage. Note that epithelial precipitates occurred only adjacent to the blastocyst. Magnification: ×33.

blastocysts and at transfer sites near blastocysts but not elsewhere in the uterus (Fig. 3) revealed that something was coming from the blastocysts and being transferred across the epithelium to the maternal circulation, rather than the reverse.

D. General Nature of Substance Transferred

That unknown something, obviously, had the property of precipitating silver ions. It must have been very efficiently removed by the maternal circulation, for no precipitates occurred in the submucosa or even in deep glands. It was probably a metabolic product rather than a stored substance, because a dead blastocyst adjacent to a normal one gave rise to no silver precipitates whatsoever (Fig. 4).

It was concentrated in the abembryonic hemisphere of implanting blastocysts, and this is a region of potential alkalinity, as shown by the

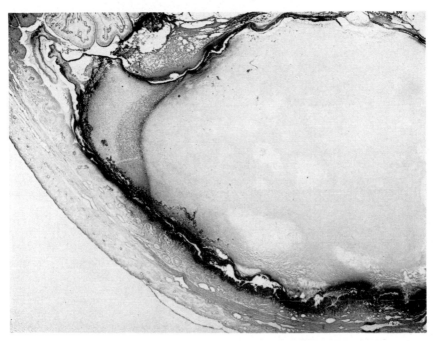

FIG. 4. At 8 days *post coitum* there are dense but widespread silver precipitates in both abembryonic blastocyst and antimesometrial epithelium. A dead blastocyst (upper left) has no dense precipitates, although both it and adjacent epithelium have been stained by silver. Magnification: ×68.

development of pH about 9 in blastocysts freshly removed from the uterus (4).

Blastocysts placed in a solution of similar or slightly higher pH become sticky all over (4). It is inferred that abembryonic adhesion (the first stage of attachment) is induced by alkalinity attending the transfer of a metabolic product from the abembryonic part of the blastocyst to the maternal circulation, but that the attachments are sharply localized at transfer sites, because alkalinity, which is potential in the abembryonic hemisphere generally, is elicited only at the sites of chemical transfer (5).

III. Implantation Chemistry

A blastocyst which was dried on a microscope slide had many crystals in the abembryonic potentially alkaline region, and where there was a crystal there was usually also an adhesion of the trophoblast to the slide. Similar crystals were obtained in greater quantity by drying the fluid from blastocysts. They shone brightly in polarized light and HCl dissolved them with bubbling. Analysis of dried blastocyst fluid by X-ray crystallography[*] showed sodium and potassium chlorides in abundance, of course, plus a small amount of calcium carbonate (calcite form). Of these substances, only the calcium carbonate is anisotropic and capable of the bubbling dissolution in HCl. I once concluded that calcium carbonate was "the" adhesion-promoting chemical and that mammals, like birds, use it to protect their eggs, but form a placenta with it instead of a shell (5). But the presence of calcium carbonate after drying does not really show that it was "the" attachment-promoting compound in the living blastocyst. In fact, its insolubility and the absence of crystals in the living blastocyst suggest that it was not even present before drying. As Dr. Lutwak-Mann recently cautioned me in conversation, in drying any biological fluid where calcium and carbonate are present, they are likely to precipitate first simply because their product is so insoluble. With this justification, and the earlier anatomical hint that the attachment promoter was a metabolic product, let us set calcium aside and consider only the carbonate. Forewarned against estimating a physiological chain of events from a single nonphysiological end product, let us consider the state of the carbonate at different times and stepwise: first in the blastocyst, next in leaving the blastocyst, then in the epithelium, and finally, if possible, in the maternal circulation.

A. IN THE BLASTOCYST

The 6- and 7-day-old unattached blastocyst *in utero* probably has an internal and external pH near 7.3 and not over 8, if one may judge from indicators observed *in vivo* with a special device (4) or from glass electrode pH meter determinations on fluid from blastocysts just removed from the uterus (5). Titration of such fluid, after it has exhibited its pH rise, on exposure to air, gives a doubly inflected curve like $NaHCO_3$ (5). The physiological pH is near the inflection where a small loss of total acid gives an appreciable pH rise but relatively much acid can be ac-

---

[*] For advice and identification of the blastocyst crystals by X-ray powder crystallography, I am indebted to Dr. J. D. H. Donnay, Department of Crystallography and Mineralogy, Johns Hopkins University, and Dr. G. Donnay, United States Geological Survey.

cumulated before the pH is greatly depressed. In other words, the living blastocyst probably contains principally bicarbonate rather than carbonate and is poorly buffered against a pH rise.

The concentration expressed as bicarbonate is three times that of maternal plasma at 6 days *post coitum,* twice at 7, and slightly less than equivalent at 8 (23). Thus, it seems proper to speak of blastocysts as heavily charged with bicarbonate a day before implantation, discharging before and during implantation, and discharged after implantation; but expression of the information also in terms of the individual blastocyst has some advantages for physiological interpretation.

The concentrations at the various times presumably reflect the balance between bicarbonate formed, bicarbonate lost, and the dilution by fluid accumulation during blastocyst expansion. Blastocyst volumes at 6, 7, and 8 days *post coitum* are about 17, 75, and 200 mm^3, respectively. Thus, the concentration drop between 7 and 8 days is approximately inversely proportional to the expansion; there is little net change in the amount of bicarbonate per blastocyst; formation and loss must be nearly equal. At 6 days, however, the volume is one-eleventh that of 8 days, whereas the concentration is only three times, not eleven times, as great. Thus, at 6 days, the blastocyst must be forming bicarbonate faster than it is losing it. This supports the anatomical inference that the then unidentified silver-precipitating substance was a metabolic product rather than something merely stored in the blastocyst.

How can a blastocyst form bicarbonate? A number of animals subjected to inadequate respiratory exchange resort to anaerobic glycolysis and maintain a tolerable pH by converting carbon dioxide and lactic acid to calcium bicarbonate and lactate, respectively, at the expense of stores of calcium carbonate (26). While the calcium metabolism has not yet been studied in the rabbit blastocyst, an analogous reaction is not proved; but it is conceivable. First, in the above reaction there is no free carbon dioxide and a blastocyst freshly removed from the uterus exhibited no bubbles when pressure was reduced by a mercury column. Second, respiratory embarrassment is consistent. The respiratory apparatus sufficient for a tissue with a moderate rate of metabolism may be inadequate for a tissue (in this case the same one) with a high metabolic rate. Fridhandler, Hafez, and Pincus recently reported that Cartesian diver measurements of the oxygen consumption of "resting" rabbit conceptuses rises, in round numbers, from 0.5 mμl. per ovum per hour to 2 on reaching the blastocyst stage, and to 3 by 4 days *post coitum.* Then there appears to be a transitory but massive increase: 80 at 4¾ days, 400 at 5 days, and a peak of 800 at 6 days. At 7 days the Cartesian diver method is inapplicable, but the Warburg respirometer indicates a drop to 200 mµl. per ovum per hour (13–15). If this indicates that a similar peak of metabolic activity occurs *in utero* at 6 days, one may at least raise the question if it can be supported aerobically. This suggests that the acquisition of the capacity for anaerobic glycolysis about the time a rabbit ovum becomes a blastocyst may be very important (15). Thus the evidence, while incomplete and circumstantial, is consistent with the interpretation that bicarbonate is accumulated about 6 days *post coitum* as result of transitory respiratory embarrassment, that its formation is approximately balanced by loss during implantation, and its concentration falls to maternal levels thereafter.

B.   In the Epithelium

From the abembryonic region, as the alkaline reaction and adhesiveness are elicited, blastocysts are losing their charge in the form of bicarbonate or carbonate (the pH varies, so the proportion probably varies). This is shown by the formation of heavy precipitates in solutions of barium hydroxide, lead chloride, or silver nitrate. Carbon dioxide could not give the precipitates with silver, and that which does precipitate with silver cannot be chloride alone since similar precipitates are formed by blastocysts in lead chloride solution; it cannot be just hydroxyl ion since a similar reaction occurs in barium hydroxide. This analysis is artificial not only in the obvious respects of an abnormal medium, but also in the subtle implication that it is describing the form in which the bicarbonate passes from blastocyst to some unspecified fluid in the uterine lumen. Actually, there is essentially no uterine lumen and no uterine fluid except the mucoid gloiolemma (9). After gloiolemma and mucolemma are penetrated by the trophoblast, the blastocyst and uterine epithelium touch. Thus, if one may draw a physiological conclusion at all, it is that the blastocyst's bicarbonate is converted into something more alkaline (carbonate, hydroxyl) either as it passes from the blastocyst or, more probably, in the uterine epithelium. Carbon dioxide "blow off" would be an expected reaction and seems probable, especially in the light of Section IV. That an alkaline state actually occurs within the uterine epithelium is suggested by the loosening and injury of epithelial cells at sites of transfer and attachment (9), and by a nonlocalized imitation of it by 0.05 N Sodium hydroxide instilled in the uterine lumen (Fig. 12).

C.   In the Maternal Circulation

It is reasonable to suppose that the epithelial cells convey the blastocyst's excretion to the maternal circulation as dissolved carbon dioxide and carbonic acid (in the blood, these substances are converted principally into bicarbonates and carried away). This inference is untested but, in company with the idea of carbon dioxide "blow off," follows from the control system about to be discussed.

IV. Endocrine Control of Chemical Transfer

Lutwak-Mann and colleagues demonstrated not only that rabbit blastocysts have a high bicarbonate concentration before implantation, but also that the endometrium becomes very rich in carbonic anhydrase during early pregnancy, especially near the time of implantation (19, 23). The carbonic anhydrase concentration is increased by progesterone and decreased by estrogen (1, 21).

A. Hypothesis: Progesterone → Carbonic Anhydrase → Bicarbonate Conversion → Alkalinity → Attachment

The above and the preceding facts may be combined into the hypothesis that progesterone promotes antimesometrial rabbit blastocyst implantation by augmenting the carbonic anhydrase concentration of the uterine epithelium, thereby aiding the transfer of bicarbonate from the blastocyst to the maternal circulation by accelerating carbon dioxide "blow off" from carbonic acid and, as a consequence of its effect on the equilibrium, favoring conversion of, for example, sodium bicarbonate to the more alkaline sodium carbonate so that there is an increase of pH at the sites of transfer. The alkalinity there renders the blastocyst (membranes or syncytial trophoblast) sticky and favors dissociation of the cellular uterine epithelium, thus promoting, first, adhesion, and then, penetration.

The various aspects of the second part have been discussed elsewhere (4, 5, 9), but it remains to be shown that the sites of chemical transfer which promote blastocyst attachment do have carbonic anhydrase, that it does function there, and that it is progesterone-dependent.

B. Carbonic Anhydrase Present and Functioning

A standard histochemical test (16) appeared to show that carbonic anhydrase was abundant in uterine epithelial cells of a pregnant rabbit but absent in a nonpregnant one (except for the cilia with spread to the apical parts of some epithelial cells) (Figs. 5 and 6). The difference was not striking, and any interpretation would be futile because control tissues (gastric mucosa, kidney) gave unconvincing reactions.

In the same two animals, a clear-cut difference was found by silver perfusions that were preceded by the instillation of an artificial blastocyst to the lumen (0.8% NaCl saturated with $CaCO_3$ and CO_2) (Figs. 7 and 8). A more precise meaning of this reaction was therefore sought.

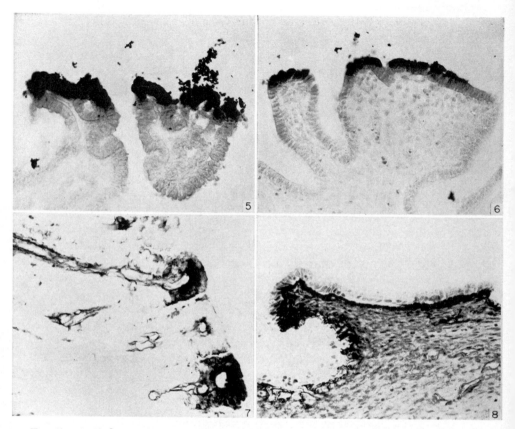

FIG. 5. At 7 days *post coitum* the epithelium in a few regions was densely stained from lumen to base by a cobalt chloride histochemical test for carbonic anhydrase. Magnification: ×225.

FIG. 6. In a nonpregnant rabbit the epithelium in a few regions was densely stained near the surface (especially the cilia) by a cobalt chloride histochemical test for carbonic anhydrase. Magnification: ×225.

FIG. 7. Silver perfusion of the pregnant animal represented in Fig. 5 shows typical epivascular precipitates. Note that the precipitates are somewhat denser toward the base of the epithelium. Magnification: ×225.

FIG. 8. Silver perfusion of the nonpregnant animal represented in Fig. 6 shows no epivascular precipitates. In fact, there are no epithelial precipitates at all in spite of obviously satisfactory perfusion of this portion of the endometrium. It is believed that this portion was reached by the artificial blastocyst solution and that the absence of precipitates indicates a lack of epithelial transfer and conversion of bicarbonate. Magnification: ×225.

1. Methods

A uterus was tied into four compartments at 2¾ days *post coitum*. At 7 days *post coitum* the compartments were variously charged with about 0.6 ml. of: 0.15 N sodium bicarbonate, water through which carbon dioxide had just been bubbled, 0.8% sodium chloride, and 0.05 N sodium hydroxide, respectively. About 8 minutes later, perfusion was begun, first with 0.8% sodium chloride and 0.1% sodium nitrite, then with 0.25 M sucrose. At 14 minutes from the time of charging, 0.5% silver nitrate was introduced. The entire uterus was fixed overnight in 10% formalin in distilled water, embedded in paraffin, and cut into sections 10 μ thick. Staining was by development for 2 minutes in 0.1% amidol, added just before use to: sodium sulfite 5 gm., sodium bisulfite 2.5 gm., distilled water 100 ml., and 3 drops of glacial acetic acid. After rinsing, fixation in sodium thiosulfate, and further rinsing, alternate slides were counterstained with methylene blue.

2. Results and Conclusion with Respect to Hypothesis

Precipitates in epithelial cells overlying vessels, imitating those seen in association with blastocysts, were found in the segment charged with sodium bicarbonate (Fig. 9) and in the one charged with carbon dioxide and water (Fig. 10). They were not found in the segments charged with sodium chloride (Fig. 11) or sodium hydroxide (Fig. 12), but it must be mentioned that the silver perfusion of these segments was very spotty although it was considered interpretable.

Since carbon dioxide supplied to the epithelium imitated the reaction of bicarbonate and the reaction of a blastocyst (be it bicarbonate or carbonate), but is itself incapable of precipitating silver, one may conclude that carbon dioxide was converted into carbonate in the epithelium. One may conclude further that this conversion was aided by carbonic anhydrase in the epithelium, because the unaided conversion (in the lumen) was too inefficient to give a precipitate. Thus, carbonic anhydrase is present and working in the epithelial cells overlying vessels in the pregnant uterus of a rabbit 7 days *post coitum*.

3. Incidental Observations and Inferences

The precipitates induced by water charged with carbon dioxide were less dense than those induced by blastocysts or 0.15 N sodium bicarbonate (Figs. 7, 9, and 10). Probably this does not vitiate the above conclusion but instead supports certain earlier ones. Even if the water had been saturated with carbon dioxide (and this is not certain), the molar concentration could have been little more than one-fifth that of the 0.15 M sodium bicarbonate solution. The latter concentration, three

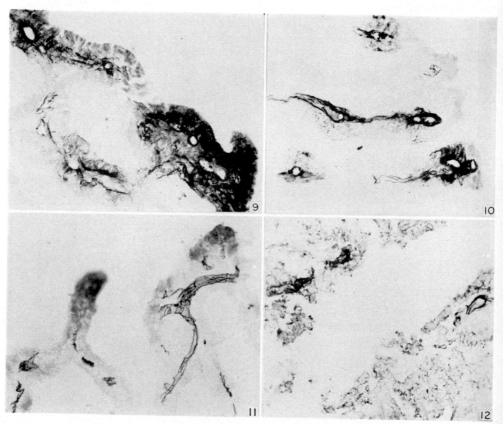

FIG. 9.   Sodium bicarbonate solution (0.15 N) in an empty horn of a pregnant rabbit 7 days *post coitum* imitated the epivascular silver precipitates seen in pregnancy. Note that they are denser toward the base of the epithelium. There are suggestions of epithelial dissociation (center and above). Magnification: ×225.

FIG. 10.   Water charged with carbon dioxide and applied as in Fig. 9 also imitated the epivascular silver precipitates of pregnancy, but tended to be lighter. Magnification: ×225.

FIG. 11.   Sodium chloride (0.8%) applied as in Fig. 9 did not give any epivascular precipitates in the few regions where perfusion was satisfactory and that the instilled solution is likely to have reached. Magnification: ×225.

FIG. 12.   Sodium hydroxide (0.05 N) applied as in Fig. 9 gave no epivascular precipitates but did cause general epithelial dissociation. Magnification: ×225.

times the maternal plasma concentration, corresponds to the maximum known concentration (6 days *post coitum*) (23) in the rabbit blastocyst. Thus, there is agreement with the demonstration by blastocysts in various reagents that the blastocyst liberates bicarbonate or carbonate rather than carbon dioxide. Carrying the reasoning back a step, into the blastocyst, the dense precipitates within 6-day-old blastocysts (Fig. 3) agree with the previously mentioned absence of bubbling under reduced pressure in showing that the blastocyst's metabolic waste accumulates as bicarbonate rather than free carbon dioxide.

It was also observed that the endometrium was dissociated generally in the uterine segment containing 0.05 N sodium hydroxide (Fig. 12). Thus, epithelial dissociation, like adhesiveness, may be attributed to the

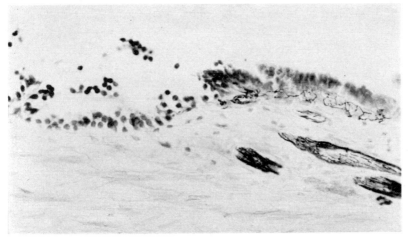

Fig. 13. Sodium bicarbonate (0.15 N) in another region of the same preparation as Fig. 9 caused obvious epithelial dissociation. Magnification: ×350.

alkalinity that accompanies bicarbonate transfer and conversion, whereas the silver precipitates are a consequence not of the alkalinity but of the bicarbonate, or more probably the carbonate, ion. Sodium bicarbonate caused not only precipitates with silver but also (Figs. 9 and 13) some epithelial dissociation. Thus, alkali induction of dissociation and presumably also alkali induction of adhesiveness may be attributed to bicarbonate or the products into which it is converted by the pregnant uterus.

C. Endocrine Control of Endometrial Carbonic Anhydrase

Silver perfusions show that bicarbonate transfer and conversion are different under different endocrine conditions. The precipitates occurred in implantation (Fig. 7) and were imitated by artificial blastocysts in the uterine lumen of rabbits that had been ovariectomized, estrogen-primed, and treated with 5 mg. per day of progesterone for a week (Fig. 14). They were not well imitated in a nonpregnant rabbit (Fig. 8) or ovariectomized ones treated with 5 to 10 μg. estradiol benzoate for a week (Fig. 15). These variations are consistent with the amounts of endometrial carbonic anhydrase found biochemically under various endocrine conditions (1, 19, 21). This gives further support to the previous conclusion that silver precipitates reveal sites of carbonic anhydrase activity, and so extends to the histological level the conclusion of Lutwak-Mann and Adams (21) that endometrial carbonic anhydrase of the rabbit is augmented by progesterone and diminished by estrogen.

The identity of silver precipitation site, chemical transfer site, and site of trophoblastic adhesion and invasion permits the physiological interpretation that progesterone promotes the function of that site during antimesometrial implantation by augmenting the carbonic anhydrase there.

D. Interference with Carbonic Anhydrase

A progesterone-dominated rabbit, prepared as described for Fig. 14 in the preceding section, was treated orally and intravenously with between 1 and 2 gm. of the carbonic anhydrase inhibitor, Diamox (sodium acetazoleamide, Lederle). The precipitates which followed the instillation of an artificial blastocyst into the uterine lumen and intravascular perfusion with silver nitrate were atypical but were not absent (Fig. 16).

This would appear to disprove the preceding conclusion, but it probably does not, for deliberate efforts to interrupt rabbit pregnancy with Diamox have failed (24) and there is no obvious loss of fertility in animal colonies routinely given sulfanilamide, another carbonic anhydrase inhibitor (20). These specific inhibitors, while effective *in vitro* (23), are apparently insufficiently effective *in vivo* within dose limits tolerable to the living animal or even at the high concentrations supplied by perfusion in acute experiments.

I have been reminded (20) that some chemical transfer and conversion may take place even without the assistance of endometrial carbonic anhydrase. That it may be sufficient for implantation is suggested by the occasional occurrence of ectopic implantation.

Against this temperate interpretation are the dramatic facts that estrogen fails to support silver precipitates, reduces carbonic anhydrase even in the presence of progesterone (21), and does interrupt early pregnancy (17), whereas the specific carbonic anhydrase inhibitors can be dismissed as merely insufficiently potent *in vivo*. The conclusion that carbonic anhydrase is essential for implantation is obvious—but it is not

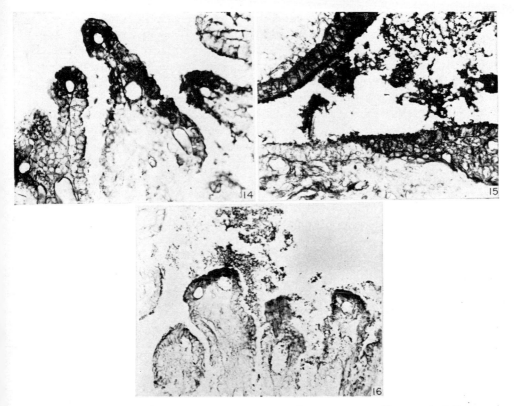

FIG. 14.   Ovariectomy, estrogen priming, and progesterone allow an imitation of the epivascular silver precipitates of pregnancy if an artificial blastocyst is provided. Note that the precipitates are denser toward the base of the epithelium. Magnification: ×220.

FIG. 15.   Ovariectomy and estrogen treatment do not allow imitation of the epivascular silver precipitates by procedures like those of Fig. 14. The epithelium may be free of precipitates (lower left) as in the nonpregnant uterus (Fig. 8) or there may be a reaction throughout the epithelium (upper left), or in both epithelium and submucosa (lower right). The reaction is usually an orange-brown stain rather than the black, granular deposits characteristic of pregnancy and progesterone; there is no particular relation to blood vessels, and the epithelial cells are usually darker near the lumen rather than near the base. Magnification: ×220.

FIG. 16.   Ovariectomy, estrogen priming, and progesterone gave atypical precipitates when the silver perfusion was preceded by Diamox given orally (125 mg.) and as 0.2% of the 750 ml. saline-nitrite and sucrose flushing solutions. The precipitates illustrated resembled those of pregnancy in being black, granular, and epivascular; they differed in being absent or lighter, rather than denser, in the basal half of the epithelium. Reactions in other regions ran the whole gamut from no precipitates at all (upper left) to ones like those of pregnancy. Magnification: ×220.

necessarily correct. Estrogen interrupts pregnancy by disrupting a number of other mechanisms, depending on the time of action and the dose (17). Thus, the carbonic anhydrase suppression may be merely contributory rather than necessary and sufficient for the abortifacient effects of estrogen.

Also warning against assuming carbonic anhydrase to be absolutely essential, rather than merely normally present and helpful, is its absence from the endometrium of many species other than the rabbit (19, 22). This variation introduces the fascinating idea that implantation in different mammals differs in fundamental chemistry just as it differs endocrinologically and anatomically.

V. Progesterone Effects on Rabbit Implantation

A. Before and During Implantation: Summary

Progesterone is required for implantation and exerts an effect on one or more mechanisms in each of the major categories.

Of the *muscular* mechanisms, blastocyst spacing is progesterone-regulated. Progesterone decreases the conductivity of uterine muscle (12) and makes the blastocyst expand (11). After a certain diameter is reached, the spacing contractions are stimulated, and after 2 days and sufficient further expansion the blastocyst becomes too large for further propulsion (9).

Among the *adhesive* mechanisms, progesterone has a preparatory function in promoting the tubal deposition of the mucolemma or mucin coat (18). This membrane, with the gloiolemma from the uterus, takes part in the first adhesive attachment (4). Probably during that attachment, as during the adhesive attachment of the trophoblast to the endometrium, progesterone helps by increasing endometrial carbonic anhydrase. This facilitates the transfer of bicarbonate from the blastocyst through the epithelial cells overlying vessels by speeding there the conversion of carbonic acid to carbon dioxide (which is removed by the maternal circulation). The attendant local liberation of alkalinity makes both membranes and trophoblast sticky.

Among the mechanisms of *invasion,* the same progesterone-regulated reaction is considered responsible for local alkali-induced dissociation of uterine epithelium which clears the path, as it were, for the intrusion of the trophoblast (which remains undissociated because it is syncytial).

B. During and after Implantation: Endometrial Convolution

The best-recognized effect of progesterone, extreme endometrial convolution, appears to be a mechanism for keeping constant the concentration of blood vessels accessible to the blastocyst. The mean distance between vessels under accessible antimesometrial epithelium in a 7-day-old specimen (99 ± 3 μ S.E.) was not significantly different from that of one 8 days *post coitum* (97 ± 3 μ S.E.) whose circumference was about double. Since simple stretching would have doubled the separation and this did not occur, one may infer that the epithelium unfolded. Moreover, nearly complete unfolding may be produced antimesometrially by artificial distention of the uterus.

It is by no means precluded that endometrial convolution has less obvious functions, such as provision of great surface for secretion or absorption of substances whose passage is not particularly facilitated at the epivascular sites adjacent to the blastocyst. The possibility of such a chemical "back door" points out that the present account should not be mistaken for a complete one. If it seems reasonably connected, it is merely because, being somewhat preliminary, it derives its support from a variety of apparently related observations; but few of these have been adequately explored by rigorous replication.

Acknowledgments

Special acknowledgment is due Mr. W. H. Duncan, Technician, for perfecting the staining by a photographic type of development of sections of silver nitrate-perfused tissue, and Mr. R. D. Grill, Photographer, for obtaining good illustrations of the resulting unusually contrasty material.

References

1. Adams, C. E., and Lutwak-Mann, C., *J. Endocrinol.* **13**, xix-xx (1955).
2. Allen, W. M., and Corner, G. W., *Am. J. Physiol.* **88**, 340-346 (1929).
3. Böving, B. G., *Anat. Record* **112**, 12 (1952).
4. Böving, B. G., *Science* **116**, 211-214 (1952).
5. Böving, B. G., *Cold Spring Harbor Symposia Quant. Biol.* **19**, 9-28 (1954).
6. Böving, B. G., *Anat. Record* **121**, 426 (1955).
7. Böving, B. G., *Am. J. Anat.* **98**, 403-434 (1956).
8. Böving, B. G., *Anat. Record* **127**, 270 (1957).
9. Böving, B. G., *Ann. N. Y. Acad. Sci.* in press.
10. Böving, B. G., *Contribs. to Embryol. Carnegie Inst. Wash.* **37** (in preparation).
11. Corner, G. W., *Am. J. Physiol.* **86**, 74-81 (1928).
12. Csapo, A., *in* "Modern Trends in Obstetrics and Gynaecology" (K. Bowes, ed.), 2nd series, pp. 20-49. Butterworth, London, 1955.
13. Fridhandler, L., Hafez, E. S. E., and Pincus, G., *Proc. Intern. Congr. on Animal Reproduction, 3rd Congr., Cambridge*, 48-58, 1956.
14. Fridhandler, L., Hafez, E. S. E., and Pincus, G., *Proc. Soc. Exptl. Biol. Med.* **92**, 127-129 (1956).
15. Fridhandler, L., Hafez, E. S. E., and Pincus, G., *Exptl. Cell. Research* **13**, 132-139 (1957).
16. Gomori, G., "Microscopic Histochemistry." University of Chicago Press, Chicago, 1952.
17. Greenwald, G. S., *J. Exptl. Zool.* **135**, 461-482 (1957).
18. Greenwald, G. S., *Anat. Record* **130**, 477-496 (1958).

19. Lutwak-Mann, C., *J. Endocrinol.* **11**, xi (1954).
20. Lutwak-Mann, C., personal communication.
21. Lutwak-Mann, C., and Adams, C. E., *J. Endocrinol.* **15**, 43-55 (1957).
22. Lutwak-Mann, C., and Averill, R. L. W., *J. Endocrinol.* **11**, xii (1954).
23. Lutwak-Mann, C., and Laser, H., *Nature* **173**, 268-270 (1954).
24. Reynolds, S. R. M., personal communication.
25. Schoenfeld, H., *Arch. biol.* (*Paris*) **19**, 701-830 (1903).
26. Von Brand, T., "Anaerobiosis in Invertebrates." Biodynamica, Normandy, Missouri, 1946.

Discussion

CHAIRMAN: E. C. HUGHES

G. PINCUS: I would just like to say something about the carbonic anhydrase reaction. We have studied it histologically and have had exactly your experience, namely, some irregularity in its demonstration by staining methods. However, we can easily determine biochemically the effect of estrogen. We have studied the actual concentration of carbonic anhydrase in the rabbit uterus using estrogen as an antagonist to progesterone, and we get very fine quantitative relationships. I think that you have outlined very beautifully the probable role of bicarbonate. We need, however, to explore somewhat more what is actually in the blastocyst fluid. For example, Dr. Fridhandler in our laboratory will shortly report the highest concentration of glycine seen in any tissue in the body, just as Dr. Lutwak-Mann has observed a very high concentration of bicarbonate. What this means I do not know. Maybe we have a glycine-carbonate-bicarbonate buffer system present. I think this is a beautiful demonstration of probabilities; but I think we need to know a lot more directly about the chemistry of the blastocyst fluid.

Finally, because I think that my remarks should end with the compliment that I really intend: I think you have exhibited such extraordinary ingenuity that almost every phenomenon that I have been puzzling about for the past few years is on the verge of explanation.

B. BÖVING: I share Dr. Pincus' dissatisfaction with the carbonic anhydrase histochemical test that depends on the incubation of acetone-fixed tissue slices in cobalt chloride and sodium bicarbonate solution. I have not yet used the manganese chloride variation. Perhaps silver perfusion, when preceded by instillation of water saturated with carbon dioxide may be regarded as a histochemical test for carbonic anhydrase. It is, however, a cumbersome procedure and would be peculiar, as a test, in showing not where the enzyme is present but only where it is functioning.

Dr. Pincus' point that we need to know more about the related chemistry is certainly well taken. I would expect that the role of calcium in both blastocyst and uterus might be of particular interest in view of its relation to cell adhesiveness.

I think that the carbon dioxide, bicarbonate, or carbonate concentrated in the blastocyst may flush out calcium from the particular cells through which it passes on its way to the maternal circulation. This, as well as the attendant high pH per se, might promote the local epithelial dissociation there. We have a suggestion of a double assurance system here.

C. G. HARTMAN: May I suggest that, for comparison, if you wish to study blastocysts devoid of stickiness (as I judge from their haphazard distribution in the uterus) you should select the opossum (gestation, 12 days, 18 hours).

A. C. ENDERS: Arguing between species is always a difficult thing. However, those of us who have dealt with delayed implantation in any or several of the about twenty-five or thirty species which exhibit this phenomenon are naturally curious concerning the initiation of those changes which you have described. We see many instances in which the blastocyst remains in the uterus for an extended period of time without showing any tendency to become invasive or to become proliferative. In some seven species that I can think of offhand, this period of delay has been altered. It has been shortened by some sort of external alteration; that is, either alteration of hormone titer or even such external alteration as changing the length of daylight has been used to produce implantation.

I wonder, in the case of the rabbit, whether you feel that the shift in carbon dioxide and hence the increased alkalinity is produced by changes in the uterus, a hormonal change, physical distention by the blastocyst, or whether it is a change in the metabolism of the blastocyst which produces this CO_2 shift and resulting alkalinity?

B. Böving: First, let me say that I don't think what I have said about the rabbit necessarily applies to mink or to mammals generally, although the hemotropism of trophoblast invasion has been found also in the macaque. Dr. R. K. Enders was kind enough to make available to me some mink that were in the stage of pregnancy when it was expected that implantation would occur within a day or so or would have just occurred. This was, I believe, April 9th; they have a very precise schedule. A silver nitrate perfusion was done at that time. In four out of five animals, so little solution entered that the specimens were not readable. Dr. Enders suggested that mink have high blood pressure, so, in a rather desperate final effort, the perfusion bottle was connected to the compressed air line, and the perfusate was driven in with a pressure of 11 pounds per square inch. In this single case, the uterus and blastocysts were stained by silver, but there was no intense black reaction in either blastocysts or epithelium. This suggests that mink blastocysts at this stage (immediately before implantation) do not have the accumulation of bicarbonate which is characteristic of rabbit blastocysts. That is why I urge that we bear in mind the possibility that mink and other mammals may have an attachment mechanism different from that of the rabbit.

What do I regard as initiating the train of events? I mentioned, perhaps too hastily, that Fridhandler, Hafez, and Pincus found a rapid increase in oxygen consumption at the blastocyst stage or just before. I think that this rapid increase in metabolism plus the deposition of the rather thick and frothy gloiolemma may cause respiratory embarrassment and accumulation of carbon dioxide within the blastocyst. This carbon dioxide is not free but, as occurs in the clam and other animals is converted to bicarbonate. There is an unusual amount of bicarbonate in the rabbit blastocyst.

I suggest that the discharge of such a bicarbonate-loaded blastocyst may be initiated by the combination of increasing endometrial carbonic anhydrase and lysis of the noncellular membranes surrounding the blastocyst.

Incidentally, if the discharge is widespread, the pH rise is widespread and may be severe as well. This occurs when a blastocyst is removed from the uterus to a carbon dioxide-absorbing Warburg apparatus, or even to an open dish. Such a general pH rise demolishes the cellular elements of the blastocyst, reduces its turgor, and makes its noncellular coverings flaccid and sticky. Reasoning backward, the healthy, turgid, nonadherent, preimplantation blastocyst *in utero* must be in an environment that limits its carbon dioxide loss, and the attaching blastocyst, which is flaccid and sticky even *in utero*, must be discharging carbon dioxide or bicarbonate, but at a rate sufficiently slow to be safe for the blastocyst as a whole. I suggest that the discharge is slowed, not only by noncellular membranes and submaximal carbonic anhydrase, but by restricting carbon dioxide or bicarbonate passage to the epithelial cells with a vessel at their base. At least, bicarbonate content is three times that of maternal plasma at 6 days *post coitum*, two times at 7 days, and equal at 8 days, and the pathways of transfer revealed by the silver perfusions are narrow until just before 8 days, when they become diffuse as a consequence of the loss of epithelial inter-cellular membranes. Yet as early as 7 days after mating pH must have risen quite high just at the localized sites of exchange, if one may judge from the fact that adhesions have occurred there. I mention this to point out that both enzymatic and anatomical aspects of uterine epithelium probably contribute to the physiological balance of the various aspects of carbon dioxide or bicarbonate discharge.

S. Zuckerman: I should like to ask a question about the first part of your paper. You first formulated a hypothesis about the spacing of the blastocysts. You then turned to the question of the presence of a blood vessel at the point of invasion of the trophoblast knob. Again you presented various hypotheses for test, ending up with the conclusion that something diffusing from the blood vessel at-tracted the blastocyst.

You presented a statistical analysis which indicated the strong probability that this was happening. But you also then showed three-dimensional pictures of the vascular network, which suggested to me certain questions. Were the blood vessels concerned arterioles or capillaries? Which way were they cut? Were they terminal vessels? How can you be sure that between the transversely and obliquely cut ends of the vessels you showed to be about 100 μ apart, there weren't vessels whose walls had been cut tangentially? Is it inconceivable that you are dealing with a histological artifact? After all, there are no vessels in the endometrium with open and cut ends.

B. Böving: Your outline of my reasoning was excellent. I should like to make clear, however, that the blastocyst spacing and the trophoblast hemotropism are related only in sequence and not as cause and effect. They are separable in time and involve structures with different orders of magnitude. The spacing occurs at 6 and 7 days after mating and concerns one or more blastocysts from 3 to 6 mm. in diameter and a whole uterine horn about 200 mm. long. The invasion site selection occurs at 7 and 8 days after mating and concerns trophoblast knobs 100 μ across, epithelial cells 5 μ in diameter, and blood vessels averaging 18 μ across.

The vessels you asked about are capillaries. So far as I recall, I have seen no vessel in contact with uterine epithelium that had a wall more complex than simple endothelium (this is especially well shown in the silver-perfused material). Sub-mucosal vessels not in contact with epithelium were neglected because of a fortu-nate hunch, later proved correct, that chemical exchange across the epithelium would concern only the vessels touching it.

I believe that essentially all such relevant vessels were detected regardless of the angle at which they were cut. Sections were 7 μ thick, so it is unlikely that any vessel was obscured by overlying tissue. Detection was usually easy because of differen-tially stained erythrocytes and, in cases of doubt, a decision included reference to adjacent serial sections. Random omissions would not influence the statistical con-clusions, and systematic omissions were tested for and found absent. Displaced erythrocytes sometimes masqueraded as a vessel, but this artifact could usually be distinguished by a plane of focus different from that of the adjacent tissue. Even if not unmasked, such artifacts could be presumed to be random and of no effect on the conclusions. Moreover, reconstruction and mapping of the material studied quantitatively showed but few points (perhaps 2% of the data) that did not connect from one section to the next in the manner of a serially sectioned vessel.

Progestational Action of Some Newer Steroids with Special Reference to Maintenance of Pregnancy

F. J. Saunders and R. L. Elton

Division of Biological Research, G. D. Searle & Co., Chicago, Illinois

I. Introduction

Some of the effects of progesterone have already been discussed in this symposium. The present paper will be restricted to a comparison of the effectiveness of various steroids in the maintenance of pregnancy in spayed animals. In general we will be concerned with various compounds related to nortestosterone although several other compounds will be discussed.

Our studies have been carried out in two species, rats and rabbits. Some of the earlier work in rabbits was the subject of previous communications (13, 15, 16), and further data will be presented in the present paper. In our earlier studies we were disappointed in that we

227

could not maintain pregnancy in rats with doses of progesterone which were adequate in rabbits. However, the work of Alexander *et al.* (1) showed that much larger doses of progesterone were needed and even 10 mg. per rat per day afforded only partial protection. Therefore, the range of doses used in this study was extended.

In each section we should like to discuss our studies in rats and then compare the effects in this species with the effects obtained in rabbits.

II. Methods

A. Rats

Normal adult female rats of the Sprague-Dawley strain were mated and breeding was checked by the finding of sperm in the vagina. The day on which sperm were found was designated as day 1. On the 8th day of pregnancy the rats were spayed by the dorsal approach. In most cases, pregnancy was confirmed by the observation of placental sites, but no attempt was made to count these since it was desired to keep the trauma to a minimum. The animals were then injected subcutaneously daily, except as noted in the tables, with the appropriate steroid in corn oil, the first injection being given shortly before oophorectomy. In a few cases 25% benzyl alcohol was added to the corn oil to increase the solubility of the steroid. All animals were sacrificed on the 18th day after mating and the uteri were placed in 70% alcohol. Twenty-four to 48 hours later the uteri were weighed, the placentas were counted and measured, and the fetuses were dissected out and weighed individually. Here and in the tables, the term "placentas" is used to designate all remnants of individual conceptuses. They ranged from minute scars in a few instances to fully maintained placentas supporting normal-sized fetuses. Any fetal remnants that could be identified as such were included in determining average fetal weights.

B. Rabbits

For the studies in the rabbits, does were mated and the ovaries were removed on the 10th to 14th day of pregnancy. In all cases, pregnancy was established by the observation of placental sites at the time of ovariectomy. Daily subcutaneous injections of the progestins were started on the day of operation. In a few cases, as shown in the tables, the compounds were administered orally. Laparotomy was performed 7–10 days after ovariectomy and the condition of the conceptuses determined. The data in the tables represent the state of the pregnancy at the time of laparotomy. In the later phases of this study, if normal-appearing fetuses were present, gestation was permitted to continue until the 30th day.

III.   Results

A.   CONTROLS

Several indices were used to assess the degree of protection as illustrated in the various tables. The data for the spayed and intact control rats are shown in Table I. When necropsy was performed on day 18,

TABLE I

EFFECT OF OVARIECTOMY ON THE COURSE OF PREGNANCY IN RATS[a]

	Controls	
	Intact	Spayed
Number of rats	10	10
Number with placentas	10	1
Average number of placentas	10.7	11
Uterine weight range (gm.)	14.3–34.6	0.11–0.22
Number with fetuses	10	0
Average number of fetuses	9.2	
Average fetal weight (mg.)	909.5	
Fetal weight range (mg.)	507–1290	

[a] Spaying was performed on the 8th day and the rats were sacrificed on the 18th day of pregnancy.

10 days after ovariectomy, placental sites could no longer be seen in the untreated animals in 9 of 10 cases. In the remaining animal, such sites were evident only as minute scars. The uterine weight gives a good overall picture of the condition of the pregnancy except for such stimulation as may be seen after estrogen treatment. The number of rats with fetuses, normal or resorbing, and the number of fetuses per rat are additional measures of protection. In the intact controls, the average fetal weight was 0.91 gm. with a range from 0.5 to 1.3 gm. Fetuses below 500 mg. may therefore be considered abnormal and probably are not viable. The following data should be kept in mind in order to assess the effectiveness of the various compounds to be discussed later in this paper.

1. In 9 of 10 spayed rats, no placentas could be seen at necropsy. In the remaining animal, the remnants were minute scars.

2. The uteri of the untreated, spayed animals weighed 0.11–0.22 gm. compared with 14–35 gm. in the intact controls.

3. The average number of placentas in the intact controls was 10.7, but the number of fetuses was only 9.2.

4. In the intact controls, the fetuses averaged 0.91 gm.

Figure 1 shows the actual fetal weights in 10 intact pregnant rats. Each dot represents one fetus and each vertical bar, one litter. This graph shows litter size as well as individual variations within each litter and between litters.

In the rabbit on the 10th day of pregnancy the uterus at the site of implantation is approximately 1 cm. in diameter. In 10 untreated spayed rabbits, sacrificed 7 days after ovariectomy, the placental sites were smaller than they were at the time of operation. In fact, in some cases resorption was nearly complete.

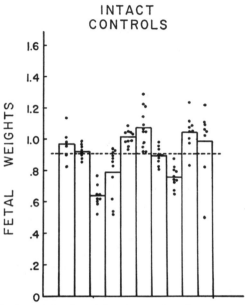

Fig. 1. Distribution of fetal weights in ten female rats sacrificed on the 18th day of pregnancy. Each dot represents one fetus and each bar, one litter. The broken line shows the average weight of all these fetuses.

B. Progesterone

Table II shows the protective action of progesterone in spayed rats. Placentas were seen in some rats at a dose of 5 mg. per kilogram and in all rats when the dose was increased to 10 mg. or more. Thus the 5-mg. dose showed some protection. The number of placentas per rat showed a tendency to increase with dose, but this may not be significant. The uterine weights reflect the fact that some of these rats had fetuses *in utero,* and at the 50-mg. dose, all rats had normal-sized fetuses. The number and size of the fetuses indicate the adequacy of protection. At the 10-mg. dose, the 2 rats in which pregnancy was maintained, had only 1 and 4 fetuses respectively. At the 20 mg. dose, each of the 4 females in which pregnancy was maintained, had 9 fetuses. Only at a dose of 50 mg. per kilogram per day was normal pregnancy maintained in all rats.

TABLE II

EFFECTIVENESS OF PROGESTERONE IN MAINTAINING PREGNANCY IN RATS SPAYED
ON THE 8TH DAY OF PREGNANCY[a]

	Daily dose (mg. per kg.):				
	1	5	10	20	50
Number of rats	7	7	10	10	10
Number with placentas	0	2	10	10	10
Average number of placentas		7.5	8.1	9.3	10.3
Uterine weight range (gm.)	0.095–	0.191–	0.277–	0.632–	16.3–
	0.262	0.291	9.6	30.4	41.5
Number with fetuses			2	4	10
Average number of fetuses			2.5	9.0	8.5
Average fetal weights (mg.)			737	1034	850
Fetal weight range (mg.)			550–	233–	84–
			983	1361	1253

[a] Rats were sacrificed on the 18th day after mating.

The distribution of the fetal weights in this series is shown in Fig. 2. At the highest dose of progesterone, 13 of 85 fetuses weighed less than the smallest fetus found in the control series and therefore were presumed to be nonviable. If we eliminate these from calculations, the average weights of the fetuses from the progesterone-treated animals exceeded the weights of those from the intact controls by 10%.

Pincus and Werthessen (10) reported that a dose of 1 mg. of progesterone per day maintained pregnancy in ovariectomized rabbits during

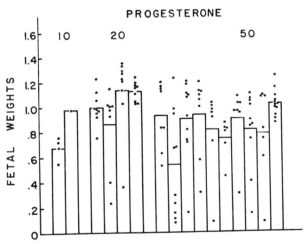

FIG. 2. Distribution of fetal weights in spayed rats receiving various doses of progesterone as indicated, in milligrams per kilogram per day. Each dot represents one fetus and each bar, one litter.

the early part of gestation while 2–3 mg. were required after the 12th day. In our rabbits, a dose of 2–3 mg. per rabbit per day was sufficient to permit the development of 1 to 11 fetuses in 16 of 18 does. In 4 of these cases the treatment was continued for 2 weeks and the fetuses were alive at necropsy. The results obtained with a graded series of doses are shown in Table III. In general these data support the conclusions of Pincus and Werthessen.

TABLE III

THE EFFECT OF VARIOUS DOSES OF PROGESTERONE IN MAINTAINING PREGNANCY IN SPAYED RABBITS

Daily dose (mg./rabbit)	Number	Living fetus(es)	Partial protection	Advanced resorption
0.5	3	1	—	2
1.	7	3	1	3
2.	7	5	2	—
2.–4.	18	16	2	—
5.	10	8	1	1

C. 17-HYDROXY-ESTREN-3-ONES

1. 17α-Ethynyl-19-nortestosterone.

The activities of 17α-ethynyl-19-nortestosterone (Norlutin) and its $\Delta^{5(10)}$ isomer, norethynodrel, (Enovid) are shown in Table IV. Pincus et al. (9) indicated that 17α-ethynyl-19-nortestosterone is ten times as

TABLE IV

THE EFFECTS OF $\Delta^{4(5)}$ AND $\Delta^{5(10)}$ 17α-ETHYNYL-17-HYDROXYESTREN-3-ONE IN MAINTAINING PREGNANCY IN RATS SPAYED ON THE 8TH DAY[a]

Daily dose (mg./kg.)	$\Delta^{4(5)}$		$\Delta^{5(10)}$		
	10	50	1	10	50[b]
Number of rats	10	5	10	10	5
Number with placentas	10	5	1	1	0
Uterine weight range (gm.)	1.2–2.7	2.1–3.2	0.31–0.75	0.36–1.5	0.55–4.3
Number with fetuses	0	0	0	0	—

[a] Necropsy on 18th day after mating.
[b] Administered orally.

active as progesterone in the Clauberg assay in rabbits, but Drill and Riegel (4) reported it only one-half as active as this standard. In our series, at a dose of 10 mg. per kilogram per day, this compound afforded only minimal protection in spayed rats. Small placentas were found in all 10 animals but no fetuses were observed in any case. Even at a dose of 50 mg. per kilogram, no fetuses were found in any of 5 rats. Some uterine enlargement was observed and this was associated with placental growth and thus does not represent an estrogenic response. In this series therefore, this compound proved less effective than progesterone in maintaining pregnancy in rats.

Three spayed rabbits were treated with 10 mg. of this compound *per os*, daily. Uterine enlargements ranged up to 2.5 cm., but there were no intact fetuses. Thus, as shown in Table V, some protection was ob-

TABLE V

THE EFFECTIVENESS OF $\Delta^{4(5)}$- AND $\Delta^{5(10)}$-17-ETHYNYL-17-HYDROXYESTREN-3-ONE IN MAINTAINING PREGNANCY IN SPAYED RABBITS

	Daily dose (mg./rabbit):			
	$\Delta^{4(5)}$	$\Delta^{5(10)}$		
Number of rabbits:	10^a	2–3	$2–3^a$	10^a
Treated	3	7	9	3
With normal fetus(es)	0	0	0	0
With partial protection	3	0	8	0
Showing advanced resorption	0	7	1	3

[a] Administered orally.

tained but the potency of this compound given orally to rabbits is less than 10% that of progesterone administered subcutaneously.

2. 17α-Ethynyl, $\Delta^{5(10)}$-estrenolone.

The $\Delta^{5(10)}$ isomer, norethynodrel, shows inherent estrogenic as well as progestational activity (9, 16). In this study, at doses of 1 or 10 mg. per kilogram per day, minute placental sites were found in only 1 of 10 animals (Table IV). There were no fetuses. Estrogenic effects were evident in the enlarged uteri, which were distended with clear fluid. Since in the Clauberg assay, the progestational activity of this compound is enhanced by oral administration, a series of 5 rats were given a daily dose of 50 mg. per kilogram orally. However, even at this massive dosage no protection was attained. In two of these rats the uterus was distended with dark blood but no fetal or placental remnants were identified.

These results are more surprising in view of the work of Lyons (8), who reported that the addition of a small amount of estrogen to progesterone greatly increased the efficacy of the latter compound in maintaining pregnancy in hypophysectomized, ovariectomized rats. In our series, the estrogenic $\Delta^{5(10)}$ isomer showed even less activity in supporting pregnancy than did the $\Delta^{4(5)}$ compound.

In spayed, pregnant rabbits, at a dose of 2–3 mg. per rabbit per day subcutaneously, no placental development was discernible and no fetuses were found in any of 7 does (Table V).

At the same dose orally, the results were somewhat variable but satisfactory protection was not obtained in any case. In 1 of 9 does, resorption was complete but in 6, the placentas at time of necropsy were at least as large as they were at the time of ovariectomy although the fetuses had been resorbed. One additional doe aborted after 4 days of treatment, with obvious growth of the fetuses during this interval. In another case, although fetuses were not found, the condition of the uterus suggested recent abortion. Even a dose of 10 mg. per rabbit per day administered orally was not adequate to maintain pregnancy.

3. 17α-Methyl, $\Delta^{5(10)}$-estrenolone.

Four rats were treated with the $\Delta^{5(10)}$, 17-methyl analog at a dose of 50 mg. per kilogram per day. Only slight protection was afforded as shown by small placentas in all animals. While there was some slight uterine enlargement, no fetuses were found in any case.

D. 17α-Substituted 19-nortestosterones

1. 17α-Ethyl.

As previously reported, 17α-ethyl-19-nortestosterone (Nilevar) will maintain pregnancy in rabbits (13). Table VI shows the protection obtained in rats. The doses used were adequate to support some placental

TABLE VI

THE EFFECTIVENESS OF 17α-ETHYL-19-NORTESTOSTERONE IN MAINTAINING PREGNANCY IN RATS SPAYED ON THE 8TH AND SACRIFICED ON THE 18TH DAY OF GESTATION

	Daily dose (mg. per kg.):			
	2	5	10	20
Number of rats	10	10	10	5
Number with placentas	9	10	10	5
Average number of placentas	8.6	10.1	9.0	11.6
Uterine weight range (gm.)	0.39–6.5	2.6–40.8	0.85–29.5	26.5–44.7
Number with fetuses	0	7	8	5
Average number of fetuses		6.3	6.4	10.6
Average fetal weight (mg.)		657	839	851
Fetal weight range (mg.)		67–1269	134–1772	55–1252

development in all cases, and fetuses were observed at the higher dose levels. However, especially at the 5-mg. dose, there were a number of fetuses subnormal in size. Complete protection was judged to have been obtained in only 2 rats at the 5-mg. dose and 3 rats at the 10-mg. dose. Twenty milligrams were required to obtain complete protection in all rats. In the Clauberg assay this compound is about five times as potent as progesterone. Its potency in maintaining pregnancy in rats is about twice that of progesterone.

In rabbits, a dose of 2 to 3 mg. per rabbit per day subcutaneously was adequate to maintain some fetuses in 10 of 14 does while in 3 additional rabbits, there was some postcastration development. Increasing the dose afforded similar protection, 5 of 6 does having 1 or more normal fetuses (Table VII). In three of these, injections were continued to 30

TABLE VII

The Effectiveness of 17α-Ethyl-19-nortestosterone in Maintaining Pregnancy in Spayed Rabbits

	Daily dose (mg./rabbit):		
Number of rabbits:	2–3	5–10	2–3[a]
Treated	14	6	5
With normal fetus(es)	10	5	0
With partial protection	3	1	5
Showing advanced resorption	1	0	0

[a] Administered orally.

days, and in two, the fetuses seemed to be fully supported. Administered orally, the 2–3 mg. dose was sufficient to promote some development in all 5 cases but there were no living fetuses in any of the does.

2. 17α-Methallyl.

Among the newer 17α-substituted 19-nortestosterones prepared in our laboratories are the 1-methallyl and 2-methallyl compounds. Both of these are potent progestins in the Clauberg assay, being respectively, five and twenty-five times as active as progesterone (5, 14). Both compounds are also potent progestins in the intrauterine assay and both are very effective in maintaining pregnancy.

Data on the 2-methallyl compound are shown in Table VIII. Even

TABLE VIII

The Effectiveness of 17α-(2-methallyl)-19-Nortestosterone in Maintaining Pregnancy in Rats Spayed on the 8th and Sacrificed on the 18th Day of Gestation

	Daily dose (mg. per kg.):			
	1	2	5	10[a]
Number of rats	10	10	10	10
Number with placentas	10	10	10	10
Average number of placentas	10.1	10.5	10.3	11.4
Uterine weight range (gm.)	0.57–27.9	11.0–37.5	22.6–40.3	4.1–37.6
Number with fetuses	7	10	10	9
Average number of fetuses	2.7	6.7	9.2	9.0
Average fetal weight (mg.)	923	813	1035	937
Fetal weight range (mg.)	434–1286	94–1354	289–1417	94–1344

[a] Administered orally.

at a dose of only 1 mg. per kilogram per day, placentas were found in all cases and fetuses in 70%. However, at this dose, only one rat showed what can be termed a normal pregnancy. At the higher doses nearly complete protection was obtained. An additional group of 10 rats was treated with a dose of 10 mg. per kilogram per day orally. All had well-developed placentas and 9 had normal-sized fetuses. Thus, administered orally, this compound is considerably more effective than subcutaneously administered progesterone.

These compounds also have been most effective in maintaining pregnancy in rabbits. This is shown in the data presented in Table IX.

TABLE IX

THE EFFECTIVENESS OF 17α-METHALLYL-19-NORTESTOSTERONE IN MAINTAINING PREGNANCY IN SPAYED RABBITS

	Daily dose (mg./rabbit):				
	1-methallyl		2-methallyl		
Number of rabbits:	2–3	5	0.05	0.1	0.5
Treated	4	2	4	7	8
With normal fetus(es)	4	2	1	2	7
With partial protection	0	0	3	5	1
Advanced resorption	0	0	0	0	0

3. *17α-Butyl and allyl.*

Limited studies have been made on these two compounds in the 19-nortestosterone series, and the results are summarized in Table X. At

TABLE X

THE EFFECTIVENESS OF 17α-BUTYL AND 17α-ALLYL-19-NORTESTOSTERONE IN MAINTAINING PREGNANCY IN RATS SPAYED ON THE 8TH AND SACRIFICED ON THE 18TH DAY AFTER MATING[a]

	Butyl	Allyl
Number of rats	5	5
Number with placentas	0	5
Uterine weight range (gm.)	0.28–0.97	1.25–34.3
Number with fetuses		2
Average number of fetuses		11.5
Average fetal weight (mg.)		870
Fetal weight range (mg.)		650–987

[a] A daily dose of 10 mg. per kilogram was used.

the dose used no protection was observed with the 17-butyl compound while the 17-allyl furnished adequate protection in 2 of 5 rats. This latter compound was also effective in maintaining pregnancy in rabbits (13).

E. 17α-Hydroxyprogesterone Esters

1. 17-Acetate.

As shown in Table XI, this compound (Prodox) exerted no protective action in rats at the dose used.

TABLE XI

Effectiveness of Esters of 17-Hydroxyprogesterone in Maintaining Pregnancy in Rats Spayed on the 8th and Sacrificed on the 18th Day after Mating

	17-acetate	17-caproate		6-Methyl-17-acetate	
Daily dose (mg./kg.)	10	10	100[a]	0.5	1.0
Number of rats	10	10	5	10	10
Number with placentas	0	1	0	10	10
Uterine weight range (gm.)	0.16–0.22	0.16–33.7	0.21–0.33	0.58–33.9	1.9–41.3
Number with fetuses		1		7	8
Number of fetuses		10		6.4	8.9
Average fetal weight (mg.)		1152		854	1154

[a] Administered orally.

2. 17-Caproate.

This compound (Delalutin) was also ineffective at the 10-mg. dose in 9 of 10 rats. In the tenth rat pregnancy pursued a normal course. Since this compound is reported to be long acting (7), it may be that it is necessary to administer it well in advance of ovariectomy. Therefore, 5 rats were treated with a single dose of 100 mg. per kilogram on the day before ovariectomy. No placentas and no fetuses were found in any case and the uterine weights only slightly exceeded those of the un-injected, spayed controls.

3. 6-Methyl-17-acetate.

Preliminary studies on this compound indicate that it is a very potent progestin. The results obtained in rats at two low doses are shown in Table XI. Although complete protection was not obtained in all cases at these very low doses, the compound appears to be about twenty-five times as active as progesterone. This estimate of potency agrees quite well with the values we have obtained in the Clauberg assay. In a preliminary study, a dose of 0.5 mg. per day maintained fetuses in all of 3 rabbits, while with a dose of 0.1 mg. per day there were no fetuses maintained in either of 2 does.

IV. Commentary

Although the role of progesterone in the maintenance of pregnancy has not been completely elucidated, several facts are well established. First, removal of the ovaries of pregnant rats or rabbits in the first

8–10 days invariably interrupts gestation. Secondly, the deficiency in the ovarian hormones can be compensated for by injections of progesterone or certain synthetic steroids. Thirdly, estrogens early in the period of gestation, can interrupt pregnancy in the rat (11, 17) and rabbit (3, 6). In the progesterone assay, estrone administered in moderate doses along with progesterone, inhibits the development of the endometrial glands in the uterus (2, 15).

In the course of these studies it appeared that some of these compounds have a specific anabolic activity, as indicated by the frequency with which the larger fetuses were observed. This effect is illustrated in the frequency diagram shown in Fig. 3. Neither progesterone nor 17α-(2-methallyl)-19-nortestosterone show anabolic activity in the levator ani

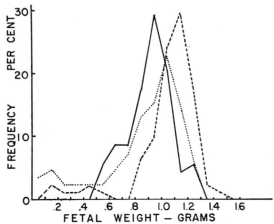

Fig. 3. Frequency distribution, in per cent, of fetal weights from control rats (solid line), rats treated with progesterone at a dose of 50 mg. per kilogram per day (dotted line) or rats treated with 17α-(2-methallyl)-19-nortestosterone at a dose of 5 mg. per kilogram per day (broken line). In all cases the mothers were sacrificed on the 18th day of pregnancy. Interval for grouping of weights was 0.1 gm.

muscle assay. The greater fetal weights observed in the present series probably reflect greater placental development afforded by these steroids.

Because of the relationship of these steroids to testosterone, the question of androgenicity becomes important. Of the three most active gestagens discussed here, two show some androgenicity. 17α-Ethyl-19-nortestosterone is 6% as androgenic as testosterone propionate as measured by the effects on the seminal vesicles and ventral prostates of castrated male rats (14). Preliminary studies indicate that approximately the same degree of androgenicity obtains for the 6-methyl-17-hydroxyprogesterone 17-acetate (12). However, by the same assay method, 17α-(2-methallyl)-

19-nortestosterone shows no androgenicity at a total dose of 5 mg. per rat and therefore was judged to be less than 1% as androgenic as testosterone propionate (12).

Certain of these steroids show a high progestational activity when administered systemically, as in the Clauberg assay, but have little or no effect when instilled directly into the uterus of the primed rabbit (13, 16). It is of interest that of the steroids we have tested the only ones which were effective in maintaining pregnancy in the rat or rabbit were those that produced a progestational response after intrauterine instillation in the rabbit. Table XII summarizes the activities of these progestins

TABLE XII

QUALITATIVE EFFECTS OF VARIOUS GESTAGENS IN SEVERAL EXPERIMENTAL PROCEDURES

| | Endometrial development | | Maintenance of Pregnancy | |
| | Subcutaneous | | | |
Compound	or oral	Intrauterine	Rat	Rabbit
Progesterone	+	+	+	+
17-Hydroxyestrenolone:				
17-Ethynyl, $\Delta^{4(5)}$	+	0	0^a	0^a
17-Ethynyl, $\Delta^{5(10)}$	+	0	0	0
17-Methyl, $\Delta^{5(10)}$	+	0	0	
19-Nortestosterone:				
17-Ethyl	+	+	+	+
17-Buytl	+	+	$?^b$	
17-Allyl	+	+	+	+
17-(1-Methallyl)	+	+	+	+
17-(2-Methallyl)	+	+	+	+
17-Hydroxyprogesterone:				
17-Acetate	+	+	$?^b$	
17-Caproate	+		$?^b$	
6-Methyl, 17-acetate	+	+	+	+

[a] Some placental development but no fetuses maintained.
[b] Inactive at doses used. May be active at higher levels.

in various test procedures. Since 17α-butyl-19-nortestosterone was very active in the intrauterine assay, we expected this compound to be effective in maintaining pregnancy. However, in our small series, no such activity was found. Similarly the failure of the 17-acetate ester of 17-hydroxyprogesterone in the maintenance of pregnancy was unexpected. This lack of activity is even more surprising in view of the very great effectiveness of 6-methyl-17-hydroxyprogesterone 17-acetate. Explanation of these differences in activities must await further study.

V. Summary

The effectiveness of progesterone and some synthetic steroids in maintaining pregnancy was studied in spayed rats and rabbits. Adequate protection was attained, but in the rat massive doses of progesterone were required (50 mg. per kilogram per day). Several of the 17α-substituted 19-nortestosterones were much more effective, the 2-methallyl compound being at least ten times as potent as progesterone. This latter compound was also shown to be effective when administered orally. 6-Methyl-17-hydroxyprogesterone 17-acetate was the most active compound tested. This compound also showed some androgenic effects when tested in castrated male rats. Such androgenic effects were not observed with 17α-(2-methallyl)-19-nortestosterone. With certain of these compounds, when pregnancy was adequately maintained, the weights of the individual fetuses exceeded those of fetuses obtained from intact rats at the same stage of gestation, thus attesting to the adequacy of the replacement therapy.

Appendix

The gross uterine development in intact and spayed control rats and in spayed rats treated with various gestagens are shown in Plates I-III. All animals were sacrificed on the 18th day after mating. Except for the uteri shown in Figs. 4 and 5 (Plate I), all uteri are from rats spayed on the 8th day of pregnancy and treated daily with the various steroids from the day of ovariectomy until necropsy.

Acknowledgment

The authors wish to acknowledge the capable assistance of Mrs. Betsy Robb in carrying out much of this work.

References

1. Alexander, D. P., Frazer, J. F. D., and Lee, J., *J. Physiol.* **130**, 148 (1955).
2. Allen, W. M., *Am. J. Physiol.* **100**, 650 (1932).
3. Courrier, R., and Raynaud, R., *Compt. rend. soc. biol.* **116**, 1073 (1934).
4. Drill, V. A., and Riegel, B., *Recent Progr. in Hormone Research* **15**, 29 (1958).
5. Elton, R. L., and Edgren, R. A., *Endocrinology* **63**, 464 (1958).
6. Greenwald, G. S., *J. Exptl. Zool.* **135**, 461 (1957).
7. Kessler, W. O., and Borman, A., *Proc. Soc. Exptl. Biol. Med.* **94**, 820 (1957).
8. Lyons, W. R., *Proc. Soc. Exptl. Biol. Med.* **54**, 65 (1943).
9. Pincus, G., Chang, M. C., Zarrow, M. X., Hafez, E. S. E., and Merrill, A., *Endocrinology* **59**, 695 (1956).
10. Pincus, G., and Werthessen, N. T., *Am. J. Physiol.* **124**, 484 (1938).
11. Saunders, F. J., *Endocrinology* **63**, 566 (1958).
12. Saunders, F. J., unpublished data.
13. Saunders, F. J., Colton, F. B., and Drill, V. A., *Proc. Soc. Exptl. Biol. Med.* **94**, 717 (1957).
14. Saunders, F. J., and Drill, V. A., *Endocrinology* **58**, 567 (1956).

PLATE I

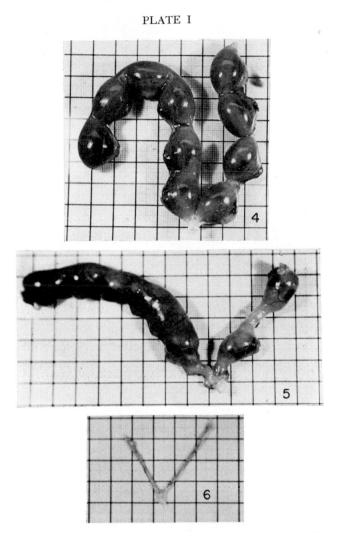

FIGS. 4 AND 5.   Uteri from intact rats showing variations observed in the normal population.

FIG. 6.   Oil-treated spayed control. No placental scars are visible 10 days after ovariectomy.

PLATE II

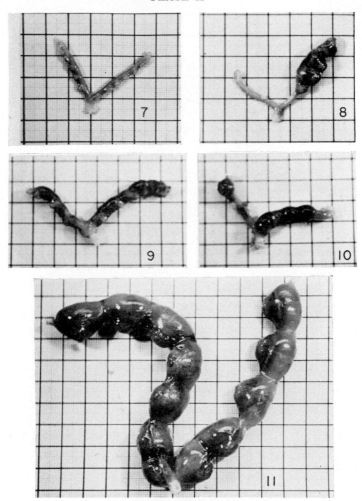

Fig. 7. Only minimal placental development is visible in this uterus from a spayed rat treated with 10 mg. of progesterone per kilogram per day.

Fig. 8. Same treatment as in Fig. 7, but larger placentas were obtained. The two largest placental sites contained only very small fetal remnants.

Fig. 9. Uterus from a rat treated with 50 mg. 17α-ethynyl-19-nortestosterone per kilogram per day subcutaneously. Definite placentas are visible but there are no fetuses remaining and the uterus is filled with blood and debris.

Fig. 10. Uterus of a rat similarly treated with norethynodrel. The uterus is filled with blood and debris and placental scars are very indistinct or absent.

Fig. 11. Uterus of a rat showing complete protection obtained with 50 mg. of progesterone per kilogram per day.

PLATE III

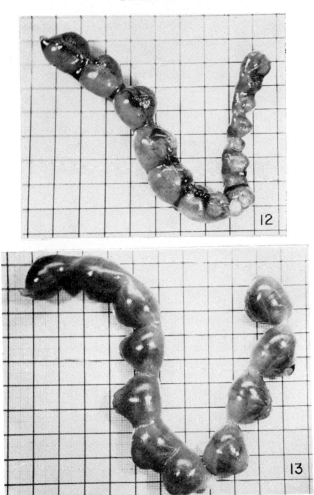

FIG. 12. Uterus of a rat which received 10 mg. of 17α-(2-methallyl)-19-nor-testosterone per kilogram per day *per os*. One horn of the uterus shows full maintenance of placentas and fetuses while the other horn shows less complete protection.

FIG. 13. Same treatment as in Fig. 12, but in this case complete fetal maintenance was attained.

15. Saunders, F. J., and Drill, V. A., *Ann. N. Y. Acad. Sci.* **71**, 516 (1958).
16. Saunders, F. J., Edgren, R. A., and Drill, V. A., *Endocrinology* **60**, 804 (1957).
17. Smith, M. G., *Bull. Johns Hopkins Hosp.* **39**, 203 (1926).

Discussion

CHAIRMAN: E. C. HUGHES

J. C. STUCKI: As Dr. Saunders has indeed correctly anticipated, I would like to comment briefly on the results he obtained with 6α-methyl-17α-acetoxyprogesterone (Provera or U-8839) a compound whose synthesis and biological activity we have very recently reported (J. C. Babcock, E. S. Gutsell, M. E. Herr, J. A. Hogg, J. C. Stucki, L. E. Barnes, and W. E. Dulin, *J. Am. Chem. Soc.* **80**, 2904 (1958)). As shown in Figs. A and B, 6α-methyl-17-acetoxyprogesterone in the Clauberg assay appears to be about 8–10 times as active as the parent compound, 17α-acetoxyprogesterone (hydroxyprogesterone acetate, Prodox, or HPA), by subcutaneous administration and about 60–80 times as potent as Prodox when administered orally. In similar assays, Prodox is about 6 times as potent as progesterone subcutaneously and about 2–4 times ethisterone when administered orally. Thus, though direct comparisons have not been made here, subcutaneously administered U-8839 would appear to be 50–60 times as potent as subcutaneously administered progesterone, and when administered orally, 120–320 times as potent as orally administered ethisterone.

We have also studied Prodox and Provera in the maintenance of pregnancy in the rat. Our data are in essential agreement with those presented by Dr. Saunders. The method employed was as follows: adult female rats were caged with fertile males overnight and smeared for sperm on the following morning. The day sperm were found was considered to be day 1 of pregnancy. On the 8th day of pregnancy, the females were bilaterally castrated if they were found to be pregnant upon examination of the uterus. Treatment, begun immediately and continued through day 20 of pregnancy, consisted of subcutaneous administration once daily of the progestin in carboxymethylcellulose suspending medium. In some groups estrone in oil was also administered subcutaneously once a day in daily doses of 1 μg. per rat. The results appear in Tables A and B. In a series of 70 intact untreated rats found by palpation to be pregnant, 68 delivered live young. Each successful mother delivered an average of 10.3 live young. The 70 rats contained an average of 11.0 implantation sites each. A net success index of 91, which has been calculated for this group, is an expression of the fact that not all pregnant animals deliver live young and that not all implantation sites develop into live young. Animals castrated on the 8th day of pregnancy and either left untreated or treated with estrone alone show absolutely no signs of pregnancy at autopsy on day 21. The administration of either progesterone alone or progesterone and estrone concomitantly results in the successful maintenance of pregnancy in some of the animals. The indices of success show that progesterone administered concomitantly with estrone is roughly four times as effective as progesterone administered alone. In confirmation of Dr. Saunders' results we found that hydroxyprogesterone acetate administered alone even in extremely high doses was not capable of maintaining pregnancy. When administered together with estrone, however, Prodox was capable of maintaining pregnancy. We feel it probable that Prodox is incapable of maintaining pregnancy when administered alone because of its virtually complete lack of inherent estrogenicity, a property not shared by the other progestins studied.

Again in confirmation of the results presented by Dr. Saunders, 6α-methyl-17α-acetoxyprogesterone administered alone to pregnant castrate rats was found to be 25–50 times as potent as progesterone administered alone for the maintenance of pregnancy. The potency of 6α-methyl-17α-acetoxyprogesterone, like progesterone, was increased by the concomitant administration of estrone. Based on limited data,

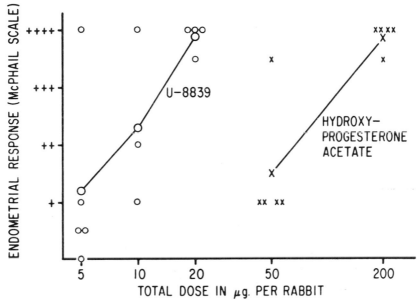

Fig. A.   Parenteral progestational activity of U-8839 and hydroxyprogesterone acetate in the estrogen-primed, immature rabbit.

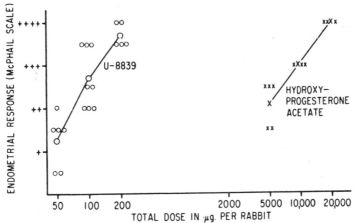

Fig. B.   Oral progestational activity of U-8839 and hydroxyprogesterone acetate in the estrogen-primed, immature rabbit.

U-8839, when administered together with estrone, is approximately 25 times as active as progesterone administered together with estrone. U-8839 was also found to maintain pregnancy effectively in one experiment where the drug was administered orally in the diet.

Dr. Saunders mentioned increasing concern over androgenicity of steroids given during pregnancy because of possible masculinizing effect on the female fetus. He has indicated that he finds 6α-methyl-17α-acetoxyprogesterone to possess 5% of the androgenicity of testosterone. We have evaluated 6α-methyl-17α-acetoxyprogesterone,

TABLE A

MAINTENANCE OF PREGNANCY IN RATS OVARIECTOMIZED ON THE 8TH DAY OF PREGNANCY

Group (compounds admin. daily)	Successful pregnancies per no. of "tries"	Live young per successful pregnancy	Net success[a] index
Intact untreated control	68/70	10.3	91
Untreated control	0/9	0	0
Estrone, 1 μg.	0/5	0	0
Progesterone, 8 mg.	5/5	4.0	36
Progesterone, 4 mg.	4/5	2.5	18
Progesterone, 2 mg.	1/5	2.0	4
Progesterone, 8 mg. + estrone, 1 μg.	4/5	5.5	40
Progesterone, 4 mg. + estrone, 1 μg.	5/5	6.8	62
Progesterone, 2 mg. + estrone, 1 μg.	5/5	3.6	33
Progesterone, 1 mg. + estrone, 1 μg.	2/5	4.5	16
HPA,[b] 100 mg.	0/5	0	0
HPA, 100 mg. + estrone, 1 μg.	2/3	2.5	15
HPA, 50 mg. + estrone, 1 μg.	1/2	5.0	23
HPA, 20 mg. + estrone, 1 μg.	0/2	0	0

[a] $\dfrac{\text{Living fetuses per experimental group}}{\text{Number of mothers per group} \times 11 \text{ implantation sites}} \times 100.$

[b] Hydroxyprogesterone acetate.

hydroxyprogesterone acetate, and progesterone in castrate male rats, using three indices of androgenicity, namely, the seminal vesicles, the ventral prostate, and the levator ani muscles (as shown in Fig. C). The compounds were administered in graded doses in oil by the subcutaneous route once a day for 10 days to groups of 10 castrate immature male rats each. Autopsies were performed on the 11th day. The results obtained show that hydroxyprogesterone acetate has no demonstrable androgenic activity as judged by any of the end points studied at any of the doses employed. Progesterone stimulated the seminal vesicles and the prostate in the doses employed, but did not stimulate the levator ani. U-8839 produced weight increases of all three androgen-responsive tissues. When one compares the potency of U-8839 and progesterone with regard to their ability to stimulate the ventral prostate, one finds that U-8839 is no more than twice as active as progesterone. Potencies with regard to seminal vesicle stimulation cannot be directly compared because the slopes of the dose-response curves for U-8839 and progesterone are clearly not the same. If minimal effective doses of the two compounds are compared, however, one can conclude that U-8839 is approximately 10 times as active as progesterone. Since U-8839 is, however, 50–60 times as active as progesterone on the basis of endometrial proliferation assays or 25–50 times as active as progesterone in maintaining pregnancy, in *equivalent progestational doses* 6α-methyl-17α-acetoxy-progesterone is clearly much less androgenic than progesterone, the natural pregnancy-maintaining hormone, and therefore would not be expected to produce masculinization of the female fetus.

TABLE B

ABILITY OF U-8839 TO MAINTAIN PREGNANCY IN RATS OVARIECTOMIZED ON THE 8TH DAY OF PREGNANCY

Daily U-8839 dose µg.	Successful pregnancies per no. of "tries"	Live young per successful pregnancy	Net[a] success index
40,000	3/3	5.3	48
20,000	3/3	9.3	85
10,000	7/7	9.0	82
5,000	4/4	9.0	82
2,500	5/5	7.8	70
1,250	4/5	5.8	42
625	4/4	7.0	64
312.5	3/3	4.7	42
150	5/5	4.4	39
75	3/5	1.3	7
40	0/3	0	0
40 + 1 µg. Estrone	2/3	1.5	9
6.05 mg./day (2.1–10.5) oral, by drug diet method	3/6	4.3	20

[a] $\dfrac{\text{Living fetuses per experimental group}}{\text{Number of mothers per group} \times 11 \text{ implantation sites}} \times 100.$

G. S. GREENWALD: There is a lengthy literature dating back to Parkes and Bellerby's original observations of about 1927 that indicates that exogenous supplies of estrogen have a deleterious effect on pregnancy. I wonder whether the failure to maintain pregnancy with some of your compounds may not be due to the *estrogenic* effect of these compounds and whether you have any information on the relative estrogenic potency of these steroids?

F. J. SAUNDERS: I think that this is a real point. The compound norethynodrel is slightly estrogenic. It is sufficiently estrogenic, I think, to interrupt pregnancy in the rat. However, Norlutin is not estrogenic, at least in the sample which we have had for our essays. It, however, did not maintain pregnancy. Neither did the butyl compound which I mentioned. Of course, we have only limited data on the butyl, but it was not estrogenic. The methyl $\Delta^{5(10)}$ estrenolone that I mentioned does have some estrogenicity.

W. M. ALLEN: Dr. David Wu and I have now accumulated considerable experience with two of the newer progestational agents. We have studied the po-
tentialities of Norlutin and Delalutin as agents for the maintenance of pregnancy
in rabbits castrated 1 day after mating and in rabbits castrated on the 12th to 14th
day of an existing pregnancy. These studies were designed to compare the capacity
of these compounds with the known effects of progesterone. Some of the results are
best shown in Table C.

It is quite apparent that both Norlutin and Delalutin act as good progestational agents and that normal-appearing embryos are found in the uterus on the

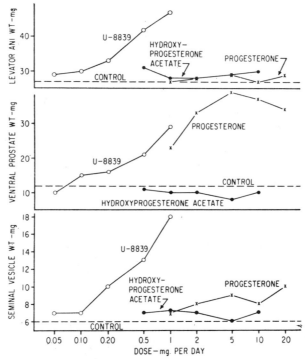

FIG. C.   Effect of U-8839, hydroxyprogesterone acetate, and progesterone on sex
glands and levator ani muscle of castrate male rats (ten animals per point).

6th day. This, of course, indicates that the progestational changes in the endometrium
are sufficiently normal to produce whatever secretions are necessary for growth
of the blastocysts after their arrival in the uterus and up to the 6th day. The number
of blastocysts recovered is somewhat below the number recovered from normal
animals, but this is not surprising as the experimental animals have been subjected
to operation.

The three compounds, progesterone, Norlutin, and Delalutin, seem to have about
equivalent activities, as judged by their capacity to produce progestational proliferation and normal-appearing embryos, when given by subcutaneous injection in sesame
oil.

The second part of the study deals with the ability of these compounds to maintain pregnancy in normally pregnant rabbits castrated on the 12th to 14th day of pregnancy. First, nine rabbits have been castrated on the 14th day of pregnancy and then have received daily subcutaneous doses of Norlutin, varying from 0.1 mg. to 8.0 mg. Exploration of these rabbits on the 21st day has shown no case in which

TABLE C

Effect of Progestational Agents on Endometrial Proliferation and Size of Blastocysts Recovered on the 6th Day after Mating[a]

Number of rabbits	Daily dose (mg.)	Progestational proliferation	Average size of blastocysts[b]	% Eggs recovered as blastocysts
Controls:				
5		4+	2.17	88.4
5	Sesame oil	4+	2.29	81.0
Progesterone:				
3	2.0	4+	2.59	82.6
3	1.0	4+	1.88	68.0
3	0.5	4+	1.58	60.9
3	0.25	3+ to 4+	1.27	57.9
3	0.125	0 to 1+	0.80	16.7
17α-Hydroxyprogesterone caproate (Delalutin)				
3	2.0	4+	2.69	75.8
3	1.0	4+	1.99	85.7
3	0.5	3+	1.49	53.6
3	0.25	2+ to 3+	0.79	54.9
3	0.125	0 to 1+	0.31	63.8
17α-Ethynyl-19-Nortestosterone (Norlutin)				
3	2.0	3+	2.19	37.0
3	1.0	3+	2.09	53.8
3	0.5	3+	1.43	60.7
4	0.25	2+	0.83	42.1
3	0.125	1+ to 2+	0.65	69.0
3	0.0625	0 to 2+	0.60	45.8
3	0.0312	0 to 1+	0.55	68.2
3	0.0156	0	0.47	48.0

[a] Ovaries removed 24 hours after mating.
[b] The size as measured does not include the zona pellucida.

the embryos had continued developing beyond the 14th day. All were in advanced stages of resorption. By this test, Norlutin does not have any value. This result led us to see if Norlutin had a detrimental effect in normally pregnant animals with the ovaries not removed. Doses of 2 and 4 mg. daily led to prompt resorption of the embryos as judged by laparotomy on the 23rd day. Daily doses of 0.5 to 1.0 mg. permitted some growth of the fetuses, but by the 32nd day all fetuses were either dead or resorbed. Delalutin, on the other hand, will maintain pregnancy to term when the dose is 2.0 mg. or more daily, provided progesterone is given for the first 2 days along with the Delalutin.

In other preliminary studies we have found that Delalutin in a dose of 2.0 mg. or more daily, will maintain pregnancy from beginning to end in rabbits subjected to ovariectomy 1 day after mating. In this respect, this agent is superior to progesterone. It is probable that the long-acting property of Delalutin provides for smooth absorption of the hormone and that this smooth absorption explains the better results at the critical time of implantation with Delalutin than are obtained with progesterone.

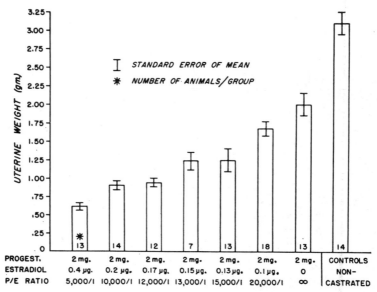

PROGEST.	2 mg.	2 mg.	2 mg.	2 mg.	2 mg.	2 mg.	2 mg.	CONTROLS
ESTRADIOL	0.4 µg.	0.2 µg.	0.17 µg.	0.15 µg.	0.13 µg.	0.1 µg.	0	NON-
P/E RATIO	5,000/1	10,000/1	12,000/1	13,000/1	15,000/1	20,000/1	∞	CASTRATED

FIG. D. Uterine weight as an index of deciduoma response of groups of oophorectomized pseudopregnant rats given progesterone alone or progesterone and estradiol.

S. ZUCKERMAN: I should like to ask a question about the tests for the androgenic properties of these compounds. Did I understand correctly that you were referring entirely to the weights of the accessory reproductive organs?

F. J. SAUNDERS: Yes.

S. ZUCKERMAN: Is there any intention of finding out whether these substances induce permanent changes in the reproductive organs. For example, could there be any deleterious effects of the treatment on the gonads and could the sex ratios be altered?

F. J. SAUNDERS: I do not know. We have all these fetuses, but we have not studied sex ratios yet. So far, all we have studied is the androgenicity in castrate male rats.

I. ROTHCHILD: I just want to make a small comment in regard to the doses of progesterone used to effect the successful maintenance of pregnancy in both your studies and those of Dr. Stucki.

I am trying to explain the discrepancies between the high doses that you found necessary and the dose that R. K. Meyer and I in 1940 used to maintain pregnancy in castrated rats. We used progesterone prepared by Dr. Marvin Spielman from cholesterol. The preparation that he had at that time was not completely pure. I mention this as a possibly important point because we were able to effect maintenance of practically normal pregnancies to term in rats castrated on the 4th day of pregnancy with doses of about 2 mg. a day.

R. E. L. NESBITT: [Remarks submitted after close of discussion] Dr. Rothchild has suggested that the marked variations in the progestational action of some of the newer steroids may be due to inhibitory effects of estrogen present in some of the compounds. It is perhaps advisable at this stage of the discussion to document the inhibition of progesterone by estrogen in experimental animals. Dr. Vincent De Feo and I have utilized a standard procedure to induce pseudopregnancy in puberal Sprague-Dawley rats by artificially stimulating the cervices of these animals. On

TABLE D

THE EFFECTS OF ADRENALECTOMY AND CASTRATION ON UTERINE WEIGHT OF PSEUDOPREGNANT RATS

Organs removed	Number of animals	Hormonal treatment	Average uterine wt. (gm.) and range
None	14	—	3.1 (2.4–3.5)
Adrenals	4	—	2.7 (2.4–2.9)
Ovaries	13	Progesterone (2 mg.)	2.0 (1.4–2.9)
Ovaries and adrenals	4	Progesterone (2 mg.)	2.0 (1.3–3.0)
Ovaries	13	Progesterone (2 mg.) and estrone (0.4 µg.)	0.6 (0.3–0.9)
Ovaries and adrenals	4	Progesterone (2 mg.) and estrone (0.4 µg.)	0.4 (0.3–0.5)

day 4 of pseudopregnancy a decidual reaction was produced by needle traumatization of the uterine horns. Bilateral oophorectomies were performed at this time and the animals were given hormonal support until sacrifice on day 9. Uncastrated animals were used as controls. Two-milligram doses of crystalline progesterone in sesame oil were given daily to all animals, alone or in combination with crystalline estrogen (estradiol), from days 4 to 8 inclusive. Thus, the progesterone:estradiol (P:E) ratios varied in the several groups of study animals as shown in Fig. D. Uterine weights were used as an index of deciduoma response. The mean uterine weight was maximum in the group of animals receiving progesterone alone, but this value was significantly less than that recorded for intact animals used as controls. The control values were unattainable in experimental animals receiving progesterone in doses up to 4 mg. per day. The mean uterine weight in other groups was directly proportional to the P:E ratio; that is, the deciduoma response (reflected by uterine weight) was related inversely to the daily dose of estrogen administered. Certain recent experiments indicate that a P:E ratio of 5000:1 is as effective in inhibiting deciduoma formation when given on days 4 and 5 of pseudopregnancy as when given from days 4 to 8 inclusive. Similar studies carried out in adult rats yielded results identical with those noted here for puberal rats. The type and magnitude of deciduoma response was the same for comparable groups of animals.

It may be of interest to this audience that our experiments seem to indicate that the inhibitory effects of estrogen upon deciduoma development is not mediated through the adrenal cortex. Certain of our experimental animals were subjected to adrenalectomy at the time of castration and were maintained on 1% sodium chloride supplementation. Other animals with intact adrenal glands were used as controls (Table D). You will notice that in all three study groups of pseudopregnant rats, namely, non-castrated animals used as controls, castrated animals supported on progesterone alone and those supported on a combination of progesterone and estradiol, the mean uterine weights were uninfluenced significantly by adrenalectomy.

The inhibitory effects of estrogen upon deciduomata were also demonstrated in pregnant rats subjected to identical hormonal studies except that bilateral oophorectomy was performed on day 4 of pregnancy instead of pseudopregnancy. The higher estrogen administrations (P:E ratios of 10,000:1 and 5000:1) restricted the development of the decidua and destroyed or removed the embryo from the implantation site. There was no sign of mesometrial deciduoma in these animals. The central portion of the antimesometrial decidua showed extravasations of blood and leucocytes. The uterus showed the effects of estrogenic stimulation, namely, increased height of epithelial cells, secretory activity, mitoses, and mucosal folds with projections into the lumen. Lower doses of estradiol, or progesterone alone, provided adequate support for the maintenance of decidua and viability of the embryos. There were some resorptions, but all animals showed well-developed fetuses at laparotomy on day 20 of pregnancy. Certain preliminary work suggests that, at least in the rat, estrogen is important in establishing proper implantation of the blastocyst. Timing must be a critical factor, however, because, if estrogen stimulation persists for more than a short period, there will be an inhibitory effect upon the decidual development.

C. W. LLOYD: I thought it might be interesting to put on the record that the 6-methyl-17-acetoxyprogesterone has apparently about the same ratio of activity in the human as compared with Prodox. Ten women with amenorrhea of various sorts were maintained on constant doses of estrogen for months and then given these compounds for 5 days. They had withdrawal bleeding about 3 days after cessation of the progestational agent. With Prodox 50 mg. daily or more was needed to do this. With this compound, we can readily do it with 5 mg. daily, usually with 2.5 mg. daily, and sometimes with 1.25 mg. daily for 5 days.

G. PINCUS: We have worked with all of these compounds and tested them principally in two respects—one for progestational activity by the carbonic anhydrase activity in the uterus of the spayed rabbit—and the ratios shown by Dr. Saunders are close to those obtained by carbonic anhydrase assay.

However, when you study the inhibition of ovulation in the rabbit, the ratios change very markedly. The 6-methyl-17-acetoxyprogesterone is in our carbonic anhydrase assay about thirteen times as active by mouth as the standard, which is Prodox. But, as an ovulation inhibitor, it is about three times as active as Prodox.

Similarly, with the 19-norsteroids, the extremely active one that Dr. Saunders showed—the 2-methallyl—is not as active an ovulation-inhibitor as one would expect on the basis of the carbonic anhydrase assay.

I might say to Dr. Allen that his experience with implantation has also been ours. Implantation will go very poorly with the two ethynyl compounds, but with the higher analog it will go very well.

The other thing that puzzles me very much is that in every progestin that we have tested so far we have never been able to get a full complement of implantations in the rabbit, no matter how high we went in the dose. You may have noted from the figures given that roughly 90% of rabbit embryos are implanted normally. We get perhaps as high as 60%. We have never obtained 90%. Does that mean that there is a residual that we cannot exceed? Or maybe it is that there is another factor needed for implantation, as suggested by Dr. Rothchild's comments.

I. ROTHCHILD: This is another thought that just occurred to me. Has anybody—Dr. Saunders or anybody else—tested these compounds and compared them with progesterone for their anesthetic effect?

F. J. SAUNDERS: We have not.

W. M. ALLEN: I would like to make a comment. At one time, in fact, I even had an article in the literature which says that you cannot maintain pregnancy from the beginning with simon-pure progesterone; and yet, if you castrate at 14 days, you are successful in a high percentage of your cases. But I looked over one of my tables, and with the Delalutin started on the day of castration, 1 day after mating, where the dose was 2 mg. a day or greater, we had 87% of the total possible number of implantations in 10 animals. All 10 had implantations.

Of course, when Dr. Horn and I used crude extracts, we came out with a highly significant number of implantations—pretty close to the ideal number. No one, I think not even Dr. Pincus himself, has come close to this with pure progesterone.

We have another series going right now to see if we can, by increasing the amount of oil, etc., possibly achieve a higher percentage. But even that, I am sure, is not going to come out anywhere near 76%.

This would raise the question that maybe progesterone isn't the hormone after all for the rabbit and perhaps 17-hydroxyprogesterone or something else may be. It is probably more likely, however, that the difficulty arises from the rapid absorption of progesterone.

We have had in this study—it is now up around 100 rabbits—very interesting observations with the Delalutin when we castrate at 14 days and give them 3 or 4 mg. per day. The animals will live and grow but they ultimately resorb. In other words, a temporary inadequacy of progesterone, if it is not too precipitous still permits growth, but it manifests its deleterious effects after several days, which I think is a rather interesting observation. But with the Delalutin given every day, there is undoubtedly a very smooth absorption with the lack of fluctuations. I have not quite given up the idea that the failure to achieve such good results with progesterone may not be due to the same thing. We are now injecting it three times in 24 hours.

W. O. NELSON: I do not want to prolong the session, but I think it might be interesting to note the effect these various compounds have on another aspect of gonadotropin inhibition. We have approached it by looking at what they do to spermatogenesis. Here, as Dr. Pincus has said in the case of ovulation, their effect shows no correspondence with their progestational activity. The compounds Norlutin and Enovid, of course, are very effective agents in suppressing spermatogenesis. Such compounds as Prodox and Delalutin are quite ineffective; 6-methyl Prodox appears to be somewhat effective by injection, at least. The methallyl compounds appear to be quite ineffective by oral administration, but are effective by injection at about three times the level of Enovid. Nilevar is interesting because it apparently is androgenic enough so that, by the time the level that is necessary to inhibit spermatogenesis is approached, the direct effect of androgen on the rat testis enters and stimulation of spermatogenesis occurs.

Gestagens in Human Pregnancy

Josef Zander

Universitäts-Frauenklinik, Cologne, Germany

I. Introduction

The role of gestagens in the physiology of reproduction is well established. With good reason Courrier has called progesterone "the hormone of the mother."

Our present knowledge is based on the biologic observations of Louis Augustus Prenant (67), Ludwig Fraenkel (29), Leo Loeb (54), and George Corner and Willard Allen (12, 14). By their work and the work of Windhaus on the identification of cholesterol, the isolation, identification, and synthesis of the most effective naturally occurring gestagen, progesterone, was possible. The work was reported independently in 1934 by four groups, Allen and Wintersteiner (3), Butenandt and Westphal (9), Hartmann and Wettstein (35), and Slotta, Ruschig, and Fels (78).

The discovery of the progesterone metabolite, pregnanediol, in the urine by Marrian (57), its identification by Butenandt (8), and the first development of a method for quantitative determination of sodium pregnanediol glucuronidate by Venning (85, 86) opened a broad field of clinical investigation.

Direct information concerning the biologically active compounds in the organism was obtained for several years only by biological tests. These were all based essentially on the original method of Corner and Allen (14). The Hooker-Forbes test (45), found a broader application.

The results obtained with this test have stirred up much discussion in recent years.

The development and practical application of physicochemical micromethods and the use of labeled steroids have increased our knowledge of the naturally occurring gestagens. I should like to mention some recent results relating to physiological aspects. The methods have been discussed elsewhere (102, 105).

II. The Naturally Occurring Gestagens

Until recently it was supposed that there is only one naturally occurring gestagen, progesterone. This was in contrast to the several compounds with estrogenic and androgenic effects. This author, together

COMPOUND		MOUSE (HOOKER-FORBES TEST)	RABBIT (CLAUBERG TEST)	HUMAN
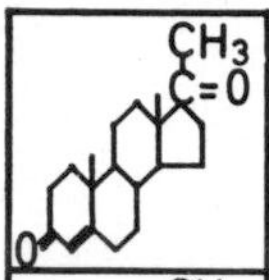 (structure) CH₃ C=O	PROGESTERONE	1	1	1
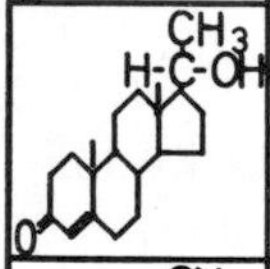 (structure) CH₃ H-C-OH	Δ⁴-3-KETO- PREGNEN-20α-OL	$\frac{1}{5}$	$\frac{1}{2}$ - $\frac{1}{3}$	AS CYCLOPENTYL PROPIONATE LESS ACTIVE THAN PROGESTERONE
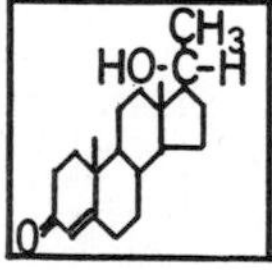 (structure) CH₃ HO-C-H	Δ⁴-3-KETO- PREGNEN-20β-OL	2	$\frac{1}{5}$ - $\frac{1}{10}$	AS CYCLOPENTYL PROPIONATE LESS ACTIVE THAN PROGESTERONE

FIG. 1.   Naturally occurring gestagens: biologic activity compared with progesterone.

with Forbes, Neher, and von Münstermann (28, 100, 101, 104), has demonstrated that there are two other substances with gestagenic activity in the organism, Δ^4-3-ketopregnen-20α-ol and Δ^4-3-ketopregnen-20β-ol (Fig. 1).

Both compounds are active in the Hooker-Forbes test and in the Clauberg test. In human beings they are active as cyclopentyl propionate esters (87); the free compounds have not yet been tested in man. The activity is always less than that of progesterone. Only in the Hooker-Forbes test is Δ^4-3-ketopregnen-20β-ol more effective than progesterone. Independently Jones and co-workers (46) isolated Δ^4-3-ketopregnen-20α-ol from human tissues and found biologic activity in the Hooker-Forbes test (69). The α-isomer occurs chiefly in human beings (101).

According to the results of Wiest (88), Short (74–76), and Gorski and co-workers (33), the occurrence of the α- and β-isomers varies in different species.

Both compounds are metabolites of progesterone. The incubation of corpora lutea of the cow with progesterone leads to conversion to Δ^4-3-ketopregnen-20β-ol (39). Wiest and Berliner (6, 88, 90) demonstrated in eviscerated rats the conversion of progesterone to Δ^4-3-ketopregnen-20α-ol. In the work of our group this conversion has been shown in human beings (100, 101). Wiest and Berliner demonstrated that the reduction of the 20-keto group is possible without the liver (6). It occurs mainly in peripheral tissues.

Thus one can say that, as with the most biologically active naturally occurring estrogens (estradiol and estrone) and androgens (testosterone and androstenedione), there is also a group of gestagens (progesterone and Δ^4-3-ketopregnen-20-ol). These compounds with biologic activity differ from each other only by two hydrogen atoms. The possibility of an oxidoreduction for the estrogen and androgen group is well known. Evidence has recently been obtained by Zander and Wiest (106) by *in vitro* experiments that there is a similar oxidoreduction in the gestagen group in human tissue.

III. The Production of Gestagens in Pregnancy

A. PLACENTA

For twenty-five years it has been known through the work of Mazer and Goldstein (58), and of Tausk and his group (1, 55) that the placenta contains substances with gestagenic effect. This has been confirmed by several groups (23, 24, 30, 34, 44, 56, 79, 84) and through the chemical identification of progesterone in placentas (19, 31, 38, 60, 63, 70). In recent years our group (105) has isolated gestagens from placentas of different stages of pregnancy and has measured them quantitatively. The results are shown graphically in Figs. 2–6.

All placentas of the second to the tenth month of pregnancy contained progesterone. In addition, the Δ^4-3-ketopregnen-20-ol fraction usually was present. The total amount of progesterone increases during pregnancy. The concentration in terms of micrograms per gram of placental tissue is higher in the second to the third month than in the later months of pregnancy.

There is a significant correlation between the increase in total gestagens and the increase in placental weight. Therefore it is possible that the increase in total gestagens is a function of the increase in placental cells and thus of placental growth.

One cannot conclude from the presence of a substance in a tissue that the substance necessarily is produced in this tissue. Therefore the evidence for placental production follows:

1. Increase in pregnanediol excretion during pregnancy [Venning (86), and others].

2. Increase in progesterone concentration in arm vein blood during pregnancy (97).

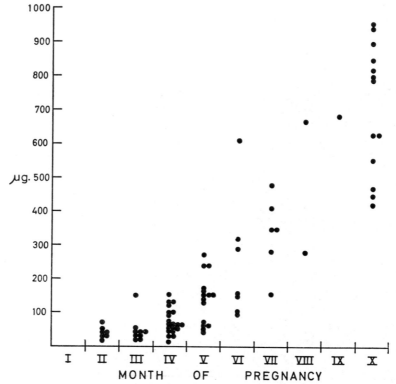

FIG. 2. Total amounts of progesterone in each of eighty placentas in the second to tenth months of pregnancy. From Zander and von Münstermann (105).

3. Increased progesterone levels in fat tissue (48).

4. Maintenance of pregnancy and of normal pregnanediol excretion after removal of the corpus luteum or of the ovaries in early pregnancy (11, 32, 52, 83).

5. Normal pregnanediol excretion in Addison's disease (51). Thus the adrenals are not the main source of gestagens.

6. No initial change of pregnanediol excretion after operative re-

moval of an abdominal pregnancy, the placenta being left *in situ* (2). After expulsion of the placenta in a normal delivery, pregnanediol excretion drops immediately.

7. Higher levels of progesterone in the uterine vein blood than in the peripheral vein blood at the end of pregnancy (49, 104).

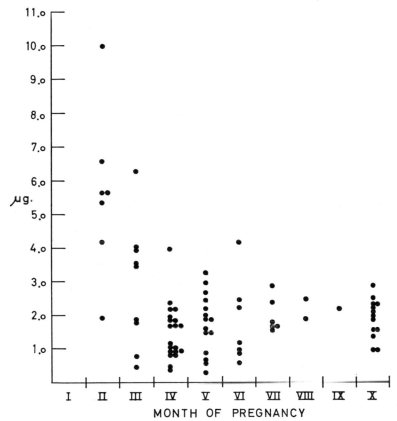

Fɪɢ. 3. Concentrations of progesterone (micrograms per gram of wet tissue) in each of eighty placentas in the second to tenth months of pregnancy. From Zander and von Münstermann (105).

8. Presence of progesterone in a chorion epithelioma (47).

9. Conversion of Δ^5-pregnenolone and cholesterol to progesterone in placental perfusion experiments (80).

10. Conversion of Δ^5-pregnenolone to progesterone by placental tissue *in vitro* (59, 71).

On the basis of this evidence there can be no doubt that the placenta produces gestagens and releases them into the blood.

The quantities released by the placenta are of interest and of practical clinical importance. Corner (13) estimated that a woman produces about 0.03 gm. progesterone in 24 hours during the corpus luteum

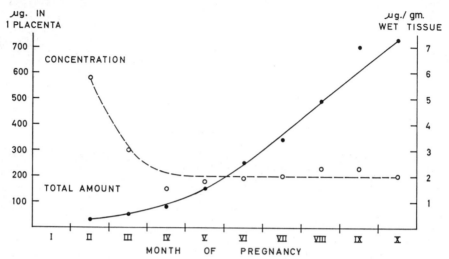

FIG. 4. Comparison of average values of concentrations (broken line), and of total amounts (solid line) of progesterone in eighty placentas in the second to the tenth months of pregnancy. From Zander and von Münstermann (105).

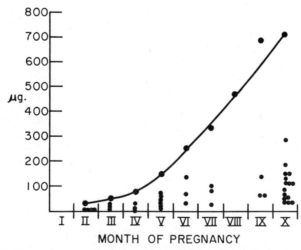

FIG. 5. Total amounts of combined Δ⁴-3-ketopregnen-20-ol (small dots) in each of forty placentas in the second to tenth months of pregnancy. The values are compared with the average values of progesterone (large dots in the line) in eighty placentas (see Fig. 4). From Zander et al. (101).

phase. This estimate appeared very high at that time but has been generally confirmed.

By measuring the excretion of pregnanediol we have attempted first to determine the order of magnitude of progesterone production in pregnancy (93). Postmenopausal women were injected with different doses of progesterone in crystal suspensions having known absorption rates. The percentage of the injected hormone which was excreted as pregnanediol was thus determined. A pregnanediol excretion which approximated that of the first third of pregnancy was reached when the

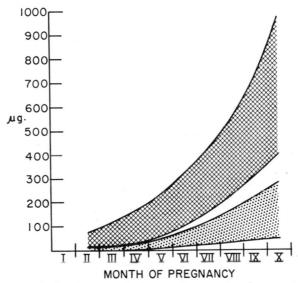

FIG. 6. Areas of distribution of the total amounts of progesterone (upper area) and of combined Δ^4-3-ketopregnen-20-ol (lower area) in placentas in the second to tenth months of pregnancy. From Zander *et al.* (101).

woman received 0.025–0.05 gm. progesterone per day. After daily injection of 0.1 gm. the excretion rate of the second half of pregnancy was reached.

In later investigations (104), the concentrations of progesterone in the blood vessels leaving the placenta, the uterine vein, and the umbilical vein were determined (Fig. 8). Using the values of Browne and Veall (7) for the rate of uterine blood flow per minute it was calculated that at the end of pregnancy 0.19–0.28 gm. progesterone passes from the placenta through the uterine vein into the maternal organism in 24 hours (98, 105).

Pearlman (61, 62) calculated progesterone production of an order of magnitude of 0.25 gm. in 24 hours for the end of pregnancy. His calculation was based on the study of isotopic dilution after administration of progesterone-16-H^3 and subsequent isolation and estimation of the specific activity of pregnanediol in the urine.

The assumption that at the end of pregnancy progesterone is released from the placenta at a rate of approximately 0.2–0.3 gm. in 24 hours is therefore well supported.

B.   CORPUS LUTEUM OF PREGNANCY

Progesterone has been isolated from corpora lutea of the second to the tenth month of pregnancy by our group (101). In addition, Δ^4-3-ketopregnen-20-ol was isolated, but the amount was too small for exact measurement. The results are shown in Fig. 7. In the material studied

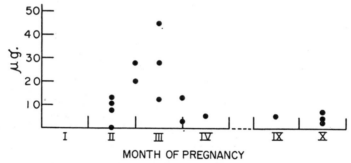

FIG. 7.   Total amounts of progesterone in each of sixteen corpora lutea of pregnancy. The amounts of the Δ^4-3-ketopregnen-20-ol fraction were too small for exact measurement.

the values for sixteen corpora lutea did not exceed values for corpora lutea of the secretory phase of the cycle. However, seven of the corpora lutea studied were from ectopic pregnancies and one was from a case of a hydatidiform mole. Corpora lutea of the tenth month of pregnancy still contained progesterone in quantities from 3.6 to 15.0 mg. per gram of tissue.

There is no doubt that the corpus luteum of the cycle produces gestagens. Therefore it is reasonable to assume that the corpus luteum is functional at least in early pregnancy.

The McGinty test has shown that in the third to fourth month of pregnancy the progesterone content is higher in ovarian blood than in peripheral blood (43). However, it is difficult to separate gestagens produced in the ovary from those produced in the placenta. Also pregnancy can be maintained following removal of the corpus luteum in early pregnancy. In such a case the excretion of pregnanediol may be unchanged (52, 83). This argues for the assumption that at least most of the gestagens come from the placenta. Davis and co-workers (15, 16) concluded from investigations with labeled acetate and cholesterol that the corpus luteum produces cholesterol until the end of pregnancy. They also considered, therefore, the possibility that progesterone is produced until the end of pregnancy.

C. Adrenal Cortex

The studies of Davis and associates (17) and Klopper and co-workers (50) and our own experiments (94) have shown that after injection of ACTH (adrenocorticotropic hormone) in women the excretion of pregnanediol increases slightly. It was concluded that the adrenal cortex may produce progesterone. Balfour and colleagues (4) recently isolated relatively large amounts of progesterone from the adrenal vein of the sheep and cow. However, there is no reason to assume that the human adrenal cortex produces significant amounts of progesterone during pregnancy.

IV.   The Importance in Pregnancy of Gestagen-Producing Glands

As already indicated, only the placenta and the corpus luteum need to be specially considered.

The older opinion was that the corpus luteum of pregnancy produces progesterone until the third or fourth month and that after this time the placenta takes over the production of the hormone. The corpus luteum of later pregnancy was considered to be without secretory activity. This opinion was based chiefly on anatomical studies of the corpus luteum and on the clinical observation that the frequency of abortion is increased during the third and fourth months.

In the light of more recent information this opinion requires reconsideration. Tulsky and Koff (83), and Davis and co-workers (15, 16) have come to the same conclusion.

The following working hypothesis may be presented regarding the physiological significance of the corpus luteum and the placenta for the production of gestagens in pregnancy.

The corpus luteum of pregnancy in man has true physiological significance as a source of gestagens only in the first days or weeks after implantation of the fertilized egg. It is significant in the first place in preventing of menstrual bleeding and of expelling the egg. Gestagen formation needs to "bridge over" only the brief period until the young trophoblast begins to produce gestagens. Even during the first month of pregnancy the trophoblast can produce the hormone in amounts sufficient to maintain pregnancy. Probably the production of gestagens in the trophoblast begins at the same time or shortly after the beginning of production of the chorionic gonadotropic hormone. The corpus luteum is probably also stimulated to produce gestagens later in pregnancy, but this production is not essential for the maintenance of pregnancy. The fetal placenta rather than the maternal corpus luteum therefore plays the essential role in maintaining pregnancy.

The following facts support this hypothesis:

1. Numerous clinical observations have shown that pregnancy is not necessarily interrupted when the corpus luteum is removed very early. Cases have been described in which the corpus luteum has been extirpated in the first month of gestation without producing abortion.

2. Many cases have been described in which the excretion of pregnanediol remained unchanged after early removal of the corpus luteum.

3. As already stated, the trophoblast of the second and third months regularly contains high levels of gestagens. The above observations point to progesterone secretion and not simply its storage. Furthermore, Plotz and Davis (66) found that after intravenous injection of progesterone-4-C^{14} only a very small part of the injected radioactivity is stored in the placenta. The increase in progesterone concentration in the second and third months of pregnancy coincides with the familiar rise of chorion gonadotropic hormone. Perhaps there is a causal relationship here.

4. According to Davis, Plotz, and co-workers (15, 16), it is possible that the corpus luteum produces progesterone until the end of pregnancy. This concept is supported by the relatively high levels of progesterone in corpora lutea of the ninth and tenth months (96, 101).

V. Gestagens in the Blood

Evidence for the release of gestagens from the placenta into the blood is supplied by biological tests and physicochemical methods. Average concentrations of progesterone in different blood vessels as revealed by the physicochemical method of Zander and Simmer (102) are shown in Fig. 8.

The amount of progesterone in arm vein blood was controversial for a long time. Our chemical studies (96, 97) have shown that the average concentration in pooled plasma samples of the second half of pregnancy is 14.2 µg. per 100 ml. Sommerville (81, 82), and Short (76) have confirmed this value.

The results of quantitative determinations of individual plasma samples of different subjects in the second half of pregnancy, obtained by the above method, are presented in Fig. 9. The concentration varied between 1 and 30 μg. per 100 ml. plasma. The highest values were ob-

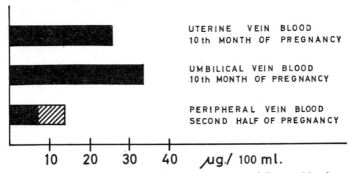

FIG. 8. Average concentrations of progesterone in different blood vessels. The black bars show the blood values. The shaded bar shows the plasma value. The data are taken from publications of Zander (96, 97), and of Zander and von Münstermann (104).

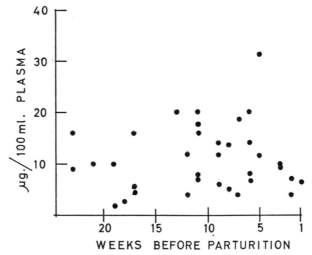

FIG. 9. Levels of progesterone in individual samples of arm vein plasma of different subjects in the second half of pregnancy.

served during the thirteenth to the fifth weeks before delivery. In eight of fifteen plasma samples during the first half of pregnancy, less than 5.0 μg. per 100 ml. must have been present (97).

These first results with a chemical method are only suggestive. One can say that the progesterone concentration almost certainly is higher during the second half of pregnancy. Whether the fall before delivery is significant is not yet clear. The Hooker-Forbes test has shown higher levels as measured in progesterone equivalents for peripheral plasma of pregnancy than has the chemical method (25, 49, 73). This interesting discrepancy requires explanation. It is possible that other biologically active compounds are detected or that the known gestagens act synergistically in this test.

VI. Inactivation and Metabolism

Many experiments have shown that progesterone disappears very rapidly from the blood (10, 37, 40, 96, 107). It has not been clear whether this is due to rapid elimination through partition into the tissues or through a true inactivation by chemical transformation of the molecule.

These questions have been further clarified by recent research. Figure 10 shows the result of a study of the blood of a 57-year-old postmenopausal woman. She received during the course of 1 minute an intravenous injection of 6.897×10^6 c.p.m. progesterone-4-C^{14} (100 µg.) in a saline-ethanol solution. The experiment was done with Wiest, Tyler, and Samuels (92). It shows that 9 minutes after completion of the injection most of the radioactivity in the blood is in the conjugated fraction. From the β-glucuronidate fraction of the conjugated steroid there were isolated by paper chromatography only two substances with the same mobility as pregnan-3α-ol-20-on and pregnane-3α,20α-diol. The largest fraction of the free steroids always showed, when separated by paper chromatography, the mobility of progesterone. In addition there were in this fraction two smaller peaks with the mobility of pregnan-3α-ol-20-on and pregnane-3α,20α-diol.

Independently, Sandberg and Slaunwhite (72) found in eight human subjects that, 15 minutes after the intravenous injection of progesterone-4-C^{14} in plasma, the level of the conjugated fraction was at least eight times the level of the free fraction. Four hours after injection 10% of the injected radioactivity had been excreted.

In our experiment we collected urine samples at shorter intervals. The results are shown in Table I. In 25 minutes after the injection a detectable amount of the total dose had been excreted. After 4 hours the amount had increased to 9%.

Of the total amount of radioactivity which appeared in the stool (Table II) the greater part was present between 24 and 47 hours.

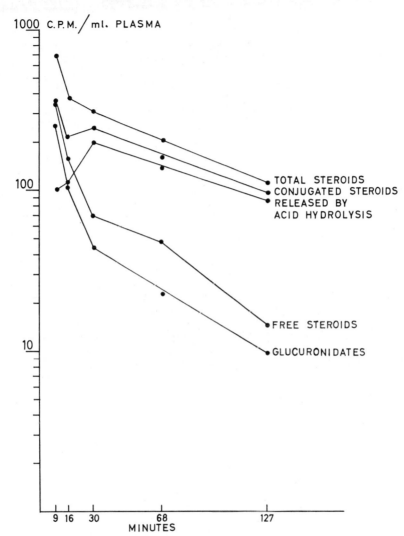

1000 C.P.M./ml. PLASMA

TOTAL STEROIDS
CONJUGATED STEROIDS
RELEASED BY
ACID HYDROLYSIS

100

FREE STEROIDS

GLUCURONIDATES

10

9 16 30 68 127
MINUTES

FIG. 10. Result of a study of the blood of a 57-year-old postmenopausal woman who had received during the course of 1 minute an intravenous injection of 100 μg. progesterone-4-C^{14} (6.897 × 10^6 c.p.m.) in saline-ethanol solution. The "free steroids" were extracted with ethylene dichloride. The aqueous residue was incubated at pH 4.5 with β-glucuronidase at 47°C. for 4 days. After extraction with ethylene dichloride to remove steroids released by β-glucuronidase, the aqueous residue was then adjusted to pH 1.0 with HCl, stored at 47°C. for an additional 4 days, then extracted with ethylene dichloride to remove steroids released by acid hydrolysis.

These experiments demonstrate not only that progesterone is swiftly eliminated from the blood, but that it is also very rapidly metabolized.

The experiments approximate physiological conditions. The blood levels obtained shortly after intravenous injection of 100 μg. are in

TABLE I

EXCRETION OF RADIOACTIVITY IN THE URINE FOLLOWING INTRAVENOUS INJECTION OF PROGESTERONE-4-C^{14}

Period of collection	C^{14} Content (c.p.m.)[a]	Per cent of injected dose	c.p.m./Min.
0– 25 min.	50,800	0.7	2,032
25– 55 min.	182,000	2.6	6,067
55–120 min.	179,000	2.6	2,754
2– 3 hr.	150,800	2.2	2,513
3– 4 hr.	74,100	1.1	1,235
4– 5 hr.	60,300	0.9	1,005
5– 6 hr.	60,800	0.9	1,013
6– 12 hr.	420,000	6.1	1,167
12– 24 hr.	442,000	6.4	613
24– 48 hr.	557,000	8.1	387
48– 72 hr.	272,000	3.9	189
Total excretion:	2,448,800	35.5	

[a] Counts per minute.

TABLE II

EXCRETION OF RADIOACTIVITY IN THE STOOL FOLLOWING INTRAVENOUS INJECTION OF PROGESTERONE-4-C^{14}

Period of collection	C^{14} Content (c.p.m.)[a]	Per cent of injected dose
0–24 hr.	383,000	5.6
24–47 hr.	1,075,000	15.6
47–75 hr.	483,000	7.0
75–95 hr.	658,000	9.5
Total excretion:	2,599,000	37.7

[a] Counts per minute.

the order of magnitude of those measured during pregnancy. Pearlman (62) recently calculated from his data and ours that the "turnover time" for progesterone at the end of pregnancy is 3.3 minutes. Forbes and co-workers (27) came to similar conclusions for the macaque monkey. This means that in this short time the total amount of circulating progesterone must have been replaced. As we have seen, the replacement in pregnancy is chiefly from the placenta. These results demonstrate the extraordinary ability of the organism to regulate progesterone levels at the end of pregnancy.

The ability to inactivate rapidly is of fundamental significance for proper and rapid regulation. Presumably the production of large amounts of gestagens in pregnancy is related to this.

The metabolism of the gestagens will be discussed only briefly. The assumption that there exist during pregnancy special metabolic conditions which lead to a higher percentage of pregnanediol excretion than in women without luteal function has been shown by Pearlman (61) to be incorrect.

In addition to hepatic and renal inactivation it has been shown by Berliner and Wiest (6, 88, 90) that inactivation of gestagens occurs also in peripheral tissues. According to Wiest (89), the peripheral tissues have relatively few enzymes for the reduction of the ring A. These tissues reduce chiefly the side chain.

New information about the excretion of the metabolites of progesterone in the bile and stool came from the work of Wiest and co-workers (91), Davis and associates (15, 16), and Sandberg and Slaunwhite (72). Sandberg and Slaunwhite (72) have postulated an enterohepatic circulation for the metabolites of progesterone in the human. The metabolites appearing in the bile and stool are not completely identified.

VII. Gestagens in Tissues

The partition of progesterone between blood and tissues also occurs very rapidly. There is a rapid taking up of progesterone by fatty tissues (48, 107). Kaufmann and Zander (48) isolated progesterone in relatively large amounts from human fat obtained during the secretory phase of the cycle and during pregnancy. Average concentrations are shown in Fig. 11.

Our earlier investigations (95) have shown that the excretion of pregnanediol after intravenous injection of large amounts of progesterone is not very different from the excretion of pregnanediol after administration of an equivalent dose in oily solution. We considered, therefore, the possibility that part of the injected progesterone is taken up by the fat and that this explains the delayed excretion of the metabolites. In fact, we found after progesterone injection in women without endogenous production of the hormone large amounts of progesterone and the Δ^4-3-ketopregnen-20-ol fraction in the body fat (48, 98, 101). The result was confirmed by Plotz and Davis (66), who made intravenous injections of progesterone-4-C^{14} in three women between the eleventh and the eighteenth week of pregnancy. These workers found 12 hours after injection of the hormone, 17.7%; 24 hours after injection, 33.7%; and 48 hours after injection, 19.6%, of the injected radioactivity in the body fat. Also the delayed excretion of the metabolites of progesterone after intravenous injection of progesterone has been confirmed (66).

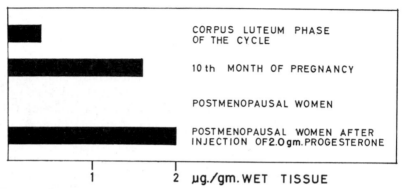

FIG. 11. Average levels of progesterone in human fat tissue. Data are taken from Kaufmann and Zander (48).

There is, therefore, no doubt that for rapid elimination of progesterone from the blood the uptake into fatty tissue is of great importance. Perhaps this mechanism in turn partly compensates for the rapid inactivation of the hormone. A part of the gestagens are taken up by the fat in their active form, and their reabsorption by the blood is correspondingly delayed.

The study of progesterone and its metabolites in the target tissues, endometrium and uterine muscle, is of interest. Within the limits of sensitivity of our method it was not possible to demonstrate endogenous gestagens in these tissues (104, 105). Injection of progesterone in mice and rats did not result in a marked uptake of the hormone in these tissues (5, 68). In the experiments already cited, Plotz and Davis (66) found in a woman in the seventeenth and eighteenth weeks of pregnancy only small amounts of the injected radioactivity in the decidua and myometrium. However, they found relatively large amounts in the decidua and myometrium of a woman in the eleventh week of pregnancy.

Wiest (89) compared a uterine horn containing deciduomata and a control horn in eviscerated female rats after injection of progesterone-

4-C^{14}. He found in the uterine horn containing deciduomata labeled steroids in higher concentration than in the control horn. Qualitative differences in the metabolites were not observed when the horns were compared. Furthermore the isotope concentrations in the ovaries, kidneys, and adrenals were higher than in either uterine horn.

The hope of finding in the target tissues high levels of gestagens or of finding a special metabolism in these sites so far has not been realized. Rather, from the present results it would appear that, in contrast to the *high* production of gestagens, the presence of relatively small concentrations of the hormone near the target cells is sufficient for their response.

For a comparative review of the concentrations of progesterone in the different tissues, average values are presented in Figs. 12 and 13.

VIII. Gestagens and the Fetus

Progesterone has been isolated by several workers from the placental blood (10, 64, 76, 104). We isolated progesterone from the umbilical vein blood and found significantly higher concentrations than in peripheral vein blood of the mother (104). Recently we investigated the problem further with larger amounts of placental blood. It was possible to isolate not only progesterone, but also Δ^4-3-ketopregnen-20α-ol (99). The results are shown in Table III. The ratio of the two gesta-

TABLE III
GESTAGENS IN CORD BLOOD

Plasma (ml.)	Progesterone (μg./100 ml.)	Δ^4-3-ketopregnen-20α-ol (μg./100 ml.)
80	63.5	7.4
1355	60.6	3.7
405	72.7	4.3
325	70.9	6.5
355	73.9	6.2

gens to each other is about 10:1. The concentration of progesterone in placental blood and umbilical vein blood is about the same. Hoffmann and Uhde (43) obtained about the same result with the McGinty test. Therefore, it is certain that gestagens pass from the placenta to the fetus. Using the values of Haselhorst and Stromberger (36) for the fetal placenta volume per minute, one can calculate that approximately 75 mg. of progesterone pass from the placenta to the fetus in 24 hours at the end of pregnancy.

Under the assumption that these gestagens are formed in the fetal placenta, the following theoretical possibilities may be suggested:

1. A part of the gestagens formed in the placenta passes via the umbilical vein into the fetus and is there inactivated by the same mechanisms as in the adult. This would involve a reduction to pregnane-

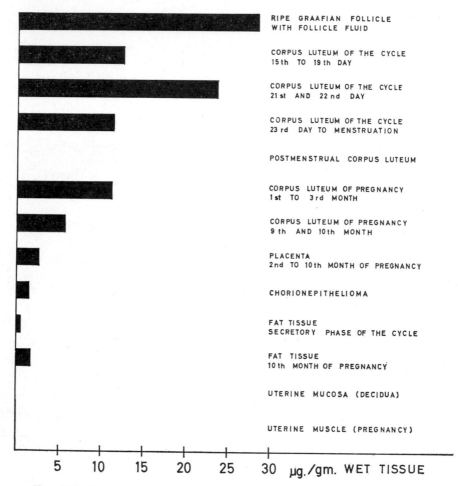

FIG. 12. Comparison of average levels of progesterone in various human tissues. Data are taken from publications of Zander and co-workers (47, 96, 101, 104).

diol. The elimination of the inactive metabolites occurs by excretion or by circulation to the mother via the umbilical arterial blood.

2. Gestagens from the placenta are metabolized in the fetus by mechanisms which do *not* exist in the adult. Their elimination occurs in the same way as in the first-listed possibility.

3. Gestagens are not altered *in* the fetus. They are excreted as biologically active substances or are passed as such to the mother.

4. There is the further possibility that the fetus itself produces gestagens. These or their metabolites are excreted or conveyed to the mother.

Of course more than one of these mechanisms may operate together.

The problem has been attacked by comparing progesterone levels in arterial and venous umbilical blood.

Hoffmann and Uhde (43), using the McGinty test, found in the arterial and venous umbilical blood approximately equal values between 5 and 15 μg. per 100 ml. serum. Forbes (26), however, found in arterial umbilical blood significantly higher "progesterone equivalent values"

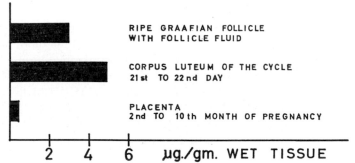

FIG. 13. Comparison of average levels of the Δ^4-3-ketopregnen-20-ol total fraction in various human tissues. Data from Zander *et al.* (101).

than in the venous blood. In the arterial blood he found up to 750 μg. per 100 ml. plasma, while the values for the venous blood were of the same order of magnitude as those obtained by physicochemical methods. Both authors have interpreted their results to mean that the fetus produces progesterone. Hoffmann and Uhde (42) implicated the fetal adrenal cortex. More information will be needed to reconcile the different quantitative results of these authors.

Information has also been sought from studies of the excretion of the newborn and of the amniotic fluid. Pregnanediol has thus far not been detected in urine of the newborn, at least by methods having a sensitivity of as little as 1 mg. (18, 103). For this reason we have injected the newborn with progesterone, but could find no pregnanediol in the urine (103). However, Philipp (65) and also Hoffmann and Uhde (41), using biological tests, found up to 4 mg. of progesterone in the urine of newborn babies in the first 24 hours after delivery. We also have isolated progesterone from the amniotic fluid (an average value of 0.14 µg. per milliliter (105), while another group has been unable to detect pregnanediol (20).

On the basis of these findings, we are inclined to think that part of the gestagens supplied to the fetus are not metabolized in the fetus and that some of the progesterone is excreted unchanged. It may be that some is returned to the mother.

According to investigations of Diczfalusy and co-workers (21, 22) on the metabolism of estrogens in the newborn one must also consider the possibility that biologically active steroids are metabolized differently in the fetal organism than in the adult.

An additional fetal source of gestagens must also be considered. Davis and co-workers (15, 16) have shown that the fetal adrenal cortex can probably synthesize cholesterol. The McGinty test (42) and the Hooker-Forbes test (103) have detected gestagenic activity in the adrenals of the fetus. However, with a physicochemical method, Gardner and Tice (31) and our group (99) have found no progesterone in this site. In vitro the biosynthesis of progesterone by neonatal adrenal tissue has not so far been clearly demonstrated (53). In the fetal liver small amounts of progesterone have only occasionally been detected by physicochemical methods (99). None was found in the fetal brain (99). Plotz and Davis (66) injected progesterone-4-C^{14} in the mother during the eleventh to the eighteenth weeks but found only relatively small amounts of radioactivity in the fetal tissues. None was found in the brain, and activity occurred in the liver in only one of three cases. The relatively highest amount was found in the adrenals.

The endocrine relations between placenta, mother, and fetus require further clarification as far as the gestagens are concerned. Evidence is still insufficient to support firm conclusions.

References

1. Adler, A., de Fremery, P., and Tausk, M., Nature **133**, 293 (1934).
2. Allen, W. M., in "Marburger Symposium." Marburg, 1951.
3. Allen, W. M., and Wintersteiner, O., Science **80**, 190 (1934).
4. Balfour, W. E., Comline, R. S., and Short, R. V., Nature **180**, 1480 (1957).
5. Barry, M. C., Eidinoff, M. L., Dobriner, K., and Gallagher, T. F., Endocrinology **50**, 587 (1952).
6. Berliner, D. L., and Wiest, W. G., J. Biol. Chem. **221**, 449 (1956).
7. Browne, J. C. McC., and Veall, N., J. Obstet. Gynaecol. Brit. Empire **60**, 142 (1953).
8. Butenandt, A., Ber. **64**, 2529 (1931).
9. Butenandt, A., and Westphal, U., Ber. **67**, 2085 (1934).

10. Butt, W. R., Morris, P., Morris, C. J. O. R., and Williams, D. C., *Biochem. J.* **49**, 434 (1951).
11. Calatroni, C. J., and di Paola, G., *Obstetr. y. ginecol. latino-am.* **3**, 145 (1945).
12. Corner, G. W., *Am. J. Physiol.* **86**, 74 (1928).
13. Corner, G. W., *Cold Spring Harbor Symposia Quant. Biol.* **5**, 62 (1937).
14. Corner, G. W., and Allen, W. M., *Am. J. Physiol.* **88**, 326, 340 (1929).
15. Davis, M. E., and Plotz, E. J., *Recent Progr. in Hormone Research* **13**, 347 (1957).
16. Davis, M. E., Plotz, E. J., LeRoy, G. V., and Gould, R. G., *Am. J. Obstet. Gynecol.* **72**, 740 (1956).
17. Davis, M. E., Test, C. E., Navori, C. A., Hryse, B., Pottinger, R. E., and Dunkle, F., *J. Clin. Endocrinol.* **12**, 697 (1952).
18. de Watteville, H., Borth, R., Mach, R. S., and Musso, E., *Acta Endocrinol.* **8**, 319 (1951).
19. Diczfalusy, E., *Acta Endocrinol.* **10**, 373 (1952).
20. Diczfalusy, E., personal communication.
21. Diczfalusy, E., Tillinger, K. G., and Westman, A., *Acta endocrinol.* **26**, 303 (1957).
22. Diczfalusy, E., Tillinger, K. G., and Westman, A., *Acta endocrinol.* **26**, 313 (1957).
23. Duyvené de Wit, J. J., and Oppers, V. M., *Ned. Tijdschr. Geneesk.* **1939**, 4001.
24. Ehrhardt, K., *Münch. med. Wochschr.* **81I**, 869 (1934).
25. Forbes, T. R., *Endocrinology* **49**, 218 (1951).
26. Forbes, T. R., *Endocrinology* **56**, 699 (1955).
27. Forbes, T. R., Hooker, C. W., and Pfeiffer, C. A., *Endocrinology* **47**, 83 (1950).
28. Forbes, T. R., and Zander, J., *in* M. E. Davis and E. J. Plotz (discussion), *Recent Progr. in Hormone Research* **13**, 379 (1957).
29. Fraenkel, L., *Arch. Gynäkol.* **68**, 438 (1903); **91**, 705 (1910).
30. Fujii, K., Hoshino, K., and Aoki, I., *Japan. Obstet. and Gynecol. Soc.* **3**, 169 (1956).
31. Gardner, L. T., and Tice, Λ. A., *Helv. Paediatr. Acta* **12**, 147 (1957).
32. Glasser, J. W. H., *Bull. Margaret Hague Maternity Hosp.* **5**, 112 (1952).
33. Gorski, J., Dominguez, O. V., Samuels, L. T., and Erb, R. E., *Endocrinology* **62**, 234 (1958).
34. Haffner, J., *Acta Obstet. et Gynecol. Scand.* **18**, 125 (1938).
35. Hartmann, M., and Wettstein, A., *Helv. Chim. Acta* **17**, 878, 1365 (1934).
36. Haselhorst, G., and Stromberger, K., *Arch. Gynäkol.* **137**, 731 (1930).
37. Haskins, A. L., Jr., *Proc. Soc. Exptl. Biol. Med.* **73**, 439 (1950).
38. Haskins, A. L., *Am. J. Obstet. Gynecol.* **67**, 330 (1954).
39. Hayano, M., Lindberg, M. C., Wiener, M., Rosenkrantz, H., and Dorfman, R. I., *Endocrinology* **55**, 326 (1954).
40. Hinsberg, K., Pelzer, H., and Seuken, A., *Biochem. Z.* **328**, 117 (1956).
41. Hoffmann, F., and Uhde, G., *Zentr. Gynäkol.* **76**, 2196 (1954).
42. Hoffmann, F., and Uhde, G., *in* "Probleme der fetalen Endokrinologie" (H. Nowakowski, ed.), Symposium der Deutschen Gesellschaft für Endokrinologie. Springer, Heidelberg, 1955.
43. Hoffmann, F., and Uhde, G., *Arch. Gynäkol.* **185**, 469 (1955).

44. Hoffmann, F., and von Lám, L., *Zentr. Gynäkol.* **65**, 2014 (1941).
45. Hooker, C. W., and Forbes, T. R., *Endocrinology* **41**, 158 (1947).
46. Jones, J. E., Berliner, D. L., and Salhanick, H. A., *Federation Proc.* **14**, 82 (1955).
47. Kaufmann, C., and Zander, J., *Acta Endocrinol.* **17**, 216 (1954).
48. Kaufmann, C., and Zander, J., *Klin. Wochschr.* **34**, 7 (1956).
49. Klein, I., and Ober, K. G., *Klin. Wochschr.* **32**, 464 (1954).
50. Klopper, A., Strong, J. A., and Cook, L. R., *J. Endocrinol.* **15**, 180 (1957).
51. Knowlton, A. I., Mudge, G. H., and Jailer, J. W., *J. Clin. Endocrinol.* **9**, 514 (1949).
52. Koff, A. K., and Tulsky, A. S., *Surg. Clin. North Am.* **33**, 3 (1953).
53. Lanman, J. T., and Silverman, L. M., *Endocrinology* **60**, 433 (1957).
54. Loeb, L., *Zentr. Physiol.* **22**, 498 (1908); **23**, 73 (1909).
55. Lucks, A., de Fremery, P., and Tausk, M., *Arch. ges. Physiol. Pflüger's* **321**, 341 (1933).
56. McGinty, D. A., McCullough, N. B., and Wolter, J. G., *Proc. Soc. Exptl. Biol. Med.* **34**, 176 (1936).
57. Marrian, G. F., *Biochem. J.* **23**, 1090 (1929).
58. Mazer, C., and Goldstein, L., "Clinical Endocrinology of the Female," p. 350. W. B. Saunders Co., Philadelphia, 1932.
59. Nissim, J. A., and Robson, J. M., *J. Physiol. (London)* **114**, 12P (1951).
60. Noall, M. W., Salhanick, H. A., Neher, G. M., and Zarrow, M. X., *J. Biol. Chem.* **201**, 321 (1953).
61. Pearlman, W. H., *Biochem. J.* **65**, 7p (1957); **67**, 1 (1957).
62. Pearlman, W. H., *CIBA Foundation Colloq. on Endocrinol.* **11**, 233 (1957).
63. Pearlman, W. H., and Cerceo, E., *J. Biol. Chem.* **189**, 79 (1952).
64. Pearlman, W. H., and Thomas, M., *Endocrinology* **52**, 590 (1953).
65. Philipp, E., *Zentr. Gynäkol.* **60**, 86 (1936).
66. Plotz, E. J., and Davis, M. E., *Proc. Soc. Exptl. Biol. Med.* **95**, 92 (1957).
67. Prenant, A., *Rev. gén. sci.* **9**, 646 (1898).
68. Riegel, B., Hartop, W. L., Jr., and Kittinger, J. W., *Endocrinology* **47**, 311 (1950).
69. Salhanick, H. A., Jones, J. E., and Berliner, D. L., *Federation Proc.* **15**, 160 (1956).
70. Salhanick, H. A., Noall, M. W., Zarrow, M. X., and Samuels, L. T., *Science* **115**, 708 (1952).
71. Samuels, L. T., Helmreich, M. L., Lasater, M. B., and Reich, H., *Science* **113**, 490 (1951).
72. Sandberg, A. A., and Slaunwhite, W. R., Jr., *J. Clin. Endocrinol. Metabolism* **18**, 253 (1958).
73. Schultz, D. H., *Am. J. Obstet. Gynecol.* **66**, 1260 (1953).
74. Short, R. V., *CIBA Foundation Colloq. on Endocrinol.* **11**, 362 (1957).
75. Short, R. V., *J. Endocrinol.* **15**, 1 (1957).
76. Short, R. V., *J. Endocrinol.* **16**, 415 (1958).
77. Short, R. V., *J. Endocrinol.* **16**, 426 (1958).
78. Slotta, K. H., Ruschig, H., and Fels, E., *Ber.* **67**, 1270, 1624 (1934).
79. Smith, G. V. S., and Kennard, J. H., *Proc. Soc. Exptl. Biol. Med.* **36**, 508 (1937).

80. Solomon, S., Lenz, A. L., Vande Wiele, R., and Lieberman, S., *Proc. Am. Chem. Soc., New York, 1954,* p. 29C.
81. Sommerville, I. F., *J. Clin. Endocrinol. Metabolism* **17**, 317 (1957).
82. Sommerville, I. F., and Deshpande, G. N., *Bull. acad. natl. méd.* (*Paris*) **122**, 229 (1958).
83. Tulsky, A. S., and Koff, A. K., *Fertility and Sterility* **8**, 118 (1957).
84. van Lankeren, C., *Arch. Gynäkol.* **160**, 150 (1936).
85. Venning, E. H., *J. Biol. Chem.* **119**, 473 (1937).
86. Venning, E. H., *J. Biol. Chem.* **126**, 595 (1938).
87. Wied, G. L., and Davis, M. E., *in* "Conference on New Compounds with Progestational Activity." New York Academy of Sciences, Section of Biology, New York, 1957. Abstracts of papers, and personal communication.
88. Wiest, W. G., *J. Biol. Chem.* **221**, 461 (1956).
89. Wiest, W. G., *Federation Proc.* **16**, 270 (1957).
90. Wiest, W. G., Berliner, D. L., and Woods, G., *Federation Proc.* **13**, 417 (1954).
91. Wiest, W. G., Fujimoto, G. I., and Sandberg, A. A., *Federation Proc.* **14**, 304 (1955).
92. Wiest, W. G., Zander, J., Tyler, F., and Samuels, L. T., unpublished results.
93. Zander, J., *Klin. Wochschr.* **30**, 312 (1952).
94. Zander, J., *Klin. Wochschr.* **30**, 873 (1952).
95. Zander, J., *Geburtshilfe u. Frauenheilkunde* **14**, 402 (1954).
96. Zander, J., *Nature* **174**, 406 (1954).
97. Zander, J., *Klin. Wochschr.* **33**, 697 (1955).
98. Zander, J., *in* "Probleme der fetalen Endokrinologie" (H. Nowakowski, ed.). Symposium der Deutschen Gesellschaft für Endokrinologie. Springer, Heidelberg, 1955.
99. Zander, J., unpublished results.
100. Zander, J., Forbes, T. R., Neher, R., and Desaulles, P., *Klin. Wochschr.* **35**, 143 (1957).
101. Zander, J., Forbes, T. R., von Münstermann, A. M., and Neher, R., *J. Clin. Endocrinol. Metabolism* **18**, 337 (1958).
102. Zander, J., and Simmer, H., *Klin. Wochschr.* **32**, 529 (1954).
103. Zander, J., and Solth, K., *Klin. Wochschr.* **31**, 317 (1953).
104. Zander, J., and von Münstermann, A. M., *Klin. Wochschr.* **32**, 894 (1954).
105. Zander, J., and von Münstermann, A. M., *Klin. Wochschr.* **34**, 494 (1956).
106. Zander, J., and Wiest, W. G., unpublished results.
107. Zarrow, M. X., Shoger, R. L., and Lazo-Wasem, E. A., *J. Clin. Endocrinol. Metabolism* **14**, 645 (1954).

Discussion

CHAIRMAN: W. M. ALLEN

G. GREENWALD: Several previous studies have indicated that the excretion of pregnanediol is higher during the luteal phase of the menstrual cycle than during pregnancy. This suggests a possible change in utilization or metabolism of progesterone in these circumstances. Do you have any data concerning this point?

J. ZANDER: I have no data about this problem. Maybe Dr. Pearlman can give you something about this.

E. H. VENNING: I was fascinated by the results coming out of Dr. Zander's work using newer microtechniques, because many years ago we tried with inadequate methods to solve similar problems. I would like to ask Dr. Zander if he has any indication as to what controls the release of progesterone from the placenta?

J. ZANDER: No. I have no information on this point. I think that today it is possible only to speculate in this respect. I don't think that there is any good evidence for the control of the release of progesterone from the placenta.

W. WIEST: I would like to express my appreciation to Dr. Zander for this excellent presentation.

He referred to some preliminary work which we did together suggesting a possible reversible oxidation-reduction reaction involving progesterone in human endometrial tissue. May I present data which supplement that work? These observations were made following the incubation of progesterone-4-C^{14} and Δ^4-pregnen-20α-ol-3-one-4-C^{14} with ovary slices taken from rats on the fifth day of pseudopregnancy, so that they were in the luteal phase. Diphosphopyridine nucleotide, adenosine triphosphate, and fumarate were added to a buffered solution at pH 7.4. It was observed that, when progesterone was incubated in this system, it was reduced to the 20α-hydroxyl product; when the Δ^4-pregnenolone, on the other hand, was incubated in the system it was oxidized to progesterone. At the end of a 3-hour incubation period, analysis of the medium, exclusive of the tissue slices, showed the same composition whether progesterone or Δ^4-pregnenolone was the substrate. In other words, an equilibrium mixture was formed from either substrate, composed of 70% 4-pregnen-20α-ol-3-one and 30% progesterone.

I think these data certainly establish the fact that there is a reversible oxidation-reduction reaction involving progesterone, and we would like to think, considering these data with those Dr. Zander mentioned, that this is a general reaction and that, therefore, progesterone must be included in the category already occupied by estrone, androstenedione, and cortisone involving the reversible reduction of these compounds to yield materials retaining hormonal activity. They also suggest the possibility that this reversible oxidation-reduction reaction might have significance in explaining the mode of action of the progestins.

W. H. PEARLMAN: I have a few questions and I would also like to make a few comments, if I may. With regard to the progesterone levels in peripheral blood, have you been able to show a progressive rise in the progesterone blood level with advancing gestation, as there is evidence for a progressive rise, although a fluctuating one, in the excretion of urinary pregnanediol? I know that you have shown a higher progesterone blood level in the latter half of gestation as compared with the first half. I am aware of the difficulties involved in this type of work and I would like to express my admiration for your beautiful presentation.

It is very interesting that Δ^4-pregnen-20β-ol-one-3 is highly active in the Hooker-Forbes test, but, if I understand correctly, you have not found any appreciable amount of this compound nor the 20α-ol steroid in peripheral blood.

The last question which I would like to pose is one relating to 17α-hydroxyprogesterone. From the literature, I notice that Zarrow and co-workers have found that this compound is exceedingly potent in the Hooker-Forbes test when Rockland Swiss mice are used. Curiously enough, as you and Dr. Forbes have found, this compound is totally devoid of progestational activity in this bioassay procedure when CHI strain of mice are employed. This raises, as you have indicated in your admirable review, the question of specificity of progestational activity of various compounds from one species to another, and indeed, among various strains of the same species. I would like to reserve my comments on other aspects of your presentation until later.

J. ZANDER: With regard to the first question, you may recall the slide showing the results of single determinations of progesterone levels in the blood of the second half of pregnancy. They did not reveal a significant increase in the blood levels of the order you can observe with the pregnanediol excretion. This, however, may be due in part to some shortcomings of the methods used. We make our single determination of progesterone using no more than 50–100 ml. of blood. In these quantities of blood the progesterone concentrations are so low that they fall within the lowest limits we can determine with our method. Thus the chance of failure of the method is relatively high in these determinations. I showed you also the very constant levels of progesterone and Δ^4-3-ketopregnen-20α-ol in placental blood. There we used larger amounts of blood, and, in addition, the levels of the gestagens are higher. Therefore, the quantitative determinations are very reliable. So I believe that we have to develop a more sensitive method with which, perhaps, we may find that the progesterone levels in the peripheral blood are more constant than those presented here. As Dr. Pearlman just mentioned, the levels in the first half of pregnancy are lower than in the second half of pregnancy.

Responding to your second point, I can only say that it was not possible to isolate the Δ^4-3-ketopregnen-20α-ol fraction from peripheral blood; but here again the reason for this may be that we did not use large enough amounts of blood to isolate the substance with our method. It is an old story, that if a substance is not found with a certain method, it doesn't necessarily mean that the substance isn't there. Maybe the concentration is too low with respect to the sensitivity of the method.

As to the last point, I think Dr. Forbes can tell more about this than I can.

T. FORBES: We tested free 17-OH-progesterone twice in our CHI mice, the second time using a sample supplied by Dr. Zarrow. Both times the material showed no activity. I ascribed the difference in reactivity between Zarrow's mice and ours to a difference in sensitivity of the strains.

As far as the Hooker-Forbes test is concerned, I would like to emphasize that this is probably best regarded as a method for detecting and measuring certain compounds and not as a test for progestational activity per se. The reason for saying this is that some compounds, such as testosterone, which have been shown to have some progestational activity by other tests are inactive in this bioassay.

Dr. Zander has already suggested two hypotheses for explaining the differences in peripheral vein blood in pregnancy, for example, between the levels of activity we found by bioassay and those which he found by a physicochemical method. One is that it seems possible that additional compounds with significant biological activity are present but not yet recognized. The other possibility is that there may be a synergism or an antagonism between known compounds which increases or decreases the biologic activity over that to be expected on the basis of gravimetric amounts. We have found that an entirely artificial mixture consisting of Δ^4-3-keto-pregnen-20β-ol and of progesterone in various proportions, when assayed by our method, showed *less* than the activity that one would predict on the basis of the separate biologic activities of the two components of the mixture. This seems to represent an antagonism; other mixtures might be synergistic.

I would like to show one slide based on some work being done with Dr. Gardner and Dr. Ray of this medical school. They obtained samples of blood from newborn babies at various intervals after birth. The samples were subjected to bioassay for gestagens. These data are obviously scanty and require amplification, but the suggestion thus far seems to be that peripheral blood gestagens disappear after perhaps the first 48 hours of life.

G. Pincus: I would like to ask about the conjugation of progesterone with protein. This seems to me to be a very important point, particularly in relation to the way it is released and metabolized; and I wonder if you have any comparative data, whether your extraction methods in one way or another allowed for the presence of protein conjugates, which have been demonstrated by Slaunwhite and Sandberg.

I would like also to say a little bit about the probable role of the adrenals in this —both the fetal and the maternal adrenals. I think the problem still unsolved about the higher activity—at least in the Forbes test—and that determined by chemical assay suggests indeed there may be some compounds of higher activity. There is still a possibility that these may be released by the adrenals. I would be particularly interested if you have any data, or Dr. Forbes has any data, on comparative biological and chemical activity in blood taken from adrenalectomized women. This would at least, I think, make a biological contribution. Certainly there are some indications that the adrenal may produce compounds that might be quite active in the Forbes test.

J. Zander: The first question I cannot answer because we have not studied the question of the binding of progesterone to proteins. The proteins are precipitated in the first extraction step of the method we use for the isolation of progesterone.

The same holds with regard to your second question. We have no experience with adrenalectomized women. Maybe Dr. Forbes has some data.

T. Forbes: We have no information on this point.

L. I. Gardner: I can say that we also have been unable to find any progesterone in the adrenal glands of newborn infants by physicochemical means [*Helv. Paediat. Acta* **12**, 147 (1957)]. We did, however, find a substance which appeared to be a steroid with an R_f slightly greater than that of progesterone. This substance, which we have called A-4, seems to be quite similar to a substance found by Robert Klein in urine of the newborn which has a very potent activity in stimulating sodium loss in a bioassay test. It had no Hooker-Forbes activity.

S. Solomon: Dr. Zander has postulated that the progesterone produced in the placenta can serve as a precursor for the biosynthesis of other steroid hormones by the fetal adrenal. I would like to report some *in vitro* experiments conducted in Dr. Lieberman's laboratory on the biosynthesis of steroid hormones by the human fetal adrenal. In collaboration with Dr. Lanman of the Department of Pediatrics of New York University we obtained fetal adrenals in Sweden, following legal abortions. These adrenals were dissected into a "fetal zone" fraction and into a fraction containing mainly adult tissue contaminated with fetal-type tissue. Both tissue fractions were incubated identically with progesterone-4-C^{14}, and after isolation and vigorous proof of radiochemical homogeneity it was found that progesterone gave rise to Δ^4-androstenedione and 17α-hydroxyprogesterone in the two types of tissues. In addition, paper chromatographic zones have been obtained bearing radioactivity and having the polarity of $C_{21}O_3$ and $C_{21}O_4$ corticosteroids. These zones are at present under investigation.

E. Ray: I would like to ask Dr. Zander if he would comment on the possibility of a progesterone-stimulating factor in the human placenta. Some years ago a luteotropic factor was demonstrated in the rat placenta as early as the eighth or twelfth day. This progesterone-stimulating factor was present as well as progesterone. In the human this would not be essential during the latter part of pregnancy when the corpus luteum itself is not essential, but perhaps a mechanism could be operating in early gestation where the placenta is exerting a progesterone-stimulating effect upon the ovary.

J. Zander: I have had no experience with this problem.

E. H. Venning: I wonder if I may add a comment on some studies we have carried out in two adrenalectomized women. We find no abnormality in the excretion of pregnanediol in these women, and it does not appear that the adrenal is an important factor in the production of progesterone in pregnancy.

W. H. Pearlman: If I may get back to the comments which I held in reserve: The figure of 3.3 minutes for the turnover time of progesterone in the blood of pregnant women, which was derived from the estimated endogenous progesterone production and the peripheral blood levels of progesterone in advanced pregnancy, is only an approximate figure. We have yet to obtain more precise figures, but it indicates the order of magnitude of the turnover time of progesterone in the living organism.

As to the question which was previously raised regarding the conversion of progesterone to pregnanediol during the luteal phase of the menstrual cycle: there have been earlier studies showing that there was an increased conversion under these circumstances and also in pregnancy. Our metabolism studies with tritium-labeled progesterone in advanced pregnancy were undertaken partly to answer that question. We did not find any striking difference in the conversion of progesterone to urinary pregnanediol in advanced pregnancy, as compared with that obtained in ovariectomized-hysterectomized women. That is to say that there may be some difference, but it is certainly not of the order of about 300%, as had been reported by earlier workers. The methods employed at that time for estimating urinary pregnanediol were not precise, but this is not to detract from the pioneering achievements of these investigators.

I. Rothchild: I would like to add a word of confirmation to what Dr. Pearlman just said. In a study that Dr. Quilligan and I did, on the conversion of progesterone to pregnanediol after intravenous, intraportal, or intrasystemic administration of progesterone in women, we found no difference in the conversion percentage in women with secretory, as compared to those with proliferative, endometria.

And the study done by Lloyd Barnes at Ohio State University on the conversion of progesterone into pregnanediol in women in early pregnancy with threatened abortion who either aborted or went to term showed exactly the same thing. There was no difference between the two groups' conversion percentage, which averaged about 10% in all cases.

W. M. Allen: I would like to ask Dr. Zander a question. He alluded to the possibility of a decline in the production of progesterone immediately or soon prior to parturition. We have already spent a good deal of time and effort in getting fertilized eggs into the uterus and getting them to flourish there. I would like to ask him if he has any additional information or would have any comments to make about the possibility of the rapid disappearance of progesterone immediately prior to the onset of labor in women.

J. Zander: The only information which we have until now on this question is reflected in the slide (Fig. 9) with the single determinations of progesterone in the second half of pregnancy which I showed in my lecture. Here you find the five concentration values in the last 3 weeks before parturition always lower than 10 μg. per 100 ml. plasma; but this is not a significant decrease in view of values obtained earlier in pregnancy. Thus we have to get more information.

As you know, Dr. Haskins has shown that in postlabor placentas the concentration of progesterone is lower than in placentas before labor. We are not able to confirm Dr. Haskins' findings in every respect, but we have plans to reinvestigate this situation. We sought to study the gestagen levels in the placenta in relation to the levels of the gestagens in the placental blood before and after labor.

E. BLOCH: I would like to make a comment regarding the question of progesterone production by the fetal adrenal. In collaboration with Dr. K. Benirschke of the Boston Lying-In Hospital, we incubated adrenals from fetuses obtained during the second quarter of gestation. The incubations were carried out with radioactive acetate, and the steroids formed were isolated by radiochemical techniques. We did not find any progesterone in the incubation extracts. On the other hand, we did find cortisol. So, unless the production of cortisol in the fetus differs as compared to the adult, one has to assume that progesterone lies on the pathway of cortisol biosynthesis. We interpret our results as indicating a very efficient conversion of progesterone to cortisol under the experimental conditions employed.

Steroidogenesis in Perfused Human Placentas

Elijah B. Romanoff

Worcester Foundation for Experimental Biology, Shrewsbury, Massachusetts

The placenta has been considered the source of the enhanced content of steroid metabolites seen in pregnancy urine. Recently some doubts have been raised as to whether the placenta is the source of these metabolites. A few years ago we undertook the perfusion of human placentas to study whether or not it could synthesize adrenocortical steroids. If the placenta is the source of metabolites in pregnancy urine it would seem that perfusates from this organ would supply sufficient material to enable characterization of its, quantitatively at least, more important product or products. In undertaking these perfusions we also hoped to study some of the factors involved in the control of secretion of steroid.

The techniques were essentially those used at the Worcester Foundation for Experimental Biology in the work on the adrenal cortex. Modifications were introduced because of organ size and for enhancing the oxygenation capacity of the pump.

The placentas used were all obtained at Cesarean section. Each placenta was cannulated at the two umbilical arteries and thoroughly flushed out with approximately 2 liters of citrated glucose-saline. The placenta was then attached to the perfusion pump. One liter of oxygenated, whole, beef blood citrated with ACD (acid citrate glucose) solution and warmed to 38°C. was pumped through the organ as a further wash. The placenta was then "conditioned," as it were, by recirculating another liter of blood through it for 1 hour. After the conditioning a control perfusion was run and then the experiment proper.

In a single-cycle perfusion the perfusing blood has gone through the placenta only once—the effluent from the vein being collected in a chilled receiver and then frozen to be worked up later. In a multicycle perfusion, blood emerging from the vein is recirculated through the placenta for the duration of the experiment.

Each perfusate was extracted four times with twice its volume of isopropyl acetate. The crude extract that resulted was partitioned between *n*-hexane and 70% aqueous methanol. The residue obtained from the 70% methanol phase was eventually chromatographed on a silica gel column. Mixtures of ethyl acetate and benzene were chosen as eluants so as to squeeze as much steroid as possible into one or two chromatogram fractions to prevent dispersion of small quantities throughout several fractions.

Δ^4-3-Ketones were measured by their optical density at 240 mμ; α-ketols, by their blue tetrazolium (BT) reducing power. 11-Deoxycorticosterone (DOC) was the reference compound in both cases; dehydroepiandrosterone (DHA) served for the Zimmermann determinations. Allen-type corrections were applied to these determinations. Porter-Silber chromogen was read against hydrocortisone. All values are given in milligram equivalents of their reference compounds.

TABLE I

BLOOD PERFUSION DATA

1. Blank blood circulated through perfusion apparatus only

Perfusion number	Blood volume (ml.)	UV 240 mμ (mg. DOC)	BT reaction (mg. DOC)	Zimmermann reaction (mg. DHA)
59	1000	0.5	1.04	0
60	1000	0.2	0.26	0.2
61	1000	0.32	0.66	0.0
62	1000	0.30	0.49	0.09
63	1000	0.98	0.34	0.22
Average mg. per 1000 ml.		0.46	0.56	0.10

2. Blood recycled through placenta for 1 hour

Control perfusion number	Blood volume (ml.)	Net production	Net production	Net production
59	610	+0.21	—0.09	0
60	490	+0.40	+0.07	+0.05
61	500	+0.22	+0.01	+0.06
62	470	+0.67	+0.03	+0.04
63	690	+0.46	+0.10	—0.11
Production: mg./hour/placenta		+0.39	+0.02	+0.04

The first set of data (Table I) is that for blood which has not been perfused through a placenta. It is citrated, whole, beef blood which has been oxygenated and pumped around the perfusion pump for at least 2 hours at 38°C. It contains streptomycin, Terramycin, and penicillin. No correction has been made for the standard amount of ACD solution used as the anticoagulant.

The next set of data (Table I) illustrates typical values obtained for control perfusions.

The net production, i.e., actual content of perfusate less blank blood equivalent, of Δ^4-3-ketone is 0.39 mg. per hour per placenta. The average production of BT- and Zimmermann-reacting substances measured is negligible.

The effect of ACTH was tested by continuous, 3-hour multicycle perfusions and by three successive 1-hour perfusions. Forty units of ACTH were added to each perfusion at the beginning of every hour.

The data (Table II) for the multicycle perfusions show that no Δ^4-3-ketone seems to have accumulated to reflect the 3 hours of continuous perfusion.

TABLE II

EFFECT OF ACTH ON STEROID PRODUCTION IN PERFUSED PLACENTA

1. Continuous recycling of perfusate for 3 hours; 40 units of ACTH added per hour

Perfusion number	Blood volume (ml.)	UV 240 mμ net production (mg. DOC)	BT reaction, net production (mg. DOC)	Zimmermann reaction, net production (mg. DHA)
59	620	0.21	−0.15	0.0
60	580	0.90	+0.08	0.01
61	650	0.22	−0.14	0.0
62	888	0.26	−0.11	−0.08
Production: mg./3hr./placenta		0.40	−0.06	−0.02

2. Three consecutive 1-hour perfusions in presence of ACTH; 40 Units of ACTH and 0.67 millicurie of radioacetate added per hour

63					Total counts
1st hr.	650	+0.47	+0.15	−0.13	6015
2nd hr.	650	+0.41	+0.15	−0.12	4355
3rd hr.	890	+0.18	+0.04	−0.18	4232
Production: mg./hr.		+0.35	+0.11	−0.14	

The average amount present, 0.39 mg., is not different from that seen in the control perfusions although the variation from placenta to placenta is quite large. The average production of BT-active material has dropped below the control value. Actually a loss of material has occurred. The same is true for the Zimmermann results.

A different picture is seen when the 3-hour multicycle perfusion is broken up into three consecutive 1-hour perfusions with the same placenta. In perfusion No. 63 (Table II) fresh blood, to which were added 40 units of ACTH and 2/3 of a millicurie of radioactive acetate, was used for each of the three successive 1-hour perfusions. These data and those for the continuous 3-hour multicycle perfusions indicate that Δ^4-3-ketone is being released by the placenta. Once a given level of these substances is reached in the circulating medium the accumulation seems to stop even though the placenta may still be continuously discharging them.

It would seem that in most of these perfusions a removal mechanism is operating to limit the blood level. The production value of 0.4 mg. of Δ^4-3-ketone per hour per placenta with or without ACTH must, therefore, be interpreted carefully. We have other perfusions which confirm the findings just presented.

The BT values for the 3-hour, multicycle perfusions show that, on the whole, α-ketol is being removed or destroyed while Δ^4-3-ketone production is being maintained. The data for placenta No. 63 suggest that ACTH may have a sustaining action, but not a stimulating one, on steroid production. The sustained production may also be due to the presentation of new supplies of precursor to the placenta when new blood supplies were used for each hour of the perfusion.

Note how meager were the radioactive counts found in the steroid fraction. Although steroid seems to be synthesized, there is no marked accumulation of radioactive steroid synthesized from the added radioactive acetate. If radioactive steroid were synthesized from the added radioactive acetate and later broken down so that, if only the steroid nucleus were left and analytically active groupings were gone, the accumulation of counts would allow us to postulate that synthesis from acetate had occurred.

The small number of counts suggests that either little or no steroid is synthesized from radioactive acetate or that once synthesized either it is later broken down into small fragments not detectable by our techniques or that the steroid is so firmly bound to protein as to be nonrecoverable by solvent extraction. Two other earlier perfusions with radioactive acetate were discarded as defective because so little radioactivity could be detected in the crude extracts. I feel, therefore, that acetate per se is not the immediate carbon source for steroid synthesis in the placenta.

The fact that BT values tend to drop with continued perfusion and Δ^4-3-ketones tend to accumulate suggested that α-ketol was being removed as rapidly as it was being synthesized. Could this be reversed if a precursor were perfused? Would we find an accumulation of α-ketol if the rate of conversion of the precursor were greater than the rate of α-ketol destruction? We know that the adrenal cortex uses progesterone as a key intermediate in its production of corticoids. Would the same hold for the placenta and allow us to bypass a block? Accordingly, we perfused several placentas with progesterone.

The data (Table III) for the blank blood used are essentially what we saw previously. The data for the control perfusions (Table IV) show that Δ^4-3-ketone production is present in all perfusions and α-ketol production is present in all but one (No. 65).

In perfusion No. 30 (Table V) we may see the results of perfusing radioactive progesterone through the placenta in a single-cycle experiment. The progesterone was metered into the placenta at the cannulation while blood was pumped through it as fast as was possible. The effluent was caught in a chilled container. From the 191 mg. of progesterone perfused we recovered 103 mg. of purified progesterone having essentially the same specific activity of the original material. I suppose that the effect of any progesterone synthesized by this placenta in reducing the specific activity would be washed out by the large amount

TABLE III

BLANK BLOOD CIRCULATED THROUGH PERFUSION APPARATUS ONLY

Perfusion number	Blood volume (ml.)	UV 240 mμ. (mg. DOC)	BT reaction (mg. DOC)	Zimmermann reaction (mg. DHA)
64	1000	0.64	0.32	0.0
65	1000	0.39	0.63	0.27
66	1000	0.40	0.19	0.0
67	1000	0.51	0.17	0.0
Average mg./1000 ml.		0.49	0.33	0.07

TABLE IV

CONTROL PERFUSIONS: BLOOD RECYCLED THROUGH PLACENTA

Perfusion number	Duration of perfusion (hours)	Blood volume (ml.)	Net production		
			UV 240 mμ. (mg. DOC)	BT reaction (mg. DOC)	Zimmermann reaction (mg. DHA)
64	1	860	+1.21	+0.52	+0.18
65	1	2140	+1.35	−0.32	−0.58
66	½	2210	+0.25	+0.26	0.0
67	½	1940	+0.67	+0.42	+0.01

of radioactive progesterone. We also were able to isolate a little over 8 mg. of 6-ketoprogesterone with a specific activity that showed that it came from the perfused progesterone. Later, the residues were either chromatographed on Celite partition columns with very fine cuts or were chromatographed on paper. We were not able to find any quantity of BT-positive material that had any significant amount of radioactivity. We were forced to conclude that in this experiment α-ketol was not formed from progesterone.

We then thought that, had we recycled the progesterone through the placenta, BT-reacting material would have been formed. We, therefore, recycled progesterone through the placenta and afterward, using another aliquot of our blood, ran mock perfusions without placentas to check

TABLE V

RECYCLE PROGESTERONE PERFUSIONS LESS BLANK CONTENT AND CONTROL PRODUCTION

Perfusion number	Progesterone (mg.)	Blood volume (ml.)	Duration of perfusion (hours)	UV 240 mμ (mg. DOC)	BT reaction (mg. DOC)	Zimmermann reaction (mg. DHA)
64	106.8[a]	700	1	1.24	+0.83	+0.10
65	112.1	1970	1	12.51	−0.08	−0.53
66	117.5	1880	1	27.8	+0.01	+0.01
67	103.8	1960	½	36.76	+0.87	+0.13
		Single Pass through Placenta				
30	191[b]	6000	1	Recovered 103 mg. progesterone and 8 mg. 6-ketoprogesterone		

[a] Progesterone was radioactive, 25,000 counts per minute per milligram. A total of 5416 counts was recovered from the steroid fraction of the column chromatogram.
[b] Progesterone was radioactive.

on our recovery methods. The data for perfusions No. 64 through No. 67 show that no BT material in any quantity would be isolated from these multicycle perfusions. More important, much of the progesterone, or rather the α/β unsaturation, had disappeared. In No. 64, practically all of it; in No. 65, almost 90%; in No. 66, almost 70%. In No. 67, which went for the shortest time (½ hour instead of 1 hour), there was the greatest recovery, and even this amounts to but 40%. Even in the single-pass experiment, No. 30, 42% of the Δ^4-3-ketone disappeared.

TABLE VI

Mock Perfusions of Progesterone: Circulation through Perfusion Apparatus for 1 Hour

Perfusion number	Progesterone (mg.)	Blood volume (ml.)	UV 240 mμ (mg. DOC)	BT reaction (mg. DOC)	Zimmermann reaction (mg. DHA)
65	107.0	1900	19.31	0.09	0.0
66	111.8	1900	5.80	0.57	0.02
67	114.6	2000	3.83	0.70	0.09

Table VI shows the data for the mock perfusions. You will note that, here, the recoveries of α/β unsaturation are, on the whole, even less than when a placenta is present. The disappearance of material here cannot be attributed to a placenta and it puts into doubt the obvious reason for its disappearance in the presence of the placenta. One may no longer say that the placenta reduces ring A and so material can no longer be detected by examining the ultraviolet spectrum at 240 mμ. In fact, the placenta may protect the Δ^4-3-ketone inasmuch as more seems to have been recovered in the presence of a placenta. We must bear in mind that the usual recovery experiments do not first pump a solution of progesterone in blood through an oxygenator for an hour or more before the blood is extracted. We think we have ruled out bacterial action because our blood contained penicillin, streptomycin, and Terramycin. On plating out samples of blood on enriched media there is some growth at 48 hours but little or none at 24 hours. If conjugates are formed (and we doubt it), they would not be extracted with isopropyl acetate; again the steroid would not be extracted if they formed firm protein complexes. It may be that ring A is being reduced and we are not detecting the reduction products or that the steroid nucleus is being attacked. In perfusion No. 64 (Table V) we perfused 106.8 mg. of radioactive progesterone having 25,000 counts per minute per milligram—a total of over 2.6 million counts. And in that part of the chromatogram where steroid should appear, a total of only 5416 counts was obtained. If the progesterone were not destroyed, it must still be in the blood residue unextractable by isopropyl acetate. Eventually we plan to hydrolyze the extracted blood residue from this experiment to see if we can recover more radioactive material.

In order to investigate the loss of α-ketol we perfused deoxycorticosterone in multicycle and in single-cycle perfusions with placentas and in a multicycle, mock perfusion without a placenta (Table VII). From the data we can see that loss of α/β unsaturation and BT reactivity seem to parallel each other, i.e., recovery values are essentially equal and this takes place also in the mock perfusion.

TABLE VII

PLACENTAL PERFUSIONS OF DEOXYCORTICOSTERONE

Perfusion number	DOC (mg.)	Type of perfusion	UV 240 mμ (mg. DOC)	BT reaction (mg. DOC)	P-S reaction (mg. "F")	Zimmermann reaction (mg. DHA)
69	103	Multicycle, 1 hr.	38.74[a]	36.93	5.92	1.6
75	119.5	Single pass, 1 hr.	34.38[a]	39.74	6.39	0.75
Mock perfusion without placenta:						
69	108.4	Multicycle, 1 hr.	30.28[a]	27.1	5.21	0.0

[a] Δ^4-3-Ketoetienic acid isolated: M.P. and infrared analysis.

The Porter-Silber (P-S) values must be carefully interpreted for they may simply reflect the P-S equivalent of the large amount of BT material present. However, because of the small amount of DOC recovered, as we shall see later, I am inclined to believe they may represent a true 17-OH α-ketol content.

We were able to recover but 8 mg. of DOC from perfusion No. 69. We isolated over 8 mg. of Δ^4-3-ketoetienic acid. When the proper chromatogram eluate of perfusion No. 75 was partitioned between a benzene-ethyl acetate mixture and sodium bicarbonate solution, 2.4 mg. of Δ^4-3-ketoetienic acid were isolated from the bicarbonate solution. When the mock perfusion was treated in the same way we were able to isolate 0.74 mg. of Δ^4-3-ketoetienic acid.

We are still working up this perfusion and further data are presented in Table VIII. From the acidic fraction of the eluate of the column chromatogram No. 69, we have evidence for the presence of at least two other substances. One seems to be saturated; it does not absorb at 240 mμ. in methanol and the absence of the characteristic maximum at 280 to 290 in H_2SO_4 confirms this. The second substance is unsaturated, but I have not as yet gone beyond the sulfuric acid chromogen. The third substance is Δ^4-3-ketoetienic acid.

TABLE VIII

A. STEROIDLIKE SUBSTANCES IN ACIDIC FRACTION FROM DOC PERFUSION No. 69

Substance	UV max. in methanol	Sulfuric Acid Chromogen Maxima	M.P.	Amount present as DOC from O.D. at 240 mμ.
1	High end absorption	267, 300, 358	—	—
2	240 mμ.	295, 355	—	0.3 mg.
Δ⁴-3-Keto-etienic Acid	240 mμ.	295	226–227.5°	8.9 mg.

B. STEROIDLIKE SUBSTANCES IN NEUTRAL FRACTION FROM DOC PERFUSION No. 69

Substance	UV max. in methanol	Sulfuric Acid Chromogen Maxima	Color reactions on paper		Running rate vs. DOC	Amount
			BT	DNPH		
4	240 mμ.	291–294	Atyp	+	origin	0.45 mg.
5	240 mμ.	299, 455, 473	Atyp	+	0.14	0.47 mg.
6						8.03 mg.
				Deoxycorticosterone isolated:		

C. STEROIDLIKE SUBSTANCES FROM SILICA GEL COLUMN ELUATES

Substance	UV max. in methanol	Sulfuric Acid Chromogen Maxima				Amount
7	236 mμ.	287, pl 340–347, 452	BT	1.5 mg. ⇆ DOC P-S neg.		3.5 mg.

In the neutral fraction of this chromatogram eluate, three unsaturated substances are present. They were detected on a paper chromatogram, benzene-formamide system, Whatman No. 540. One is DOC and the other two are more polar than DOC. The first one remained at the origin, the second ran 0.14 times as fast as DOC. Both reacted with BT but did not give the rapid blue-red that is characteristic of an α-ketol. As you see, the amount of DOC isolated is very small, 8.03 mg.

From one of the post-DOC column eluates we were able to isolate one other substance. This is unsaturated, has a negative Porter-Silber, its BT value is 1.5 mg., while its Δ^4-3-keto value is 3.5 mg. equivalents of DOC. The hypochromic shift of the UV peak in methanol to 236 mμ. and the plateau in the 340–347 mμ. region of the sulfuric acid chromogen suggests that a 6β-OH compound may be present.

The isolation of Δ^4-3-ketoetienic acid was totally unexpected. It is present in the single-cycle perfusion, No. 75, in much less amount— 2.4 mg.—compared to the 8.9 mg. found in the multicycle perfusion. It would seem that with increased time of contact more of the DOC is converted to the acid. We worked up the mock perfusion of DOC for its etienic acid content. We were able to isolate 0.74 mg. of this substance. At first we were disappointed in this because we thought we had an identifiable conversion product produced solely by the placenta and an explanation for our apparent lack of results in corticoid synthesis. But the fact that oxygenated blood can also produce this substance from DOC —albeit in much smaller amounts—is suggestive of a mechanism or pathway for the disappearance of hormones both from the circulation and the placental circuit. The fact that α-ketol disappears in our regular control perfusions while the Δ^4-3-ketone persists for a longer time could be explained by our finding that the side chain of DOC is converted into a non-BT-reducing substance with a Δ^4-3-ketone ring A. The possibility exists that this is another mechanism for hormone inactivation in the body other than via reduction and conjugation.

The last compound on which we have a bit of data is dehydroepiandrosterone. We were particularly interested as to whether the placenta could transform the Δ^5-3β-hydroxy grouping to a Δ^4-3-ketone. In Table IX we have some data: Approximately 100 mg. of DHA were metered into each of the placentas during a single-cycle perfusion. Perfusions No. 70 and No. 77 show little increase in Δ^4-3-ketone, but No. 71 shows a remarkable increase—11.12 mg.—about 10% conversion of the added DHA. Note also the BT value, 15.07 mg. The Zimmermann values show but 40% to 50% recovery for No. 70 and No. 77. For No. 71 where the Δ^4-3-ketone was increased, the Zimmermann dropped to 29%.

We took an aliquot of the column chromatogram eluate of the No. 71

TABLE IX

Placental Perfusion of Dehydroepiandrosterone (DHA) Perfusate Recycled for 1 Hour

Perfusion number	Blood volume (ml.)	UV 240 mμ. (mg. DOC)	BT reaction (mg. DOC)	P.-S. reaction (mg. "F")	Zimmermann reaction (mg. DHA)
A. Blank blood					
70	1000	0	0.16		0
71	1000	0	0.72	0.06	0
77	1000	0.02	0.19		0.02
B. Control perfusion, continuous recycling for 1 hour		Net prod.	Net prod.	Net prod.	Net prod.
70	1000 (45 min.)	0.37	0.16		0.04
71	1650 (60 min.)	0.0	1.17	−0.04	0.12
77	1670 (75 min.)	0.36	0.43		0.0
C. DHA perfusion, single-cycle; DHA metered into placerta at cannulation		Content less blank	Content less blank	Content less blank	Net prod.
70	6900 (45 min.)	2.81	0.15		43.0
71	2798 (60 min.)	11.12[a]	15.07	−0.09	28.7
77	6400 (80 min.)	2.75	0.64		45.2

[a] 6β-OH-Δ⁴-androsten-3,17-dione isolated.

TABLE X

PILOT PAPER CHROMATOGRAM OF DHA PLACENTAL PERFUSION No. 71

Substance	RR/DOC	UV Maximum	Sulfuric acid chromogen	Color reactions on paper			Amount calc. (mg. DOC)
				BT	Zimm.	UVP	
1	0.29	High end absorption	313 mμ., 363 mμ	Atyp.	Purple	–	
2	0.81	236 mμ[a]	290 mμ., 355 mμ.	Atyp.	Purple	+	6.22
3	3.2	High end absorption	305 mμ., 400–410 mμ.	–	Purple	–	DHA isolated

[a] 6β-Hydroxy-Δ⁴-androstene-3,17-dione: M.P. and comparison of infrared spectra for free and acetylated compounds with authentic specimens.

perfusion and ran it on Whatman No. 540 paper in the benzene-formamide system (Table X). We were able to detect three substances. The polar substance was saturated and a 17-ketone. The second substance was 6β-OH Δ⁴-androstene-3,17-dione, and we subsequently isolated 6.2 mg. of it. The last substance was DHA.

We have partially worked up a mock perfusion of DHA, and, fortunately, we couldn't find any Δ⁴-3-ketone in it.

We may, therefore, say that the perfused placenta seems to be able to produce Δ⁴-3-ketone from precursors either endogenous or in blood; that ACTH may have some effect in sustaining production of steroid; that the placenta's ability to form α-ketol and its ability to form Δ⁴-3-ketone are masked by the capacity it (as well as that of oxygenated blood) has to destroy the side chain; that evidence could not be found that it forms 17-ketosteroid; that it can convert the α-ketol side chain of DOC to an acid, as shown by the isolation of Δ⁴-3-ketoetienic acid from DOC perfusates; that it can form Δ⁴-3-ketone from a Δ⁵-3β OH compound; and that it can hydroxylate at the 6-position to give a 6β-hydroxyl.

The finding that the placenta as well as blood can oxidize a simple α-ketol to an acid suggests that this may be a mechanism whereby the blood inactivates and removes excess hormone in the normal body and that the placenta may use this as a means to protect the fetus from excess maternal hormones or the mother from excess fetal hormones. It also points up one of the hazards in interpreting data obtained from perfusion experiments.

Discussion

CHAIRMAN: W. M. ALLEN

P. L. PERLMAN: In your first table, the difference between your blank perfusion and your placental perfusion without ACTH in terms of UV 240 mμ was about 0.4 mg. In your second table, with ACTH it is also about 0.4 mg.

Now, did you intend to convey an impression that ACTH elicited a net increase over your perfusion and of the placenta by 0.4 mg. or no increment?

E. B. ROMANOFF: No. I did not intend to give you this impression. I would have liked to have seen it but, on the basis of all the experimental data we have, ACTH does not stimulate, but possibly may sustain, the production of steroids. Does that answer your question?

P. L. PERLMAN: What do you mean by "sustain"?

E. B. ROMANOFF: By sustain, I mean that where the production of steroid would fall at an earlier interval, the ACTH may enable the placenta to continue to produce steroid for a longer interval.

I would also like to point out in these data that where we did the three 1-hour successive perfusions there is really an accumulation of Δ⁴-3-keto and BT material which is much higher than that in the continuous 3-hour multicycle perfusion. Now, this sustained output may very well be due to having added at hourly intervals a new precursor which the new blood was bringing to the placenta.

T. FORBES: In connection with the disappearance of progesterone from the blood *in vitro*, as noted by Dr. Romanoff, I might mention work that Dr. Hooker and I did about ten years ago. We obtained plasma from a pseudopregnant rabbit, assayed part of the plasma, and stored the rest of it at body temperature. We removed samples at fairly short intervals for further assay and found that the progesterone level dropped about 50% in 5 hours. We then repeated this experiment, first heating the plasma to 80°C. for an hour and then storing it as before. We found that the disappearance of the progesterone was very much less. We took this to suggest that inactivation of the gestagens might be enzymatic. Dr. Roger Short of the University of Cambridge has recently confirmed the inactivation of progesterone in stored blood.

S. J. FOLLEY: In connection with the disappearance of progesterone from the blood that you observed, it might be interesting to note that some time ago in collaboration with Dr. W. Klyne of the Post Graduate Medical School at Hammersmith, we perfused a bovine udder with whole blood containing progesterone. The udder, of course, is a target organ for this hormone. In a control experiment in which the blood containing progesterone was recycled through the apparatus without the udder we also observed substantial disappearance of progesterone.

W. PEARLMAN: Did you have a control for the mock perfusion experiments in placentas substituting, let's say, a plasma protein solution—in other words, getting rid of the iron in the form of hemoglobin, which might have some effect? It seems to me that, in such a perfusion, your chances of getting oxygenation of the molecule might possibly occur. I think it would be very interesting.

Do you really know whether the ring A was reduced—or possibly it was oxidized? It seems to me that situation would be more to be expected.

May I ask: Have you tried any addition of gonadotropin to these placenta perfusions? I would like to know whether the gonadotropin which the placenta produces might possibly have some effect in stimulating progesterone production.

E. B. ROMANOFF: On the first point that you made about the iron present, this may be the case. We have not tried placental plasma perfusions with precursor. We have done perfusions with plasma alone and the results we have are essentially what we get with whole blood. We have begun looking for reduced compounds.

We have added gonadotropin. We have not done enough experiments with it, but, in those that we have done, two of the four experiments showed a gradual rise in α-ketol with continued perfusion. In the other two, one showed a drop and the other simply maintained its output. These are all the data I have.

E. H. VENNING: I was most interested in Dr. Romanoff's findings with regard to the possibility that ACTH may increase the corticoid output in the placenta. We have been studying this problem also and have approached it in a somewhat different manner from Dr. Romanoff. This work has been carried out by Miss Sybulski. She has incubated placental tissue *in vitro* in Krebs-Ringer solution and has measured the release of various steroids into the incubation medium.

The following steroids have been separated by paper chromatographic procedures and are shown in Table A. Over a 3-hour period, 135.9 μg. progesterone per 100 gm. tissue, 13.8 μg. cortisone, 3.2 μg. cortisol, and 1.0 μg. aldosterone were obtained. We were surprised at the high ratio of cortisone to cortisol in placental tissue. The administration of either chorionic gonadotropin or ACTH had no significant effect on the products of any of these steroids.

In experiment II (Table A), you will see the rapid disappearance of progesterone and cortisone in the incubation medium at different periods of time. During the first hour of incubation very large amounts of progesterone and cortisone were being released, diffused from the tissue. Betweeen 1 and 3 hours, and 3 and 5 hours, the progesterone released was maintained at a relatively constant rate, while the cortisone had decreased to 1.2 and 0.7 µg.

Table B shows that prolactin had no effect on the production of progesterone, cortisone, or cortisol from placental tissue. When cortisol was added to the incubation medium, higher amounts of cortisone were obtained, thus showing that placental tissue was capable of converting cortisol to cortisone.

TABLE A

STEROIDS PER 100 GRAMS PLACENTA AFTER 3 HOURS OF INCUBATION. SEPARATION BY PAPER CHROMATOGRAPHY[a]

Experiment I	Progesterone (µg.)	Cortisone (µg.)	Cortisol (µg.)	Aldosterone (µg.)
Control	135.9	13.8	3.2	0.94
C.G.[b] 32 U./gm.	137.1	14.1	3.7	1.02
ACTH 5 I.U./gm.	129.9	14.3	3.5	0.93
Experiment II (µg. steroids/100 gm./hr.)				
Period 0–1 hr.	90.5	21.3	—	—
1–3 hr.	20.3	1.2	—	—
3–5 hr.	17.0	0.7	—	—

[a] Micrograms per 100 gm. placenta.
[b] C.G. = chorionic gonadotropin.

TABLE B

INCUBATION STUDIES ON HUMAN PLACENTA[a]

Period	0–3 Hours			3–6 Hours		
	Progesterone	Cortisone	Cortisol	Progesterone	Cortisone	Cortisol
Control	77.1	7.2	2.9	41.5	0.8	0
Prolactin, 1.5 U./gm.	77.1	6.6	2.9	34.2	0.8	0
374 µg. Compound F/100 gm.	93.9	65.0	35.1	—	—	—

[a] Micrograms steroids per 100 gm. tissue per 3 hours.

W. M. ALLEN: Do you have a comment, Dr. Romanoff?

E. B. ROMANOFF: I have no data for the conversion of progesterone to hydrocortisone.

L. I. GARDNER: The suggestion that the placenta might act as a sort of steroidal barrier between mother and fetus would seem to be of considerable interest in view of the *in vivo* experiments that Migeon and colleagues have made. They infused cortisol intravenously into pregnant women at term who were about to have elective Cesarean sections, and then measured the concentrations of cortisol in the peripheral plasma of the mother and in the umbilical cord plasma. They found that, irrespective of the concentrations obtained by infusing different amounts of cortisol into the mother, there was always a constant ratio between maternal peripheral concentration and the fetal concentration, thus suggesting that the placenta was having the controlling influence as to how much cortisol it permitted to pass through.

P. TROEN: May I ask Dr. Venning one question? In Table A, the first experiment, do the figures for cortisone and hydrocortisone represent the values after the amount present in the tissue before incubation had been subtracted?

E. H. VENNING: These represent amounts released into the incubation media. Curiously enough, after incubation, if we extract the tissue, hydrolyze it with alkali, we still obtain relatively high amounts of progesterone remaining in the tissue that have not been released over the 5-hour period of incubation. This appears to be held in the tissue and is not readily released under the conditions of these experiments.

E. B. ROMANOFF: [Added during correction of remarks] I should like to point out that the data I have presented may be interpreted other than that the placenta is synthesizing steroid. Dr. Venning's remarks emphasize the possibility that these data also may be interpreted as a simple release of steroid during the perfusion. That is, steroid possibly bound to protein is simply being released. However, I would like to believe that the "washing" which the placentas received before the experiment proper would seem to argue against this.

Perfusion Studies of the Human Placenta

PHILIP TROEN[*]

Department of Medicine, Harvard Medical School and Department of Medical Research and Yamins Research Laboratory, Beth Israel Hospital, Boston, Massachusetts

I. Introduction

The human placenta has been considered an endocrine organ for many years. Despite its unique quantity and variety of secretions and its availability for study in both normal and abnormal clinical states, much remains to be learned of placental endocrine function. To obtain direct data on placental endocrine function we began our studies using perfusion of the intact placenta. Among the reasons for adopting this approach was the hope that perfusion of the intact gland would provide a more nearly physiologic approach than other techniques and also yield larger amounts of material for analysis.

Reports of placental perfusion study are relatively few. About ten years ago a few brief reports appeared (5, 6) in which isolated cotyledons of placenta were perfused in search for pressor and antidiuretic factors and for demonstration of chorionic gonadotropin and estrogen production. In the last few years additional reports have appeared, including studies of estrogen production and interconversion by perfused cotyledons (15, 16) and of steroidogenesis by the perfused intact placenta (11, 18, 21).

Our initial efforts of placental perfusion began three and a half years ago in Dr. Alexander Albert's laboratory at the Mayo Clinic. With the help of Dr. Harold Mason we began a study concerning possible production of corticosteroids by the placenta. At that time much evidence suggested this might take place (see below). Despite perfusion of

---

[*] Ziskind Teaching Fellow.

several score placentas by varying techniques, the corticosteroid material (as measured by Porter-Silber chromogens) extractable from the perfusate over 3–4 hours of perfusion rarely was significantly greater than the amount of preformed material liberated from the placenta during perfusion (26).

We were able to establish, however, that the placenta contained more corticosteroid than could be accounted for on the basis of the corticosteroid content of the maternal and fetal blood present in the placenta (26). A similar conclusion was reported by Salhanick et al. (20).

Further perfusion studies using various techniques, analyzing for various hormones, and trying various stimuli were relatively unsuccessful, considering the quantity of hormones known to be produced by the placenta in vivo.

The studies have been continued at the Beth Israel for the past two and a half years. The following technique of perfusion has become standard. A placenta obtained directly after delivery from a normal patient is brought to the laboratory in ice-cold saline. After suitable preparation, the umbilical vein is catheterized. A modified Tyrode's solution containing penicillin and streptomycin is used for perfusion. Pulsatile flow is used and the fluid recycled at a rate of about 170 cc. per minute. The perfusing fluid is replaced every hour. The perfusing fluid leaves the placenta through the umbilical arteries which are incised on the fetal surface of the placenta. The perfusing fluid is exposed to an atmosphere of 95% oxygen and 5% CO_2 and maintained at pH 7.4. The system is maintained at 37–38°C. Appropriate hormones may be added to the perfusing fluid and suitable aliquots may be taken for analysis. Cultures of the perfusate show no significant bacterial contamination.

After considerable further experiments, it became increasingly apparent that firm data were needed indicating that the general metabolic processes of the placenta were continuing under our conditions of perfusion. The apparent metabolic (12) and histologic (30) aging of the placenta at term raised the distinct possibility that only a terminal metabolic activity might be obtainable in the perfused intact placenta. Perfusion thus might result only in the extraction of substances from a dead organ.

II. Citrate Metabolism

A parameter to resolve this possibility of an unresponsive gland was available. Villee and associates (28, 29) had done excellent studies on certain reactions of the Krebs cycle in placental homogenates. As a major source of energy for the cell, the reactions of the Krebs cycle seemed an excellent index of the continuing metabolic activity of the perfused placenta. Equally important was the previous demonstration by Villee and associates (28, 29) of the ability of estradiol to stimulate the rate of utilization of citrate through the reactions of the Krebs cycle in homogenates or purified preparations. This afforded an opportunity to determine the responsiveness of our preparation and also to compare this responsiveness with the results obtained in placental homogenates. In conjunction with Dr. Edwin E. Gordon we, therefore, began a study of citric acid metabolism of the perfused placenta measuring citrate disappearance and α-ketoglutaric acid accumulation with and without added hormones (24, 25).

Four groups of three placentas each were perfused. The four treatment groups were: (a) control, (b) added estradiol-17β (at a concentration of 3.57 × 10⁻² millimoles per liter), (c) added human chorionic gonadotropin (HCG) at a concentration of 20,000 international units (I.U.) per liter and (d) estradiol and HCG added together. Citric acid was present initially in all perfusion fluid at a concentration of 5 millimoles per liter.

TABLE I

CITRATE UTILIZATION[a]

Group[b]	Hour								Mean
	1	2	3	4	5	6	7	8	
Control	125.3	97.7	89.0	80.7	114.3	136.3	111.0	100.3	106.8
Estradiol	161.3	73.3	129.3	98.3	123.7	92.0	95.0	177.0	118.8
HCG[c]	176.0	100.3	48.0	69.3	102.7	57.3	187.7	248.0	123.7
Estradiol plus HCG	123.3	115.0	139.7	131.3	101.3	304.7	329.3	371.7	202.0

[a] Figures are milligrams per hour per placenta.
[b] Each treatment group consists of three placentas.
[c] Human chorionic gonadotropin.

Some of the results obtained may be summarized as follows (see Table I):

1. Significant citrate disappearance took place during each hour of the 8 hours of perfusion.

2. The addition of estradiol to the perfusing fluid caused no significant change in the amount or pattern of citrate disappearance.

3. The addition of HCG to the perfusing fluid was associated with a significant ($P < 0.05$) increase in citrate disappearance during the eighth hour compared with that of the control group.

4. Estradiol and HCG added together to the perfusing fluid caused a significant ($P < 0.02$) increase in the mean hourly citrate disappearance per gland. There was also a significant regression on time

($P < 0.001$) with a marked increase in citrate disappearance during the sixth, seventh, and eighth hours of perfusion.

5. Evidence for the citrate disappearance being a metabolic process was the ability of fluoroacetate to inhibit ($P < 0.01$) the stimulation of citrate disappearance produced by added hormones.

6. Other studies were performed measuring changes in circulating potassium during the perfusion. The absence of any significant change indicated minimal disturbances of gross cellular integrity. Furthermore, the absence of change in citrate level of perfusate reincubated outside the placenta after perfusion indicated no release into the perfusion fluid of the enzymes or cofactors necessary for citrate disappearance.

Thus, a previously undescribed action of HCG—more striking in the presence of estradiol—was noted. Several mechanisms of action were possible, but the data did not allow any conclusions. It is of interest that Talalay and Williams-Ashman (22) have shown that the locus of action of steroids on this Krebs-cycle activity is on a transhydrogenase system rather than directly on an isocitric dehydrogenase.

The biologic significance of the time lag noted before stimulation of citrate utilization by the placenta occurred is not clear. Pincus (18) in studying placental steroidogenesis also cited a lag period before the effect of sheep pituitary gonadotropin became apparent.

These results showing metabolic activity which could be stimulated or inhibited provided a basis for the expectation that our perfusion technique could be extended to the study of other metabolic processes of the placenta.

III. Corticosteroid Production

The next phase of our studies was a return to the problem of corticosteroid production by the placenta (23). Using the same perfusion technique, ten placentas were perfused for periods up to 12 hours: seven placentas for 12 hours, two for 8 hours, and one for 6 hours. Aliquots of each hour's perfusate were extracted with methylene chloride and the extract assayed for Porter-Silber chromogens as a test for 17,21-dihydroxy,20-ketosteroids. The residue was incubated with mammalian β-glucuronidase, then again extracted with methylene chloride and the extract tested for Porter-Silber chromogens. The yield of the first extract is called the "free" portion and the yield of the postincubation extract is called the "conjugated" portion. The sum of the free and conjugated is called "total." The results of this study are shown in Fig. 1 expressed as mean cortisol equivalents for each hour of perfusion. The mean cumulative production of Porter-Silber material during 12 hours of perfusion was 8.2 mg. with a range from 0.75 to 14.9 mg. The mean hourly production of the placenta increased almost linearly from 0.13 mg. in the first hour to 1.5 mg. during the twelfth hour. The mean cumulative ratio of free to conjugated was 2 with a range of 0.15 to 4.5.

In contrast to our earlier studies with perfusion for a shorter period of time and measurement of the "free" material only, these amounts represent significantly more material than can be shown to be present in the placenta at the start of perfusion. Extraction of placental tissue

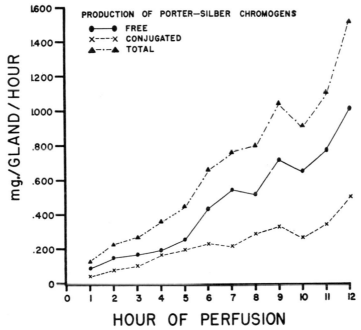

Fig. 1.   Mean hourly production of Porter-Silber chromogens by perfused intact placentas. The results are expressed in milligrams of cortisol equivalents. The values represent means of ten placentas. The total Porter-Silber material is the sum of the free and conjugated.

yielded less than one-twentieth the amount of the Porter-Silber material obtained from the perfusate. This provides further support for the production of the Porter-Silber material by the placenta during perfusion rather than the release of preformed material.

Studies have been started to identify the Porter-Silber material produced. Some examples of the results now being obtained follow:

Figure 2 represents a countercurrent distribution curve of a total extract. An aliquot of perfusate was first incubated with β-glucuronidase, then extracted with ethyl acetate. The cleaned extract then was subjected to a 59-tube countercurrent distribution in a Craig-Post automatic machine, using the solvent system indicated. The result of assay of the Porter-Silber chromogens in the upper phase are expressed in micrograms

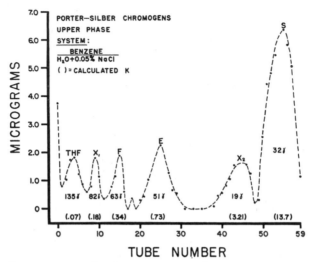

FIG. 2. Countercurrent distribution of a total extract of placental perfusate. See text.

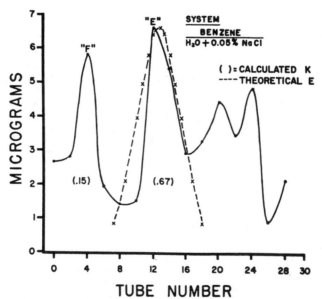

FIG. 3. Countercurrent distribution of an extract of "free" Porter-Silber chromogens from placental perfusate. See text.

of cortisol equivalents per tube. Six distinct peaks may be seen. The calculated partition coefficients (K) coincide with published ones for compounds F, E, S, and tetrahydro F (4). The shapes of these curves also correspond closely to the theoretical curves. Two additional peaks are as yet unidentified. The amount of material present in each fraction is indicated in the figure. The total amount of Porter-Silber material

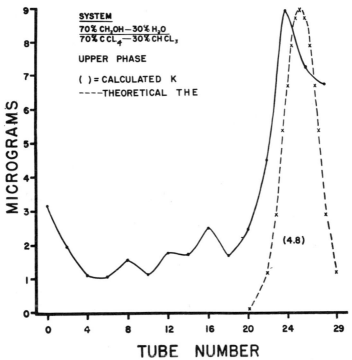

FIG. 4. Countercurrent distribution of an extract of "conjugated" Porter-Silber material from placental perfusate. See text.

represented by these six fractions accounts for 80% of the amount obtained by the methylene chloride extract analysis described earlier.

Countercurrent distribution of separate free and conjugated (or hydrolyzed) material, respectively, from another perfusion are shown in Figs. 3 and 4. The contents of tubes near the peak marked "F" in Fig. 3 were chromatographed, yielding blue-tetrazolium-staining material with a mobility identical to that of known cortisol. Similar chromatography has not been accomplished for the peak marked "E". The latter corresponds closely to the theoretical distribution for cortisone. In Fig. 4 is shown a peak of "conjugated" Porter-Silber material from the same run.

This corresponds only approximately to the curve of tetrahydrocortisone. The nature of this unknown has not yet been determined.

Figure 5 shows the results obtained on chromatographing perfusate from another placenta and eluting the various zones for Porter-Silber assay. A concentration of ultraviolet-absorbing, Porter-Silber-reacting material is noted in areas corresponding to and adjoining standard cortisol and cortisone. Other, more polar, material is also present.

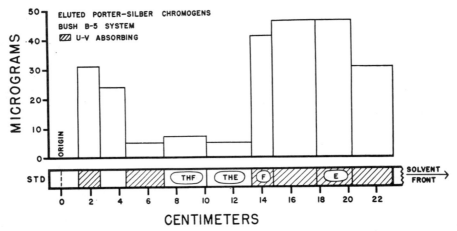

Fig. 5. Porter-Silber chromogens, expressed as cortisol equivalents, eluted from separate areas of a chromatogram of a total extract of placental perfusate.

Further studies to establish synthesis and aid in identification have been done. Carbon-[14]-labeled acetate was added to the perfusion fluid at the start of runs 10 and 12 of another perfusion. Figure 6 shows a paper chromatogram of a "free" extract of perfusate from run 10 of this perfusion. Depicted are the blue-tetrazolium-staining areas of the perfusate material compared to standard steroids. The upper curve represents the radioactivity present in the chromatogram as determined by a "strip scanner;" the radioactivity peaks coincide with two of the blue-tetrazolium-staining areas. The hydrolyzed extract for conjugated material in the same run was similarly chromatographed (Fig. 7). Blue-tetrazolium-positive areas were obtained as indicated, but no radioactivity was present.

Figure 8 shows the results of the free extract of run 11. Blue-tetrazolium-positive spots with superimposed radioactivity are again observed. The hydrolyzed aliquot extract once again had no radioactivity.

The chromatograms of the free and hydrolyzed aliquots of run 12 are shown in Fig. 9 and Fig. 10, respectively. Radioactivity coincident with a blue-tetrazolium-positive area is now seen for the first time in the hydrolyzed aliquot. Similar results are seen in run 13 extracts (Fig. 11 and Fig. 12).

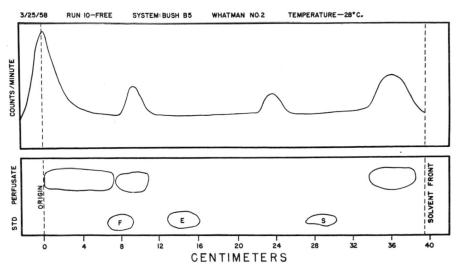

FIG. 6. Chromatogram of free material extracted from placental perfusate showing blue-tetrazolium-staining areas and localization of radioactivity. Positions of standard steroids are shown for reference. Placenta perfused with C^{14}-acetate.

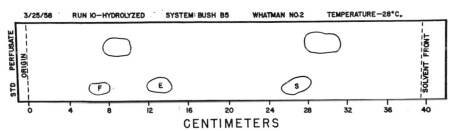

FIG. 7. Chromatogram of material extracted after hydrolysis of placental perfusate showing blue-tetrazolium-staining areas. There was no radioactivity present. Positions of standard steroids are shown for reference. Placenta perfused with C^{14}-acetate.

It must be stressed that the countercurrent distribution and chromatograms seen are not representative of those obtained on all perfusions. Not only is there marked variability in quantity of Porter-Silber material produced, as indicated above, but there is also some apparent variation in the nature of the material extracted. Care has been taken to avoid false-positive results with the analytical methods used. The material used for perfusion was studied singly and in combination and after perfusion through the apparatus without a placenta. No positive Porter-Silber reaction was obtained. The Porter-Silber material extracted from the placental perfusate showed a peak absorption of 410 mμ.

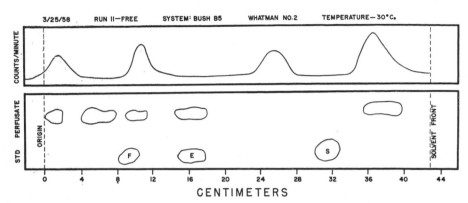

FIG. 8. Chromatogram of free material extracted from placental perfusate showing blue-tetrazolium-staining areas and localization of radioactivity. Position of standard steroids are shown for reference. Placenta perfused with C14-acetate.

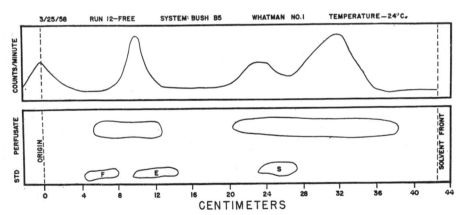

FIG. 9. Chromatogram of free material extracted from placental perfusate showing blue-tetrazolium-staining areas and localization of radioactivity. Positions of standard steroids are shown for reference. Placenta perfused with C14-acetate.

The data on corticosteroid production available at this preliminary stage may be summarized as follows:

1. Production of significant amounts of Porter-Silber chromogens takes place in the perfused placenta.

2. The amount produced per hour increases with successive hours during 12 hours of perfusion.

3. About one-third of the total Porter-Silber material produced appears to be in the form of a conjugate liberated after incubation with β-glucuronidase.

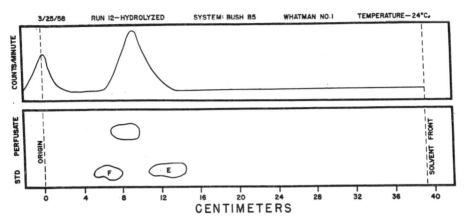

FIG. 10. Chromatogram of material extracted after hydrolysis of placental perfusate showing blue-tetrazolium-staining areas and localization of radioactivity. Positions of standard steroids are shown for reference. Placenta perfused with C[14]-acetate.

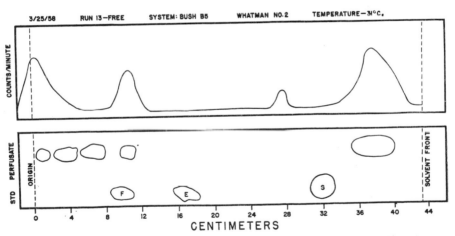

FIG. 11. Chromatogram of free material extracted from placental perfusate showing blue-tetrazolium-staining areas and localization of radioactivity. Positions of standard steroids are shown for reference. Placenta perfused with C[14]-acetate.

4. Most of the total Porter-Silber material measured can be accounted for as comprising a group of compounds which (a) are blue-tetrazolium-positive, (b) are often ultraviolet-absorbing, (c) have partition co-

efficients often corresponding to those of known steroids, (d) have mobilities on paper chromatograms close to those of known steroids, (e) appear to incorporate radioactivity from C^{14}-labeled acetate.

Further rigorous fractionation and identification are necessary. Such studies are in progress. An important possibility being explored is that the compounds produced by the placenta may be transformed in the perfusate itself, either during the process of recycling or during the analytical process. This possibility is suggested also by the finding of Levitz et al. (16) that, after perfusion through an isolated cotyledon, perfusing fluid acquires the ability to interconvert estrone and estradiol.

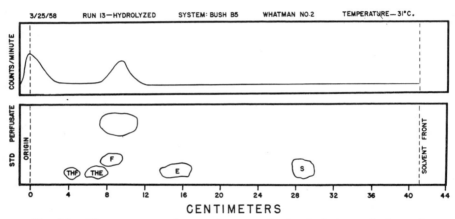

FIG. 12. Chromatogram of material extracted after hydrolysis of placental perfusate showing blue-tetrazolium-staining areas and localization of radioactivity. Positions of standard steroids are shown for reference. Placenta perfused with C^{14}-acetate.

Numerous reports have appeared concerning this problem of possible placental corticosteroid production. Clinical studies such as those of Jailer and Knowlton (13) suggested a possible extra-adrenal source of corticosteroid activity in pregnant Addisonians. Several reports have, in addition, indicated increased excretion of corticosteroids during pregnancy (27), although other studies have not confirmed this (10). The finding of increasing blood levels of corticosteroids in pregnancy (9) (as measured by the Porter-Silber method) seemed also to indicate increased production of these hormones during pregnancy. The report of corticosteroids in placental tissue (3, 7, 14) suggested to some that the site of production of these corticosteroids was the placenta. However, more recently several reports have appeared which suggest that the placenta is *not* the source of extra-adrenal corticosteroids during pregnancy and even that there is no increased production of corticosteroids during pregnancy. Examples of the former are two reports (1, 2) on blood and urine levels of corticosteroid during pregnancy in Addisonian patients. No significant amount of plasma cortisol or urinary corticosteroids was found in the blood or urine of these patients. Migeon *et al.* (17) in studies of the metabolism of C^{14}-labeled cortisol administered to pregnant women near term found that the half-life of free radioactivity in plasma was twice that observed in control subjects and the amount of radioactivity released from plasma by β-glucuronidase hydrolysis was smaller than normal. This and other data suggested "that the increase in plasma free 17-hydroxycorticosteroids observed near term is related to a slower rate of catabolism of cortisol rather than to a more rapid rate of its production."

Pincus (18) recently reported his findings on steroidogenesis in the perfused intact placenta. Using chromatographic separation before assaying for three types of steroids (Δ^4-3-ketones, 17-ketosteroids, and α-ketols), he found a gradual decline of output of all steroid types with several fractions often falling to zero by the second hour of the 4-hour perfusions. There appeared to be no steroids of the cortisol type in the perfusate. The α-ketols were largest in groups with polarities similar to cortisol and tetrahydrocortisol, respectively. ACTH seemed to cause transformation of the former group to the more reduced forms in the latter group without increasing total steroid output. In all of the fractions studied, radioactive steroids were obtained after perfusion with radioactive acetate.

No data will be presented today on the questions raised by the apparent conjugation of steroid to glucuronides in the placenta. It is of interest, though, to mention the high content of β-glucuronidase activity in placental tissue (8). We have demonstrated this also to be present in placental perfusate. The significance of this is not yet clear. Further studies are in progress.

The data presented today indicate that the placenta has the *in vitro* capacity to produce corticosteroids or, more precisely, compounds with certain characteristics of corticosteroids. It cannot necessarily be inferred that the perfused state is precisely indicative of the *in vivo* function of the placenta. The hormonal and nonhormonal factors possibly affecting placental metabolism *in vivo* require much further study.

IV. Estrogen Metabolism

Study of the aspect of estrogen metabolism to be reported here briefly was motivated, in part, by the finding of the joint effect of HCG and estradiol on citrate metabolism. A possible mechanism for this action is an alteration of estrogen metabolism by the HCG. It has already been shown by Ryan and Engel (19) and Levitz *et al.* (16) that placental tissue slices and perfused cotyledons, respectively, can cause interconversion of estradiol and estrone. Neither study reported formation of estriol as a metabolite. That such conversion occurs someplace during pregnancy is, of course, evident from the large excretion of estriol during pregnancy and the relatively large estriol content of the human placenta.

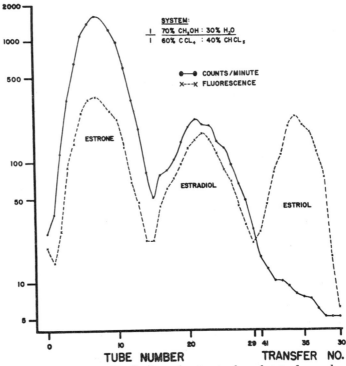

Fig. 13. Countercurrent distribution of extract of perfusate from placenta perfused with C^{14}-estradiol. Carrier estradiol, estrone, and estriol were added before extraction.

Studies were performed with the addition of C^{14}-labeled estradiol-17β to the perfusion fluid and evidence of conversion of this to other labeled estrogens was sought. To an aliquot of perfusate, carrier estradiol, estrone, and estriol were added. The perfusate was extracted and the extract subjected to countercurrent distribution in an appropriate solvent system (Fig. 13). Aliquots from each tube of the final distribution were then assayed for radioactivity and for the fluorescence obtained with estrogens. Two peaks of radioactivity were obtained. These coincided with the observed distribution of the added estrone and estradiol as determined by fluorimetry. In addition, both sets of curves coincided with the theoretical curves of distribution for these two estrogens in the solvent system used. Of the radioactivity extracted from the perfusate, 15–20% was estradiol and 80–85% was estrone.

Similar studies were done with the addition of HCG plus radioactive estradiol to the perfusion fluid. The perfusate was then processed in the same fashion as before with carrier estradiol, estrone, and estriol added

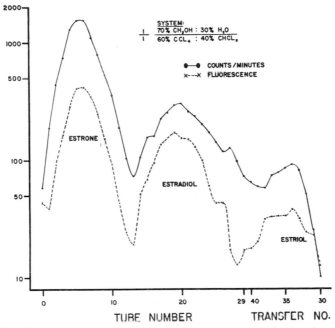

FIG. 14. Countercurrent distribution of extract of perfusate from placenta perfused with C14-estradiol and human chorionic gonadotropin. Carrier estradiol, estrone, and estriol were added before extraction.

before extraction. On countercurrent distribution the same coincidence of radioactivity and fluorescence peaks was noted for estrone and estradiol as previously. In addition, there was now for the first time a third peak of radioactivity clearly separable from and more polar than those of estradiol and estrone (Fig. 14). This third peak coincided with the fluorimetric curve of added carrier estriol and had a calculated partition coefficient identical to the theoretical one for estriol. These results indicate that under these conditions HCG alters the metabolism of estradiol with the formation of a third substance in detectable amounts. This is probably estriol but the possibility of other polar estrogen metabolite(s) cannot as yet be excluded. Of the radioactivity extracted from the HCG-treated perfusions, 15–35% was estradiol, 65–80% was estrone and 1–5% was the third metabolite.

This previously undescribed action of HCG on estrogen metabolism plus the action on citrate utilization suggest that HCG has indeed some function even beyond the first trimester of pregnancy.

V. Conclusion

Perfusion studies of the intact human placenta have yielded data describing two new effects of human chorionic gonadotropin on citrate metabolism and estrogen metabolism, respectively, and indicating that corticosteroid production and conjugation may take place in the human placenta.

Further application of the technique of perfusion as well as of other methods of study will be necessary to enlarge our understanding of the endocrine functions of the human placenta.

Acknowledgments

The author acknowledges the skilled and loyal technical assistance given by Mrs. Margaret Proctor, Miss Frances Cochios, Miss Mary Coakley, and Miss Florence Cohen.

Placentas were obtained through the kind cooperation of Dr. Harold Rosenfield, Chief, Obstetrical Service, Beth Israel Hospital.

This work was supported by grants from the Milton Fund of Harvard University, The United States Public Health Service, and the Massachusetts Heart Association.

References

1. Baulieu, E. E., Bricaire, H., and Jayle, M. F., *J. Clin. Endocrinol. and Metabolism* **16**, 690 (1956).
2. Baulieu, E. E., de Vigan, M., Bricaire, H., and Jayle, M. F., *J. Clin. Endocrinol. and Metabolism* **17**, 1478 (1957).
3. Berliner, D. L., Jones, J. E., and Salhanick, H. A., *J. Biol. Chem.* **223**, 1043 (1956).
4. Carstensen, H., *Acta Soc. Med. Upsaliensis* **61**, 26 (1956).
5. Chesley, L. C., and McFaul, I. E., *Am. J. Obstet. Gynecol.* **58**, 159 (1949).
6. Chesley, L. C., *Bull. Margaret Hague Maternity Hosp.* **2**, 71 (1949).
7. DeCourcy, C., Gray, C. H., and Lunnon, J. B., *Nature* **170**, 494 (1947).
8. Fishman, W. H., and Anlyan, A. T., *Cancer Research* **7**, 808 (1947).
9. Gemzell, C. A., *J. Clin. Endocrinol. and Metabolism* **13**, 898 (1953).
10. Gray, C. H., *Ann. endocrinol. (Paris)* **15**, 22 (1954).
11. Hagopian, M., Pincus, G., Carlo, J., and Romanoff, E. B., *Endocrinology* **58**, 387 (1956).
12. Hellmann, L. L., Harris, B. A., Jr., and Andrews, M. C., *Bull. Johns Hopkins Hosp.* **87**, 203 (1950).

13. Jailer, J. W., and Knowlton, A. I., *J. Clin. Invest.* **29**, 1430 (1950).
14. Johnson, R. H., and Haines, W. J., *Science* **116**, 456 (1952).
15. Levitz, M., Condon, G. P., and Dancis, J., *Federation Proc.* **14**, 245 (1955).
16. Levitz, M., Condon, G. P., and Dancis, J., *Endocrinology* **58**, 376 (1956).
17. Migeon, C. J., Bertrand, J., Wall, P. E., *J. Clin. Invest.* **36**, 1350 (1957).
18. Pincus, G., *in* "Transactions of the Third Conference on Gestation" (C. A. Villee, ed.), p. 91. Josiah Macy, Jr. Foundation, New York, 1957.
19. Ryan, K. J., and Engel, L. L., *Endocrinology* **52**, 287 (1953).
20. Salhanick, H. A., Neal, L. M., and Mahoney, J. P., *J. Clin. Endocrinol. and Metabolism* **16**, 1120 (1956).
21. Solomon, S., Lenz, A. L., Vande Wiele, R., and Lieberman, S., *126th Meeting Am. Chem. Soc., New York, Sept. 12–17, 1954.*
22. Talalay, P., and Williams-Ashman, H. G., *Proc. Natl. Acad. Sci. U.S.* **44**, 15 (1958).
23. Troen, P., *J. Clin. Invest.* **37**, 936 (1958). (Abstract.)
24. Troen, P., and Gordon, E. E., *J. Clin. Invest.* **36**, 932 (1957). (Abstract.)
25. Troen, P., and Gordon, E. E., *J. Clin. Invest.* **37**, 1516 (1958).
26. Troen, P., Mason, H. L., and Albert, A., unpublished observations (1955).
27. Venning, E. H., *Endocrinology* **39**, 203 (1946).
28. Villee, C. A., and Gordon, E. E., *J. Biol. Chem.* **216**, 203 (1955).
29. Villee, C. A., and Hagerman, D. D., *J. Biol. Chem.* **205**, 873 (1953).
30. Wislocki, G. B., and Bennett, H. S., *Am. J. Anat.* **73**, 335 (1943).

Discussion

CHAIRMAN: W. M. ALLEN

P. PERLMAN: I would like to ask Dr. Troen about the specificity of the response to the chorionic gonadotropin. Did you do any experiments in which you added inactive preparations of chorionic gonadotropin or other proteinaceous materials? You were dealing with a Tyrode's solution to which you added some protein, and I wonder if the effect you got was simply increased solubility of your substrate in the reaction causing a better reaction mixture or something of that kind?

P. TROEN: We have not done such studies. I should mention, however, that the Tyrode's solution used for perfusion quickly becomes protein-containing by virtue of material washed from the placenta. This amount of protein is far in excess of the amount added as chorionic gonadotropin.

F. HAAG: I don't think I clearly understood the effect you had on autoclaving your dextrose-containing substrate. Would you repeat that?

P. TROEN: This was an aside. It has no relation to the data presented here. We found during the early months of perfusions at Rochester that autoclaving a dextrose-containing solution can produce large quantities of Porter-Silber-reacting material. Our present perfusion technique does not use autoclaved solutions. We have had no false-positive problems with the results reported today.

W. J. WATERS: I was interested in your remark about conjugation on the part of the placenta. We have been interested in bilirubin metabolism in the newborn and the role of conjugation. On several occasions we have used homogenates of placenta obtained at Cesarean section and have been unable to demonstrate significant conjugation of bilirubin in an *in vitro* system. I would wonder, then, if the apparent recovery of conjugated steroid in your experiments would not possibly represent β-glucuronidase activity of material already present in the placenta rather than the production of conjugated steroid.

P. TROEN: There is not this amount of conjugated steroid material present in placental tissue to begin with. The amounts in the perfusate are far in excess of the tissue content. Other people also have not been successful in getting the placental tissue, slice and homogenate, to conjugate bilirubin. One of the items on our agenda is to try to perfuse the intact placenta with bilirubin to see whether conjugation of this does also take place.

Metabolic Studies of the Mechanism of Action of Estrogens[*]

DWAIN D. HAGERMAN AND CLAUDE A. VILLEE

Department of Biological Chemistry, Harvard Medical School, and the Research Laboratories of the Boston Lying-in Hospital, Boston, Massachusetts

I. Introduction

It is unnecessary to review here the morphologic effects of estrogenic hormones, either endogenously produced by the animal under consideration or given exogenously by an investigator. All the known effects can be summarized in the phrase "growth of target organs". This phrase properly emphasizes that only certain genetically determined tissues will respond dramatically to estrogens and that in general estrogens lead to a building up of new tissue, an endergonic synthetic process.

The biochemist has at his disposal four fundamental techniques for the study of the mechanism of action of a hormone:

First, he may examine the chemical composition of the tissues under the influence of either endogenous or exogenous hormones.

Second, he may examine the metabolism of the intact animal or of surviving tissues of the animal *in vitro* under conditions of hormone lack or plenty.

Third, he may study the effects of the hormone when it is added to surviving tissues from untreated animals.

Fourth, he may investigate the effects of the hormone on isolated enzymes or enzyme systems.

* The original investigations described in this paper were supported by grants from the Charles A. King and Marjorie King Fund and from the National Institutes of Health, United States Public Health Service.

All of these techniques have been used in studies of the mechanism of action of estrogens, and the results of some of these investigations form the basis of the present discussion.

II. The Influence of Estrogens on Chemical Composition of Target Organs

A dramatic effect on first the water content and then the dry weight of the immature rodent uterus is induced by injected estrogen (2). It has been suggested that this uptake of water is related to vasodilatation with possible permeability changes in the uterine vessels (26), but there is no doubt that protein synthesis occurs during the later phase of increase in dry weight. The ionic composition of the uterus at the point of maximal water imbibition suggests that the fluid is largely extracellular (7, 63). Similar, but less dramatic, changes in the water content of human endometrium during the normal menstrual cycle under the influence of endogenous estrogen have been described (40) and denied (57). The glycogen content of endometrium, determined chemically, varies with the menstrual cycle, most authors finding a maximum during the secretory phase (50, 55, 80) when the tissue is dominated by progesterone. However, increases of uterine glycogen content have also been reported as the result of estrogen action alone (65, 75). There is a slight increase in lecithin and free cholesterol in the uterine mucosa late in the estrous cycle (47).

Both ribonucleoprotein and deoxyribonucleoprotein are present in maximal amounts in human endometrium in the late proliferative phase (56), uterine ribonucleic acid synthesis is increased by injecting estrogen into rats (64), and the purine and pyrimidine composition of endometrial nucleic acids varies with the menstrual cycle (13). These facts suggest that these substances are being actively metabolized, which may be related to the fact that estrogen increases the vaginal tissue content of organic phosphate (4).

Likewise, the enzyme content of estrogen-sensitive tissues varies with the amount of estrogen present in the animal. Examples of this phenomenon include β-glucuronidase (11, 46), alkaline glycerophosphatase (30), and fibrinolysin (48). The arginase content of rat kidney is said to increase following estrogen injection (37). Certain other enzymes, e.g., phosphorylase (79) and adenosinetriphosphatase (29), have been reported to be more active when progesterone is dominant. And to conclude this noninclusive list of biochemical changes induced by estrogens, there is the curious observation that the hormone increases the urinary excretion of citric acid (54). All these observations fit rather well the idea that the function of estrogen is to increase the rate of tissue synthesis, as indeed was postulated by the morphologists before the chemical analyses were done.

III. The Influence of Estrogens on Tissue Metabolism

In this section we shall restrict ourselves to measurements of metabolism of tissues taken from animals in various endocrine states, i.e., the hormone is acting *in vivo* although the biochemical measurements may be done *in vitro*. A series of papers has appeared since 1931 which, taken together, clearly show that under appropriate experimental conditions estrogens will increase the over-all rate of metabolism of target tissues as measured by oxygen consumption. The tissues investigated include the rodent uterus (5, 8, 31, 33, 34, 35, 41, 51, 59, 60, 64), the sow uterus (36), the human endometrium (21), and in one report, the pituitary (67). Some investigators did not obtain such effects (10, 49). In addition, increased rates of glycolysis *in vitro* in surviving tissues from estrogen-treated animals were reported (5, 21, 31, 32, 51, 58, 77, 78). Under similar experimental conditions an increased rate of uptake of phosphorus by estrogen-stimulated tissue has been observed (17, 76), increased protein synthesis was reported (28), and the incorporation of C^{14}-labeled glycine into rat uterine protein was found to be stimulatable by pretreatment of the animal with estradiol-17β (44). These important modern studies were later extended to a demonstration of an estrogen-increased rate of incorporation of radioactive glycine and formate into protein, lipid, and the nitrogenous bases adenine and guanine (45), while it was found that with serine as substrate, estradiol increased the incorporation of the amino acid into protein, adenine, and guanine, but not into lipid. Serine conversion to carbon dioxide was also increased (24).

All of these observations can be fitted into a pattern of increased localized metabolic activity which coincides with the preparation of a special tissue for a special function which is undertaken only at intervals. To reiterate, an important part of this preparation is the synthesis of new tissue.

IV. The Influence of Estrogens Added to Tissues in Vitro

Very shortly after purified preparations of estrogens became available, experiments were tried in which these materials were added to surviving tissues of various kinds. It was reported, for instance, that estrogens added *in vitro* increased the oxygen consumption of pituitary (66), and increased anaerobic glycolysis (9) and oxygen consumption (33) of rat uteri. Other investigators (59) were unable to demonstrate any metabolic effects of estrogens added *in vitro* to surviving tissues.

This sort of experiment was first tried in our laboratory in 1951, and we found that the addition of as little as 1 µg. of estradiol-17β per milliliter of incubation medium to slices of human endometrium *in vitro* caused consistent increases in oxygen consumption and increased the rates of oxidation of radioactive glucose and pyruvate to carbon dioxide (19–21). These experiments were extended to slices of human placenta because of the greater availability of this tissue (72), and similar results were obtained. The effects were obtained without any intervention of the metabolic systems of the intact animal and were therefore interpreted as reflecting a primary effect of estrogen on the oxidative, energy-supplying systems of target tissues.

V. The Influence of Estrogens on Specific Enzyme Systems

A number of investigators have examined the problem of mechanism of action of steroid hormones by adding the hormones to tissue homogenates under conditions such that one enzymatic reaction predominates. Thus, inhibition of glycerophosphate oxidation (25), inhibition of diphosphopyridine- or triphosphopyridine-linked enzymes (18), inhibition of succinoxidase (42, 43), inhibition of over-all oxygen consumption (14), and inhibition of alkaline phosphatase (1) have all been reported. Experiments in which no inhibitions were found have also been published (6).

The results of such enzyme-inhibition studies are inherently difficult to interpret, since in many of the experiments very unphysiologic amounts of hormone were used and the tissues were usually not "target organs," but in general the experiments with estrogens pointed toward effects on the oxidative pathways of metabolism.

Since estradiol had affected the metabolism of placenta slices when added *in vitro*, we examined the effect of the hormone on tissue homogenates (72). It was easy to demonstrate that estradiol stimulated the metabolism of these preparations, and the greatest effect on oxygen consumption was observed when glucose, acetate, pyruvate, or citrate were used as substrates; smaller effects were seen when other constituents of the Krebs tricarboxylic acid cycle were used. It is evident from an examination of Fig. 1, which outlines the pathways of intermediary metabolism, that an effect of estrogen upon the oxidation of citric acid to α-ketoglutaric acid would explain these results. Direct examination of the rate of conversion of citrate to α-ketoglutarate by a placental homogenate confirmed the existence of an estradiol stimulation of this reaction.

It was possible to demonstrate that this estradiol-stimulatable conversion of citrate to α-ketoglutarate occurred in the soluble protein fraction of a placental homogenate, obtained by ultracentrifugation which removed insoluble debris, nuclei, mitochondria, and microsomes (68). Studies of such soluble placenta enzyme systems with a variety of substrates and cofactors (70) indicated clearly that the oxidation of isocitrate to oxalosuccinate (which then spontaneously decarboxylates to α-ketoglutarate) was the reaction affected by estradiol. Investigation of the cofactor requirements of this reaction (15, 68, 71) indicated that in addition to isocitric acid as a substrate and the placental enzymes, only diphosphopyridine nucleotide (DPN) and a divalent cation such as mag-

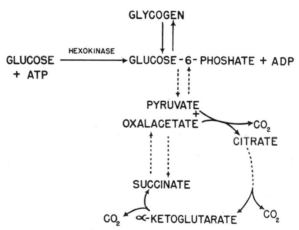

FIG. 1.   Pathways of intermediary metabolism.

nesium or manganese were required. Accordingly, the estrogen-sensitive enzyme was formulated as a DPN-linked isocitric dehydrogenase which catalyzed the reaction:

$$\text{Isocitrate} + \text{DPN}^+ \longrightarrow \alpha\text{-ketoglutarate} + CO_2 + \text{DPNH} + H^+$$

Attempts to purify the enzyme system involved were not altogether satisfactory (22), and we had concluded that some other cofactor must be involved when Talalay and Williams-Ashman (61) pointed out that such was indeed the case and that the cofactor was triphosphopyridine nucleotide (TPN), required in minute amounts.

Their observations were readily confirmed in our laboratories (74), and the estrogen-sensitive enzyme system of placenta is now believed to be a transhydrogenase, an enzyme system which transfers hydrogen ions and electrons from reduced TPN to DPN:

$$\text{TPNH} + \text{DPN}^+ \rightleftharpoons \text{DPNH} + \text{TPN}^+$$

This reaction can be coupled to any TPNH generating system, such as isocitric dehydrogenase, glucose-6-phosphate dehydrogenase, etc.

VI. Steroid Specificity of the Estrogen-sensitive Placental Enzyme System

Measuring either the production of α-ketoglutarate or reduced DPN in a system in which the transhydrogenation reaction is coupled to isocitrate oxidation, the stimulating activity of a number of steroids has been examined. Some of the results obtained are summarized in Table I (71). These results have been confirmed and extended by Hollander (27) and indicate that the enzyme system is quite specific. Introduc-

TABLE I

STIMULATING ACTIVITY OF VARIOUS STEROIDS

Compound	% Stimulation compared to estradiol-17β, 1 μg./ml.
Estrone, 1 μg./ml.	95
Equilin, 1 μg./ml.	95
Equilenin, 1 μg./ml.	98
Estradiol-17α, 1 μg./ml.	0
19-Nortestosterone, 1 μg./ml.	19
Estriol, 10 μg./ml.	8
Testosterone, 17 μg./ml.	14

tion of unsaturation into ring B of the steroid molecule, as in equilin and equilenin, does not affect the activating ability, but the configuration in ring D is quite specific.

Inhibitors for the activating process have also been found (73). Notable among these are stilbestrol, estradiol-17α, an analog of stilbestrol (1,3-di-p-hydroxyphenylpropane), and estriol. Since the inhibition induced by these compounds can be reversed in the in vitro system by adding large amounts of estradiol, the inhibition is of the competitive type, and probably involves the binding of the compounds involved to the estrogen-sensitive enzyme (22).

If this hormone effect is to be important in physiological control, it must be effective at very small concentrations and a graded response to different amounts of the hormone would be anticipated. That such is indeed the case may be seen from Fig. 2 (69). As little as 0.003 μg. estradiol per milliliter produces a clear-cut response, and the dose-response curve is typically sigmoid. This phenomenon has been utilized as an assay method for estrogens in urine (16) and in tissues (23, 39).

VII. Mechanism of the Estrogen Effect on the Placental Enzyme System

Two different mechanisms have been proposed for the effect of estrogen on the placental enzyme system. One of these states that the estrogen acts to convert an inactive enzyme to an active form. When

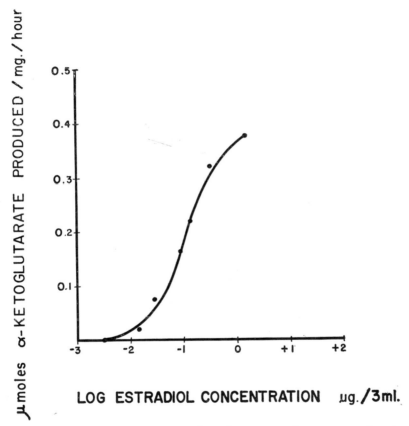

FIG. 2. Dose-response curve of α-ketoglutarate production as a function of estradiol concentration.

this hypothesis was formulated, it was believed that the estrogen acted upon a specific placental isocitric dehydrogenase. However, the theory is equally applicable to an action of the hormone on a transhydrogenase. The kinetics of the over-all reaction are consistent with this theory (22), and from these kinetics apparent binding constants for the enzyme-hormone complex have been calculated. The effects of the inhibitors mentioned above can also be interpreted in the terms of this theory as a competition of the activator and an inhibitor for a site on the enzyme.

Alternatively, the hormone may act as a coenzyme for the transhydrogenation. The reaction may be formulated as follows:

$$\text{Estrone} + \text{TPNH} + \text{H}^+ \rightleftharpoons \text{Estradiol} + \text{TPN}^+$$

$$\text{Estradiol} + \text{DPN}^+ \rightleftharpoons \text{Estrone} + \text{DPNH} + \text{H}^+$$

and is the interpretation favored by Talalay and Williams-Ashman (61). This reaction scheme implies that the estrogen-sensitive transhydrogenation in placenta is mediated by the placental estradiol-17β dehydrogenase characterized by Langer and Engel (38). This enzyme will utilize either DPN or TPN as hydrogen acceptor, as required by the theory. However, it is present in tissues such as rat liver (52), human ileum, liver, and adrenal (53); but human ileum, liver, and adrenal do not respond dramatically to estrogen injections, and the metabolism of rat or human liver homogenates is not affected by estradiol *in vitro* (68). Again, rabbit liver homogenates readily dehydrogenate estradiol to estrone but do not contain any estrogen-stimulatable transhydrogenase system (74a).

Establishment of the true mechanism of estrogen action in this system will obviously require either the separation of two enzymes, one an estrogen-sensitive transhydrogenase and the other an estradiol-17β dehydrogenase, or conclusive proof of their identity. Experimental evidence in this area is as yet contradictory. Talalay and associates have reported a hundredfold purification of the dehydrogenase without separation of the transhydrogenase activity (62). Furthermore, they find identical inhibition of the two activities by sulfhydryl reagents. Conversely, we have obtained a partial separation of the two activities by

TABLE II
RELATIVE ENZYME ACTIVITIES

Preparation	Estradiol-17β dehydrogenase: transhydrogenase ratio
$S_{57,000}$	9.0
40% Ammonium sulfate precipitate	8.9
Langer procedure	29
Alcohol precipitate—$Ca_3(PO_4)_2$ gel adsorption and elution	3.6

simple protein fractionation techniques (Table II). Moreover, we find that the sulfhydryl reagent *p*-chloromercurisulfonic acid causes a 50% inhibition of the transhydrogenase reaction at a concentration of 10^{-5} *M*, while the same degree of inhibition of the dehydrogenase requires ten times more inhibitor, 10^{-4} *M*.

It is known that the mitochemical transhydrogenase of heart muscle is inhibited by thyroxine (3). Similarly, the placental estrogen-sensitive enzyme is inhibited by thyroxine, and the inhibition can be overcome by increasing amounts of estrogen. Clearly, further careful experimental work is required before the mechanism of action of estrogen in this system may be considered to be known.

VIII. Physiologic Significance of These Observations

It was pointed out earlier that the effect of estrogens in the whole animal is one of stimulating growth of specialized tissues. At the biochemical level, growth involves utilization of energy derived from the oxidation of substrates for the synthesis of new bonds, and frequently, the reduction of newly formed chemical moieties, such as fatty acids, cholesterol, and the nitrogenous bases of nucleic acids.

The major fraction of the cell's biologically useful energy is derived from the oxidation of reduced DPN via the cytochrome system. At the same time, a large fraction of substrate oxidation in the cell leads to the production of reduced TPN, not DPN. It is clear that hormonal control of the transfer of hydrogen ions and electrons from TPN to DPN will influence the over-all rate of cell metabolism and hence the amount of energy available for synthetic processes. This was, in fact, implied in our early experiments in which the oxygen consumption of tissue slices of target organs was increased by the addition of estrogen *in vitro*.

It presently appears that the reductive processes involved in biological syntheses are reactions utilizing TPNH. Since the estrogen effect on the transhydrogenation reaction is in the direction of decreasing the amount of TPNH (the cell ordinarily contains a large amount of reduced TPN and a small amount of reduced DPN) (12), it would appear that estrogens could only hinder these reductive syntheses if its only function were to decrease the amount of TPNH. This prediction does not agree with the experimentally demonstrated increased rate of incorporation of glycine into lipid in the estrogenized rat uterus, for example (45).

But in addition to the reductive reactions, most biochemical syntheses utilize energy for the activation of substrates. If this is the rate-limiting step for the over-all reaction, then a stimulation of transhydrogenation by estrogen would increase the rate of oxidative metabolism of the tissue and thereby increase the amount of energy available for use in synthetic reactions.

A further difficulty is that the effect on transhydrogenation does not satisfactorily explain the activity in the whole organism of such synthetic estrogens as stilbestrol, 17α-ethynylestradiol, and 1-*cis*-bisdehydrodoisynolic acid, particularly if the estrogens serve as cosubstrates in a coupled oxidation-reduction.

Despite these difficulties of interpretation which probably cannot be resolved until the complex dynamic metabolic interrelationships of the intact cell are better understood, and despite the existence of two hypotheses as to the exact mechanism of the estrogen effect on the transhydrogenation reaction, it would now appear that the major mechanism of action of estrogen at the molecular level is better understood than that for any other hormone.

The close correlation between the changes in endometrial metabolism under the influence of endogenous estrogens and the changes that can be induced by the addition of estrogens *in vitro* (21) and the existence of an isolated enzyme system which can account for these changes provide, it seems to us, good evidence that the phenomenon under study is the one that operates in the intact animal.

Desirable as a unitary hypothesis for the mechanism of action of a hormone is, these experiments do not exclude other sites of action for the hormone. Nevertheless, an estrogen stimulation of the transhydrogenation reaction in target cells can explain, with a minimum of accessory hypotheses, all of the known effects of the natural estrogens, simply on the basis of additional availability of energy to the cell. What the cell does with this energy is presumably genetically determined and unaffected by the hormone.

References

1. Aldman, B., Diczfalusy, E., Högberg, B., and Rosenberg, T., *Biochem. J.* **49**, 218 (1951).
2. Astwood, E. B., *Endocrinology* **23**, 25 (1938).
3. Ball, E. G., and Cooper, O., *Proc. Natl. Acad. Sci. U.S.* **43**, 357 (1957).
4. Bengtsson, L. P., *Acta Endocrinol. Suppl.* **13**, 1 (1953).
5. Carrol, W. R., *Proc. Soc. Exptl. Biol. Med.* **49**, 50 (1942).
6. Case, E. M., and Dickens, F., *Biochem. J.* **43**, 481 (1948).
7. Cole, D. F., *J. Endocrinol.* **7**, 12 (1950).
8. David, J. C., *J. Pharmacol. Exptl. Therap.* **43**, 1 (1931).
9. Dirscherl, W., *Congr. intern. biochim. 2e Congr. Paris 1952 Chim. biol.* **VIII**, 16 (1952).
10. Dreyfuss, M. L., *Am. J. Cancer* **38**, 551 (1940).
11. Fishman, W. H., Kasdon, S. C., Bonner, C. D., Fishman, L. W., and Homberger, F., *J. Clin. Endocrinol.* **11**, 1425 (1951).
12. Glock, G. E., and McLean, P., *Biochem. J.* **61**, 381 (1955).
13. Gold, N. I., and Sturgis, S. H., *J. Biol. Chem.* **206**, 51 (1954).
14. Gordan, G. S., and Elliott, H. W., *Endocrinology* **41**, 517 (1947).
15. Gordon, E. E., and Villee, C. A., *J. Biol. Chem.* **216**, 215 (1955).
16. Gordon, E. E., and Villee, C. A., *Endocrinology* **58**, 150 (1956).

17. Grauer, R. C., Strickler, H. S., Wolken, J. J., and Cutuly, E., *Proc. Soc. Exptl. Biol. Med.* **75**, 651 (1950).
18. Guidry, M. A., Segaloff, A., and Altschul, A. M., *Endocrinology* **50**, 29 (1952).
19. Hagerman, D. D., and Villee, C. A., *Arch. Biochem. Biophys.* **40**, 481 (1952).
20. Hagerman, D. D., and Villee, C. A., *J. Biol. Chem.* **203**, 425 (1953).
21. Hagerman, D. D., and Villee, C. A., *Endocrinology* **53**, 667 (1953).
22. Hagerman, D. D., and Villee, C. A., *J. Biol. Chem.* **229**, 589 (1957).
23. Hagerman, D. D., Wellington, F. M., and Villee, C. A., *Biol. Bull.* **112**, 180 (1957).
24. Herranen, A., and Mueller, G. C., *J. Biol. Chem.* **223**, 369 (1956).
25. Hochster, R. M., and Quastel, J. H., *Ann. N. Y. Acad. Sci.* **54**, 626 (1951).
26. Holden, R. B., *Endocrinology* **25**, 593 (1939).
27. Hollander, V. P., Nolan, H., and Hollander, N., *J. Biol. Chem.* **233**, 580 (1958).
28. Jeener, R., *Biochim. et Biophys. Acta* **2**, 439 (1948).
29. Jones, H. W., Wade, R., and Goldberg, B., *Am. J. Obstet. Gynecol.* **64**, 1118 (1952).
30. Jones, H. W., Wade, R., and Goldberg, B., *Obstet. Gynecol. Survey* **8**, 398 (1953).
31. Kerly, M., *Biochem. J.* **31**, 1544 (1937).
32. Kerly, M., *Biochem. J.* **34**, 814 (1940).
33. Khayyal, M. A., and Scott, C. M., *J. Physiol. (London)* **72**, 13 P (1931).
34. Khayyal, M. A., and Scott, C. M., *Quart. J. Exptl. Physiol.* **24**, 249 (1934).
35. Khayyal, M. A., and Scott, C. M., *Quart. J. Exptl. Physiol.* **25**, 77 (1935).
36. King, J. L., *Am. J. Physiol.* **99**, 631 (1932).
37. Kochakian, C. D., *Am. J. Physiol.* **151**, 126 (1947).
38. Langer, L. J., and Engel, L. L., *J. Biol. Chem.* **233**, 583 (1958).
39. Loring, J. M., and Villee, C. A., *Acta Endocrinol.* **25**, 371 (1957).
40. McLennan, C. E., and Koets, P., *Obstet. Gynecol. Survey* **8**, 704 (1953).
41. MacLeod, J., and Reynolds, S. R. M., *Proc. Soc. Exptl. Biol. Med.* **37**, 666 (1938).
42. McShan, W. H., Meyer, R. K., and Erway, W. F., *Arch. Biochem.* **15**, 99 (1947).
43. Meyer, R. K., and McShan, W. H., *Recent Progr. in Hormone Research* **5**, 465 (1950).
44. Mueller, G. C., *J. Biol. Chem.* **204**, 77 (1953).
45. Mueller, G. C., and Herranen, A., *J. Biol. Chem.* **219**, 585 (1956).
46. Odell, L. D., and Fishman, W. H., *Am. J. Obstet. Gynecol.* **59**, 200 (1950).
47. Okey, R., Bloor, W. R., and Corner, G. W., *J. Biol. Chem.* **86**, 307 (1930).
48. Page, E. W., Glendening, M. B., and Parkinson, D., *Am. J. Obstet. Gynecol.* **62**, 1100 (1951).
49. Pincus, G., and Graubord, M., *Endocrinology* **26**, 684 (1940).
50. Randall, L. M., and Power, M. H., *Proc. Staff Meetings Mayo Clinic* **17**, 158 (1942).
51. Roberts, S., and Szego, C. M., *J. Biol. Chem.* **201**, 21 (1953).
52. Ryan, K. J., and Engel, L. L., *Endocrinology* **52**, 277 (1953).
53. Ryan, K. J., and Engel, L. L., *Endocrinology* **52**, 287 (1953).
54. Schorr, E., Bernheim, A. R., and Taussky, H., *Science* **95**, 606 (1942).
55. Spyker, M. A., and Fidler, R. S., *J. Clin. Endocrinol.* **2**, 365 (1942).
56. Stein, R. J., and Stuermer, V. M., *Am. J. Obstet. Gynecol.* **61**, 414 (1951).

57. Stuermer, V. M., and Stein, R. J., *Am. J. Obstet. Gynecol.* **61**, 668 (1951).
58. Stuermer, V. M., and Stein, R. J., *Am. J. Obstet. Gynecol.* **63**, 359 (1952).
59. Sweeney, B. M., *J. Lab. Clin. Med.* **29**, 957 (1944).
60. Szego, C. M., and Roberts, S., *Recent Progr. in Hormone Research* **8**, 419 (1953).
61. Talalay, P., and Williams-Ashman, H. G., *Proc. Natl. Acad. Sci. U.S.* **44**, 15 (1958).
62. Talalay, P., Williams-Ashman, H. G., and Hurlock, B., *Proc. Natl. Acad. Sci. U.S.* **44**, 862 (1958).
63. Talbot, N. B., Lowry, O. H., and Astwood, E. B., *J. Biol. Chem.* **132**, 1 (1940).
64. Telfer, M. A., *Arch. Biochem. Biophys.* **44**, 111 (1953).
65. Telfer, M. A., and Hisaw, F. L., Jr., *Acta Endocrinol.* **25**, 390 (1957).
66. Victor, J., and Anderson, D. H., *Am. J. Physiol.* **120**, 154 (1938).
67. Victor, J., and Anderson, D. H., *Am. J. Physiol.* **122**, 167 (1938).
68. Villee, C. A., *J. Biol. Chem.* **215**, 171 (1955).
69. Villee, C. A., *Fertility and Sterility* **8**, 156 (1957).
70. Villee, C. A., and Gordon, E. E., *J. Biol. Chem.* **216**, 203 (1955).
71. Villee, C. A., and Gordon, E. E., *Bull. soc. chim. Belges* **65**, 186 (1956).
72. Villee, C. A., and Hagerman, D. D., *J. Biol. Chem.* **205**, 873 (1953).
73. Villee, C. A., and Hagerman, D. D., *Endocrinology* **60**, 552 (1957).
74. Villee, C. A., and Hagerman, D. D., *J. Biol. Chem.* **233**, 42 (1958).
74a. Villee, D. B., Villee, C. A., and Hagerman, D. D., unpublished observations (1958).
75. Walaas, O., *Acta Endocrinol.* **10**, 175 (1952).
76. Walaas, O., and Walaas, E., *Acta Physiol. Scand.* **21**, 18 (1950).
77. Walaas, O., Walaas, E., and Löken, F., *Acta Endocrinol.* **10**, 201 (1952).
78. Walaas, O., Walaas, E., and Löken, F., *Acta Endocrinol.* **11**, 61 (1952).
79. Zondek, B., and Hestrin, S., *Am. J. Obstet. Gynecol.* **54**, 173 (1947).
80. Zondek, B., and Stein, L., *Endocrinology* **27**, 395 (1940).

Discussion

CHAIRMAN: G. PINCUS

S. J. FOLLEY: Did I understand Dr. Hagerman to say that synthetic reactions in cells require TPNH rather than DPNH? Because surely the biosynthesis of fatty acids is linked to DPNH rather than TPNH. It is true that certain investigators have claimed that there is a separate system specific for TPNH which synthesizes short-chain acids, but I believe the synthesis of long-chain acids depends mostly on a DPNH-linked system.

D. HAGERMAN: Not knowing much about the synthesis of fatty acids, I have been content to take the opinion of experts from whom I gather that the TPNH system is the important one.

S. J. FOLLEY: Of course, it is known that the pentose phosphate oxidation cycle is a TPN cycle.

I wonder if you had considered the possibility of estrogen being concerned in shifts of the metabolism of carbohydrate between the pentose phosphate and glycolytic pathways. In the case of the mammary gland, which is another target organ for estrogen, as lactation gets under way there seems to be an increasing emphasis on the pentose phosphate cycle whereas the activity of the glycolytic pathway remains more or less constant. It seems possible that there may be some tie-up there with your results.

D. HAGERMAN: I would agree that that is a possibility. Some experiments that we have done with differentially labeled glucose in the presence and absence of estrogen in this enzyme system would fit quite satisfactorily into such a formulation.

W. W. WESTERFELD: It would seem to me that "transhydrogenase" is just another name for an enzyme which catalyzes the oxidation and reduction of substrate system (such as estradiol $\rightleftarrows$ estrone) and which has the additional characteristic of using both DPN or TPN as cofactors. The net result of the reaction is a transfer of hydrogen between the pyridine nucleotides, with the substrate acting as an intermediate carrier. If this is a correct evaluation, then the only requirement for transhydrogenase activity is a dehydrogenating enzyme capable of reacting with both DPN and TPN, and acting in the presence of its appropriate substrate. Is the estradiol-estrone reaction unique in this respect, or are there numerous enzyme-substrate systems which would exhibit transhydrogenase activity?

D. HAGERMAN: Transhydrogenase reactions may well be important in the control of the relative rates of reactions in many cells. The unique property of our system is that it involves a hormone. The enzyme is in some way intimately related to this hormone and is found in significant concentrations only in those tissues which we know from other experimental evidence are stimulated by that hormone.

As far as other steroids are concerned, you have seen on the slides the ones that have been tested and found active in this system. We have tried many other steroids and none of them has any significant stimulating activity.

Dr. Zander suggested this morning that progesterone and Δ^4-3-ketopregnen-20α-ol might be involved in a similar reaction. Progesterone does not have any appreciable activity in our placental transhydrogenase system despite the fact that human placenta contains a hydrogenase for progesterone. It should be pointed out that we presently believe this reaction to be mediated by a specific pyridine nucleotide transhydrogenase, not a coupled oxidation-reduction system.

S. ROBERTS: Certain corticosteroids are known to inhibit many of the metabolic effects of estrogens on the uterus. Have you tried cortisol or any other corticosteroids in this system, with or without estrogen?

C. VILLEE: Yes. We have tried both cortisol and cortisone. Neither one had either a stimulatory or an inhibitory effect on the enzyme system.

B. RUBIN: I would like to ask Dr. Hagerman: It is my understanding, which is rather limited, that this transhydrogenase is unusual in being in the supernatant fraction of the high-speed run, whereas most nucleotide transhydrogenases have been demonstrated in the insoluble microsomes. Is this correct?

D. HAGERMAN: Yes. I believe that this is correct if you restrict yourself to organisms higher than bacteria. The transhydrogenase which is probably best characterized and most certainly a true transhydrogenase without intervention of co-substrates, is the heart muscle mitochondrial transhydrogenase which Ball and Cooper have recently described.

G. PINCUS: I would like to take the opportunity to ask one question. In view of the recent demonstration of the apparent TPNH deficit in diabetes, have you made any study of tissues of diabetic animals or studied the effects of insulin on this system?

D. HAGERMAN: We have not examined the effects of insulin on this reaction. The transhydrogenase system that is obtained from the placentas of diabetic women is apparently perfectly normal in amount and character. It should be pointed out, however, that the women from whom these placentas came were scrupulously controlled with insulin, so probably the experiment is inconsequential.

W. PEARLMAN: Would you like to make a comparison of the estrogen concentration required to be effective in the enzyme systems under discussion and the estrogen concentration which normally obtains in the living organism, particularly at the site of the target organ of hormone action? I think that such a comparison might be interesting to make at this point.

D. HAGERMAN: Such a comparison cannot be readily made because of the difficulty in knowing just how much estrogen is present in the tissue. There is enough estrogen in the normal placenta to stimulate partially the enzyme that is prepared from that same placenta. If you add more estrogen to such a preparation, you can obtain a further stimulation. By appropriation purification of the enzyme system, you can reduce the amount of estrogen and reduce the amount of enzyme activity.

The activity goes down proportionally to the reduction in hormone, and it would appear to go to zero when the hormone concentration is zero, although that is a slight extrapolation.

W. PEARLMAN: In this connection I recall certain studies by Biggers and co-workers on the action of various estrogens on the vagina of the mouse in tissue culture; the effective dose of estrone was found to be less than 10^{-5} μg. for one-sixth of a mouse vagina in tissue culture.

What is the order of concentration in which you get the first noticeable effects of estrogen in the enzyme systems discussed—particularly the removal of hydrogen from isocitric acid? What are the minimal concentrations of estradiol?

D. HAGERMAN: You can detect with certainty as little as 0.003 μg. of estradiol or estrone per milliliter of incubation medium. You can detect, if you are willing to do a number of experiments and take an average, probably an order of magnitude lower than that. This works out to less than 10^{-9} M as an effective concentration for the hormone, and I would guess that the hormone in the whole animal is not far below that concentration.

S. GELFANT: Because of the known *in vivo* effects of estrogen on nontarget organ tissues, have you made any studies *in vitro* of tissues other than uterus—or nontarget organs?

D. HAGERMAN: As I mentioned earlier, we have examined the metabolism of rat liver, kidney, lung, heart, the metabolism of human fetal liver and kidney, and in no case have we found any evidence for the existence of the estrogen-sensitive transhydrogenase in these tissues. That does not say it is not there, of course.

F. HAAG: You have mentioned the interference of sulfhydryl compounds in this reaction. I wonder, did you study any possible correlation between sulfhydryl compounds already present in the tissues studied with this reaction; or was this strictly on the addition of such compounds to the system?

D. HAGERMAN: The experiments to which I referred were altogether a biochemist's attempt to differentiate between two enzyme activities by the addition of powerful sulfhydryl blocking agents.

C. VILLEE: I believe Dr. Haag may have misunderstood the statement. It was not sulfhydryl groups which were added, but substances such as *p*-chloromercuri-sulfonic acid, which is known to inhibit sulfhydryl groups. That these inhibit the enzyme, leads to the inference that the enzyme contains sulfhydryl groups which are essential for its activity.

I. ROTHCHILD: It is always interesting to hear generalizations that attempt to explain the great many variations in the behavior of a particular organ, or portion of an organ, or of a hormone—as in this case, the estrogens.

I want to make sure I understand you correctly. In your concluding statements you generalize that the estrogens affected the metabolism of certain tissues or rather affected the oxidation processes within certain cells and that the energy derived from this was then used by the particular cells for their own particular purpose. Is that right?

D. HAGERMAN: Yes, approximately.

I. ROTHCHILD: How would you attempt to tie this in with another very important effect of estrogen—a fairly significant one—namely, the inhibition of FSH (follicle-stimulating hormone) secretion by the pituitary gland?

D. HAGERMAN: It is possible that the estrogen may affect a transhydrogenase system in the pituitary.

As I mentioned, experiments have been reported in the literature in which estrogens apparently do have a stimulatory effect on the metabolism of the pituitary. This might result in an inhibition of the systems which produce the protein hormone by a stimulation of oxidative reactions which reduce the amount of building blocks available for production of the hormone; and so on.

R. HERNE: Diczfalusy and co-workers found a difference between estradiol and polymerized estradiol phosphate; the latter was shown to be a potent inhibitor of some esterases. Do you have any experience with polyestradiol phosphate?

D. HAGERMAN: No, sir. We have had no experience with that material.

C. SZEGO: I would like to ask a somewhat easier question than the one on the pituitary that was just asked.

Without attempting to detract from this valuable and brilliant series of studies performed by Drs. Hagerman and Villee, I would like to know whether they visualize the effect of estrogen on the enzyme system as having anything whatsoever to do with the initial hyperemia, the vasodilatation, and the associated increase in capillary permeability of the target organ?

D. HAGERMAN: That would be much easier to answer, Dr. Szego, if I knew what the mechanism for the production of increased permeability was.

C. SZEGO: Recently, in our laboratories, my colleague, Dr. Eugene Spaziani, has done some very interesting studies which I believe will throw some light upon this question.

Dr. Spaziani found that an early and acute effect of estrogen was to promote the liberation and dissipation of endogenous histamine from the uterus. This was clear cut when estrogen was administered intravenously to ovariectomized adult rats. Similarly, it was observed by Dr. Spaziani that when intact animals were sacrificed in late proestrus and estrus, their intrinsic uterine histamine was significantly lower than in animals studied at phases of the estrous cycle characterized by lower endogenous estrogen levels.

He then proceeded to study the effects of histamine and, later, of a histamine liberator, compound 48-80—which I can't name chemically because its structure is somewhat uncertain [cf. J. L. Mongar and H. O. Schild, J. Physiol. **118**, 461 (1952)] —instilled into the uterus of the ovariectomized rat. To his surprise and mine, the hyperemia, the vasodilatation, and the increase in water uptake were similarly brought about by these compounds without the intervention of estrogen at all.

The next logical step for him was to attempt to block estrogen action in terms of these early correlates of hormone activity as measured on the uterine target, with standard histamine blocking agents. Of the four antihistamines which were studied, he observed that Benadryl hydrochloride and Chlor-Trimeton maleate were capable of interfering with the early uterine uptake of water, as well as with the hyperemia, which were elicited by estrogen [E. Spaziani and C. M. Szego, *Endocrinology* **63**, 669 (1958)].

Hence his hypothesis at the moment—and I think he is as close to the primary action of estrogen as one can be in terms of time course of the response of the rat uterus—is as follows: The early uterine response to estrogen: the vasodilatation and the hyperemia, the associated increase in capillary permeability, the uptake of sodium, water, perhaps also the transfer of glucose and the increase in glycolysis which were reported from our laboratories some years ago [C. M. Szego and S. Roberts, *Recent Progr. in Hormone Research* **8**, 419 (1953)], all of which occur before any augmentation of oxidative metabolism, are brought about by the release of uterine histamine by estrogen. Thus he suggests that histamine is the local mediating substance for the primary effects of the hormone.

D. HAGERMAN: Do you suppose that the synthesis or release of the histamine could involve a transhydrogenation reaction?

C. SZEGO: Unfortunately, related studies on histidine decarboxylase have not yet been performed. To my knowledge, however, this is not an oxidative step. I doubt, moreover, if there is actually enough time elapsed for new histamine production.

I forgot to mention that Dr. Spaziani found no increase in histaminase to account for the disappearance of histamine from the uterus. The point here is, of course, the local liberation of intrinsic, preformed histamine.

D. HAGERMAN: I would like to point out at this juncture that in the purified enzyme system, the increased rate of transhydrogenation—measured optically by absorbance of reduced pyridine nucleotide at 340 μ—takes place immediately upon the addition of the hormone. So there is no problem about time elapsed for the initiation of the transhydrogenation reaction at least.

If the transhydrogenation reaction is coupled to four or five or eight or ten other sequential reactions, it is quite possible that two or three minutes might pass before the end reaction in such a chain would show a change in rate.

G. PINCUS: I would like to interject a comment at this point. I think Dr. Hagerman has answered the thousand questions about "when" and "how" in terms of near or remote biochemical sequences. We could go on with this forever. This has been very familiar to all of us who have worried about the mechanism of hormone action. I think that the factual linking up of the mysteries to the known is the real problem.

S. ZUCKERMAN: I should like to ask a question in relation to Dr. Szego's remarks. She is certainly aware of Dr. Shelesnyak's observation that histamine introduced into the uterine lumen causes a decidual response. The same reaction may occur when histamine is given systemically. Histamine releases may also bring about the response, and, correspondingly, blocking agents can prevent them.

In which way would Dr. Szego correlate the observations that she has reported with those which Shelesnyak has now confirmed several times?

C. Szego: Dr. Spaziani was, of course, well aware of the work of Dr. Shelesnyak on the mechanism of implantation. I should point out that the former, in our laboratory, made his observations primarily during the 3 or 4 hours following estrogen administration or the administration of histamine or histamine liberators.

Dr. Spaziani has some preliminary data on effects as late as 24 hours, which I think he would be very reluctant to have me mention at this stage, but since this question arose I will have to. It appears that 24 hours after the instillation of histamine into the uterus, there has been induced the kind of increase in epithelial cell height and activity of glands that estrogen itself might bring about.

Now, this is not an original observation. There is some literature—the French literature particularly [E. Spaziani, Ph.D. Thesis, University of California, Los Angeles, Jan. 1958]—that describes similar studies, over a longer period, however. All this appears to support the suggestion earlier advanced from these laboratories [S. Roberts and C. M. Szego, *Physiol. Revs.* **33**, 593 (1953)] that some aspects of growth may have been very much dependent upon the early influx of substrate that was brought about by the altered permeability of the uterine vessels and that the increased substrate concentration itself modified the subsequent metabolism during the later cell division phases.

Estrogen Excretion of the Pregnant Woman

J. B. Brown

Clinical Endocrinology Research Unit (Medical Research Council), University of Edinburgh, Edinburgh, Scotland

The daily excretion of estriol, estrone, and estradiol has been studied in women during complete menstrual cycles followed by cycles in which they became pregnant, throughout pregnancy, delivery, the puerperium, and lactation, and until normal menstrual cycles had been re-established. Most of the findings reported here have already been published (1). They also include results from a woman (D. H) who was artificially inseminated and became pregnant during the period of study. This case is interesting because the successful insemination was performed on the day of the mid-cycle peak of estrone and estradiol excretion; previous inseminations performed at the time of the rise in basal temperature had been unsuccessful. Urinary pregnanediol and gonadotropin were also estimated in this case.

Methods

In this investigation, the methods for collecting and preserving urine samples, for estimating urinary estrogens, pregnanediol, and gonadotropins, and for recording basal temperatures were the same as those described in Chapter 3.

In all the cases studied, the previous and present pregnancies were uncomplicated. Deliveries were spontaneous except in subject 10, for whom forceps were required. Lactation was established in all cases:

Subject 7, aged 33; para—2.
Subject 8, aged 28; para—2.
Subject 9, aged 27; para—1.
Subject 10, aged 29; para 0.

Subject D. H., aged 30; para 0, treated for sterility due to impotence of her husband. A successful artificial insemination with her husband's semen was performed during the second menstrual cycle studied. The pregnancy proceeded uneventfully to term.

Results

The results obtained from subject 8 over a period of time which included a complete menstrual cycle and the cycle in which she became pregnant are shown in Fig. 1. The urinary estrogen results were very similar in the two cycles until the 24th day, in that they showed both the ovulation peak and the subsequent luteal rise. In the first cycle the estrogen levels decreased after the 24th day and menstruation followed; in the second cycle, when pregnancy had occurred, the levels continued

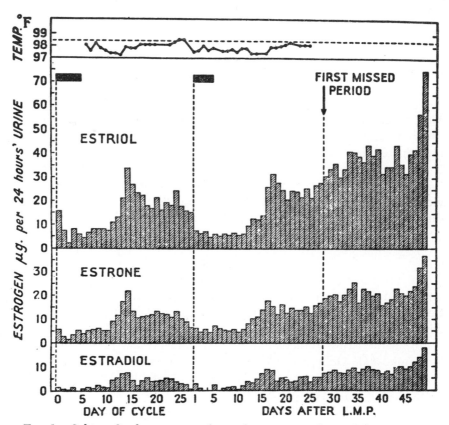

FIG. 1.   Subject 8: the amounts of estriol, estrone, and estradiol excreted per 24 hours and also the variations in basal temperature, during a normal cycle, the cycle in which pregnancy occurred, and early pregnancy. Horizontal bar indicates menstrual period. From Brown (1).

to increase gradually. About 7 weeks after the last menstrual period, the estrogen levels began to increase at a much greater rate. Such an increase was observed at about this time in all three women studied (subjects 7, 8, and D. H.). It is possible that this abrupt change in the estrogen excretion curve is due to a change-over from the corpus luteum to the placenta as the major source of estrogens.

Similar results were obtained for subject D. H. (Fig. 2). However, in this case, the most poorly defined ovulation peak and luteal maximum yet observed were found, and in spite of these conception occurred. These results probably represent the lowest levels of estrogen excretion during an ovulatory menstrual cycle which can be considered as normal. In contrast the luteal phase rise in pregnanediol was one of the highest yet observed (3). In both cycles, the peak of estrone and estradiol excretion occurred on the 11th day; the rises in pregnanediol and basal temperature occurred 3 days later. In the first cycle, the specimens which probably contained the gonadotropin peak could not be assayed; in the second cycle the gonadotropin peak occurred 1–2 days after the estrogen peak. The day of the estrone/estradiol peak of the second cycle was successfully predicted on the basis of the similarity between the emerging pattern and the pattern of the previous cycle. An artificial insemination performed on this day was successful. The first indication of conception was a sharp rise in gonadotropin excretion 10 days after the insemination, due presumably to the appearance of chorionic gonadotropin in the urine. The increase in gonadotropin excretion was followed by a rise in estrogen output and by maintenance of the high luteal-phase levels of pregnanediol. Although little can be concluded from a single case, it is interesting to note that previous artificial inseminations performed at the time of the rise in basal temperature on the 14th day of the cycle had been unsuccessful; the successful insemination was performed on the day of the estrone/estradiol peak which occurred some 3 days earlier. The result might have been fortuitous, but, on the basis of the estrous cycle in animals, it might be expected that the height of estrogen secretion in women might also be the best time for conception.

The results from subjects 7–10 throughout their pregnancies are shown in Fig. 3, plotted on a logarithmic scale. Those for subject 8 are also shown for a week after delivery. After about the 7th week, the urinary estrogen levels increased rapidly and were soon outside the range found during the menstrual cycle; they followed a smooth exponential curve which flattened somewhat toward the end of pregnancy. The estrone and estradiol levels at labor were approximately 100 times higher than those during the luteal phase of the menstrual cycle, the estradiol levels being about one-third of the estrone levels. The urinary estriol levels rose approximately a thousandfold during this time. It is interesting to note that the increases in estrone and estradiol between the 10th week and term were approximately thirtyfold; the weight of the placenta increases over this time from an average of 20 gm. to an

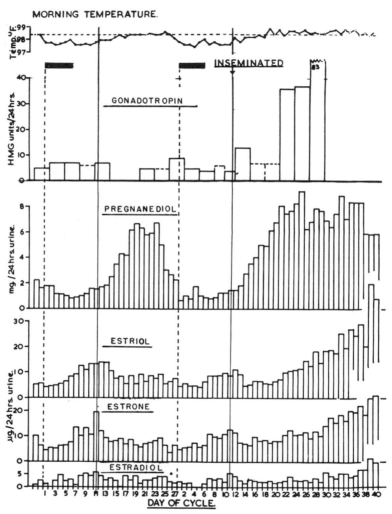

Fig. 2. Mrs. D. H.: the amounts of gonadotropins, pregnanediol, estriol, estrone, and estradiol excreted per 24 hours and also the variations in basal temperature, during a normal cycle, the cycle in which pregnancy occurred, and early pregnancy. Gonadotropin assays: ——— = results by the mouse uterus test. – – – – = results by the mouse uterus test in which the reading was actually less than the figure shown. The vertical line indicates the day of the mid-cycle peak of excretion of estrone and estradiol. Horizontal bar indicates menstrual period. From Brown *et al.* (2).

average of 600 gm.,* which is also thirtyfold. There were no consistent changes in estrogen excretion which could be correlated with the onset of labor. After delivery, the urinary estrogen levels fell rapidly; estrone

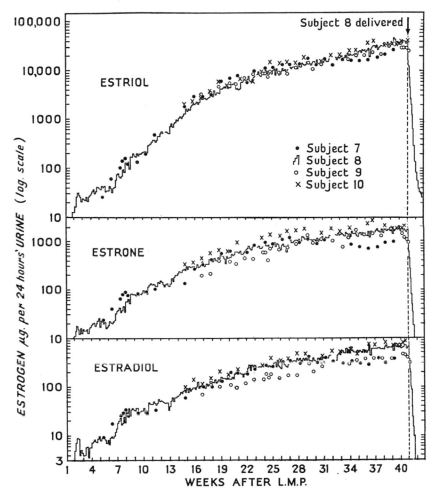

FIG. 3.   Excretion of estriol, estrone, and estradiol during pregnancy in four subjects and during the puerperium in subject 8. From Brown (1).

and estradiol reached nonpregnancy values within 5 days and estriol reached these values within 25 days after delivery (subject 8, Fig. 4). Levels were low during lactation and reached a minimum of 4 μg. total

---

* These figures were kindly supplied by the Obstetric Medicine Research Unit (Medical Research Council), Aberdeen. They have been reported by Walker (4).

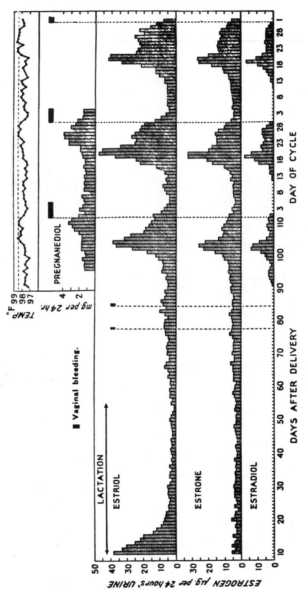

Fig. 4. Subject 8. During lactation and until the onset of menstruation, excretion of estriol, estrone, and estradiol was measured. Thereafter, until the end of the third menstrual period following delivery pregnanediol was measured in addition and variations in basal temperature were recorded. From Brown (1).

estrogen per 24 hours at the time when lactation became inadequate and suckling was discontinued. Thereafter the amounts increased slowly.

After the period of lactation amenorrhea, there was slight vaginal bleeding on the 78th and the 84th days after delivery when the total estrogens excreted had risen to approximately 15 µg. per 24 hours, levels approaching those encountered in anovulatory menstrual cycles. Soon after this, measurable amounts of estradiol appeared in the urine and the amount of all three estrogens rapidly increased and decreased in the manner characteristic of ovulation. However, the estrogen levels did not rise again to a definite luteal maximum and menstrual bleeding began 8 days after the "ovulation" peak. That ovulation, followed by a shortened luteal phase, had occurred was confirmed by morning basal temperature and urinary pregnanediol measurements. An ovulation peak followed by a somewhat shortened luteal phase of 10 days was seen during the next menstrual cycle, and during the third menstrual cycle there was a normal luteal maximum and the estrogen levels throughout were almost identical with those during the menstrual cycle preceding pregnancy.

Acknowledgments

I wish to thank my colleagues Drs. A. I. Klopper and J. A. Loraine for their permission to report our combined studies on subject D. H. which are yet unpublished.

References

1. Brown, J. B., *Lancet* i, 704 (1956).
2. Brown, J. B., Klopper, A., and Loraine, J. A., *J. Endocrinol.* **17**, 401 (1958).
3. Klopper, A., *J. Obstet. Gynaecol. Brit. Empire* **64**, 504 (1957).
4. Walker, J., *Cold Spring Harbor Symposia Quant. Biol.* **19**, 39 (1954).

Discussion

CHAIRMAN: G. PINCUS

C. G. HARTMAN: I note that in your curve of estrogen output there is a kink at about the sixth week of the 267-day gestation period. In the monkey there is a slight change in the consistency of the uterus (probably reflecting a depression of the endocrines) at about the fourth week of the 168-day gestation.

In man and monkey these endocrine changes appear at about the time the corpus luteum regresses and the mode of embryonic nutrition changes from the invasive type to the orderly establishment of the placental circulation. The ovary now surrenders to the placenta the primacy in the endocrine control of pregnancy. It seems to me that the kink in the curve comes about the time this transition is made.

E. EICHNER: Some time ago we produced pseudocyesis in a group of eight women. These women had been normally menstruating before that time. They received increasing doses of progesterone and chorionic gonadotropin by injection and estradiol pellet implants at 10-day to 2-week intervals over a 3-month period. The study continued for a total of 6 months. Daily urines were collected and our results showed well within the range of the speaker with reference to estrone, estriol, estradiol. However, despite increasing amounts of estradiol implanted in these patients, we never got a level much above your 7–10-week level. Culdoscopy demonstrated completely atrophic ovaries. The uteri on the other hand were approximately the size of a 7–8-week gestation and stayed that way. The vaginal spreads were the typical dirty spreads of pregnancy. The endometrial biopsy showed decidua which varied at times.

Bradbury, on seeing some of the results, thought that it was degenerating decidua. Some of the local gynopathologists called them growing decidua. The estrogenic affect on the patient persisted for well over two years after the experiment was stopped. I just wanted to comment on the question of the amount of material recovered in the urine. These being State Hospital patients, all urines which did not have adequate creatinine were discarded as being improperly collected.

One other question I would like to ask the speaker is with reference to the insemination at the estrone peak. Since it takes 24 hours to collect the urine, and quite some time to run the urine, how do you pick the day on which you inseminate?

J. B. BROWN: The urinary estrogen excretion of an individual is usually similar in pattern and amount from cycle to cycle. This is illustrated by the first two figures shown. If the urinary estrogens are determined throughout one cycle, it is usually possible to predict with reasonable accuracy the dates of events in the following cycle. The emerging pattern in the second cycle (Fig. 2) was in fact the same as that found during the first cycle. An estrogen determination can be completed in a day, and it was possible to guess on the afternoon of the eighth day that the estrone-estradiol peak was going to be on the eleventh day. It was fortunate that the prediction was correct because this was about the most difficult case we could have started with. The estrogen levels were the lowest and the patterns of excretion the least definite of any individual we have yet studied. In fact, if she had not conceived, we might have been tempted to consider her estrogen excretion was abnormal.

G. PINCUS: Did you have any cases which failed?

J. B. BROWN: One might have expected that this success would have stimulated more gynecologists to try the method. However, this is the only case that has been presented to us and it was successful.

G. PINCUS: This is known as the phenomenon of the first experiment.

P. TROEN: You inferred from your data that estriol was probably directly produced by the placenta. There is a report by Levitz and associates [M. Levitz, G. P. Condon, and J. Dancis, Federation Proc. 14, 245 (1955)] on perfusion of C^{14}-acetate into an isolated cotyledon from human placenta. From the perfusate, they isolated radioactively labeled estrone and estradiol in small yields, but no estriol. I believe there may still be some doubt as to whether estriol is made primarily by the placenta or whether it is primarily a metabolite of estradiol and estrone. The data we presented this morning indicated that the latter pathway may be operative in the placenta itself. We are doing further experiments on this problem, but the data are still too preliminary to report.

J. B. BROWN: I agree with you entirely. The subject still is quite open.

J. ZANDER: My comment refers to the same question as Dr. Troen's. It is known from the work of Dr. Diczfalusy that there are significantly larger amounts of estriol than of the other two estrogens in the human placenta. In collaboration with

Dr. Erica Brendle we have recently started some studies on estrogen concentrations in different tissues, using a modification of Dr. Brown's method which is useful for isolation of estrone, estradiol, and estriol from tissues. Dr. Diczfalusy's findings in placental tissues were confirmed. But it was quite interesting that, pooling five corpora lutea with a total weight of 5.27 gm., we found only a very small amount of estriol. The concentration of estrone was 0.47 µg. per gram of corpora lutea; of estradiol, 0.63 µg. per gram of tissue; of estriol, only 0.02 µg. per gram of tissue. This shows that the relative amounts of these three estrogens differ also in the main estrogen-producing tissues during cycle and pregnancy—corpus luteum and placenta.

J. B. BROWN: We have tried to determine whether the corpus luteum produces estriol. There is some evidence from Furuhjelm's work using histological methods that it does. Estradiol, estrone, and estriol were administered separately to human subjects and the amounts of estrone, estradiol, and estriol excreted in the urine as a result of the administration were measured. It was found that the ratio of estrone:estradiol:estriol excreted in the urine following the administration of estrone or estradiol was practically constant for any individual, and the total excreted represented about 25% of the dose. Of this approximately half was estriol. In the case of administered estriol, 80% of the dose was excreted unchanged as estriol. In other words, administered estriol is approximately eight times more effective in raising the urinary estriol levels than the same amount of estradiol. This should also apply to endogenous estrogens. If the corpus luteum does secrete appreciable amounts of estriol, then it would be expected that more estriol relative to the other estrogens would be excreted in the urine during the luteal phase of the cycle than during the follicular phase. However, it has been found that the ratio of the three estrogens excreted in the urine by an individual remains constant throughout the menstrual cycle. This is interpreted as evidence that corpus luteum does not produce significant amounts of estriol.

E. H. VENNING: Dr. Brown, I was wondering if you really meant that ovulation did not occur in that cycle which preceded menstruation or do you believe that the rise in estrogens can occur without ovulation?

J. B. BROWN: The question whether a peak of estrogen excretion resembling that found during an ovulatory menstrual cycle is in itself sufficient evidence of ovulation is still undecided. All the current tests for ovulation are tests for a functioning corpus luteum. Regular estrogen peaks have been observed in a case suffering from cystic glandular hyerplasia who showed no evidence of a functioning corpus luteum.

E. H. VENNING: A number of years ago we followed six women after delivery until the appearance of the first menstrual bleeding. In all these women, pregnanediol was excreted before the occurrence of the bleeding, suggesting that ovulation had occurred.

J. B. BROWN: It occurred in this woman, too.

E. H. VENNING: But you suspected, I gathered, that the rise in pregnanediol had not been adequate.

J. B. BROWN: No, a rise in pregnanediol excretion occurred in this case, indicating that ovulation had taken place. However, the duration of this rise and the length of the luteal phase were much shorter than the average. I was speculating about an exaggeration of this effect where the luteal phase was so evanescent that it could not be detected. Would the estrogen peak still imply that ovulation had occurred?

G. Pincus: On the question of the estriol excretion, I should mention that Dr. Levy in our laboratory has isolated estriol as a metabolite of C^{14} estradiol perfused through the rat liver; so that the possibility of a conversion outside of a placental site exists. This, incidentally, is the first demonstration of such an effect, but none the less appears to be real.

C. Villee: I might mention that about a year ago Dr. Hagerman and I incubated some fetal liver with radioactive estradiol and Dr. Lewis Engel has been working on this for the last year, satisfying himself that the product was estriol. He told me just the other night that he is now satisfied that it is estriol. This is another demonstration of conversion of estradiol to estriol by the liver—fetal liver in this case.

J. B. Brown: Diczfalusy has shown that the estrogen metabolism of newborn infants is unusual in that only estriol is recovered in the urine following the administration of estradiol.

Metabolic Studies in Pregnancy

ELEANOR H. VENNING AND JOHN C. BECK

McGill University Clinic, Royal Victoria Hospital, Montreal, Canada

I. Introduction

Pregnancy is an anabolic state and the continued retention of nitrogen, calcium, sodium, potassium, fluid, and other elements has been well established. It has been shown by Coons *et al.* (5) that the retention of sodium may exceed the requirements of the growing uterus and products of conception in some normal pregnant women. Among the many factors suggested as contributing to this retention, the alterations in renal function and capillary permeability, increased venous pressure, and increased production of antidiuretic, adrenal cortical, and estrogenic hormones have frequently been implicated.

The rise in the output of urinary estrogens during pregnancy has been recognized for many years, and the sodium- and fluid-retaining properties of these hormones are well known. The progressive increase in the levels of blood and urinary corticosteroids has also been confirmed by many investigators and appears to be due to increased secretion from the adrenal as well as a delayed metabolism of the hormones in pregnancy. The demonstration of significant increases in the excretion of aldosterone (7, 8, 9, 11–13, 16), a potent sodium-retaining hormone, has further emphasized the participation of the adrenal cortex in this respect. In Fig. 1 is shown the rising output of aldosterone in pregnancy. These values were obtained from ten normal pregnant women. Near term, aldosterone excretion ranges from 15 to 90 µg. per day while in nonpregnant women the range is from 2 to 7 µg. per day.

In order to study the relationship between excretion of aldosterone and corticoids and the retention of sodium and fluid, metabolic studies

have been carried out in five pregnant women (15). The pregnant
women chosen for this study had been followed in the antenatal clinic;
their antenatal history and physical and laboratory examinations were
normal throughout and all the patients delivered normally and had no
complications throughout the puerperium. They were admitted to
hospital approximately 2–3 weeks before the expected time of delivery

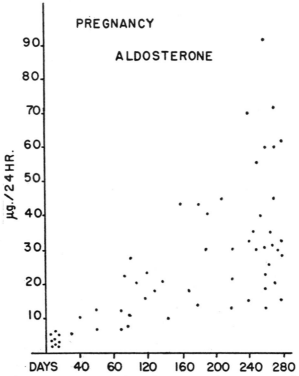

Fig. 1. Aldosterone excretion throughout normal pregnancy determined by
bioassay.

and remained for 7–12 days after delivery. Throughout the study they
were maintained on a constant intake of fluid, electrolytes, protein, and
calories. Their caloric intake varied from 2025 to 2035 calories, the
protein from 78 to 80 gm., and the fat and carbohydrate were 83 and
224 gm., respectively. The fluid intake was maintained at 2000 ml. The
daily sodium intake was constant at 130 meq. except for those days
when sodium thiosulfate was administered intravenously for the measurement of extracellular fluid volume. Potassium intake was maintained
at 102 meq. A supplement of 245 mg. of vitamin C was given daily.

All the food served to them was eaten except on the day immediately before or after delivery.

Complete 24-hour collections of urine were made, and sodium, potassium, and nitrogen balances were measured. The stools were not collected and factors for fecal loss of 1.7 gm. for nitrogen, 10.0 mcq. for potassium, and 4.0 meq. for sodium were used in the calculations of the balances. It has been shown that the fecal loss of these constituents is relatively constant and independent of the intake. It was not possible to obtain an accurate collection of the amniotic fluid, and the blood loss at the time of the delivery was estimated; these were not included in the balances.

The serum sodium, potassium, and nonprotein nitrogen (NPN) were followed, and periodic determinations of blood and plasma volume, total body fluid, and extracellular fluid space were made. Radioiodinated serum albumen was used for the determination of blood and plasma volume. These studies were carried out by Dr. L. Lowenstein. Total body water was measured using antipyrine (4), and the extracellular fluid space with sodium thiosulfate (6), both determinations were made by Dr. L. McLeod. The excretion of 17-hydroxycorticosteroids was determined by the Porter-Silber reaction (11) and aldosterone by the bioassay of Venning et al. (14). The aldosterone fraction was separated from other urinary corticoids by two systems of paper chromatography prior to bioassay.

II. Results

The results of these studies are shown in Figs. 2 7. For the balances, the intake is plotted from the zero line downward and the urinary excretion is plotted upward from the intake line and is represented by the crosshatched area. The fecal excretion is represented by the area above the zero line, positive balances by the blank areas below the line. The loss from discharge of blood and lochia during the puerperium was not measured and is not included in the balance.

CASE 1 — J.L. (Fig. 2). This patient, aged 25 years, weighed 130½ lb. on admission. She lost 3 lb. during the 31-day period in the antepartum phase, 11½ lb. at delivery, and a further 5½ lb. during the subsequent post-partum period. The hemoglobin levels remained at 85 gm.% in the ante-partum period, decreased to 82 gm.% at delivery, and rose again following delivery. The total blood and plasma volume increased slightly up to the time of delivery and then decreased gradually in the post-partum period. Ten days before delivery the total blood volume was 5.21 liters and 10 days after parturition it had decreased to 3.85 liters. The potassium balance remained positive in the ante-partum phase, showing an average daily retention of 10 meq. per day over the 30-day period. Following delivery a diuresis of potassium occurred on the first and fourth post-partum days. The serum potassium

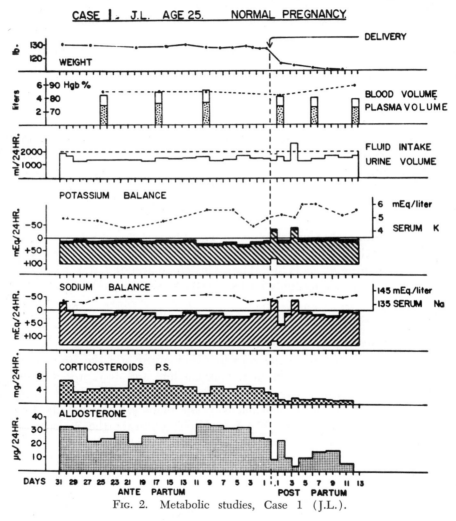

FIG. 2.   Metabolic studies, Case 1 (J.L.).

which had varied between 4.3 and 5.7 meq. per liter in the ante-partum period reached a peak of 6.0 meq. per liter on the fifth and seventh days post partum. The sodium balance was positive throughout the ante-partum period except for the first day on the diet and the patient retained an average of 15 meq. per day. A diuresis of sodium occurred on the day of delivery and again on the fourth day post partum. The serum sodium ranged between 136 and 141 meq. per liter in the ante-partum period and were slightly higher in the post-partum period.

The nitrogen balance was positive in the ante-partum period averaging a retention of 1.3 gm. nitrogen per day. The urinary nitrogen increased on the first and fourth days post partum at a time when similar effects were observed with regard to sodium and potassium. The serum NPN rose following delivery (Fig. 7).

The excretion of corticosteroids ranged between 4.3 and 7.0 mg. per day in the ante-partum period, decreased following parturition, and reached levels of 3.0 mg. per day by the fourth day post partum. The aldosterone varied between 24 and 43 µg. per day in the ante-partum period to 9.0 mg. per day on the day of delivery, and on the second day post partum showed a temporary rise to 23 µg. per day and then subsequently was excreted at lower levels.

CASE 2 — C.B. (Fig. 3). This patient, aged 30 years, weighed 122 lb. When placed on the controlled diet she appeared to maintain her weight fairly well, losing only 1½ lb. over 21 days in the ante-partum period. The hemoglobin was 84 and 88 gm.%, decreased to 64 gm.% following delivery, and subsequently returned to 73 gm.% on the ninth day post partum. The total blood volume increased from 5.89 liters to 6.10 liters and following delivery showed values of 4.5 liters and 3.56 liters on the second and ninth days post partum. The urinary corticosteroids remained between 4.5 and 7.6 mg. per day during the ante-partum period and showed only a slight decline following delivery. The aldosterone levels, which were initially 12 µg. per day, gradually rose within a period of 15 days to 55 µg. per day and remained between 34 and 44 µg. for the remainder of the ante-partum period. Following delivery a significant decrease in the excretion of aldosterone occurred on the second day post partum; on the third day it increased to 33 µg. and then subsided to levels observed in nonpregnant women. These changes in aldosterone excretion were reflected in the sodium balance which became increasingly positive with the rising output of aldosterone, and the diuresis of fluid and sodium which occurred following parturition was associated with the decrease in the levels of aldosterone. The potassium balance followed a somewhat similar trend to that of sodium and both serum sodium and potassium increased to higher levels following delivery. The nitrogen balance shown in Fig. 7 was positive in the ante-partum period and showed a negative balance in the post-partum period although the patient was maintained on the same intake of protein.

CASE 3 — K.B. (Fig. 4). This patient, aged 32 years, weighed 166 lb. and lost only 3 lb. over the 18-day ante-partum period. Her hemoglobin remained around 72% throughout the study. The total blood

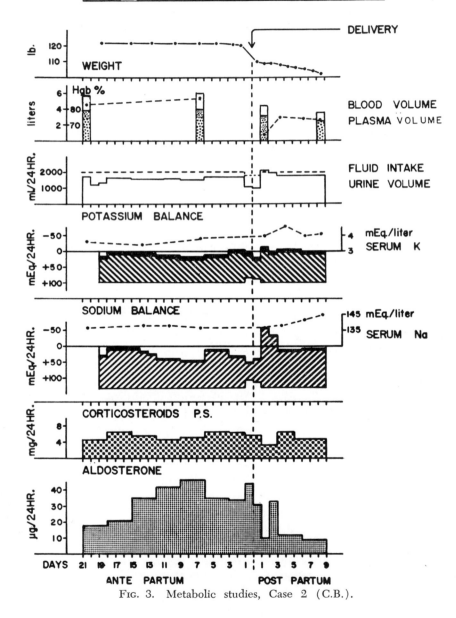

FIG. 3. Metabolic studies, Case 2 (C.B.).

volume showed values of 6.2 and 5.7 liters on the thirteenth and fifth days ante partum and decreased to 4.53 liters and 4.30 liters on the fourth and seventh days post partum. Total body water measured on

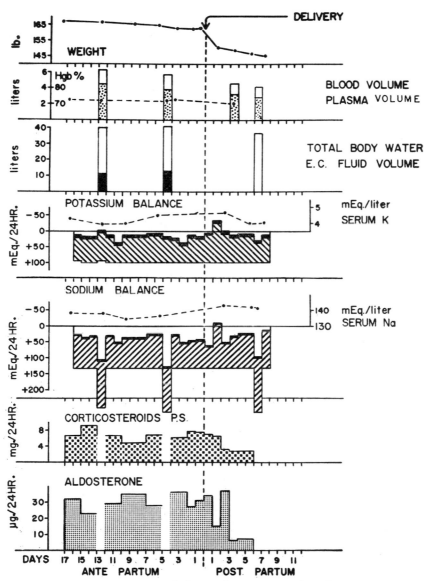

Fig. 4.   Metabolic studies, Case 3 (K.B.).

the same days ante partum was 39.8 liters and 41.3 liters, respectively, and on the seventh day post partum had decreased to 37.0 liters. The potassium balance was positive and averaged a daily retention of 13 meq. potassium in the ante-partum period. Following delivery, a diuresis occurred on the second day post partum, and after this episode the balance was positive for the remainder of the study. The sodium balance was relatively constant throughout the ante-partum period showing an average daily retention of 36.5 meq. sodium. In determining this average, the days on which the patient received an additional amount of sodium in the form of sodium thiosulfate, for the determination of extracellular fluid space, were omitted. A diuresis of sodium occurred on the second day post partum and this was associated with a fall in aldosterone. In this patient the aldosterone excretion had remained fairly constant in the ante-partum period, averaging 30 μg. per day. On the second day post partum it decreased to 15 μg. per day, increased again on the third post-partum day to 35.7 μg. and then fell to low levels. The corticosteroids varied between 4.6 and 8.7 mg. per day before delivery and decreased to 3.0 mg. after delivery. This patient retained an average of 1.35 gm. nitrogen per day in the ante-partum period, and following delivery the diuresis of nitrogen coincided with that of sodium and potassium. The serum NPN increased after delivery.

CASE 4 — J.B. (Fig. 5). This patient, aged 32 years, weighed on admission 134 lb. She lost 3 lb. during the first 3 days on the controlled diet, then appeared to maintain her weight fairly well, losing only 2 lb. in the following 20 days. She showed a metabolic picture somewhat similar to that of Case 2 in that there was a progressive increase in the output of aldosterone associated with increasing retention of sodium. The aldosterone excretion during the last week of gestation was around 60 μg. per day. On the day of delivery the level decreased to 15 μg. per day and a diuresis of sodium, fluid, potassium and nitrogen occurred simultaneously. A subsequent rise in aldosterone occurred and sodium was again retained. When aldosterone again decreased the sodium output increased. The urinary corticosteroids showed only a slight change after delivery, decreasing from an average of 5.6 mg. to 4.9 mg. per day. The blood volume measured only once in the ante-partum period, was 5.69 liters. It decreased to 4.22 and 3.40 liters on the second and ninth days post partum. The total body water increased from 37.1 liters to 38.6 liters between the eighteenth and eleventh days ante partum and in the post-partum period was 35.0 and 30.7 liters. The nitrogen balance and serum NPN values are shown in Fig. 7.

CASE 5 — E.F. (Fig. 6). This patient, aged 30 years, weighed 160 lb. on admission and lost 5½ lb. over a period of 15 days in the antepartum period. The aldosterone excretion varied between 15 and 32 μg.

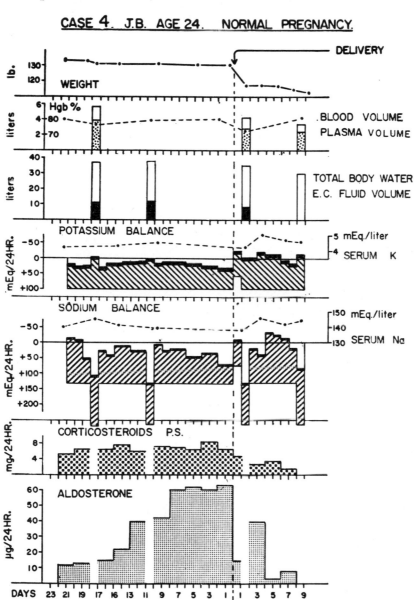

Fɪɢ. 5. Metabolic studies, Case 4 (J.B.).

per day and rapidly decreased following delivery to levels of 3 and 2 μg. per day. No aldosterone assay was carried out on the second day post partum, and it seems probable that a temporary rise which occurred

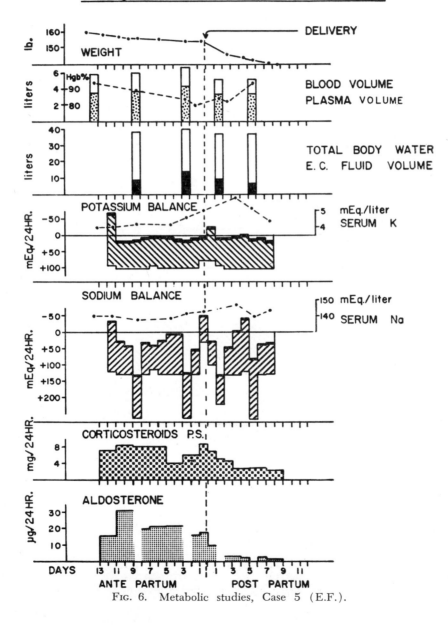

FIG. 6. Metabolic studies, Case 5 (E.F.).

in the other patients was missed in this one. This patient retained an average of 18 meq. sodium per day in the ante-partum period. The negative sodium balance on the day of delivery may be due in part to the low intake on that day. A second diuresis of sodium occurred later in the post-partum period. The blood and plasma volumes, as well as the total body water and sodium thiosulfate space, increased slightly up to

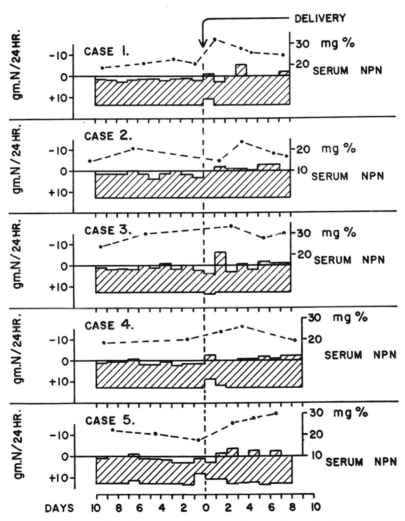

Fig. 7.   Nitrogen balances studies in Cases 1–5.

TABLE I

AVERAGE DAILY BALANCE FOR NITROGEN, POTASSIUM, AND SODIUM IN ANTE-PARTUM (AP) AND POST-PARTUM (PP) PERIODS AND EXCRETION OF ALDOSTERONE AND 17-OH-CORTICOSTEROIDS AND WEIGHT LOSS

	Period (days)	Weight loss (gm./24 hr.)	N (gm./24 hr.)	K (meq./24 hr.)	Na (meq./24 hr.)	Aldosterone (μg./24 hr.)	17-OH Corticosteroids (mg./24 hr.)
Case 1	30–20 AP	90.6	+0.7	+ 6	+13	27	5.3
	20–10 AP	0	+1.5	+ 7	+15	26	5.5
	10– 1 AP	68.0	+1.7	+17	+17	31	4.3
	1–12 PP	181.0	−0.2	+ 4	+ 6	12	3.1
Case 2	19–10 AP	0	+0.9	+ 4	+18	26	5.6
	10– 1 AP	90.6	+1.6	+11	+34	45	5.6
	1– 9 PP	362.0	−0.9	− 2	+ 6	19	4.9
Case 3	15–10 AP	45.3	+1.4	+13	+36	28	7.0
	10– 1 AP	90.6	+1.3	+13	+37	32	5.5
	1– 6 PP	159.0	−0.3	+ 1	+21	17	3.9
Case 4	20–10 AP	68.0	−0.5	+12	+23	20	6.3
	10– 1 AP	45.3	+1.4	+17	+41	55	6.7
	1– 8 PP	226.0	−0.8	− 7	0	16	3.0
Case 5	10– 1 AP	113.3	+0.9	+ 6	+18	19	6.8
	1– 6 PP	125.0	−0.8	− 2	+ 8	5	3.8

the time of delivery, and all showed significant decreases in the post-partum period. The nitrogen balance and values for serum NPN are shown in Fig. 7.

III. Correlation of Balances with Steroid Excretion

The average balances per day for 10-day periods or less in the ante- and post-partum periods are shown in Table I together with the average daily output of aldosterone and 17-OH corticosteroids and weight loss. This table brings out several facts. There is no correlation between the nitrogen balance and the weight lost nor does there appear to be any relationship between the retention of nitrogen and potassium. The changes in potassium and sodium balance follow the same trend except in patient 1 who shows an increasing retention of potassium just prior to delivery without similar changes in sodium balance. In both the ante-partum and early post-partum periods the sodium retention is more closely associated with changes in aldosterone than with 17-OH corticosteroid excretion.

IV. Effect of Administration of Sodium Thiosulfate on Sodium Balance

The additional sodium intake due to the administration of sodium thiosulfate for the measurement of extracellular fluid space varied from 125 to 137 meq. The percentage of sodium excreted on the days on which this determination was carried out is shown in Table II. Before delivery and up to the second post-partum day, 39.4 to 58.5% of the

TABLE II

PER CENT OF SODIUM EXCRETED BEFORE AND AFTER DELIVERY FOLLOWING ADMINISTRATION OF SODIUM THIOSULFATE

Days	Case 3	Case 4	Case 5
Ante partum			
18th	—	58.5	—
13th	56.5	—	—
11th	—	49.0	—
9th	—	—	49.5
5th	52.0	—	—
3rd	—	—	40.2
Post partum			
2nd	—	49.0	39.4
6th	—	—	68.0
7th	65.0	—	—
9th	—	68.0	—

total sodium intake was excreted. From the sixth to the ninth days post partum, 65 to 68% of the sodium was eliminated. At this time the aldosterone output had decreased to low levels. These results indicate that sodium was more readily retained during the pregnant state than after the first week of post partum.

V. Comments

These five normal pregnant women showed variations in their metabolic behavior although they were maintained on similar and constant intakes. In two of the cases there was a rapid accumulation of sodium and potassium in the last week of pregnancy, and this was associated with a rising level of urinary aldosterone. In the other three cases where the aldosterone values remained relatively constant, less variation was observed in the sodium balances. In each patient, however, the excretion of sodium and potassium followed somewhat similar trends although the magnitude of the changes seen in the sodium balance were greater than those observed in the potassium balance. When additional sodium was administered as sodium thiosulfate, a greater proportion of this was retained in the ante-partum period than in the post-partum period.

The excretion of sodium, potassium, and nitrogen fluctuated considerably in the post-partum periods although the patients continued to be maintained on the same intake. There appeared to be definite periods of diuresis of these constituents occurring simultaneously. While all patients showed a retention of sodium, potassium, and nitrogen in the ante-partum period, all gradually lost weight. This could not be explained by loss of water, as periodic measurements of total body water and blood volume showed that there appeared to be a slight expansion of these fluid spaces near term. These observations suggest that possibly the diet may not have been adequate and that fat was being utilized for the synthesis of lean tissue. Following parturition the positive balances previously observed tended to be reduced or to become negative.

The variations occurring in the levels of serum sodium appeared to be independent of change in balance. Only three of the patients consistently showed decreased levels of serum sodium in the ante-partum period while in the post-partum period higher levels were observed in agreement with some of the earlier investigations. Similar trends were noted for the levels of serum potassium, and only in one patient were the levels below the normal range before delivery.

The changes occurring in blood and plasma volumes, total body water, and sodium thiosulfate space following delivery are in accord with values reported by previous investigators (17, 18, 19, 20). In the ante-partum period it was not possible to correlate these findings with sodium balance or aldosterone excretion, as these determinations were made only at infrequent intervals.

Although fluctuations were observed in the excretion of the Porter-Silber corticosteroids, the values were higher in the ante-partum period than in the post-partum period. While increased levels of these hormones may contribute to some extent to the retention of sodium observed in late pregnancy, these metabolic studies reveal that in those cases where sodium was rapidly accumulating in the body little change in the excretion of these hormones was observed. This retention of sodium was more closely associated with a rising output of aldosterone rather than with changes in the excretion of 17-OH corticosteroids. Similarly in the post-partum period the diuresis of fluid and sodium was associated with a decrease in aldosterone excretion. This loss appeared to act as a stimulus, and in several of the patients a temporary rise in aldosterone excretion followed. This increase in aldosterone was always associated with a positive sodium balance. During this period the corticosteroids continued to decrease.

The stimulus for the increased secretion of aldosterone in pregnancy is not clear. The excretion of this hormone increases in the presence of an expanded total fluid and extracellular space, conditions which in the healthy nonpregnant individual lead to a reduction in aldosterone excretion (2, 3, 10). Recent studies of Bartter (1) suggest that the control of aldosterone secretion may reside in some undefined function of the intravascular volume. It is possible that the demands of the rapidly growing uterus and products of conception may in some manner alter the fluid balances in the maternal organism and lead to a decrease in the "effective intravascular volume" controlling aldosterone excretion. At the present time satisfactory methods are not yet available to test this theory.

VI. Summary

Metabolic-balance studies carried out in late pregnancy and in the early puerperium show that changes in sodium excretion are more closely associated with changes in aldosterone excretion than with 17-OH-corticosteroid excretion. Following parturition a diuresis of fluid, sodium, potassium, and nitrogen occurs simultaneously. While the excretion of 17-OH-corticosteroids rapidly returns to levels observed in the nonpregnant state, the aldosterone excretion fluctuates and is inversely related to the excretion of sodium.

Acknowledgments

We are greatly indebted to Dr. I. Dyrenfurth and Dr. L. Caligaris for their assistance in these investigations; to Dr. M. Sabin for the clinical supervision of the patients; to Dr. L. McLeod for the determination of total body water and sodium thiosulfate space; and to Dr. L. Lowenstein for the measurement of total blood and plasma volume.

References

1. Bartter, F. C., *Scand. J. Clin. & Lab. Invest.* **10**, Suppl. 31, 50 (1957).
2. Bartter, F. C., Liddle, G. W., Duncan, L. E., Jr., Barber, Y. K., and Delea, C., *J. Clin. Invest.* **35**, 1306 (1956).
3. Beck, J. C., Dyrenfurth, I., Giroud, C. J. P., and Venning, E. H., *A.M.A. Arch. Internal Med.* **96**, 463 (1955).
4. Brodie, B. B., Axelrod, J., Soberman, R., and Levy, B. B., *J. Biol. Chem.* **179**, 25 (1949).
5. Coons, C. M., Coons, R. R., and Shiefelbusch, A. T., *J. Biol. Chem.* **104**, 759 (1934).
6. Frank, H. A., and Carr, M. H., *J. Lab. Clin. Med.* **45**, 973 (1955).
7. Gornall, A. G., Gwilliam, C., and Hall, A. E. D., *J. Clin. Endocrinol. and Metabolism* **16**, 950 (1956).
8. Koczorek, K. R., Wolff, H. P., and Beer, M. L., *Klin. Wochschr.* **35**, 497 (1957).
9. Martin, J. D., and Mills, I. H., *Brit. Med. J.* **2**, 571 (1956).
10. Muller, A. F., Riondel, A. M., and Mach, R. S., *Lancet* **270**, 831 (1956).
11. Porter, C. G., and Silber, R. H., *J. Biol. Chem.* **185**, 201 (1950).
12. Rinsler, M. G., and Rigby, B., *Brit. Med. J.* **2**, 966 (1957).
13. Venning, E. H., and Dyrenfurth, I., *J. Clin. Endocrinol. and Metabolism* **16**, 426 (1956).
14. Venning, E. H., Dyrenfurth, I., and Giroud, C. J. P., *J. Clin. Endocrinol. and Metabolism* **16**, 1326 (1956).
15. Venning, E. H., Dyrenfurth, I., Sabin, M., Lowenstein, L., and Beck, J. C., *J. Clin. Endocrinol. and Metabolism* in press.
16. Venning, E. H., Primrose, T., Caligaris, L. C. S., and Dyrenfurth, I., *J. Clin. Endocrinol. and Metabolism* **17**, 473 (1957).
17. Chesley, L. C., and Boog, J. M., *Surg. Gynecol. Obstet.* **77**, 261 (1943).
18. Caton, W. L., Roby, C. C., Reid, D. E., and Gibson, J., *Am. J. Obstet. Gynecol.* **57**, 471 (1949).
19. Tysoe, F. W., and Lowenstein, L., *Am. J. Obstet. Gynecol.* **60**, 1187 (1950).
20. Seitchik, J., and Alper, C., *Am. J. Obstet. Gynecol.* **68**, 1540 (1954).

Discussion

CHAIRMAN: G. PINCUS

H. HELLER: I should like to ask Dr. Venning a question and also make a comment.

Going through the literature on the changes in water metabolism and pregnancy, I have been very confused by the contradictory opinions and reports. Is there any clear evidence that water is retained in the pregnant women beyond the requirements of the fetus and the reproductive organs? Can Dr. Venning help me by giving me her conclusions?

Secondly, she mentioned the difficulty of explaining the potassium and nitrogen diuresis. I would suspect—admittedly purely from results on animals—that oxytocin rather than vasopressin may have something to do with this. Oxytocin has been shown to increase urinary potassium as well as sodium excretion under certain circumstances. I would like to have her comment on that.

E. H. VENNING: We feel that the methods that have been used for measuring total body water and extracellular fluid space are not sensitive enough to enable us to place too much emphasis on these changes.

There have been studies done where sodium has been measured in the products of conception, the uterus, placenta, fetus and amniotic fluid, and blood lost at the time of delivery. These authors claim that the amount of sodium retained by the woman during pregnancy exceeded that which was lost at delivery.

I don't know of any exact determination with regard to water balance. One might assume that water loss or retention would follow sodium to some extent.

It is true that after delivery all these patients lose weight in a much more rapid fashion than they did prior to delivery, although maintained on the same diet. Their blood volume and total body water continued to decrease over the period studied in the puerperium and I understand it takes several weeks for them to come into equilibrium. At the end of these studies we are still at a stage where the blood volume and total body water is increased above that which is found in normal nonpregnant females.

W. V. MACFARLANE: Dr. Venning has presented an account of many nicely controlled events here, but there is one other on which we have made some experiments: that is temperature.

I do not know what the thermal picture was for these patients; but this same type of endocrine picture does appear. If the human creature is made to sweat, there is about 24–48 hours later, in a cool environment, diuresis. Sweating is associated with almost immediate aldosterone production and the diuresis is primarily of sodium and to a lesser extent of potassium.

Some of the changes recorded in pregnancy could conceivably be due to the different thermal environments in which the patients existed. I would be interested to know if the patients were in air-conditioned quarters in Montreal.

The other matter that is very interesting is the very large sodium retentions which occur late in pregnancy without weight gain, but rather with weight loss. You could think perhaps of fat being reduced and replaced by water but it does not look as though the fluid volume increases proportionately to the sodium retention.

There are two possibilities—one being storage in the fetus. That does not seem anywhere near enough to account for some of those data.

The sodium must, therefore, I suppose go into the bone. I wonder if perhaps some Na^{24} or something of this sort might help in resolving the distribution.

Is the aldosterone there as a cause or an effect? Bull in Belfast maintains that it is the mean atrial pressure that determines aldosterone output. So, if fluid begins to be retained, perhaps by estrogen, aldosterone could be a product of increased stimulation of some receptor mechanism for volume, which would make it a secondary product rather than a primary cause of any of these fluid disturbances.

I don't know if you have opinions on this.

E. H. VENNING: I really do not know whether it is cause or effect. After delivery, it seems as if it might be the result of the diuresis, that loss of fluid and sodium might stimulate aldosterone production. During pregnancy I suspect that changes occurring in the maternal circulation are stimulating aldosterone production and this in turn must have some physiological effect. One cannot quite rule out an effect of aldosterone upon sodium metabolism.

It is very difficult with these types of experiments to measure the so-called "critical spaces" in order to determine what is actually happening in the body. All we are measuring is the total turnover per day.

In the ante-partum period, the patients were not sweating. I think Dr. Beck could answer this question better than I could. I don't know about the days immediately after delivery. We certainly have a great variation in temperature in Montreal and these patients were not in air-conditioned rooms.

J. C. BECK: These patients were in cool rooms. The only excessive sweating which occurred would be on the day of delivery. There was none either ante partum or in the post-partum period. There are a couple of other things that I think one might mention.

The first is pure hypothesis and that is that the post-partum loss of potassium and nitrogen which is seen, might be due to the mobilization of a great deal of the breakdown products of uterine muscle which must in part be excreted.

The other feature, of course, is that delivery is a stress to the organism and a portion of the observed rise in urinary nitrogen and potassium might be the classical metabolic response to damage, which has been so well described.

This might also be true of the secondary rise in aldosterone which is seen post partum and is something which one again can hypothesize about. This temporary second peak usually occurring in the 24–48-hour period is very similar to the temporary rise which Dr. Venning and our associates have observed in patients undergoing surgical operations.

Finally, a few comments about Dr. Heller's suggestions.

The problem of the measurement of fluid comparments in man is a very vexing one, indeed, because of poor methods. Similarly the problem of relating an increase, if such is demonstrated, to the body mass of a pregnant woman is an almost impossible one. People who have attempted to relate it to a gain in body weight have been unsuccessful and these factors have led to much of the confusion in the literature. Relating it to changes in subcutaneous adipose tissue thickness has been attempted, and all these have been unsatisfactory.

However, I think that the progressive loss of weight which follows delivery in spite of a constant dietary intake and the post-partum diuresis certainly suggest that increased amounts of fluid were aboard which are gotten rid of in the post-partum period.

P. TROEN: I wonder whether the role of the placenta in relation to the production of hormones—either 17-hydroxycorticosteroids or aldosterone—might be more accurately represented as a potential one—perhaps fulfilled in some pregnancies and not in others or, indeed, even changing in varying times in the same pregnancy. The appropriate conditions for placental production are not yet clear. Although this may not be as satisfying teleologically to some as an all-or-none role for the placenta, it seems at present the best way of resolving such troublesome data as the inconstant presence of glucocorticoids or aldosterone in the urine of adrenalectomized pregnant women such as has just been presented—as well as the data on corticosteroid production by the perfused placenta as presented this morning.

Finally, in relation to aldosterone production by the placenta, I had not mentioned this finding this morning because it is very preliminary, but in our placental perfusates there has been some material with some physicochemical characteristics of aldosterone. It is inconstant and has not been subjected to bioassay.

W. PEARLMAN: Perhaps there is another explanation for aldosterone production in adrenalectomized pregnant women and that is the possibility that placental progesterone reaches the fetal adrenal cortex to undergo conversion to aldosterone. The tremendous outpouring of progesterone into the blood stream in late pregnancy is impressive and, as Dr. Zander has pointed out, a goodly portion of placental progesterone enters the fetal circulation.

E. H. VENNING: I think that is a possibility, Dr. Pearlman.

G. PINCUS: I would like to ask one question about the possible role of anxiety in your patients. Remember you found that students at examination exhibited increased aldosterone secretion. Were these patients perhaps a little upset?

E. H. VENNING: I would think parturition would be a very disturbing experience. Actually it did not rise immediately before parturition. The rise in aldosterone occurred after delivery and following or associated with the diuresis of fluid and sodium.

The Neurohypophysis during the Estrous Cycle, Pregnancy, and Lactation

H. HELLER

Department of Pharmacology, University of Bristol, England

I. Introduction

Much interest has lately been taken in the role of oxytocin in relation to seminal transport, labor, and lactation, but little attention has been paid to neurohypophyseal function as a whole during the various phases of the reproductive cycle. Considering the clinical importance of changes in the water metabolism during the menstrual cycle and pregnancy, this is rather astonishing. Alterations in the secretion of the antidiuretic hormone (ADH) in these physiological situations and during lactation would not be unexpected. Adrenocortical and ovarian function vary in these conditions. That is to say there are fluctuations in the secretion of substances which are known to influence the metabolism of water and the electrolytes and which may therefore be suspected to evoke a regulatory response of the neurohypophysis. There is also the possibility—suggested by recent findings of Dingman (15, 16) and Gaunt (19) and their co-workers that cortisol-like compounds influence hormone storage in the posterior pituitary by acting on the hypothalamus. Similar effects may conceivably be exerted by other steroid hormones. A further type of evidence may be adduced in this connection: The results of Harris (22), Cross (9), Abrahams and Pickford (1), and Bisset *et al.* (4) show that whatever the stimulus applied to the neurohypophysis, the gland liberates simultaneously both vasopressin and oxytocin. In other words whenever the secretion of oxytocin is postulated, the release of ADH and the possibility of its effect on water metabolism has to be taken into account.

These and similar considerations suggested an inquiry into the role of ADH during the reproductive cycle. Ideally, perhaps, hormone concentrations in the blood should have been measured, but very low levels of ADH in plasma cannot as yet be estimated with the necessary precision. Measurements of the output of antidiuretic activity in the urine meet the difficulty that the recovery from the urine even of injected vasopressin varies considerably: in adult male rats, for example, from 3 to 29% of the injected dose (24). As a first approach therefore the hormone content and the vasopressin:oxytocin ratios (V/O) were determined in pituitary glands obtained from pregnant and lactating rats, and from rats killed during the various stages of the estrous cycle.

A discussion of these results forms the first part of this paper. However, since hormone concentrations in the blood are influenced not only by the rate of release but also by the rate of removal, some recent experiments on the fate of vasopressin and oxytocin in male and female rats will also be reported.

II. Hormone Content and Hormone Ratios in the Neurohypophysis of Rats during the Estrous Cycle

Figure 1 shows the content of pressor and oxytocin activity in the posterior pituitary of groups of adult albino rats which were killed by decapitation at various stages of their estrous cycle. The glands were extracted with 0.25% acetic acid immediately after removal. Pressor activity was assayed on the rat blood pressure (10) and oxytocic activity on the rat uterus (29). Significant differences were obtained between rats in diestrus and rats in proestrus and between animals in estrus and animals in metestrus. The differences in hormone content between proestrus and estrus were not significant, but the differences between the rats in diestrus and estrus were highly so ($P < 0.001$). It will also be noted that the amount of glandular pressor and oxytocic activity during the cycle fluctuated in the same directions and to about the same extent. Consequently the V/O ratios during the four stages shown remained much the same. These results were calculated by comparing glandular hormone content per 100 gm. body weight, but they were not materially affected by using different criteria of comparison such as hormone content per gland or hormone content per milligram neuro-hypophyseal tissue.

The mean hormone content of glands removed in diestrus compared with that of male rats of the same strain which had been killed during the same period of experimentation ($P_V > 0.6$, $P_O > 0.4$).*

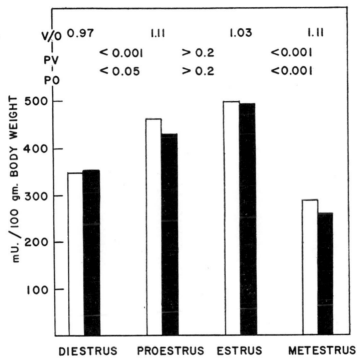

FIG. 1. Hormone content of the neurohypophysis of adult albino rats during four stages of the estrous cycle. □ = pressor activity; ■ = oxytocic activity; V/O = vasopressin:oxytocin ratio; P = limit for the probability of a difference between two series.

It would appear then that vasopressin and oxytocin accumulate in the pituitary during the follicular phase of the estrous cycle and that this is followed by a rather more abrupt depletion after ovulation. Figure 2 summarizes these results in a semischematic diagram.

The interpretation of these findings in terms of changes of neuro-hypophyseal function is difficult. As usual in this type of experiment one

---

* P_V = Limit for the probability of a difference between the two series of vasopressin estimations. P_O = the same for oxytocin.

cannot say whether, for example, an increase of glandular hormone content signifies decreased release or increased synthesis. Nor can much guidance be obtained from the comparatively scanty studies of the water metabolism during the estrous and menstrual cycles. Krohn and Zuckerman (31), who measured the urine output of a pig-tailed macaque (*Macaca nemestrina*) during its menstrual cycle, noted a "dramatic rise" in urine volume at the middle of the cycle when, as Zuckerman (51) has shown, the amount of estrogen available is con-

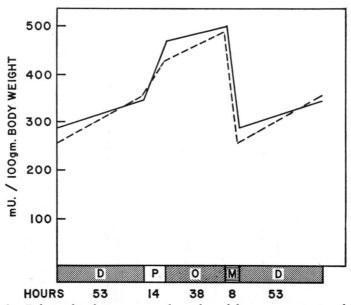

FIG. 2. Relationship between neurohypophyseal hormone content and the time course of the phases of the estrous cycle. Semidiagrammatic. Duration of phases according to Long and Evans (32). ——— = pressor activity; – – – – = oxytocic activity; D = diestrus; P = proestrus; O = estrus; M = metestrus.

siderably reduced. Gilbert and Gillman (20) have reported similar findings in female baboons (*Papio ursinus*). However, the metabolic situation in this type of mammal is complicated by the special water requirements of the sexual skin. Similarly there is not much systematic information about the renal response to water ingestion during the menstrual or estrous cycle. Our own investigations on rats are not sufficiently advanced to be reported but Pickford (37) has observed marked changes in the pattern of water diuresis in dogs just before and during estrus: On the day before the appearance of vulval swelling became marked there was scarcely any increase in the rate of urine flow following the administration of the test dose of water. On the following days the response returned slowly to the excretory pattern usually seen in males. Cyclical fluctuations in the excretion of sodium and potassium were also observed in these experiments.

There is thus the suggestion that the changes in spontaneous urine output and in the response to an administered water load during the course of the female sexual cycle are related to the secretion of estrogens. But while this may be so, it must not be forgotten that cyclical edema in women occurs usually just before menstruation, i.e., during the luteal phase. Moreover, the edema may be of a character which is held by Thorn (43) to be compatible with an increased release of ADH.

We have just started some experiments which may eventually throw some light on the influence of estrogens on the neurohypophysis. When 0.5 µg. estradiol monobenzoate per 100 gm. were injected for 3 days into bilaterally ovariectomized rats, high values for pressor and oxytocic activity were found in the glands, which were, however, not significantly different from those in ovariectomized rats receiving control injections. Another group of ovariectomized animals were injected with 2.5 µg. estradiol per 100 gm. The glandular vasopressin content was again as high as in rats in estrus ($P > 0.5$), but this time there was a clear difference ($P < 0.01$) between these animals and the controls, whose hormone levels resembled those found in rats in diestrus ($P > 0.3$). The number of glands analyzed is as yet insufficient to permit valid conclusions, but it is clear that these experiments will have to be continued and that the effect of progesterone on ovariectomized animals will also have to be investigated.

III. The Neurohypophysis during Pregnancy

Figure 3 shows the mean hormone content of the neurohypophyses of rats killed during the first, second, and third weeks of pregnancy. There was little difference between these stages both in terms of vasopressin and oxytocin content and in the values for the V/O ratios. The mean values for vasopressin were as high as those for animals in estrus ($P > 0.5$). The values for oxytocin were somewhat lower, approximately on the level of those of rats in diestrus ($P > 0.7$). The V/O ratios in the pregnant animals were higher than those found in the glands of nonpregnant rats, but the significance of this finding is uncertain. Acher et al. (2), who investigated rats killed on the tenth and the twenty-first day of gestation found likewise little difference between the hormone content of the glands of their two groups.

The hormone content of glands removed shortly before and during labor has not as yet been investigated.

The high hormone content found throughout pregnancy is in some contradiction to the results of Malandra (33), who observed an increase of Gomori-positive material in the pituitaries of rats during the second half of pregnancy. However, it may be assumed that the ac-

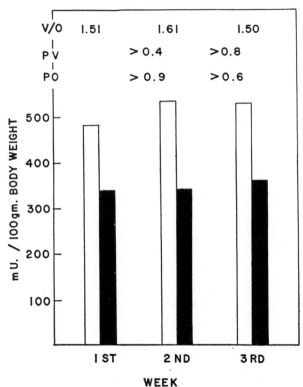

FIG. 3.   Hormone content of the neurohypophysis of rats killed during the first, second and third weeks of pregnancy. □ = pressor activity; ■ = oxytocic activity; V/O = vasopressin:oxytocin ratio; P = limit for the probability of a difference between two series.

cumulation of active material is easier—and therefore sooner detectable by bioassay than by the evaluation of morphological criteria.

With regard to the possibility of changes of posterior pituitary function during pregnancy, it may be recalled that Morrison (35) was unable to demonstrate water retention in pregnant rats in excess of that required for the formation of reproductive tissue. Even more significantly, Hoffman et al. (28) failed to find an impairment of water diuresis in normal pregnant rats. It may well be that the relatively high levels of the glandular storage of vasopressin found in pregnancy are determined by the increased secretion of corticosteroids (11, 34) and that the effects of the increased production of estrogens are antagonized by the diuretic action of the cortisol-like hormones (19) or by progesterone which, under certain conditions has also been shown (39, 49) to produce a diuresis and to lower body water. It is clear however, that these complex endocrine interrelationships require further elucidation.

IV. Hormone Content and Hormone Ratios in the Neuro-hypophysis of Lactating Rats

The hormone content and the hormone ratios in glands of lactating rats have been investigated by Dicker and Tyler (13) and Acher et al. (2). Both groups of workers found that the V/O ratio increased significantly during lactation. We were therefore surprised when estimation of the V/O ratio in a series of 16 lactating rats killed from 1 to 21 days after labor gave a mean ratio of 1.15 ± 0.11. This is a value well within the limits found in males or nonpregnant adult females. However, when compared with rats during the last week of pregnancy (Fig. 4) the content of both pressor and oxytocic activity had decreased markedly ($P < 0.001$) during lactation. This is in agreement with similar findings of van Dyke et al. (45) in lactating dogs but disagrees with the report of Acher et al. (2).

The decrease in hormone content found is in accordance with reports (5, 33, 41) that the amount of neurosecretory material in the rat posterior pituitary decreases during lactation.

But why were our V/O ratios so much lower than those obtained by the other workers [Acher et al. (2), for instance, obtained ratios up to 3]? The methods of assay were the same, but, while we extracted the glands with acetic acid immediately after removal, most of their results seem to have been obtained by following the pharmacopoeial procedure, i.e., they first "dried" the glands with several portions of acetone and only then extracted with acetic acid. We therefore repeated the assays of extracts of glands from lactating rats but this time used the "acetone method." The results were as follows: The mean values for vasopressin were much the same as before, but we found considerably less oxytocic activity in this type of extract. The mean V/O ratio for 22 glands was 1.64 ± 0.10, i.e., it was significantly higher ($P < 0.001$) than that obtained with the other method of extraction.

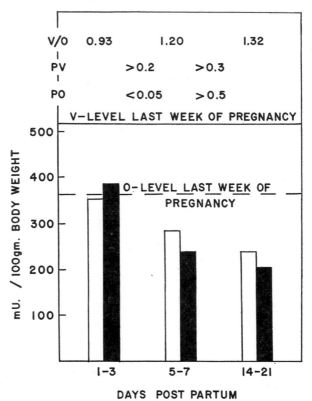

FIG. 4. Hormone content of the neurohypophysis of lactating rats. ▢ = pressor activity; ▨ = oxytocic activity; V = vasopressin; O = oxytocin; *P* = limit for the probability of a difference between two series.

A. The Solubility of Oxytocin in Acetone

This difference suggested that oxytocin is more soluble in acetone, or, more correctly, in watery acetone, than vasopressin. The following experiment was therefore done: Twenty posterior pituitary glands of adult male rats were dried over P_2O_5, powdered and mixed. The powder was then divided into five portions. One of these was extracted with acetic acid only, the others were first treated with acetone to which small volumes of water had been deliberately added. All extracts were assayed for pressor and oxytocic activity in the usual manner. Pretreatment with the acetone-water mixtures did not demonstrably alter the vasopressin content of the gland powder. However, as revealed by the increase in the V/O ratios (Fig. 5), the amounts of oxytocic activity residual after treatment with acetone decreased with a rise in the water content of the acetone mixture. It ought to be stressed that it is very difficult to free acetone completely of water and that therefore even our "dry" acetone contained at least 0.1% water.

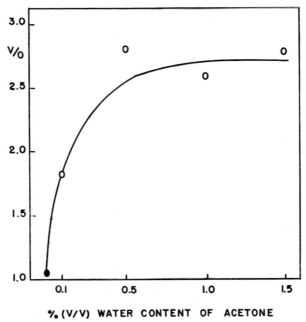

%(V/V) WATER CONTENT OF ACETONE

Fig. 5. Effect of the water content of acetone on the solubility of oxytocin. O = V/O ratio in the acetic acid extract of powdered rat neurohypophyses after preliminary treatment with watery acetone. ● = V/O ratio obtained by extraction with 0.25% acetic acid only. The same powder was used throughout. For further details see text.

Similar experiments were done with fresh ox glands, half of which were extracted with acetic acid only and half according to the procedure prescribed by the British Pharmacopoeia, which involves preliminary drying with acetone. The mean V/O ratios obtained with the latter method tended again to be higher but the differences were within the fiducial limits of the assay methods. It had therefore to be shown by other means that oxytocin was removed by the organic solvent: Acetone with which neurohypophyseal tissue had been treated was evaporated under reduced pressure and the residue taken up in saline. Using a recently developed method (26) which permits the visualization of micrograms of active neurohypophyseal peptides, the solution was then subjected to unidimensional chromatography (Fig. 6). A spot at the same R_f value as that of synthetic oxytocin (Syntocinon,

Sandoz) will be noted. Another chromatogram (Fig. 7, AE) of the
acetone residue solution was not stained, the areas parallel to reference spots of Pitressin and Syntocinon were extracted and the eluates
assayed. No pressor or antidiuretic activity was found but the test
for oxytocic activity was positive. A further test showed that this
oxytocic activity could be inactivated with thioglycolate. There can
therefore be little doubt about the preferential solubility of oxytocin
in watery acetone. This result agrees with the general experience (3, 17,
30) that oxytocin is better soluble in organic solvents than is vasopressin.

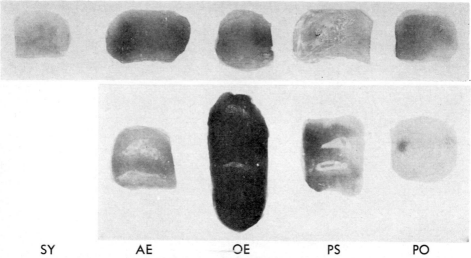

SY   AE   OE   PS   PO

Fig. 6.   Unidimensional chromatogram of posterior pituitary extracts and preparations.
SY = synthetic oxytocin (Syntocinon, Sandoz); AE = residue of acetone extract of fresh
ox posterior pituitary lobe dissolved in 0.9% NaCl solution; OE = acetic acid (0.25%)
extract of fresh ox posterior pituitary; PS = Pitressin (Parke, Davis & Co.); PO = Pitocin
(Parke, Davis & Co.). Spots were developed by the method of Heller and Lederis (26).
Amounts of preparation applied: Syntocinon, 1700 mU.; Pitressin, 1700 mU.; Pitocin,
3400 mU. For further explanations see text and Fig. 7.

While showing that *some* oxytocin is lost in the acetone when
pituitaries are extracted by the pharmacopoeial method these results
do not explain why ratios derived from acetone-treated glands of
lactating animals were higher than those of males or nonpregnant
females. Or—to put it in slightly different terms—they do not explain why the amount of acetone-extractable oxytocin was higher
in one instance than in the other. The phenomenon is not an isolated
one. It has also been encountered—and to an even more pronounced
degree—in another physiological situation, namely in newborn and
infant rats (Fig. 8).

The larger amounts of oxytocic activity extracted by acetone from the glands of lactating animals are not likely to have been due to differences between the water content of these glands and those of the controls. A large volume of acetone (about 6.5 ml. per milligram

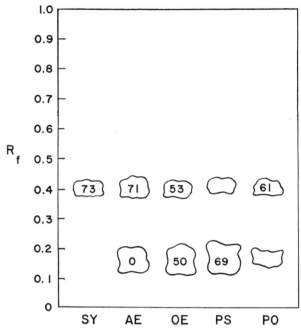

FIG. 7. Chromatogram of posterior pituitary extracts and preparations. SY = synthetic oxytocin (Syntocinon, Sandoz); AE = residue of acetone extract of fresh ox posterior pituitary dissolved in 0.9% NaCl solution; OE = acetic acid (0.25%) extract of fresh ox posterior pituitary; PS = Pitressin (Parke, Davis & Co.); PO = Pitocin (Parke, Davis & Co.). After the solution had been chromatographed the spots were eluted with distilled water and the eluates assayed biologically. The oxytocic activity was found at $R_f = 0.40$, the pressor activity at $R_f = 0.14$. The figures inside the spots denote the percentage recovery of the activities of the solutions applied at zero. Note that in contrast to Pitocin no spot at the R_f of vasopressin was found in the chromatogram of the Syntocinon solution. The "vasopressin spot" of the acetone residue solution (AE) contained no detectable pressor activity.

neurohypophyseal tissue) was used for extraction, which would make any differences between the dilution of the acetone by the water content of the glands negligible. Since the oxytocic activity of hypothalamic extracts was found to have the same R_f value as that of glandular oxytocin (26), it is also unlikely that the acetone-extractable oxytocic activity in the pituitary derived from a precursor of the glandular hormone with a different solubility. Whether, therefore, under certain circumstances oxytocin is more easily released by organic solvents from the cytoplasmic granules in which, according to Pardoe and Weatherall (36), it is held in the pituitary or whether, as again suggested by the results of these authors, the proportion of "free" to "bound" oxytocin may change, remains a subject for further enquiry.

How do the results just reported affect the question of the differential release of oxytocin during lactation? The following conclusions are tenta-

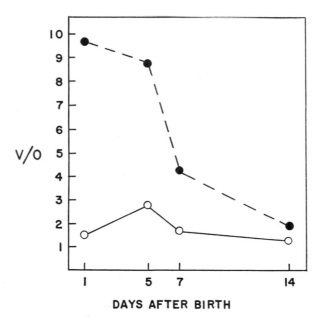

FIG. 8. Vasopressin:oxytocin ratio of the extract of infant rat pituitary glands. ●–––● = glands "dried" with acetone and subsequently extracted with dilute acetic acid; ○–––○ = glands extracted with acetic acid only.

tively offered: (a) Oxytocin *and* vasopressin are depleted from the posterior pituitary of the lactating rat. (b) The high V/O ratios previously reported for this species (2, 13) appear to be due to the preferential extraction of oxytocin by watery acetone. (c) Our failure to demonstrate preferential depletion of oxytocin in the glands of lactating rats may have been due to the state of our animals. It remains a possibility that it could be shown in rats killed immediately after suckling or in animals whose litters had not been artificially restricted to six as in the present series.

V. The Fate of Oxytocin in Male and Female Rats

A. THE FATE OF VASOPRESSIN

Ginsburg and Heller (21), Crawford and Pinkham (8), and Dicker (12) have shown that the antidiuretic activity of intravenously injected Pitressin* disappears very rapidly from the circulation in rats. The decay follows an exponential course, the half-life being in the region of 1 minute. The main sites of clearance are the liver and the kidneys. Both organs have been shown (27) to inactivate the hormone *in vitro* and *in vivo* with great rapidity. A small fraction of intravenously injected ADH appears in the urine within the first minutes after injection (27).

The quick disappearance of ADH from the circulation and its speedy inactivation in the kidneys may be regarded as a necessary correlate to Verney's (46) theory of the mechanism of water diuresis. This theory implies that after the ingestion of water the hypothalamic osmoreceptors are inhibited by the dilution of the blood and the resulting fall in effective osmotic pressure, and that therefore the release of ADH from the pituitary ceases. However, water diuresis would still not occur with the promptness it does unless the circulating hormone disappeared quickly and unless, presumably, any hormone in the renal tubular epithelium was also rapidly inactivated.

B. THE DISAPPEARANCE OF OXYTOCIN FROM THE CIRCULATION OF MALE RATS

It is difficult to make a similar physiological postulate for the inactivation of oxytocin, but it seemed of interest to study the fate of another cyclopeptide, and in particular one whose target organs differ from those of vasopressin. Such work has therefore been recently undertaken by my colleagues M. Ginsburg and M. W. Smith. They have developed a new method for the extraction of oxytocin from plasma which consists essentially in the precipitation of the plasma proteins with 10 volumes of dry acetone. The recovery of added oxytocin in twelve experiments was 84.5 ± 3.2%. The extracts were assayed on the superfused rat uterus.

When 200 mU. (milliunits) Pitocin per 100 gm. body weight were injected intravenously into anesthetized male rats, it was found (Fig. 9) that the disappearance of oxytocic activity followed an exponential course with a half-life of 1.66 ± 0.13 minutes, the plasma activity falling from 18.6 ± 1.4 mU./ml. one minute after injection to levels near the

---

* It is not known whether the batches used contained arginine- or lysine-vasopressin or a mixture of these peptides.

limit of the detectability (0.5 mU./ml.) 6 minutes later. Thus oxytocin seems to behave much like vasopressin both in the manner and in the rate of its clearance from the blood.

After ligation of the celiac and superior mesenteric arteries, division of the descending colon and left colic artery, and ligation of the portal vein, the disappearance of oxytocin was slightly retarded (half-life =

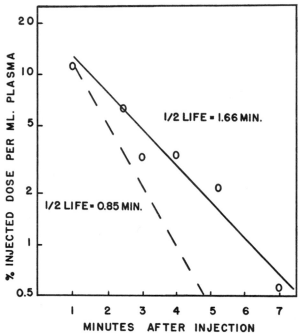

Fig. 9. Rate of disappearance of antidiuretic and oxytocic activity from the arterial blood of anesthetized *male* rats injected intravenously with 100 mU. Pitressin per 100 gm. or with 200 mU. Pitocin per 100 gm. ————— = antidiuretic activity; —o— = oxytocic activity. Semilogarithmic. Mean half-life of antidiuretic activity = 0.85 ± 0.03 minutes; mean half-life of oxytocic activity = 1.66 ± 0.13 minutes.

2.12 ± 0.2 minutes) while removal of both kidneys had a greater effect, increasing the half-life to 2.95 ± 0.2 minutes; in both circumstances the concentration in plasma fell exponentially with time (Fig. 10).

When both operations, i.e., bilateral nephrectomy *and* exclusion of the splanchnic vascular area were combined in the same animal, the concentration of oxytocin in plasma fell during the 6–8 minutes following the injection at a rate slower, but not significantly different from that in rats which had been nephrectomized only (Fig. 11). However, when the concentration of oxytocin reached between 3 and 7 mU. per milliliter of plasma a steady level was maintained, no further fall in concentration being observed up to 26 minutes after the injection. This finding suggests that in male rats the clearance of oxytocin—like that of vasopressin—is dependent upon the kidneys and organs of the splanchnic area.

The quick equilibration of oxytocin in a volume apparently larger than that of the inulin space in such animals raises an interesting question with regard to the state of the hormone in the blood. We (25)

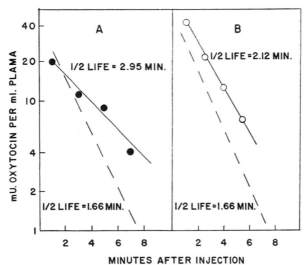

FIG. 10.   A.   Effect of bilateral nephrectomy on the rate of disappearance of oxytocic activity from the circulation of male rats. – – – = intact rats (mean half-life = 1.66 ± 0.13 minutes); ●———● = nephrectomized rats (mean half-life = 2.95 ± 0.20 minutes).   B.   Effect of exclusion of the splanchnic vascular bed. – – – – – intact rats (mean half-life – 1.66 ± 0.13 minutes); ○———○ = rats with splanchnic circulation excluded (mean half-life = 2.12 ± 0.20 minutes). All rats received 200 mU. Pitocin per 100 gm. intravenously.

have been able to show by means of dialysis experiments that vasopressin and oxytocin equilibrate at a higher level in (human) plasma than in saline. This is in agreement with the recently published findings of Thorn and Silver (44), who found that native ADH circulated as a "definite protein peptide complex," associated very likely with the β-globulin fraction. Dingman (14) has presented similar evidence. It would seem, therefore, that either the nature of the protein bond or complex is such that it does not prevent the penetration of oxytocin into the extravascular space or that the doses used in our experiments were so large that a fraction of the injected hormone remained unbound.

There are reasons why the values for the half-lives of oxytocin
and vasopressin as established in our experiments in rats should be
accepted with some reservation so far as the fate of the *endogenous*
hormones is concerned. We used Pitressin and Pitocin, and these

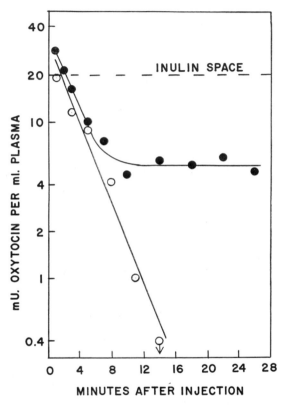

FIG. 11.   Effect of simultaneous exclusion of renal *and* splanchnic vascular beds
on the disappearance of oxytocic activity from the blood of male rats. O———O =
bilaterally nephrectomized rats; ●———● = nephrectomy plus exclusion of splanchnic circulation; – – – – = concentration of oxytocic activity if distributed in the
inulin space of the second group of animals. All rats received 200 mU. Pitocin per
100 gm. intravenously.

preparations can be shown in chromotograms (Fig. 6) (26) to contain
impurities [probably other peptides (38, 50)] with similar R_f values
as those of the neurohypophyseal hormones. Such "contaminating" compounds may conceivably compete with the hormones for removal. Experiments with pure vasopressins and oxytocin are therefore needed.
Moreover, the hormone doses which had to be injected were relatively

large and are likely to have produced vascular effects which may not occur at more physiological concentrations.

C. The Fate of Oxytocin in Female Rats in Estrus and during Lactation

The disappearance of oxytocin from the circulation of female rats in estrus was not significantly different from that in male rats. The half-life was 1.73 ± 0.0 minutes. Removal of the kidneys and exclusion

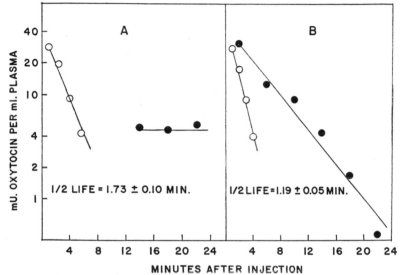

Fig. 12. A. Rate of disappearance of oxytocic activity from the blood of anesthetized *female* rats in estrus. O———O = intact rats (mean half-life = 1.73 ± 0.10 minutes); ●———● = rats with renal and splanchnic circulation excluded. B. Rate of disappearance of oxytocic activity from the blood of anesthetized lactating rats. O———O = intact rats (mean half-life = 1.19 ± 0.05 minutes); ●———● = rats with renal and splanchnic circulation excluded. All rats received 200 mU. Pitocin per 100 gm. intravenously.

of the splanchnic circulation in virgin females (Fig. 12A) resulted in the same phenomenon as in males, namely a fall in concentration during the first minutes after the intravenous injection and maintenance of the hormone level thereafter.

In intact lactating rats the half-life of oxytocin was significantly shorter (1.19 ± 0.05 minutes) than in intact female controls. When the renal and splanchnic vascular beds were excluded from the circulation in lactating animals, the oxytocic activity in the plasma did not "level out" as in the controls but fell to concentrations beyond the limits of detectability (Fig. 12B), suggesting that during lactation the clearance of oxytocin is not solely dependent on the kidneys and organs in the splanchnic vascular area.

We have so far not been able to extend our experiments to pregnant animals, but some interesting results on the plasma clearance of oxytocin in pregnant women have recently been obtained in Caldeyro-Barcia's laboratory by Sica-Blanco and Gonzales-Panizza (40): In mid-pregnancy when the concentration of "oxytocinase" [which has been found during pregnancy and in primates only (6)] is low (7, 48), they found a half-life of 3–5 minutes for intravenously infused oxytocin, a figure which—considering the differences in circulation time—agrees remarkably well with the results obtained in nonpregnant female rats.

D. Comparison of the Fate of Vasopressin and Oxytocin

Figure 13 compares the results of our experiments on the fate of vasopressin and oxytocin. The two peptides were found to have half-lives of a similar duration in the circulation and their main sites of clearance (the kidneys and the splanchnic vascular area) appear to be the same. It would seem therefore that changing two amino acids in the octopeptide chain does not produce important differences in the way the body handles these compounds. Since corticotropin (ACTH) has been shown (42) to have a half-life of similar duration as the neuro-

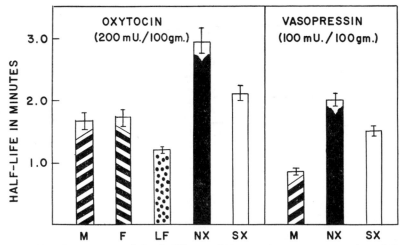

Fig. 13.   Comparison of the half-lives of Pitocin (oxytocic activity) and Pitressin (antidiuretic activity) under various experimental conditions. M = male rats, F = female rats, LF = lactating rats, NX = rats with bilateral nephrectomy, SX = rats with splanchnic circulation excluded.

hypophyseal hormones and since insulin (18, 23, 47) seems to share their main sites of inactivation, a common pathway for the metabolism of peptide hormones begins to emerge. However, the results obtained in lactating rats show that this pathway is liable to be modified under certain physiological conditions.

VI. Summary and Conclusions

The amounts of pressor and oxytocic activity in the neurohypophysis of adult female rats have been shown to rise during the follicular phase of the estrous cycle and to fall markedly and rapidly in metestrus. The vasopressin:oxytocin ratio did not alter significantly during the cycle. These results suggest that the neurohypophysis should be added to those endocrine glands which may undergo a phasic change during the estrous cycle.

The hormone content and the V/O ratios of pregnant rats remained essentially the same during the first, the second, and the third weeks of pregnancy.

In lactating rats which suckled their young there was a significant depletion in the amounts of pressor and oxytocic activity in the pituitary. No preferential depletion in oxytocin could be demonstrated but our results suggest that the state of the stored hormone or of structures concerned in its release is altered in lactating animals.

Oxytocin (Pitocin) injected intravenously into unanesthetized male and female rats has been shown to disappear rapidly from the circulation. The decrease of oxytocic activity followed an exponential course with a half-life of less than 2 minutes. The half-life of the antidiuretic activity of Pitressin was of similarly short duration.

As in the case of vasopressin, the kidneys and the splanchnic vascular area could be shown to be the main sites of clearance of oxytocin from the blood.

The half-life of oxytocin in lactating rats was significantly shorter than that in nonlactating controls. Further results suggest that in lactating animals the mammary gland participates to a substantial extent in the removal of oxytocin from the circulation.

References

1. Abrahams, V. C., and Pickford, M., *J. Physiol.* (*London*) **126**, 329 (1954).
2. Acher, R., Chauvet, J., and Olivry, G., *Biochim. et Biophys. Acta* **22**, 428 (1956).
3. Acher, R., and Fromageot, C., *Ergebn. Physiol. biol. Chem. u. exptl. Pharmakol.* **48**, 286 (1955).
4. Bisset, G. W., Lee, J., and Bromwich, A. F., *Lancet* ii, 1129 (1956).

5. Brightman, M. W., *Anat. Record* **121**, 268 (1955).
6. Caldeyro-Barcia, R., and Poseiro, J. J., paper presented at the conference on "The Uterus," New York, 1958. In press.
7. Carballo, M. A., and Méndez-Bauer, C., *Proc. 2nd Uruguayan Congr. Obstet. Gynecol. 1957,* in press.
8. Crawford, J. D., and Pinkham, B., *Endocrinology* **55**, 699 (1954).
9. Cross, B. A., *J. Physiol. (London)* **114**, 447 (1951).
10. Dekanski, J., *Brit. J. Pharmacol.* **7**, 567 (1952).
11. Devis, R., *Gynécol. et obstét.* **53**, 57 (1954).
12. Dicker, S. E., *J. Physiol. (London)* **124**, 464 (1954).
13. Dicker, S. E., and Tyler, C., *J. Physiol. (London)* **121**, 206 (1953).
14. Dingman, J. F., *Am. J. Med. Sci.* **235**, 79 (1958).
15. Dingman, J. F., and Despointes, R. H., *J. Clin. Endocrinol. and Metabolism* **16**, 936 (1956).
16. Dingman, J. F., and Thorn, G. W., *J. Clin. Endocrinol. and Metabolism* **15**, 871 (1955).
17. Dudley, H. W., *J. Pharmacol. Exptl. Therap.* **21**, 103 (1923).
18. Elgee, N. J., and Williams, R. H., *Proc. Soc. Exptl. Biol. Med.* **87**, 352 (1954).
19. Gaunt, R., Lloyd, C. W., and Chart, J. J., *in* "The Neurohypophysis" (H. Heller, ed.), p. 233. Academic Press, New York, 1957.
20. Gilbert, C., and Gillman, J., *S. African J. Med. Sci.* **20**, 133 (1955).
21. Ginsburg, M., and Heller, H., *J. Endocrinol.* **9**, 283 (1953).
22. Harris, G. W., *J. Physiol. (London)* **107**, 430 (1948).
23. Haugaard, N., Vaughan, M., Haugaard, E. S., and Stadie, W. C., *J. Biol. Chem.* **208**, 549 (1954).
24. Heller, H., *J. Pharm. and Pharmacol.* **7**, 225 (1955).
25. Heller, H., *Ciba Colloquia Endocrinol.* **11**, 3 (1957).
26. Heller, H., and Lederis, K., *Nature* **182**, 1231 (1958).
27. Heller, H., and Zaidi, S. M. A., *Brit. J. Pharmacol.* **12**, 284 (1957).
28. Hoffman, F. G., Knobil, E., and Caton, W. L., *Endocrinology* **55**, 114 (1954).
29. Holton, P., *Brit. J. Pharmacol.* **3**, 328 (1948).
30. Kamm, O., Aldrich, T. B., Grote, I. W., Rowe, L. W., and Bugbee, E. P., *J. Am. Chem. Soc.* **50**, 572 (1928).
31. Krohn, P. L., and Zuckerman, S., *J. Physiol. (London)* **88**, 369 (1937).
32. Long, J. A., and Evans, H. M., *Mem. Univ. Calif.* **6**, 1 (1922). Cited from Mandl, A. M., *J. Exptl. Biol.* **28**, 576 (1951).
33. Malandra, B., *Z. Zellforsch. u. mikroskop. Anat.* **43**, 594 (1956).
34. Martin, J. D., and Mills, K. H., *Clin. Sci.* **17**, 137 (1958).
35. Morrison, S. D., *J. Physiol. (London)* **134**, 650 (1956).
36. Pardoe, A. U., and Weatherall, M., *J. Physiol. (London)* **127**, 201 (1955).
37. Pickford, M., *in* "Modern Views on the Secretion of Urine" (F. R. Winton, ed.), p. 128. Churchill, London, 1956.
38. Ramachandra, L. K., and Winnick, T., *Biochim. et Biophys. Acta* **23**, 533 (1957).
39. Selye, H., and Basset, L., *Proc. Soc. Exptl. Biol. Med.* **44**, 502 (1940).
40. Sica-Blanco, Y., and Gonzales-Panizza, V., *Proc. 2nd Uruguayan Congr. Obstet. Gynecol. 1957,* in press.
41. Stutinsky, F., *Ann. endocrinol. (Paris)* **14**, 722 (1953).
42. Sydnor, K. L., and Sayers, G., *Proc. Soc. Exptl. Biol. Med.* **83**, 729 (1953).

43. Thorn, G. W., *Am. J. Med.* **23**, 507 (1957).
44. Thorn, N. A., and Silver, L., *J. Exptl. Med.* **105**, 575 (1957).
45. van Dyke, H. B., Adamsons, K., Jr., and Engel, S. L., *in* "The Neurohypophysis" (H. Heller, ed.), p. 65. Academic Press, New York, 1957.
46. Verney, E. B., *Proc. Roy. Soc.* **B135**, 25 (1947).
47. Weisberg, H. F., Friedman, A., and Levine, R., *Am. J. Physiol.* **172**, 709 (1949).
48. Werle, E., and Semm, K., *Arch. Gynäkol.* **187**, 449 (1956).
49. Wilbrand, U., and Humke, W., *Z. Geburtshilfe u. Gynäkol.* **144**, 183 (1955).
50. Winnick, T., Winnick, R. E., Acher, R., and Fromageot, C., *Biochim. et Biophys. Acta* **18**, 488 (1955).
51. Zuckerman, S., *J. Physiol.* (*London*) **86**, 31P (1936).

Discussion

CHAIRMAN: F. L. HISAW

E. H. FRIEDEN: With reference to the figure which Dr. Heller showed of the disappearance of oxytocin in animals in which both the kidney and the splanchnic circulation were removed, I would like to suggest a possibility other than explaining this entirely on the basis of distribution into tissue spaces.

Many years ago du Vigneaud showed that the posterior lobe hormones, when treated with reducing agents, did not, as many other hormones do, show complete inactivation. Instead, a rather curious thing happened. As I recall, the activity of these substances was reduced to about half of the initial activity under *in vitro* conditions with a variety of reducing agents.

It might be possible that some of this apparent inactivation might simply be due to the specific redox conditions in the circulation at the time, resulting in a partial reduction of the disulfide group in the hormone.

H. HELLER: I am very interested in this suggestion. But if it applied, the neurohypophyseal hormones should also be rapidly inactivated *in vitro*. However, we found no decrease in antidiuretic or oxytocic activity when rat blood was incubated with Pitressin for 30 minutes.

S. J. FOLLEY: I was interested in Professor Heller's results on the ratio of oxytocin and vasopressin in the posterior pituitary of the lactating rat.

I would like to mention briefly some results on goats obtained in our laboratory a few years ago: the object of these experiments was primarily to see whether we could detect any depletion in either of the two principles, particularly oxytocin, as a result of milking. The experiments were carried out by Dr. Margaret Macaulay, and she assayed goat posterior lobes for oxytocic activity by the isolated rat uterus method and for vasopressin activity on the blood pressure of the anesthetized rat. She wasn't able to do a large series of experiments because she had to leave the department before the research was completed; but I thought you might be interested to hear her results. These show that the ratio of the two hormones was unity in almost every case, both in dry goats and in lactating goats, irrespective of whether they were killed immediately after milking or after an interval of 24 hours, that is, when the udders were engorged with milk. Lactation had no effect on the ratio which was usually one to one, and we could detect no depletion of either hormone as a result of milking.

However, later studies which have indicated the probable amounts of oxytocin released in response to the milking stimulus, under physiological conditions, have shown that we could not have expected to detect any depletion because amounts released are rather small in comparison with the oxytocic content of the goat posterior pituitary.

H. HELLER: I am, of course, well acquainted with the interesting findings of Dr. Folley's laboratory. It is quite conceivable that different species of mammals behave differently. Differential depletion in lactating goats may not be demonstrable —or may not be present—but it has, as he knows, been reported to occur in rats and in dogs. However, I think we have now shown that another phenomenon obtains in the glands of lactating rats, namely a change in the physicochemical state of at least part of the glandular oxytocic hormone content which, if one is permitted to think teleologically, may be aimed at facilitating the release of oxytocin in a situation where larger quantities are needed.

S. ZUCKERMAN: Would Professor Heller elaborate a bit further about the variations in the hormonal content of the posterior pituitary during the phases of the estrous cycle? You referred to observations which I made some twenty years ago on the extraordinary changes which take place in the water balance of the pig-tailed monkey; and you also referred to the fact that similar changes take place in the baboon. They also take place, I believe, in other species of mammal, and the magnitude of the phenomenon is worth noting. I once had a baboon—before the period of the study of the pig-tailed monkey—which on one occasion had retained in its sexual skin an amount of water equal to 30% of its body weight.

You have demonstrated phasic variations in the hormonal content of the neuro-hypophysis. I am wondering whether you regard them as being somehow directly responsible for the changes in the water balance of the tissues of the body during the cycle, or whether you regard them as representing a secondary or accessory mechanism which operates, say *via* the kidney, in order to retain fluid in the body —fluid which has been "bound" as a result of hormonal mechanisms quite distinct from those which you describe now. The changes in water retention and elimination are so pronounced in species of monkey with a sexual skin that I think it reasonable to suppose that more than one mechanism is involved. That is to say, a mechanism which is concerned with the retention and release of water in the tissues, both intracellular and intercellular—and another which operates, say, on the kidney.

I should be very grateful if you would expand a little more your views, or your speculations, on this particular topic.

H. HELLER: I think you have put your finger on the most important point. There are obviously two possibilities. First, the changes in the hormone content of the neurohypophysis during the cycle may be due to a regulatory response of the gland to distortions of the body water compartments caused primarily by one or several steroid hormones. On the other hand, I suppose that at this stage we cannot exclude the possibility that the neurohypophysis is somehow in phase with the changing functions of the anterior pituitary during the estrous cycle. And there again one might ask oneself whether the two glands are, as it were, working in series or working in parallel. I think that these are possibilities that must be explored experimentally.

S. ZUCKERMAN: May I add a further point? The balance of probability, I think, is that we have two mechanisms working in parallel—one mechanism operating on the kidney and another which exercises its effect on the tissues generally and par-ticularly on those of the reproductive tract. I think it is worth recording here that fluid which is deposited in the sexual skin—and I believe in all the reproductive organs—as a result of estrogenic stimulation cannot be retained there by means of the administration of vasopressin after the estrogenic stimulus ceases operating.

I think it is worth noting this fact although I am fully aware that since these experiments were carried out there have been considerable advances in our knowledge of the pharmacology of the posterior lobe. No doubt one ought to repeat the work with much larger quantities of vasopressin.

H. HELLER: I heartily agree with this. While there have been considerable advances in our knowledge of the effects of the neurohypophyseal and adrenocortical hormones on the metabolism of water generally, astonishingly little experimental work has been done on the water metabolism during the estrous and menstrual cycles since you published your papers. Moreover, while the influence of various steroid hormones on the water metabolism during the menstrual and estrous cycles and during pregnancy has at least been considered, the posterior pituitary appears to have been forgotten. It seems to me from our results that its function during these physiological conditions should at last be investigated, quite irrespective of the possibility that there may be direct effects of the steroid hormones on the water metabolism which have no connection with changes in neurohypophyseal function.

The Physiology of Relaxin in Laboratory Animals

Bernard G. Steinetz, Vivian L. Beach, and Robert L. Kroc

Warner-Lambert Research Institute, Morris Plains, New Jersey

I. Introduction

A. Pubic Symphysis and Connective Tissue Effects of Relaxin

Until recently, the function(s) of relaxin have been considered to be related primarily to the softening of the pelvic ligaments during pregnancy in many mammalian forms [for reviews see Hisaw and Zarrow (42) and Sher and Martin (65)]. The histological and histochemical changes associated with interpubic ligament formation in pregnant or relaxin-treated nonpregnant mice have been intensively studied by Hall (31, 32, 36), Crelin (11, 12, 15, 17) and Storey (72). The histochemical changes in the connective tissue of the guinea pig pubic symphysis have been thoroughly reviewed by Hisaw and Zarrow (42). Very recently, Boucek and associates (6, 7, 22, 60) have reported effects of relaxin on the histology and chemistry of sponge-biopsy connective tissue obtained from the rat dorsum. These include changes in mast cells, collagen, water, and cholesterol synthesis.

B. Effects of Relaxin on Structures Other than the Pubic Symphysis

1. Mammary Glands

In 1945, Hamolsky and Sparrow (38) reported interaction of estrogen, progesterone, and relaxin in stimulating growth and lobulation of the mammary glands of ovariectomized immature rats. This effect was confirmed by Smith (67). On the basis of quantitative DNA determinations, Wada and Turner (76) reported recently that relaxin plus estrogen effectively stimulated lobule-alveolar growth in intact and castrated, but not hypophysectomized mice. A daily dose of 750 μg. crystalline progesterone was required to produce an effect similar to that observed with 80 μg. of the relaxin-containing extract similarly injected. The authors hypothesized that the action of progesterone on mammary development may be indirect, and mediated via the endogenous formation of relaxin.

2. Uterus

a. *Inhibition of spontaneous uterine motility.* In 1950 Krantz and associates (50) demonstrated that aqueous extracts of swine corpora lutea inhibited the spontaneous motility of guinea pig uteri *in vivo.* Similar effects were obtained with known relaxin-containing extracts on mouse and rat uterine segments *in vitro* by Sawyer and co-workers (64) and on guinea pig uteri *in vivo* by Felton *et al.* (23). These observations have been amply confirmed (4, 52, 57, 76a).

b. *Inhibition of deciduoma formation.* Frieden and Velardo (28) reported inhibition of deciduoma formation by relaxin injection in rats, but this effect was not confirmed subsequently by Zarrow and Brennan (80) or by Velardo (75).

c. Cervical softening. Relaxin-induced softening of the uterine cervix was observed by Graham and Dracy in cows (30) and in estrogen-primed gilts by Zarrow *et al.* (82). On the contrary, Smith and Nalbandov (66) reported that estrogen treatment induced constriction of the uterine cervix in swine and that neither progesterone nor relaxin therapy modified this effect. Kroc *et al.* (52) observed increased dilatability of the spayed rat cervix following small estrogen doses, but constriction of the cervical canals when large doses of estrogen were injected. Further, relaxin increased cervical dilatability regardless of estrogen treatment, and this effect was potentiated by concomitant progesterone administration. Similar observations have been presented by Cullen and Harkness (19), who used a more objective technique for measuring cervical circumference.

d. Biochemical changes in the uterus. Although the biochemistry of the "relaxed" guinea pig symphysis pubis has been studied by Frieden *et al.* (24–26), Perl and Catchpole (61) and Catchpole *et al.* (8), the biochemical events accompanying uterine and cervical effects of relaxin treatment have only recently been investigated. Zarrow and Brennan (79) observed a rapid increase in uterine water content of relaxin-treated immature rats. Uterine water increases were also recorded following a single injection of relaxin in estrogen-primed, spayed rats (70), and these were accompanied by large but transient increases in glycogen concentration, dry weight, and total nitrogen. Daily treatment with repository relaxin maintained these changes in water, carbohydrate, and protein composition (52). This may be an effect peculiar to relaxin, since elevated uterine water levels were not maintained with continued estrogen treatment; in fact, if sufficient estrogen were given, the relaxin effect was inhibited.

Zarrow and associates (82) also reported changes in the water content and histochemically demonstrable mucopolysaccharides of the sow cervix following relaxin injection. Kroc *et al.* (52) described an increase in water and glycogen content of the cervix of the estrogen-primed spayed rat and mouse when the animals were treated with relaxin.

C. Effects of Relaxin in Pregnant Animals

Although extreme pelvic relaxation and the accompanying increase in the diameter of the birth canal are presumably essential to normal delivery in the guinea pig, this is apparently not true in many other species including the mouse, which normally forms a long interpubic ligament during the last week of gestation. Crelin (10) observed normal spontaneous delivery of viable young in mice in which the pubic bones had been sutured together to prevent any separation whatsoever. An extra-innominate effect of relaxin on the mechanism of parturition in the mouse has been suggested by Smithberg and Runner (68, 69), Hall (37), and by Steinetz and associates (71). Kroc *et al.* (52) further proposed a functional role of relaxin in the termination of pregnancy in the rat, a rodent in which pubic symphyseal changes are minimal during pregnancy, according to Crelin (14).

D. Problems in Relaxin Research

It is apparent that a wide variety of effects have been ascribed to the action of relaxin. However, relaxin research has been hampered by several difficulties:

1. The hormone has never been isolated or characterized in pure form.

2. There is lack of standardization of relaxin extracts used by different laboratories.

3. Low-potency extracts necessary to evaluate possible nonspecific polypeptide effects are seldom used by investigators.

4. Many workers have failed to recognize the importance of potentiating and prolonging the activity of injected protein hormones.

E. Standardization of Relaxin Extracts, Vehicles, and Control Procedures

The studies presented in the following sections have been performed with these points in mind. All extracts used were manufactured by essentially the same method. Materials were bioassayed against a reference standard by one or both of the methods previously described (51–53). These are: (a) palpation of the pubic symphysis of estrogen- and relaxin-primed guinea pigs, following administration of relaxin; (b) direct measurement by transillumination of the interpubic ligament in estrogen-primed mice, following administration of relaxin. A third method—inhibition of spontaneous motility of estrous mouse uterine horns or segments *in vitro* (52)—was used extensively as a check on the other two methods because of persistent, but as yet unconvincing, reports of a separate, water-soluble "uterine-relaxing factor" present in swine ovaries (23, 27, 50). The three assay methods were in good agreement, and when ten to twenty animals were used at each of three dose levels of standard and unknown, the limits of error generally fell within ± 20–40% of the potency estimates, at $p = 0.95$.

In all preliminary studies of new hormonal properties a low-potency control extract (isolated by the same procedure but prepared from nonpregnant ovaries) was tested in parallel with the higher potency material, on an equivalent nitrogen basis in order to rule out nonspecific polypeptide effects.

The hormone was always injected in one or more repository vehicles, because previous data repeatedly demonstrated the relative ineffectiveness of saline solutions of relaxin in mice and rats.

F. Outline of the Studies Presented

The experiments presented below are concerned with the following problems:

1.   The distribution of relaxin in tissues of various vertebrates. Such studies provided clues as to choice of species for experimental work and gland extirpation-replacement, as well as indications of universality of the hormone.

2.   Potentiation and prolongation of relaxin activity by repository vehicles and complexes. These experiments yielded important information regarding choice of vehicle and number of injections necessary in exploring new effects of the hormone.

3.   Interaction of relaxin and steroids on the pubic symphysis of the mouse. These studies provided a relatively simple method for studying the relationships of exogenous and endogenous hormones which exert effects on one type of connective tissue.

4.   Interaction of relaxin and steroids on the rat uterus and cervix. Relaxin, estrogen, and progestagens were observed to interact in altering uterine and cervical weight, chemical composition, and physical properties.

5.   Role of relaxin in pregnancy and parturition. In Section VI, evidence is presented suggesting that relaxin conditions the response of the pregnant uterus to oxytocin; may be responsible for the increasing dilatability of the rat cervix with advancing gestation; and may play a role in placental detachment.

II. Sources of Relaxin

The potential importance of relaxin in endocrine physiology is suggested by its wide distribution among vertebrates. Hisaw and Zarrow (42) have summarized previous bioassay information regarding the relaxin activity in sera, ovaries, uteri, and placentas of various mammals and in the ovaries of birds. Table I is intended to supplement their report by presenting additional data pertinent to tissue, sex, and species

TABLE I
APPROXIMATE RELAXIN ACTIVITY OF TISSUES OF VARIOUS VERTEBRATE SPECIES

Subject	Tissue	Activity: G.P.U. per gm. or ml.	No activity by G.P. sym. pub. assay
Shark—pregnant	Ovaries[a]	4–10	Liver
Rooster	Testes[b]	2–5[e]	
Whale, fin—pregnant	Ovarian stroma[c]	0–1.2	
Fetal length 4'6"–10'4"	Corpus luteum[c]	24	
Fetal length 4'6"–10'4"	Placenta[c]	0.6–1.4	
Fetal length 4'6"–10'4"	Endometrium[c]	0–2	
Fetal length 4'6"–10'4"	Liver[c]	0–1.4	
Whale, blue—pregnant	Corpus luteum[c]	536	
Fetal length 13'0"	Placenta[c]	1	
Mouse, preg. 16–17 days	Ovary[d]	114	Placenta
Mouse, preg. 19 days	Ovary[d]	200[e]	Uterus
Mouse, preg. 19 days	Serum[d]	0.1	Kidney Serum
Rat, nonpregnant	Ovary[d]	2	
Rat, preg. 13 days	Ovary[d]	290	
Rat. preg. 15 days	Ovary[d]	98–141	Serum
Rat, preg. 21 days	Ovary[d]	720	
Rat, preg. 21 days	Placenta[d]	1–4 (?)	
Cat—Preg. late	Serum	1.5	
	Placenta[d]	0.5	
Dog—estrous	Serum	0.3	
Rabbit—Preg. 28 days:	Serum[a]	5–15[e]	Brain
	Ovary[a]	9	Liver
	Uterus[a]	3	Muscle
	Placenta[a]	137[e]	Adrenal
	Mammary gland[a]	9	Fetus
	Spleen[a]	3	
	Kidney[a]	5–27	
	Heart[a]	6	
	Lung[a]	9	
Sow—nonpregnant	Ovary-luteal[a]	4	Pancreas
Preg. 1.5"–7" fetuses	Ovary-luteal[a]	675[e]	Kidney Spleen Placenta

[a] Homogenate.
[b] Acid extract.
[c] Methanol-dried.
[d] Acetone-dried.
[e] Confirmed by mouse pubic ligament test.

distribution of this hormone. All assays were performed by guinea pig symphysis pubis palpation, and in some instances by the mouse ligament method as well.

Definite relaxin activity was found in homogenates of pregnant shark ovaries, implying the presence of the hormone early in vertebrate phylogeny. No activity was observed in assays of "ripe" ovaries of a bony fish, the striped mullet (*Mugil cephalus*).

Extracts of rooster testes induced pelvic relaxation in guinea pigs and mice, suggesting a role of relaxin in the physiology of the male. However, no activity was detected in testes of boars or stallions when extracts or homogenates were injected at relatively high dose levels.

The presence of relaxin activity in such nonreproductive structures as spleen, kidney, heart, and lung of pregnant rabbits may simply be due to the vascularity of these organs. The circulating blood level of hormone was found to be higher in the rabbit than in any other species tested. However, no activity was observed in liver, muscle, or brain when these were assayed at identical dose levels.

Relaxin activity was present in the ovaries of nonpregnant sows and rats, and in the serum of the estrous dog. These findings are suggestive of a role of the hormone in the normal cycles of such animals.

The general distribution of relaxin in the tissues of pregnant mammals correlates with the hypothesis that the ovary may be the primary source of hormone in animals which require this organ throughout gestation, *e.g.*, mouse, rat, and sow. In animals in which the ovaries are expendable throughout the latter part of gestation, the placenta may produce relaxin (42). Thus, relaxation of the pelvic ligaments occurs regardless of midterm castration in pregnant guinea pigs (9, 41). Csapo (18) has recently shown that the function of pregnancy maintenance shifts from the corpus luteum to the placenta late in pregnancy in the rabbit. The data of Hisaw and Zarrow (42) suggest that both these organs may produce relaxin in this species. Also, castration at mid-term generally did not induce a fall in serum-relaxin levels of rabbits in which pregnancy was maintained by progesterone injection (42).

In the mouse, there is considerable evidence that ovariectomy or failure of luteal function prevents the normal separation of the pubes during the last week of pregnancy (58, 59, 68, 69). The placenta, but not the hypophysis, is apparently necessary for relaxin production by the ovary in the pregnant mouse (59).

Whereas very high relaxin activity was detected in pregnant rat ovaries, only questionable activity was found in placentas, even at huge doses. Bloom and associates (4) assayed relaxin-type extracts of a variety of tissues of pregnant rats using an *in vitro* uterine motility inhibition test. They detected definite inhibitory activity in ovarian extracts, but not in similar extracts of metrial gland or other placental areas.

III. Potentiation and Prolongation of Relaxin Activity by Repository Agents and Complexes

A. Potentiation of the Mouse Pubic Symphysis Response to Injected Relaxin

Early relaxin research was hampered by failure to recognize the importance of achieving sustained action of this hormone. Despite the short half-life of injected relaxin reported by Zarrow and Money (81), and the important observations of Kliman and Greep (49) that suitable repository vehicles were thirty to seventy times as effective as saline in potentiating relaxin action on the mouse pubic symphysis, inconclusive or negative findings continue to be accumulated by some investigators who still employ water or saline as the injection medium.

Figure 1 illustrates the potentiating effects of various types of vehicles on the quantitative response of the pubic symphysis of the estrogen-primed mouse to single injections of relaxin.

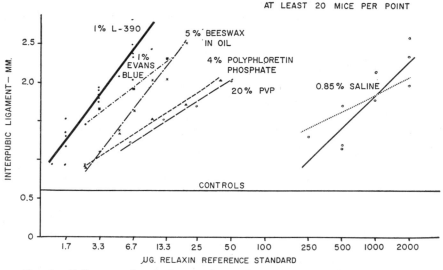

Fig. 1. Influence of vehicle on the 24-hour response of the mouse pubic symphysis to a single injection of relaxin. All mice were primed with 5 μg. estradiol cyclopentylpropionate on day zero. On day 7 the animals received single subcutaneous injections of relaxin in the doses and vehicles indicated. Interpubic ligament length was measured 24 hours later.

The curves illustrated with relaxin in saline solution are not typical, in that generally no dose response whatsoever was obtained. One per cent L-390 (benzopurpurine 4-B) and 5% beeswax in peanut oil not only markedly potentiated relaxin activity, but the dose-response curves were relatively steeper than those obtained with Evans Blue, PVP (polyvinyl pyrrolidone), or polyphloretin phosphate. Accordingly, 1% L-390 and 5% beeswax in peanut oil have been used routinely for relaxin bioassay in the mouse. With beeswax-oil, only 1/150th and with L-390 1/300th of the equivalent dose of relaxin in saline solution is necessary to produce long interpubic ligaments in the mouse.

B. Prolonged "Relaxation" of the Guinea Pig Pubic Symphysis

There are no reports of potentiation of relaxin activity in guinea pigs. However, repository preparations have now been found to maintain extreme pubic symphyseal relaxation for long periods of time in this species. In order to obtain this effect, it was necessary to elevate the relaxin dose to 100-1000 times that required to elicit a strong response in the usual 6-hour test system (52). A similar phenomenon has been reported by Junkmann (48) in the case of repository estrogens.

Figure 2 illustrates the duration of action of some relaxin repository preparations in maintaining pubic symphyseal relaxation in estrogen-primed guinea pigs, as determined by daily manual palpation following single injections equivalent to 10 mg. of relaxin reference standard W1164-A, Lot 8. Single, or even multiple injections of 10 mg. in saline solution failed to maintain the degree of relaxation observed when animals were treated with single injections of effective repository preparations such as a suspension in beeswax-oil, or a tannic acid complex in oil. 20% gelatin, carbowax, or plain sesame oil were relatively ineffective vehicles.

In order to obtain a semiquantitative estimate of effectiveness, relative areas under the curves were calculated, assigning an arbitrary value of 1 to the area observed with a single injection of relaxin in saline solution.

Ten daily injections of 10 mg. each in saline solution (total dose= 100 mg.) were only 3.1 times as effective as a single injection in the same vehicle, suggesting that most of the hormone may be wasted when administered this way. On the other hand, single injections of 10 mg. as a tannic acid complex in oil, or simply as a suspension in beeswax-oil demonstrated a nine- to tenfold increase in efficacy. A complex containing 0.2% zinc was intermediate in effectiveness, yielding a relative value of 4.2 when compared with the saline preparation.

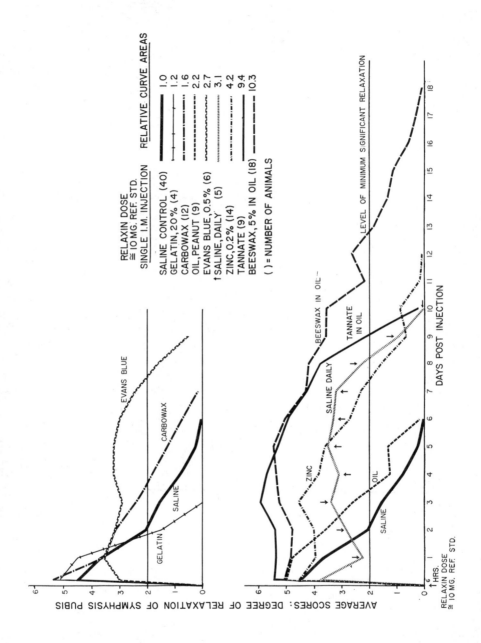

IV. Interaction of Relaxin and Steroids on the Pubic Symphysis of the Mouse

A. REVIEW OF THE PROBLEM

It has long been known that estrogen priming is a prerequisite to optimal effects of relaxin on the pubic symphysis of the guinea pig and mouse (42). This need for prior estrogenization is analogous to that observed in studies of progesterone effects on the endometrium and mammary glands.

Other relationships of relaxin and steroids have been observed, and the effects appear to be related to target organ and species. Thus, in the guinea pig and rabbit, pretreatment with estrogen and progesterone has been reported to induce the endogenous formation of relaxin by the uterus (42–44). This phenomenon has been confirmed (54–56, 77, 78), casting considerable doubt on the interpretation of data of many investigations employing rabbits and guinea pigs for the study of estrogenic and progestational hormone effects and for the assay of progestagens.

In the mouse, though, Hall (35, 36) failed to induce interpubic ligament formation with various combinations of estrogen and progesterone. However, progesterone injection was found to inhibit or retard interpubic ligament formation in mice (16, 33, 34, 71), and thus, failure to induce ligament elongation with estrogen and progesterone does not prove that endogenous relaxin was not formed in amounts too small to overcome the inhibition. Gardner and Van Heuverswyn (29) long ago observed prevention of interpubic ligament formation in pregnant mice treated with testosterone. Kliman (1955, personal communication) discovered that cortisone injection prevented pubic symphyseal separation in the relaxin-treated mouse. Additional relevant data have been reported by Horn (45, 46), who found that thiouracil or thyroid feeding inhibited interpubic ligament formation during pregnancy in mice and also altered the response of ovariectomized nonpregnant animals to injected relaxin.

Clearly, a variety of hormones are capable of exerting direct or indirect effects on the mouse pubic symphysis, and thus this target organ

---

FIG. 2. Effect of relaxin repository preparations on duration of relaxation of the guinea pig symphysis. The animals were previously estrogen- and relaxin-primed (52). Guinea pigs were then injected intramuscularly with 10 mg. standard relaxin activity in 0.5 ml. of the preparations indicated. The pubic symphysis was palpated manually by two operators, and the degree of loosening evaluated subjectively (52) at 6 hours post injection and daily thereafter.

has provided a useful tool for the study of hormonal effects on one type of connective tissue.

B. A QUANTITATIVE METHOD FOR STUDYING HORMONAL INTERACTIONS ON THE MOUSE PUBIC SYMPHYSIS

A standardized quantitative procedure has been developed for the assessment of steroidal inhibition of interpubic ligament formation in relaxin-treated mice (Fig. 3). Virgin females (weighing 18–20 gm.) are

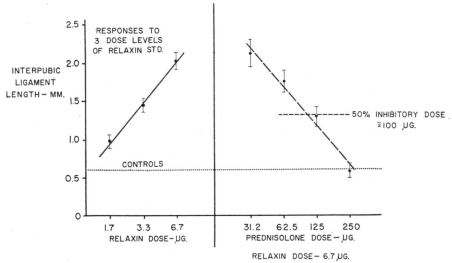

FIG. 3. Quantitative inhibition by prednisolone acetate of the mouse pubic symphysis response to relaxin. All mice were primed with 5 μg. estradiol cyclopentylpropionate on day zero. On day 7, groups of ten to twenty mice were injected subcutaneously with graded doses of relaxin (left side of figure) or 6.7 μg. relaxin plus graded doses of prednisolone acetate (right side of figure). Controls received only vehicle. Interpubic ligament lengths were measured 24 hours post injection.

primed with a single subcutaneous injection of 5 μg. estradiol cyclopentylpropionate on day 0. On day 8, mice receive: (a) placebo, (b) graded doses of the relaxin standard in 1% L-390 (benzopurpurine 4-B), (c) the highest dose of standard (in L-390) plus graded doses of the inhibitor. Animals are sacrificed 24 hours later and the interpubic ligament lengths measured directly at 13 times magnification under transillumination (52). In a valid test, inhibition should range from 0 to greater than 50%. The interpolated 50% inhibitory dose of steroid is used for potency comparisons, as different slopes may be obtained with different compounds.

C. Effects of Several Types of Steroids on the Mouse Pubic Symphysis Response to Relaxin

Figure 4 illustrates a spectrum of inhibition curves obtained with representative steroids. Inhibition was not directly related to androgenic, progestational, or anti-inflammatory properties. The 19-nortestosterones, particularly 17α-ethyl-19-nortestosterone, were exceptionally potent. This compound was approximately 200–250 times as active as progesterone in this test, whereas it was only 5–10 times as potent by

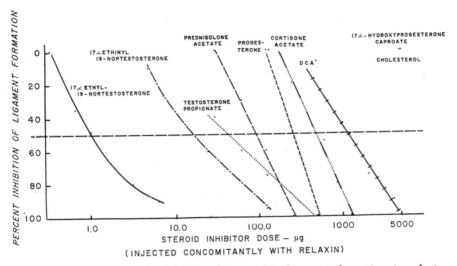

Fig. 4. Acute steroid inhibition of interpubic ligament formation in relaxin-treated, estrogen-primed mice. The various inhibitors were evaluated by the method illustrated in Fig. 3. The data are summarized here plotting percentage inhibition of interpubic ligament formation against steroid dose.

usual progestational criteria (62). Similarly, it was 50 times as active as testosterone propionate as a relaxin inhibitor, but is reputedly a weaker androgen (63).

17α-Hydroxyprogesterone caproate, although more active than progesterone in the rabbit (47), did not inhibit the relaxin response in the mouse at a dosage of 5 mg. The meaning of this is unclear at present, but could be important from the standpoint of lack of interference of the two hormones at the time of parturition. DCA (deoxycorticosterone acetate) the only progestationally active adrenal steroid tested (74) was not as potent as the antiinflammatory compounds, cortisone, and prednisolone.

D. INDIRECT INHIBITION OF INTERPUBIC LIGAMENT FORMATION BY
ACTH AND GONADOTROPIN

It has also been possible to assess endogenous steroid formation due
to injection of tropic hormones. When zinc-ACTH was injected concomitantly with the standard dose of relaxin in intact animals, interpubic ligament formation was almost completely inhibited (Fig. 5).
The corticotropin preparation had no effect on relaxin-induced pubic

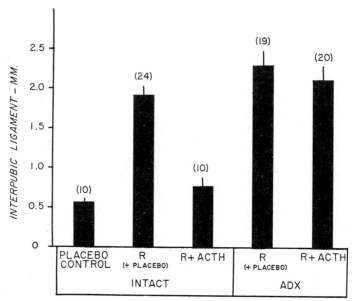

FIG. 5. Effect of ACTH on relaxin-induced interpubic ligament formation in
intact and adrenalectomized mice. All mice were primed with 5 μg. ECP on day
zero. Adrenalectomy was performed on day 2. The indicated doses of relaxin and
ACTH were injected on day 7. Interpubic ligament lengths were measured 24
hours later.

separation in adrenalectomized mice, suggesting that inhibition had
been mediated via the adrenal glands.

Similarly, sheep anterior pituitary gonadotropin injections depressed
interpubic ligament formation in intact, but not in ovariectomized immature mice treated concomitantly with relaxin (Fig. 6). Since ligament
elongation is complete approximately 15–18 hours after relaxin injection
(52), the ovary must have produced inhibitory substances (progestagens?) rather rapidly in response to tropic stimulation, and long before
ovulation and corpus luteum formation could occur.

V. Interaction of Relaxin and Steroids on the Uterus and Cervix of the Spayed Rat

A. Review of the Problem

Some of the interactions of steroids and relaxin on the guinea pig and mouse pubic symphysis have been described above. Further work has been done using the rat uterus as the target organ. Zarrow and Brennan (79) reported that relaxin injection induced a rapid rise in

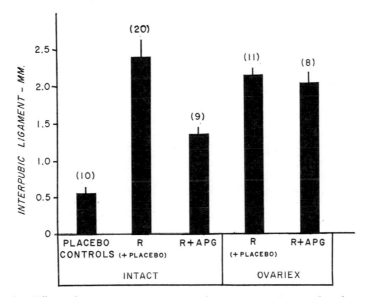

Fig. 6. Effect of anterior pituitary gonadotropin on relaxin-induced interpubic ligament formation in intact and ovariectomized mice. All mice were primed with 5 μg. ECP on day zero. Ovariectomy was performed on day 2. The indicated doses of relaxin and sheep anterior pituitary gonadotropin were injected on day 7. Interpubic ligament lengths were measured 24 hours later.

water content of uteri of immature rats and that this effect could be prevented by cortisone or progesterone (80). They further claimed that relaxin had a progesterone-sparing action in the Clauberg rabbit test (80). Kroc *et al.* (52) previously reported that an estrogen priming was necessary for optimal effects of relaxin on the spayed rat uterus but that excessive estrogen reduced the effectiveness of relaxin. This group also observed an increase in cervical "dilatability" ascribable to the action of relaxin and found that this effect was potentiated by progesterone (52). Cullen and Harkness have made similar observations on

TABLE II

EFFECT OF ESTROGEN, PROGESTERONE, AND RELAXIN ON THE CERVIX OF THE SPAYED RAT

Treatment[b]			No. of rats	Cervical weight		Cervical dilatability		Ratio: % dilatability increase / % weight increase		
Estrogen prime	Relaxin (mg.)	Progesterone (mg.)		mg./100 gm.	SE±	Mm.	SE±	Versus no ECP control	Versus 5 μg, ECP control	Versus 50 μg, ECP control
None	0	0	5	6	0.4	1.40	0.03	1.00 (Control)		
	5	0	5	9	0.4	2.69	0.12	1.28		
	0	5	5	4	0.4	0.33	0.08	0.36		
	5	5	5	8	0.9	2.42	0.08	1.30		
5 μg, ECP[a]	0	0	12	26	2.0	2.11	0.07	0.35	1.00 (Control)	
	5	0	10	56	5.0	3.85	0.21	0.28	0.85	
	0	5	8	17	1.0	1.62	0.05	0.41	1.19	
	5	5	9	58	6.0	4.11	0.16	0.32	0.90	
50 μg, ECP	0	0	10	36	3.0	1.42	0.13	0.17	0.48	1.00 (Control)
	5	0	8	46	3.0	2.88	0.11	0.27	0.77	1.59
	0	5	10	27	2.0	1.83	0.08	0.29	0.84	1.72
	5	5	8	64	5.0	3.79	0.21	0.26	0.73	1.50

[a] ECP = estradiol cyclopentylpropionate × 1, s.c., day 0.

[b] Injected s.c. daily, days 8–14; relaxin in 0.1 ml. 5% beeswax in peanut oil; progesterone in 0.1 ml. sesame oil.

the rat cervix, using a more objective technique for measuring cervical stretch (19).

B. PITFALLS IN ASSESSING CERVICAL SOFTENING

Kroc and associates (52) cautioned that measurements of cervical "dilatability" do not take into account the cervical hypertrophy which occurs when the atrophic cervix of the spayed animal is subjected to hormonal influences. Table II illustrates this point. Estrogen or relaxin, and the combination of estrogen, relaxin, and progesterone, induced an obvious increase in the absolute stretchable diameter of the cervix. However, these increases were generally not as great percentagewise as the increases in tissue mass which occurred concomitantly. This became evident when ratios of the dilatability increase to the weight increase were related to the castrate control values. If the cervix values of the animals primed with 5 μg. of estrogen are taken as base line (similar to values obtained in normal cycling rats) subsequent relaxin-progesterone treatment did not increase dilatability more than weight as reflected in the ratio of the respective increases. Elevating the estrogen level to 50 μg., on the other hand, reduced absolute and relative dilatability while increasing the mass of the cervical portion of the uterus. Thus, the data are really in agreement with those obtained by Smith and Nalbandov in sows (66); i.e., estrogen constricts the cervix. Only when the 50-μg. priming dose was used did relaxin or relaxin plus progesterone actually increase "dilatability" more than could be accounted for by growth alone. The foregoing is not intended to imply that an increase in cervical tissue mass is not an important or desirable hormonal effect. It merely serves as a caution in interpreting as *softening effects,* data which demonstrate an increase in diameter or circumference of the cervical canals. These may simply be due to over-all growth of the structure and *not* to changes in consistency or composition. Biochemical criteria are necessary for establishment of the latter. Kroc *et al.* (52) have reported that the increased cervical dilatability due to relaxin injection in the rat is accompanied by an increase in water content of the structure. Zarrow and colleagues (82) observed increased cervical water content and changes in mucopolysaccharides following relaxin injection in sows. Unfortunately, chemical data on possible collagen changes due to relaxin are lacking. Harkness and co-workers (40) did not observe pregnancy-type increases in the collagen content of cervices of spayed rats treated with combinations of estrogen and progesterone. Whether relaxin influences cervical collagen is still a matter of conjecture.

C. Synergism of Estrogen, Progestagens, and Relaxin in Modifying the Composition of the Uterus

Kroc *et al.* (52) also presented evidence of synergism between progesterone and relaxin in modifying the weight and composition of the

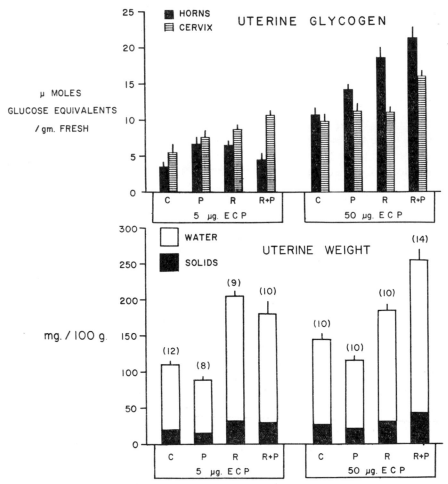

Fig. 7. Effects of relaxin and progesterone on uterine composition in estrogen-primed ovariectomized rats. All rats were ovariectomized 14 days before receiving a single subcutaneous injection of 5 or 50 μg. estradiol cyclopentylpropionate (ECP). On the 7th day after estrogen priming, 7 daily injections of relaxin (1 mg.) in beeswax-oil, progesterone (5 mg.) in oil, their combination (doses indicated), or placebo (control = C) were begun. Rats were sacrificed 24 hours after the last injection. Parentheses indicate total number of animals per group. Vertical lines represent one standard error.

uterus of the estrogen-primed, spayed rat. This effect is illustrated in
Fig. 7. All rats were ovariectomized 2 weeks before receiving a priming
dose of 5 or 50 μg. estradiol cyclopentylpropionate (ECP). One week

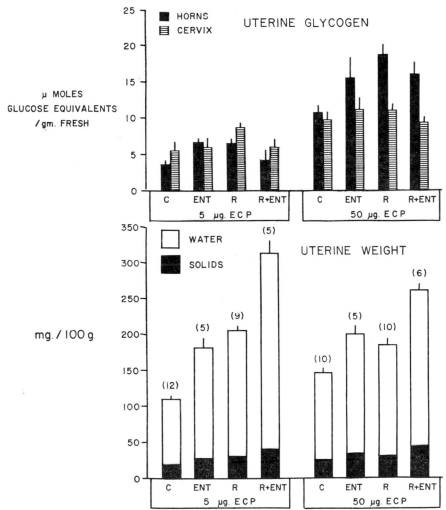

FIG. 8. Effects of relaxin and 17α-ethyl-19-nortestosterone on uterine composition in estrogen-primed ovariectomized rats. All rats were ovariectomized 14 days
before receiving a single subcutaneous injection of 5 or 50 μg. estradiol cyclopentylpropionate (ECP). On the 7th day after estrogen priming, 7 daily injections of
relaxin (1 mg.) in beeswax-oil, 17α-ethyl-19-nortestosterone (1 mg.) in oil, their
combination (doses indicated), or placebo (control = C) were begun. Rats were
sacrificed 24 hours after the last injection. Parentheses indicate total number of animals per group. Vertical lines represent one standard error.

after injection of the estrogen, daily administration of relaxin and progesterone, separately or as a combination, or placebo was begun and
continued for an additional 7 days. Progesterone injections significantly
depressed uterine weight in comparison to values of placebo-treated
controls following 5 or 50 µg. estrogen priming. Relaxin administration
induced significant *increases* in wet and dry weight following either
estrogen-priming dose. In rats primed with 5 µg. ECP, progesterone did
not alter the relaxin effect. However, following the 50-µg. ECP dosage,
progesterone and relaxin synergized to induce a significantly greater
uterine weight (wet and dry) than was observed in any of the factorial
control groups. The glycogen concentrations of uteri were increased by
relaxin or progesterone. The increases, however, appeared to be estro-
gen-limited. Glycogen concentration did not necessarily reflect glycogen
deposition. Progesterone treatment (following either estrogen-priming
dose) increased glycogen concentration while decreasing uterine weight.
The absolute amount of glycogen per uterus remained constant. Relaxin
induced roughly a twofold increase in glycogen concentration while
uterine weight was increased 50–100%. Thus, the absolute increase in
total glycogen was three- to four-fold. Cervix glycogen concentration was
only markedly affected by estrogen and combinations of relaxin and
progesterone.

Figure 8 illustrates a similar study in which 17α-ethyl-19-nortes-
tosterone (ENT) was substituted for progesterone in the experimental
design. This compound was extremely potent in inhibiting the response
of the mouse pubic symphysis to relaxin (see Section IV). ENT was
reported to be seventy times more potent than testosterone in antag-
onizing the effects of estradiol on the uterus (21) and was also effective
as an inhibitor of vaginal cornification (20). The data shown in Fig. 8
demonstrate the great difference between acute and priming dosages
of estrogen. Thus, ENT actually induced a further increase in uterine
weight of the estrogen-primed spayed rat. Uteri of animals injected
with combinations of ENT and relaxin were much heavier than those
of rats receiving either substance alone. Uterine-glycogen concentration
was not markedly influenced by treatment with combined relaxin and
ENT because glycogenesis was masked by large concomitant increases
in uterine water content.

D.   ESTROGEN AS AN INHIBITOR OF UTERINE WATER ACCUMULATION

Whereas a well-known effect of estrogens is the induction of rapid
increases in uterine water concentration (1, 2), 17β-estradiol itself may
inhibit water accumulation due to injection of relaxin or ethylnortes-
tosterone (Fig. 9).

When spayed rats were treated with ENT and relaxin either separately or as a combination, significant elevation of uterine water content was observed. When spayed animals were primed with 5 μg. estradiol cyclopentylpropionate 1 week earlier, relaxin and the combination of relaxin and ENT induced an even greater increase in uterine water levels. However, when the estrogen priming dose was raised to 50 μg. ECP, there was a marked suppression of the effects of relaxin and ENT.

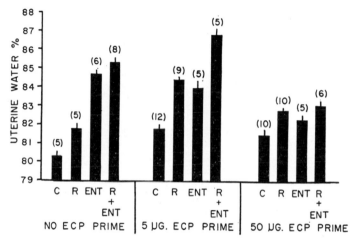

Fig. 9. Effects of estrogen pretreatment on uterine-water response to relaxin and 17α-ethyl-19-nortestosterone in ovariectomized rats. Fourteen days after ovariectomy, rats were primed with a single subcutaneous injection of 5 or 50 μg. estradiol cyclopentylpropionate, or left untreated. Seven days later, daily injections of relaxin (1 mg. in beeswax-oil), 17α-ethyl-19-nortestosterone (1 mg. in oil), or placebo (C) were initiated and continued for an additional 7 days. Parentheses indicate number of rats. Vertical lines represent one standard error. [Reproduced with permission from "The Uterus," New York Academy Science Annals (52).]

It is postulated that endogenous estrogen itself may be responsible for the failure of uteri of rats to give a positive Astwood response (3, 5) during the period of vaginal cornification.

E. ESTROGEN AS A CERVICAL CONSTRICTOR

Similar effects of "too much" estrogen were observed in studies of the rat cervix (Fig. 10). In this experiment, all rats were primed with 5 μg. estradiol cyclopentylpropionate. One week later, daily injections of relaxin and 17β-estradiol, administered separately or as a combination, and placebo were initiated. Relaxin increased cervical water content and "dilatability" significantly, whereas 17β-estradiol greatly reduced cervical elasticity without significantly altering water concentration. 17β-Estradiol partially inhibited the effect of relaxin when the two hormones were injected concomitantly.

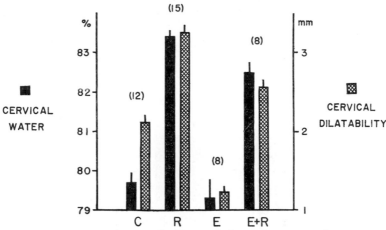

FIG. 10. Effects of relaxin and 17β-estradiol on the cervix of estrogen-primed ovariectomized rats. Rats were ovariectomized 2 weeks before receiving a single dose of 5 μg. estradiol cyclopentylpropionate. Seven days after priming, 7 daily injections of relaxin, in beeswax-oil, 17β-estradiol in oil, or their combination were given. Vertical lines represent one standard error.

VI. Role of Relaxin in Pregnancy and Parturition

A. REVIEW OF THE PROBLEM

As previously indicated in Section II, relaxin is present in relatively large amounts in the ovaries and/or placentas of pregnant mammals. This observation is in agreement with previous publications of Hisaw and Zarrow (42). The exact functions of relaxin, particularly during the earlier phases of pregnancy remain unclear. The ability of this hormone to inhibit spontaneous uterine motility *in vivo* or *in vitro* (4, 23, 52, 57, 64, 76a) would suggest a possible role in pregnancy maintenance. Indeed, Hall (37) has reported that relaxin treatment reduced the daily progesterone requirement for pregnancy maintenance in the spayed (day 14) mouse from 1 mg. to 0.5 mg. Unfortunately, a constant dose of estrogen was also administered in these experiments, and it is not yet established that a higher dose of estrogen would not have had a similar progesterone-sparing action. In view of the five- to tenfold reduction in the progesterone-maintenance dose afforded by small concomitant estrogen doses in spayed pregnant rats (52), this activity of relaxin must remain open to question.

Similarly, the reported progesterone-sparing action of relaxin in the Clauberg rabbit test (80) is suggestive of an effect on implantation, but definitive proof is still lacking. Finally, the evidence of synergism between relaxin, progesterone, and estrogen reported in Section V circumstantially favors a role in pregnancy maintenance, of some balanced levels of these hormones.

The hormonal involvement in the mechanism of parturition remains unclear. Csapo (18) postulated that withdrawal of the "progesterone block" against coordinated contractile impulses and oxytocic agents might be the primary factor in initiating delivery. The evidence for this viewpoint was derived from extensive and brilliant studies on the contractile mechanics and physicochemistry of the uterus of the pregnant and nonpregnant rabbit. Unfortunately, the rabbit is one species in which the blood level of relaxin is extremely high in late pregnancy (42) and in which injected estrogen and progesterone have been reported to induce the *endogenous* formation of relaxin by the uterus (43). Thus, there must be considerable reservation in accepting Csapo's *interpretation* of his data, for undoubtedly, relaxin was present as a complicating factor.

The circumstantial evidence, at least, for hormonal factors involved in parturition of the mouse are slightly clearer. Newton (58) and Newton and Lits (59) reported that the simultaneous presence of placentas and ovaries is necessary for parturition in this species. An important corollary to this observation is the reported lack of normal interpubic ligament formation in the absence of ovaries or placentas, suggesting that relaxin might play a role in delivery. Smithberg and Runner subsequently studied the hormonal aspects of fertilization, implantation, pregnancy maintenance, parturition, and lactation in prepuberally pregnant (68), and genetically sterile (69), mice. In such animals, heat and ovulation were induced by injection of gonadotropin, and males were accepted. Corpora lutea were generally nonfunctional, but progesterone injection successfully induced implantation of fertilized ova. The ovaries remained nonfunctional and could be removed without detriment to the pregnancy. If the pregnancy were maintained on progesterone alone parturition failed, even though injections were stopped in order to withdraw the hormone and remove the "progesterone block." Pubic symphyseal separation did not occur. However, injection of repository relaxin on the 13th, 16th, and 19th days induced normal interpubic-ligament formation, and viable young were born spontaneously at approximately the normal time for the strain used. Hall (37) has recorded similar successful spontaneous delivery of viable young in adult female mice spayed on the 14th day of gestation and maintained on progesterone, estrogen, and relaxin. When progesterone and estrogen were the only therapies, parturition generally failed even after treatment was discontinued.

B.   EFFECTS OF PROGESTERONE AND RELAXIN ON SPONTANEOUS PARTURITION IN MICE

Some effects of progesterone and relaxin on the time of parturition in intact and in ovariectomized mice are shown in Fig. 11. A surprising observation is that *2.5 mg.* progesterone had to be injected daily to prolong pregnancy in *intact* mice, whereas *1 mg.* daily produced this effect

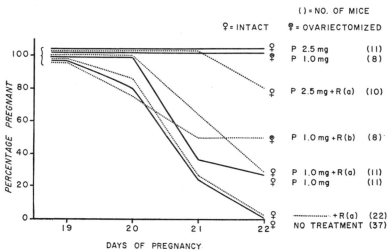

FIG. 11.   Influence of progesterone and relaxin on time of parturition in intact and ovariectomized pregnant mice. Ovariectomy was performed on day 16 in groups indicated. Injections (daily doses indicated) were initiated on day 16 and continued throughout the experiment.

in *ovariectomized* mice. This strongly suggests that mere progesterone withdrawal is not the initiating factor of parturition in this species and the ovariectomized mice which received relaxin in addition to the 1 mg. progesterone dose delivered their litters before the 22nd day of pregnancy despite continuation of the progesterone treatment. Delivery did not occur in any of the spayed mice treated with progesterone alone. Relaxin had no significant effect on time of parturition in intact animals.

C.   EFFECTS OF RELAXIN, PROGESTERONE, AND ESTROGEN ON OXYTOCIN-INDUCED PARTURITION IN MICE

Steinetz and his group (71) provided a possible extrasymphyseal mechanism for the effect of relaxin on parturition. Their revised data are shown in Figs. 12 and 13. The study involved the delivery response to oxytocin injection on the 19th day of pregnancy in intact, unilaterally or bilaterally ovariectomized mice treated with various combinations of progesterone, 17β-estradiol, and relaxin.

Steroids were injected daily on days 16, 17, and 18, and relaxin was administered in beeswax-oil on days 16 and 18. On day 19, individually caged animals received 0.5 I.U. oxytocin in 20% PVP subcutaneously, and labors and deliveries were observed for 4 hours. Oxytocin response was calculated in terms of percentage of each litter delivered (71).

Under these conditions, intact control mice were induced to deliver an average of 30% of their litters. Pretreatment with relaxin or 17β-estradiol did not alter delivery response, but combined relaxin and 17β-estradiol therapy significantly increased deliveries to about 65% (Fig. 12).

Progesterone injection obliterated oxytocin response, and concomitant treatment with 17β-estradiol did not significantly improve responsiveness in such animals. Mice treated with progesterone and relaxin, or a combination of progesterone, relaxin, and estrogen, were induced by means of oxytocin, to deliver a significantly higher percentage of their litters than mice treated with progesterone alone.

Figure 13 illustrates the effects of oxytocin in a similar experiment in which animals were unilaterally or bilaterally ovariectomized on the 16th day of pregnancy. Operative trauma was apparently not a factor, since sham-operated mice were similar to unoperated animals in the order of their response to oxytocin injection.

Unilateral ovariectomy increased the percentage of each litter delivered with oxytocin to 92%. When similarly operated animals were treated with progesterone, the response was reduced to about the level in intact controls. Relaxin did not prevent this effect of progesterone.

Bilaterally ovariectomized mice maintained by progesterone injection were unresponsive to oxytocin. Concomitant treatment with a variety of dosages of 17β-estradiol did not alter the delivery response. Complete details of effects of individual estrogen dosages have been published (71). Ovariectomized mice which were treated with a combination of progesterone and relaxin were nearly as responsive as unilaterally ovariectomized animals when oxytocin was injected.

Thus, the data suggest that endogenous progestagen secretion in the mouse is proportional to the amount of ovarian tissue present, and that response to oxytocin may depend upon the relative proportions of substances similar to or identical with progesterone and relaxin. The data also suggest that removal of the "progesterone block" against oxytocin does not necessarily induce parturition, since unilaterally ovariectomized untreated mice, or bilaterally ovariectomized mice maintained on progesterone and relaxin were highly responsive to injected oxytocin, and yet did not abort spontaneously. Even when pregnancy in intact mice was prolonged by progesterone treatment, concomitant relaxin therapy maintained oxytocin responsiveness of the delivery mechanism when inductions were performed on the 23rd day of gestation (52).

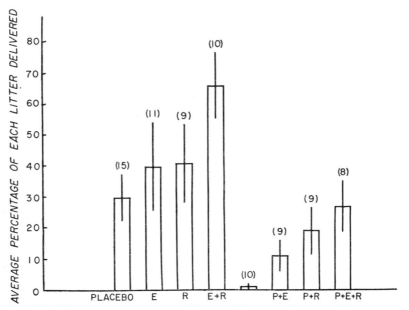

FIG. 12.   Effects of progesterone, 17β-estradiol, and relaxin on delivery response of intact mice to oxytocin injection on the 19th day of pregnancy. Average percentage of each litter delivered due to oxytocin injection (0.5 I.U. in 20% PVP) was calculated by averaging values obtained in individual animals according to the formula:

$$\frac{\text{Fetuses delivered}}{\text{Fetuses } in \ utero \text{ and delivered}} \times 100$$

D.   FACTORS INFLUENCING CERVICAL DILATABILITY IN PREGNANT RATS

Despite accumulating evidence that relaxin softens the uterine cervix, the cause of increased dilatability in the pregnant animal is unclear (71, 73). In the rat, there is a progressive softening of the cervix with advancing gestation (Fig. 14). These data are in agreement with previous reports of Uyldert and De Vaal (73) and Harkness and Harkness (39). Steinetz and associates (71), and Crelin (13) demonstrated a similar phenomenon in the pregnant mouse. In the rat, cervical water concentration paralleled increased dilatability until the 16th day of pregnancy.

Later softening was not accompanied by further water accumulation, suggesting the operation of another mechanism (Fig. 14).

A pertinent observation was recorded in experiments on pregnancy maintenance in rats which were ovariectomized on the 15th day of pregnancy (Fig. 15). In this particular strain (Charles River Wistar) a daily dose of 10 mg. progesterone was necessary to maintain a normal complement of living fetuses. As little as 1 or 2 mg. progesterone was re-

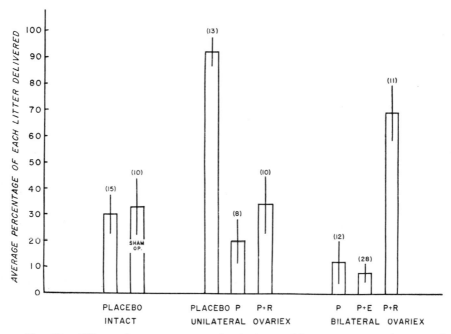

Fig. 13. Effects of progesterone and relaxin on delivery response of uni- and bilaterally ovariectomized mice to oxytocin injection on the 19th day of pregnancy. Operations were performed on day 16 of pregnancy. Average percentage of each litter was calculated as described for Fig. 12.

quired daily when 1 μg. 17β-estradiol was also supplied, but daily injection of 5 mg. progesterone was necessary when the estradiol dose was reduced to 0.1 μg. Measurements on the cervix revealed that "dilatability" was roughly inversely proportional to pregnancy maintenance. Thus, when adequate therapy was instituted, the cervix failed to soften to the degree observed in intact control animals. Conversely, when most or all of the litter was lost, the cervix was markedly dilated. Bioassays did not detect relaxin activity in placentas of such animals. On the other hand, relaxin injection induced a dose-proportional increase in cervical softening in spayed pregnant rats on adequate estrogen-progesterone therapy (Fig. 16). Cervical water content decreased below the control level in spayed rats maintained only on estradiol and progesterone. Depending on dose, relaxin injection restored cervical water concentration to normal or above normal levels.

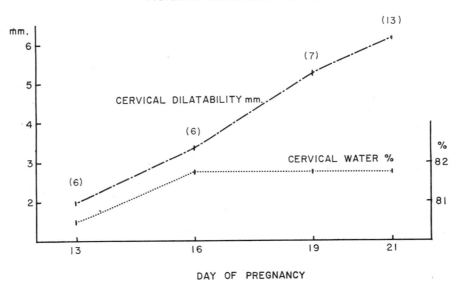

FIG. 14. Progressive softening of the cervix with advancing gestation in normal pregnant rats. Numbers of rats sacrificed at each time interval are indicated in parentheses. Vertical bars indicate ± standard errors of the mean values observed.

E.   EXPERIMENTAL PARTURITION IN RATS

In order to assess the functional significance of the effect of relaxin on the cervix, rats spayed on the 15th day of pregnancy were maintained on 2 mg. progesterone and 1 μg. 17β-estradiol daily with or without 1 mg. relaxin daily in wax-oil. Progesterone was withdrawn by giving 1 mg. on day 20 and then discontinuing therapy. 17β-estradiol and relaxin injections were continued through the 22nd day (the normal time of parturition in this strain). Animals were observed daily through the 23rd day when they were sacrificed. Living and dead births were recorded in both groups. However, all thirteen of the rats treated with 17β-estradiol and progesterone alone had retained placentas; an average of seven per rat on day 23 (Table III). There were also a few living and dead young *in utero*. In contrast, fourteen of the fifteen relaxin-treated animals had fully emptied their uteri by the 23rd day. The one animal with retained placentas in this group also retained dead fetuses *in utero*. Retained placentas were firmly attached to the uterine wall, and it appeared that this was associated with failure of the myometrium to contract at the uteroplacental junctures. According to Csapo (18) there is a gradient of progestational hormone emanating from the pla-

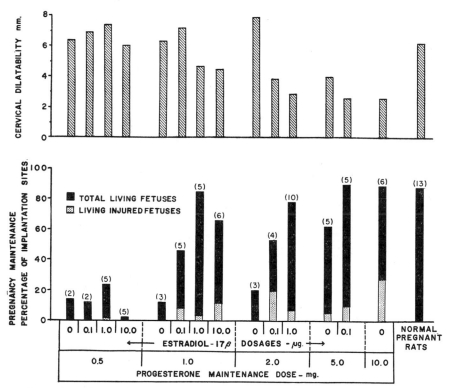

Fig. 15. Effects of progesterone and 17β-estradiol on pregnancy maintenance and cervical dilatability in rats spayed on the 15th day of gestation. Steroids were injected daily in the dosages indicated from the 15th through the 20th day of pregnancy. Rats were sacrificed on day 21, success of maintenance was evaluated and cervical dilatability was measured. Numbers of rats shown in parentheses.

centa, and the concentration is highest in the myometrium directly over placentas. His data could also be interpreted as an ability of the uteroplacental juncture to concentrate circulating progestin. In any event, it appears possible that relaxin may influence progestagen clearance from the tissue or directly overcome progestational effects on the myometrium.

Cervical dilatability was similar in both groups, suggesting again that parturition effects were due to the action of relaxin on the uterine delivery mechanism, as has previously been proposed in the mouse (71).

It appears that the cervix may achieve full *dilatability* by either an active or passive process; that is, by hormonal stimulation, or lacking

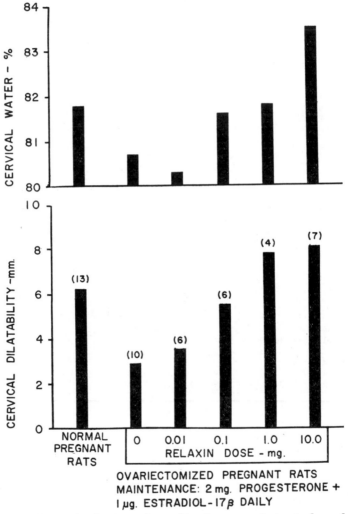

FIG. 16. Effects of relaxin on the cervix of rats ovariectomized on day 15 of pregnancy and maintained by injection of progesterone and 17β-estradiol. Steroids and relaxin were injected daily on days 15 through 20 of pregnancy. Necropsy was performed on day 21. [Reproduced with permission from "The Uterus," New York Academy of Science Annals (52).]

TABLE III

EFFECT OF RELAXIN ON SPONTANEOUS PARTURITION IN SPAYED (DAY 15) PREGNANT RATS MAINTAINED ON PROGESTERONE AND ESTRADIOL[a]

Treatment[b]	No. of rats	Percentage of mothers with retained placenta	Average no. of placentas per mother	Average no. of fetuses in utero per mother		Cervical dilatability (mm.)
				Living	Dead	
Progesterone + estradiol	13	100	7.0 ± 0.9	1.6 ± 1.0	1.5 ± 0.5	6.9 ± 0.7
Progesterone + estradiol + relaxin	15	7	0.5 ± 0.5	0	0.07 ± 0.07	8.0 ± 0.3

[a] Animals sacrificed 23 days post mating.
[b] Progesterone, 2 mg. daily days 15–19, 1 mg. day 20. Estradiol-17β, 1 μg. daily days 15–22. Relaxin, 1 mg. daily days 15–22.

that, by the mechanical pressures exerted upon it by the contents of the contracting uterus.

VII. Summary and Conclusions

1. The occurrence of substances with relaxin-like activity is not restricted to the female mammal; such substances have been demonstrated to occur in the ovaries of elasmobranchs and in the testes of birds.

2. The importance of repository vehicles in experimental relaxin research has been emphasized. A mouse test for estimation of relaxin potentiators, and a guinea pig test for evaluating sustained-release vehicles, have been described.

3. Relaxin and steroids interact in a variety of ways at the uterine, cervical, and pelvic levels. Relaxin importantly alters uterine composition, and progesterone synergizes relaxin with respect to this effect, in estrogen-primed animals. A role of relaxin in balance with the steroidal hormones in normal pregnancy maintenance is postulated.

4. Estrogens may inhibit uterine water uptake as well as induce it. The importance of prior estrogenization in the study of the effects of relaxin, progesterone—and even 17β-estradiol itself—has been emphasized.

5. Relaxin may play a role in parturition in the rat and mouse. Changes in the balance of relaxin and progesterone alter the delivery response to oxytocin injection. Relaxin may also exert an effect on placental detachment.

6. Withdrawal of the progesterone "block" against oxytocin does not necessarily induce parturition in the mouse. "Progesterone-dominated" uteri may be "unblocked" by relaxin treatment, as judged by delivery response to subsequently injected oxytocin.

7. Marked cervical softening fails to occur prior to parturition in spayed pregnant rats adequately maintained on estrogen and progesterone. Relaxin replacement therapy in such animals restores the normal prepartum increase in cervical dilatability. However, the "unfavorable" cervix also appears to become fully stretchable during abortion or parturition.

Acknowledgments

Gratitude is expressed to Mr. Paul Nemith, Mrs. R. Dun, Miss R. Nussbaum, and Mr. R. Blye for technical assistance during various phases of this work, and to Mrs. F. Mackenzie and staff for animal care.

Special thanks are due Messrs. John Doczi and Joachim Anschel for invention and preparation of many of the repository forms of relaxin used and for their invaluable suggestions in planning and executing the experiments reported in Section III.

The pure 17α-ethyl-19-nortestosterone (Nilevar) used in these studies was generously supplied by Dr. Victor Drill, G. D. Searle and Company.

The 17α-ethynyl-19-nortestosterone was kindly furnished by Dr. Dan McGinty of Parke, Davis and Company.

The authors express appreciation to the officers of Warner-Lambert for continued interest and encouragement over the years in basic research into the mechanism of hormone action in reproductive processes.

References

1. Astwood, E. B., *Anat. Record Suppl.* **70**, 5 (1938).
2. Astwood, E. B., *Endocrinology* **23**, 25 (1938).
3. Astwood, E. B., *Am. J. Physiol.* **126**, 162 (1939).
4. Bloom, G., Paul, K.-G., and Wiqvist, N., *Acta Endocrinol.* **28**, 112 (1958).
5. Boettiger, E. G., *J. Cellular Comp. Physiol.* **27**, 9 (1946).
6. Boucek, R. J., "Biochemical and Histologic Aspects of *in Vivo* Cultivated Connective Tissue," *in* Lectures on Orthopedics and Rheumatic Diseases, Dedication Volume, pp. 155-158. Hospital for Special Surgery, New Haven, Conn. Quinnipiack Press, Inc., 1956.
7. Casten, G. G., and Boucek, R. J., *J. Am. Med. Assoc.* **166**, 319 (1958).
8. Catchpole, H. R., Joseph, N. R., and Engel, M. B., *J. Endocrinol.* **8**, 377 (1952).
9. Courrier, R., and Kehl, R., *Compt. rend. soc. biol.* **128**, 181 (1938).
10. Crelin, E. S., *Proc. Soc. Exptl. Biol. Med.* **86**, 22 (1954).
11. Crelin, E. S., *Anat. Record* **124**, 279 (1956).
12. Crelin, E. S., *Science* **125**, 650 (1957).
13. Crelin, E. S., *Anat. Record* **130**, 401 (1958).
14. Crelin, E. S., and Brightman, M. W., *Anat. Record* **128**, 467 (1957).
15. Crelin, E. S., and Grillo, M. A., *Anat. Record* **127**, 407 (1957).
16. Crelin, E. S., and Honeyman, M. S., *Anat. Record* **127**, 407 (1957).
17. Crelin, E. S., and Levin, J., *Endocrinology* **57**, 730 (1955).
18. Csapo, A., *Am. J. Anat.* **98**, 273 (1956).
19. Cullen, B. M., and Harkness, R. D., *J. Physiol.* (*London*) **140**, 46P (1958).
20. Edgren, R. A., *Acta Endocrinol.* **25**, 365 (1957).
21. Edgren, R. A., and Calhoun, D. W., *Proc. Soc. Exptl. Biol. Med.* **94**, 537 (1957).
22. Elden, H. R., Sever, R. J., Noble, N. L., and Boucek, R. J., *Federation Proc.* **16**, 293 (1957). (Abstract No. 1256.)
23. Felton, L. C., Frieden, E. H., and Bryant, H. H., *J. Pharmacol. Exptl. Therap.* **107**, 160 (1953).
24. Frieden, E. H., *Endocrinology* **59**, 69 (1956).
25. Frieden, E. H., and Hisaw, F. L., *Endocrinology* **48**, 88 (1951).
26. Frieden, E. H., and Martin, A. S., *J. Biol. Chem.* **207**, 133 (1954).
27. Frieden, E. H., Noall, M. W., and de Florida, F. A., *J. Biol. Chem.* **222**, 611 (1956).
28. Frieden, E. H., and Velardo, J. T., *Proc. Soc. Exptl. Biol. Med.* **81**, 98 (1952).
29. Gardner, W. U., and Van Heuverswyn, J., *Endocrinology* **26**, 833 (1940).
30. Graham, E. F., and Dracy, A. E., *J. Dairy Sci.* **35**, 499 (1952).
31. Hall, K., *J. Endocrinol.* **5**, 174 (1947).

32. Hall, K., *J. Endocrinol.* **5**, 314 (1948).
33. Hall, K., *Quart. J. Exptl. Physiol.* **35**, 65 (1949).
34. Hall, K., *J. Endocrinol.* **7**, 54 (1950).
35. Hall, K., *J. Endocrinol.* **12**, 247 (1955).
36. Hall, K., *J. Endocrinol.* **13**, 384 (1956).
37. Hall, K., *J. Endocrinol.* **15**, 108 (1957).
38. Hamolsky, M., and Sparrow, R. C., *Proc. Soc. Exptl. Biol. Med.* **68**, 8 (1945).
39. Harkness, M. L. R., and Harkness, R. D., *J. Physiol.* (*London*) **131**, 19P (1956).
40. Harkness, M. L. R., Harkness, R. D., and Moralee, B. E., *J. Physiol.* (*London*) **135**, 270 (1957).
41. Herrick, E. H., *Anat. Record* **39**, 193 (1928).
42. Hisaw, F. L., and Zarrow, M. X., *Vitamins and Hormones* **8**, 151 (1950).
43. Hisaw, F. L., Zarrow, M. X., Money, W. L., Talmage, R. V., and Abramowitz, A. A., *Endocrinology* **34**, 122 (1944).
44. Hisaw, F. L., Zarrow, M. X., Talmage, R. V., Money, W. L., Abramowitz, A. A., *Anat. Record* **84**, 456 (1942).
45. Horn, E. H., *Anat. Record* **130**, 417 (1958). (Abstract No. 356.)
46. Horn, E. H., *Anat. Record* **130**, 418 (1958). (Abstract No. 357.)
47. Junkmann, K., *Arch. exptl. Pathol. Pharmakol. Naunyn-Schmiedeberg's* **233**, 244 (1954).
48. Junkmann, K., *Recent Progr. in Hormone Research* **13**, 389 (1957).
49. Kliman, B., and Greep, R. O., *J. Clin. Endocrinol. and Metabolism* **15**, 847 (1955).
50. Krantz, J. C., Jr., Bryant, H. H., and Carr, C. J., *Surg. Gynecol. Obstet.* **90**, 372 (1950).
51. Kroc, R. L., Beach, V. L., and Stasilli, N. R., *Federation Proc.* **15**, 113 (1956). (Abstract No. 367.)
52. Kroc, R. L., Steinetz, B. G., and Beach, V. L., *Ann. N. Y. Acad. Sci.* **75**, 942 (1958).
53. Kroc, R. L., Steinetz, B. G., Beach, V. L., and Stasilli, N. R., *J. Clin. Endocrinol. and Metabolism* **16**, 966 (1956).
54. Marois, M., *Compt. rend. soc. biol.* **142**, 1407 (1948).
55. Marois, M., *Compt. rend. soc. biol.* **143**, 370 (1949).
56. Marois, M., *Compt. rend. assoc. anat.* **36**, 11 (1949).
57. Miller, J. W., Kisley, A., and Murray, W. J., *J. Pharmacol. Exptl. Therap.* **120**, 426 (1957).
58. Newton, W. H., *J. Physiol.* (*London*) **84**, 196 (1935).
59. Newton, W. H., and Lits, F. J., *Anat. Record* **72**, 333 (1938).
60. Noble, N. L., and Boucek, R. J., *Circulation Research* **5**, 573 (1957).
61. Perl, E., and Catchpole, H. R., *Arch. Pathol.* **50**, 233 (1950).
62. Saunders, F. J., and Elton, R. L., Chapter 12 in this volume.
63. Saunders, F. J., and Drill, V. A., *Endocrinology* **58**, 567 (1956).
64. Sawyer, W. H., Frieden, E. H., and Martin, A. C., *Am. J. Physiol.* **172**, 547 (1953).
65. Sher, I. H., and Martin, G. J., *Exptl. Med. Surg.* **14**, 89 (1956).
66. Smith, J. C., and Nalbandov, A. V., *Am. J. Vet. Research* **19**, 15 (1958).
67. Smith, T. C., *Endocrinology* **54**, 59 (1954).
68. Smithberg, M., and Runner, M. N., *J. Exptl. Zool.* **133**, 441 (1956).
69. Smithberg, M., and Runner, M. N., *J. Heredity* **48**, 97 (1957).

70. Steinetz, B. G., Beach, V. L., Blye, R. P., and Kroc, R. L., *Endocrinology* **61**, 287 (1957).
71. Steinetz, B. G., Beach, V. L., and Kroc, R. L., *Endocrinology* **61**, 271 (1957).
72. Storey, E., *J. Pathol. Bacteriol.* **74**, No. 1, 147 (1957).
73. Uyldert, I. E., and De Vaal, O. M., *Acta Brevia Neerl. Physiol. Pharmacol. Microbiol.* **15**, 49 (1947).
74. Van Heuverswyn, J., Collins, V. J., and Williams, W. L., *Proc. Soc. Exptl. Biol. Med.* **41**, 552 (1939).
75. Velardo, J. T., *Am. Assoc. Anat. Abstr.* Paper No. 417 (1958).
76. Wada, H., and Turner, C. W., *Proc. Soc. Exptl. Biol. Med.* **99**, 194 (1958).
76a. Wada, H., and Yuhara, M., *Sci. Repts. Fac. Agr. Okayama Univ.* **9**, 11 (1956).
77. Zarrow, M. X., *Anat. Record* **96**, 32 (1946).
78. Zarrow, M. X., *Endocrinology* **42**, 129 (1948).
79. Zarrow, M. X., and Brennan, D. M., *Proc. Soc. Exptl. Biol. Med.* **95**, 745 (1957).
80. Zarrow, M. X., and Brennan, D. M., *Ann. N. Y. Acad. Sci.* **75**, 981 (1958).
81. Zarrow, M. X., and Money, W. L., *J. Pharmacol. Exptl. Therap.* **93**, 180 (1948).
82. Zarrow, M. X., Neher, G. M., Sikes, D., Brennan, D. M., and Bullard, J. F., *Am. J. Obstet. Gynecol.* **72**, 260 (1956).

Discussion

CHAIRMAN: F. L. HISAW

E. H. FRIEDEN: This is perhaps apart from the most excellent material which was presented by Dr. Kroc, but the question I have is with reference to prolonged effects of relaxin in mice. We have found, as many others have, I think, that guinea pigs treated repeatedly with relaxin lose their sensitivity to this hormone. We have attributed this phenomenon to the development of an antibody—probably of rather limited species specificity—since the response to relaxin of pregnant rabbit serum, for example, in animals which have been treated repeatedly with relaxin from sow ovaries, does not disappear quite as rapidly. I wonder if, Dr. Kroc, you have found any evidence for the appearance of resistance in mice treated for long periods of time with relaxin?

R. KROC: We have found that guinea pigs become unresponsive after a time, corresponding with your experience. In mice I am not sure that we can answer that question because the mice, when once they are markedly relaxed, stay relaxed—that is, for 4 or 5 weeks, at least. However, it is rather interesting that the ligament of the normal, pregnant mouse, which at first pregnancy reaches 3–4 mm., regresses relatively rapidly post partum so that the ligament by 5 days later is only 1 mm. or 1½ mm. long. However, if on the 19th day of pregnancy, the mouse is injected with a milligram or two of our standard relaxin in wax-oil, and then posted 5 days post partum, not only will the ligament have persisted, but it will be greatly elongated —up to 6, 7, 8 mm. So, there appears to be a very definite dynamic regression following parturition which we have not yet completely elucidated in our attempts experimentally. However, testosterone and progesterone in high dosage will involute established ligaments.

S. L. LEONARD: In spite of the enormous amount of data that was presented by Dr. Kroc and his co-workers on relaxin, I would like to add another effect of relaxin upon the uterus. This has to deal with the effect of relaxin upon the concentration on the enzyme phosphorylase of this enzyme—I am referring to active phosphorylase, the one which is the key enzyme in the last step in the formation of glycogen in tissue, that is, the conversion of glucose-1-phosphate to glycogen. It so happens, as far as we can determine in our laboratory (Dr. J. Kostyo) and from the work of others, that the rat uterine glycogen is located primarily, if not entirely, in the myometrium. Now, of all the steroids, only those with estrogenic activity have the power of increasing glycogen in the uterus of the rat. No other steroid, unless it has estrogenic properties, is capable of doing so. Likewise, we have been able to show recently that active phosphorylase can be increased in the uterus of the rat only with those steroids which are also capable of causing the deposition of glycogen. The effect of estrogen is very rapid. Within 6 hours one can detect the change of the inactive to active phosphorylase.

When Dr. Kroc's work appeared in which he showed that another hormone, relaxin, not a steroid presumably, was also capable of increasing uterine glycogen in the rat, interest was immediately aroused as to whether it also works the same way as estrogen in increasing active phosphorylase.

The method by which Dr. Kroc has shown that the relaxin increases glycogen in the rat uterus is to prime the rats with estrogen a week, at least, prior to the administration of relaxin. I became a little impatient. I did not want to wait so long. So I thought: it was just the estrogen priming of the rat which was important so why not castrate a rat which was in heat, the animal having already primed its own uterus for the possible effects of relaxin? I castrated some rats which were in heat and 24 hours later gave them an injection of 0.5–1 mg. of a potent relaxin preparation provided by Dr. Kroc, and within 12 hours I found that the uterine weight increased by 41% and active phosphorylase increased by 21%. The ratio of the active to the total potential phosphorylase in the uterus increased by 38%. If one calculates the increase of the phosphorylase on the basis of the whole uterus, the amount of active phosphorylase is almost doubled in 12 hours. By 24 hours, the effect has worn off. It begins to wear off, as Dr. Kroc mentioned, without continued treatment or without the proper vehicle to sustain the effect. These are only preliminary experiments, but they are sufficient, I believe, to suggest that the results will be substantiated by further work.

F. L. HISAW: Thank you. Those are very interesting observations.

S. J. FOLLEY: I would like briefly to mention some results showing an interaction between relaxin and estrogen and progesterone in regard to another target organ, the mammary gland. I will show a slide, if I may. These experiments were carried out on groups of goats spayed in infancy. The experiments were begun when the goats reached 18 months of age. Each of the curves represents the mean results for a group of three goats. The udders were developed by treatment with estrogen and progesterone over a period of 150 days, which is roughly the gestation period of the goat, and twice-daily milking was begun at the end of the treatment period.

One of the objects of the experiment was to compare the mammogenic effect of microcrystal suspensions of estradiol with that of similar suspensions of hexestrol, but that is beside the point now.

There are therefore two experiments. In the first one the udders were developed with estradiol and progesterone microcrystals given at intervals. One of the groups received in addition, during the last part of the treatment period, relaxin which was kindly supplied by Dr. Kroc. The lower two curves show a similar experiment in which, instead of estradiol, hexestrol microcrystal suspensions were used.

It is evident from the slide that in both experiments the relaxin treatment has had a lasting depressing effect on the milk yield. Whether this is a functional effect exerted through the pituitary, or, as we think more likely, an effect on mammary growth, will not become apparent until we have been able to carry out quantitative histological investigations on the udders of these goats. This we have not yet been able to do.

R. KROC: As I remember your data, Dr. Folley, you treated with aqueous relaxin in the morning and you treated with relaxin-beeswax oil at night.

In our discussions here at the meeting, I have suggested to Dr. Folley that it might be a good idea—if he has more spayed goats that he will run for 150 days—to try an extract from us which will have the same total nitrogen content, be made exactly the same way, and that would be, in essence, a low-potent control extract so that one could demonstrate that it was not a nonspecific polypeptide effect—a point which I think should always be kept in mind when dealing with substances which are still not pure.

E. C. REIFENSTEIN, JR: Dr. Kroc has shown us the differences between the action of various progestagens on relaxin. I wonder if he could give us any information about the effectiveness of various estrogens in priming for the relaxin response. Has he observed any quantitative or qualitative differences between the free estradiol which was injected repeatedly (each day) and the ester which was given as a single injection to induce an action for a long time. Does he have any information on the efficacy of other esters? What about the effect of diethylstilbestrol?

R. KROC: Mr. Chairman, I think I should share the answers with Dr. Steinetz. Do you have any comments?

B. STEINETZ: Actually we have found that in terms of total dosage of estrogen, the long-acting esters were much more effective in inducing an estrogen priming. In other words, if we injected estradiol-17-β daily we had to give somewhere in the neighborhood of ten times as much estrogen to achieve the same degree of priming as obtained with a single dose of a long-acting ester.

We have tested several other long-acting estrogens particularly with reference to priming for the mouse pubic symphysis assay. I might say that estradiol valerate was just about the equivalent of estradiol cyclopentylpropionate in that respect. Stilbestrol, for some reason, we found was a very poor priming agent in the dosages in which we used it.

G. S. GREENWALD: These remarks are directed primarily to Dr. Leonard:

We recently carried out some experiments involving the incorporation of S-[35]-methionine in the uterus of the spayed mouse. The studies involved autoradiographic and chemical techniques and they show an interesting incorporation of methionine in relation to the myometrium.

In the untreated castrate, the methionine is incorporated only by the longitudinal muscle layer. Similarly, the pattern is the same with the progesterone-treated castrate —methionine is incorporated only by the longitudinal layer.

However, with estrogen, the incorporation is also in the circular muscle layer in addition to the longitudinal layer. This is the same distribution that W. B. Atkinson and H. Elftman (Endocrinology 40, 30, 1947) found for alkaline phosphatase in the uterus of the spayed mouse. That is, in the longitudinal muscle layer, there is apparently no hormonal dependence for alkaline phosphatase, but the circular layer requires estrogen for the synthesis of the enzyme.

I wonder whether Dr. Leonard has done any histochemical studies on phosphorylase or glycogen to see whether this same distribution holds true?

S. L. LEONARD: No. That is one that is in the books to do—the histochemically determined distribution of phosphorylase. There is a new method, rather recent I believe.

I do think the distribution of the enzyme along with the glycogen should be investigated further, particularly following relaxin. Now we have a nonsteroidal hormone (which is the important thing that I want to bring out) that will increase glycogen in the uterus.

F. L. HISAW: If there is no objection, the Chair would like to take the privilege of showing three slides. These slides represent the work of the younger (H. L. Hisaw, Jr.) of us—that is the F_{-1} instead of the F generation—who probably would present them much better if he were here to do it, but I will try to take his place.

I would like to mention three different effects: (1) The effects of relaxin on the uterus of a monkey in combination with estrogen and progesterone; (2) the effect on the cervix; and (3) a peculiar effect on the blood-vascular system of the endometrium.

All the monkeys weighed between 5 and 6 kg., were adults in perfect health, castrated, all primed—first with 10 µg. of estradiol for 20 days and then put on experiments in which estriol happened to be used because we were studying it for another purpose. I think estradiol would do just as well. Estriol was used at a rather high dose of 0.5–1.0 mg. per day, plus 2.0 mg. progesterone. That was the basic treatment for 20 days. This treatment plus the simultaneous injection of relaxin daily for the 20-day period constituted the test for the effects of relaxin.

The first slide shows cross sections of four uteri: (1) One uterus shows the effects of the estrogen-progesterone treatment alone. (2) The second was given the same treatment and in addition a thread was placed through the uterus to induce a decidual reaction. In these two uteri it is important to note the relatively thick myometrium in relation to the endometrium. (3) The third shows the effects of large doses of estrogen and 2 mg. progesterone daily for several months. Such treatment produces a marked overgrowth of myometrium and a great reduction of endometrium. (4) The fourth uterus is that of an animal given estriol, progesterone, and relaxin for 20 days. The myometrium is thin in relation to a thick endometrium. There is a marked increase in endometrial stroma as shown by the wide separation of denser areas containing the spiral arteries. This action of relaxin has been referred to as producing a "watermelon" uterus.

The second slide shows sagittal sections of the cervices of four monkeys: one monkey received estriol; two, estriol plus progesterone; and one estriol, progesterone, and relaxin. The cervix, under estriol alone, is large, firm, shows marked development of the glands and the ventral colliculus is a very prominent structure. The cervices of the two animals on estriol and progesterone are smaller than that of the monkey given only estriol and are soft and pliable; the glands have discharged most of their secretion. Monkeys given estriol and progesterone have some relaxin in their blood but apparently not enough to cause marked modification of the reaction. However, when relaxin is added to the treatment, the effects described for estriol and progesterone become much more pronounced. The cervix is extremely soft, the walls are thin, and the ventral colliculus is strongly reduced.

The next slide shows the effects on the endometrium when relatively small doses of estrogen are used (10 µg. estradiol), instead of large doses of estriol. That is, the treatment given was 10 µg. estradiol plus 2 mg. progesterone daily—with and without relaxin—for 20 days following a priming treatment of 10 µg. estradiol daily for

20 days. The effects to be noted are those on the endometrial stroma and blood vessels.

Decidual cells or changes resembling a decidual reaction are rarely if ever seen in monkeys during a normal menstrual cycle nor are they developed when 10 μg. estradiol and 2 mg. progesterone are given as described above. The result is a fully developed progestational endometrium. However, when relaxin is added to such a treatment there is a decidualike reaction in the stroma and the glands are markedly reduced probably by pressure exerted by the surrounding tissue. Also, the capillaries and venules below the surface mucosa of the uterine lumen become greatly dilated and the cells of the endothelium show hypertrophy and hyperplasia. A similar modification of the blood vessels at the borders of a developing placenta has been described by G. B. Wislocki and G. L. Streeter, *Contr. Embryol. Carneg. Inst.* **27**, 1 1938 and referred to as "cytomorphosis" of the endothelium. The meaning of this is not clear, but it is not seen when large doses of estriol are given with the same dosage of progesterone and relaxin as is used here. It may in some way be related to placentation.

Effects of Relaxin in the Human

MARTIN L. STONE

Department of Obstetrics and Gynecology, New York Medical College Metropolitan Medical Center, New York, New York

I. Introduction

Although most of us accept the existence of relaxin as a nonsteroid hormone of pregnancy, its clinical status is still very controversial (13). Suggested uses include treatment of dysmenorrhea, prevention and treatment of premature labor, softening of the term cervix and treatment of collagen diseases.

Unfortunately studies reporting on these uses in humans have been conflicting or confusing. One of the first reports was that of Abramson and Reid (1), who were successful in arresting premature labor in a small series of patients treated with intramuscular relaxin. All five patients delivered normal infants at term. Similarly favorable results were reported by Folsome and his co-workers (6) in a group of 40 patients in premature labor. The fetal salvage rate was 71%, and complete arrest of labor occurred in 57.7% of the patients. McCarthy *et al.* (7) concluded from their study that relaxin did inhibit premature contractions in "uncomplicated" cases of premature labor but that it was of little use if the membranes were ruptured.

Paradoxically, it has also been reported from these and other studies that in many cases the use of relaxin was followed by rapid cervical dilatation and prompt delivery (4, 6). Eichner *et al.* (4) used relaxin in patients about to undergo therapeutic termination of pregnancy by means of dilatation and curettage. It was his impression that the cervix was softer and the use of the drug contributed to the ease of cervical

429

dilatation and evacuation of the products of conception. Maclure (8) used relaxin to assist in the induction of labor in a series of fifteen cases of retained dead fetus. In eleven of these cases, induction was facilitated. Birnberg and Abitbol (2) have reported softening of the term cervix and significant shortening of labor in a selected group of patients given relaxin.

Reports on the use of relaxin for control of dysmenorrhea, threatened abortion, and toxemia of pregnancy have been interesting but inconclusive (10). Studies and case reports on nonobstetric therapeutic applications of relaxin are beginning to appear in the literature. These include cases of scleroderma, bile duct fibrosis, chronic cirrhosis, and other disturbances involving connective tissue (3, 9, 10).

At the New York Medical College we have been unimpressed with the results in treatment of premature labor and have directed our attention to evaluating the effects of relaxin on the term cervix (12, 14).

II. Material and Method

To date the series includes 97 pregnant women at or near term in whom indicated or elective induction of labor was contemplated. Indications for induction included toxemia of pregnancy, diabetes, Rh sensitization, and retention of a dead fetus *in utero*. There were also several patients under investigation for metabolic changes in anemia of pregnancy in whom induction had to be performed for study purposes. The only criteria for selection was the condition of the cervix. All patients had an unripe, unfavorable cervix of firm consistency, without effacement or dilatation and in the posterior location. All patients were examined by the same investigator in order to rule out differences in the interpretation of the status of the cervix.

A. Dosage

The patients received 2 cc. (40 mg.) of relaxin* intramuscularly on the evening prior to induction. On the following morning 6 cc. in 500 cc. G/W was administered by continuous intravenous drip. The rate of infusion was 60 drops per minute. Two hours after completion of the relaxin infusion, intravenous oxytocin drip was started according to the technique previously described (15).

B. Controls

In order to obtain some degree of control, patients who went into labor spontaneously or whose membranes ruptured spontaneously were

---

* Clinical supplies of this material under the trade name Releasin were furnished by Warner-Chilcott Laboratories.

excluded from the study. No amniotomy was performed as part of the induction technique. Further control was achieved by giving other patients selected according to the same criteria of cervical status, a placebo instead of relaxin and then following it with oxytocin according to the plan outlined above.

III. Results

If labor did not result and delivery did not follow the above regime, the case was considered a failure. We have been encouraged by our results to date (Table I). Sixty-two patients received relaxin and oxytocin and 35 patients received placebo and oxytocin. Of the relaxin-treated patients, 43 or 71.5% were successfully induced. In 19 patients, 28.5%, the attempt at induction failed. In a control group, only 8 patients, 22.8%, were successfully induced and there were 27 failures, 77.2%.

TABLE I
RESULTS IN INDUCTION OF LABOR

	Successful	Unsuccessful	Total
Relaxin	43 (71.5%)	19 (28.5%)	62
Placebo	8 (22.8%)	27 (77.2%)	35

Softening of the cervix as determined on vaginal examination was a fairly constant finding in all cases treated with relaxin. This does not mean that there was increased effacement or dilatation prior to the use of oxytocin. The effect of relaxin on the cervix was not clinically demonstrable in less than 3 hours after its administration. In a few cases where the routine could not be carried out after the relaxin had been administered, we had the opportunity to observe the transient nature of the relaxin effect. The cervix became soft but on re-examination the next morning, it had again become firm and reverted to its original condition.

In four additional cases the relaxin-oxytocin combination was used because of retention of a dead fetus. All four cases were successfully induced. Some of them had previous unsuccessful attempts of stimulation of labor. The surprisingly uniform effective action of the compound in these cases in whom induction of labor is notoriously difficult merits special consideration.

IV. Reactions

Very little untoward reaction to the drug was noted. One patient developed an urticarial type rash which responded promptly to antihistaminics. Two patients had chills suggesting a pyrogenic reaction. There were no adverse effects on blood pressure, pulse, temperature, or blood count. Relaxin is apparently compatible with other drugs including oxytocin, analgesics, and anesthetics.

V. Comments

There is little reason to doubt the existence or biologic activity of relaxin. However, some of the successful uses reported can be doubted. Its use in premature labor seems illogical to us. Premature labor is a nebulous condition with no demonstrable etiologic factor in 60% of cases. The other 40% are related to varying obstetrical and medical conditions, many of which would not be amenable to relaxin therapy even if relaxin did all that is claimed for it. In many of the series the status of labor when the drug was started was not reported. It is probable that the successes include cases that were not in true or advanced labor.

Relaxin will soften the cervix. This statement does not imply that relaxin dilates the cervix or initiates labor in humans. Oxytocin, either endogenous or exogenous, is still necessary to produce effective uterine contractions.

On the basis of the softening effect, relaxin may be an effective adjunct to the medical induction of labor and may make delivery possible in patients with an unfavorable cervix. This may be especially valuable in cases of retained dead fetus. In addition to the readily understandable psychic trauma these patients may suffer, we must add the recently recognized danger of hypofibrinogenemia, particularly in isoimmunized mothers.

The one report of marked shortening of labor with relaxin involved patients who received supplemental oxytocin in the presence of advanced cervical dilatation and effacement and ruptured membranes. It is our thought that the short labors in these patients should be credited to the action of oxytocin used under ideal conditions (11).

Variations in results have also been ascribed to differences in dosage and products. In our study, aqueous relaxin in the form Releasin was the product used either intramuscularly or intravenously or both. Releasin is assayed by an objective method using the mouse pubic symphysis test. We have had no experience with oral or newer repository forms of relaxin. The latter give promise of being even more effective than the original aqueous products.

In our study untoward reactions were minimal. There were no adverse effects on blood pressure, pulse, temperature, or blood count. Relaxin is apparently compatible with other drugs including oxytocics, analgesics, and anesthetics. However, it should be emphasized that relaxin is a protein substance and the dangers of reactions exist. We have been able to find one fully authenticated case of death following administration of relaxin (5). If repeated administration is contemplated, skin testing is strongly recommended.

In an attempt to confirm our clinical impressions of the effect of relaxin on the term cervix, we have performed cervical biopsies before and after relaxin therapy. The specimens were subjected to special histochemical stain and analysis. To date, in 14 cases, we have been unable to demonstrate any objective changes in the connective tissue of the cervix which might be attributed to relaxin.

VI. Summary

1. Relaxin is a nonsteroid hormone of pregnancy apparently concerned with preparation for parturition.

2. Suggested clinical uses in the human include treatment of dysmenorrhea, prevention and treatment of premature labor, softening of the term cervix, and treatment of collagen and connective tissue diseases.

3. Relaxin does soften the cervix of pregnant women and thus it appears to be a worth-while adjunct to the medical induction of labor. In a series of 62 patients treated with relaxin and oxytocin, successful induction was obtained in 71.5%. In a control group of 35 patients who received placebo and oxytocin, the success rate was 22.8%. Both groups were selected on the basis of an unfavorable cervix.

4. While better methods of assay are now available, final word on form and optimum dosage will have to await further basic and clinical studies.

5. Although relatively nontoxic, the protein nature of relaxin makes the possibility of sensitivity reactions an ever-present problem.

6. There is no doubt that much more work needs to be done to acquire a fuller understanding of this interesting hormone and to establish its proper place in obstetrics. It is hoped that other investigators will use relaxin in an effort to reproduce the reported results and confirm its effect on the cervix. It is this action of relaxin and perhaps its effect in collagen diseases which offer the most promise for future clinical use.

References

1. Abramson, D., and Reid, D. E., *J. Clin. Endocrin. and Metabolism* **15**, 206 (1955).
2. Birnberg, C. H., and Abitbol, M. M., *Obstet. and Gynecol.* **10**, 366 (1957).
3. Casten, G. G., and Boucek, R. J., *J. Am. Med. Assoc.* **166**, 319 (1958).
4. Eichner, E., Waltner, C., Goodman, M., and Post, S., *Am. J. Obstet. Gynecol.* **71**, 1048 (1956).

5. Evans, James A., *Lahey Clin. Bull.* **10**, 190 (1957).
6. Folsome, C. E., Harami, T., Lavietes, S. R., Massell, G. M., *Obstet. and Gynecol.* **8**, 536 (1956).
7. McCarthy, J. J., Erving, H. W., and Laufe, L., *Am. J. Obstet. Gynecol.* **74**, 134 (1957).
8. Maclure, J. G., *Bull. Univ. Miami School of Med.* (June, 1957).
9. Molander, D. W., and Sands, R. X., *Clin. Research Proc.* **6**, 146 (1958).
10. Sands, R. X., and Stone, M. L., *Western J. Surg. Obstet. Gynecol.* **66**, 115 (1958).
11. Stone, M. L., and Gordon, M., *N. Y. State J. Med.* **54**, 2310 (1954).
12. Stone, M. L., Sedlis, A., and Zuckerman, M., *Bull. N. Y. Med. Coll. Flower and Fifth Ave. Hosp.* **19**, 87 (1956).
13. Stone, M. L., Sedlis, A., and Zuckerman, M., *Am. J. Obstet. Gynecol.* **76**, 544 (1958).
14. Stone, M. L., Sedlis, A., and Zuckerman, M., Transactions of the Conference on the Uterus, *Ann. N. Y. Acad. Sci.* in press.
15. Stone, M. L., and Tanz, A., *Obstet. and Gynecol.* **1**, 346 (1953).

Discussion

CHAIRMAN: F. L. HISAW

E. EICHNER: Through the courtesy of Dr. Kroc I have been working on relaxin in humans for somewhat over five years. We treated patients with the gelatin and the saline material cyclically through several cycles, attempting to see what would develop insofar as ureteral dilatation, cervical softening, changes in the endometrium, and other alterations. It was noted at that time that despite the reports in the literature that progesterone had an "anti" effect on relaxin, our patients seemed to respond better in the progestational or luteal phase of their cycle with cervical softening and several other changes.

One patient developed a mild, minimal degree of ureteral dilatation which disappeared. One patient had a minimal degree of separation of the symphysis which also could not be developed again. As to the problem of antihormone as presented by Dr. Frieden, we were never able to verify this or to go further with the subject on this patient.

Insofar as the balance of the human work was clinical, we discovered that there was a rather long latent period before relaxin became effective—anywhere up to 48 or 72 hours. It was for this reason that our original injections were given around the clock with saline and gelatin added.

In the original experiments on cervical dilatation, the patients received injections of relaxin the night before, the following morning, and before going to surgery; so they received quite a bit of material, some of it intravenously. We found that we did not get adverse reactions on I.V. injection. We raised our I.V. dosage schedule so that, instead of talking in guinea pig units, we can now go to milligrams. In an attempt to stop labor we have given over 200 mg. of relaxin in a single injection, I.V., and have given probably over a gram of it to one patient.

With the relative cost of the material you see that our treatment was rather heroic, but in selective cases we were able to stop labor with the cervix dilated up to 6 or 7 cm. providing the initiating cause of labor did not continue. That's a rather vague statement, but again we have no end point with which we can work.

In many cases, even in term labor, we were able to modify contractions and to stop them for short periods of time with a massive I.V. injection of relaxin. Many of these patients lost that period of time out of their labor and then when contractions picked up went ahead to rather precipitous labor and delivery. This started us on the project of cervical softening which we had noted previously.

Unfortunately, cervical softening, as Dr. Stone has emphasized, does not mean cervical dilatability insofar as labor is concerned. You can manually dilate the cervices; you can do an accouchement without difficulty; but somehow or other labor itself does not always seem to be progressive, and in some patients we have had some interference with Pitocin working during the high peaks of relaxin efficiency, and in other patients there has apparently been no difficulty. There are other processes involved which at the present time are completely and totally unclear.

In an attempt to stop premature labor, if 5 or 10 mg. per minute, I.V., is not effective, give up. With that dosage we have maintained a complete cessation of contractions for several hours.

I want to ask Dr. Stone about the selection of the patients who received the placebo. There were two treated cases to one placebo patient. Were these alternate cases, alternate serial numbers, or did he merely pick those that he thought would be most effectively treated? One last comment is that we have used the products made available to us by both drug houses that are now marketing relaxin and on the schedules that we have used, we cannot tell the difference between these materials in the cessation of labor. The possibility, as Dr. Kroc has mentioned, that we may be getting an amino acid or foreign protein rather than a relaxin reaction has to be considered.

On the question of cervical dilatation, we ran a double blind on materials from the two concerns plus saline in patients in the last 2 weeks of pregnancy and statistically we were not able to determine any difference in cervical softening 2 hours after an I.V. injection of an adequate amount of relaxin.

M. STONE: Thank you, Dr. Eichner. I think one place wherein we are in complete agreement is that the dosage used by Dr. Eichner is probably higher than anyone has used, so no one can argue with the results that he has obtained. We never have had as much relaxin for our entire study as he can use in one patient.

While it doesn't stop premature labor at least it does not hurt the patient and that's a contribution in itself.

As far as the selection of patients, the reason there were more in the treated group is, as Dr. Nesbitt reminded me, that we like to induce labor when it is indicated. In most cases, since this was not a blind study, the patients needed the induction because of an unfavorable cervix during toxemia, or were in the group who had had radioactive B[12] and we had to get the fetus out so we could measure it in the placenta before it was all gone. So there was a greater number of patients in the treated group in the hope that the treatment would help us successfully deliver the patients without waiting for a favorable cervix or doing a Cesarean section. The patients were selected to receive the placebo in an attempt to obtain controls using patients with an unfavorable cervix at term.

E. C. HUGHES: I appreciate the fairness of Dr. Stone's paper this morning.

With respect to prematurity our experience here on a small series of cases has not been very happy. Relaxin has not prevented any patient from continuing in labor. When you consider the various factors involved in prematurity—alterations of hormone levels, the changes in the placenta, and the picture as a whole, I personally cannot see how relaxin can alter the situation. In our hand, it has not.

We also have not had very happy results in respect to softening and dilatation of the cervix in delayed labor. The clinical observation of softening of the cervix is so extremely difficult to evaluate that I think until we get some objective method of determining this, we can't say relaxin actually has a specific action upon the cervix. Labor itself, various analgesics, rupture of the membranes, will often soften the cervix. The normal physiological changes that occur at this time are so dramatic that so far we have not been able to feel that relaxin has affected the cervix in any appreciable manner.

However, I think more clinical studies together with the investigations that have been going on here are needed. Certainly those in the clinical field would appreciate a medication of this type that could help the progress of labor; but until we can get that, I feel we have to have more objective methods of determining the effect upon the cervix.

E. EICHNER: I just want to show these slides in response to Dr. Hughes' comments. The first slide shows the effect of a single I.V. injection of 200 mg. of relaxin in a patient with a multiple string gauge TKD (tokodynamometer) on the abdomen. Just consider the second channel because the others start working at a later time. The first two contractions are approximately 2 minutes apart, at which time the 200 mg. of relaxin was given I.V. The next contraction is technically tamped down, followed through, and then you see what happens during the next half hour or so. [Contractions were diminished.—Ed.] In the third channel, that is the third line, the contractions are beginning to recur again at this time.

The next slide shows a recording by an intrauterine balloon. The relaxin is given about a third way over from the left-hand side of the film; that one little spike resulted from a rectal examination which jarred the recording catheter, but within 6 or 7 minutes we then get our response in the irregular contractions. Now this is approximately one-third of the dose that was given before, and within 15 or 20 minutes the contractions are back again where they were.

The third slide merely shows the difficulties in recording. Top line is the recording of intrauterine balloon and the bottom line is a surface TKD. Fetal movement, picked up as a contraction in the bottom line, gives a false impression of what is occurring. In the top line there is minimal distortion, but note the succeeding excellent contraction.

M. STONE: I think Dr. Eichner's last slide is the important one, showing the difficulty in interpreting uterine tracings. Kelly and Possé, with whom I had the privilege of working, used the intrauterine electrodes of Karlsen and did some studies of the effects of relaxin on uterine activity. They couldn't demonstrate any objective changes that they could attribute just to the relaxin. Here we see in the third slide that intra-abdominal or intrauterine or fetal movements, all play a role in interpreting relaxin effects. There are many problems in following the pattern, particularly with one injection. As Dr. Eichner said, one rectal exam changed things quite a bit.

I agree with Dr. Hughes that the hope for us clinicians will come from the work of the group in this room. If you can give us a simple way of finding the blood level in humans and can tell us that the blood level normally is so much in premature labor, either high or low, and that if we give a dose of 40 mg. we can expect to get a given response, then, of course, we can evaluate this.

Something worth while has come out of all this. While there is no tremendous series, if we had a relaxin registry, and maybe we ought to start that at Harvard, and pooled the results of different clinicians, we could perhaps see that the original enthusiastic articles in the literature about fetal salvage are perhaps no longer to be considered valid. But I think we could conclude that relaxin exists, that it has biologic activity. If we as clinicians cannot properly use it, well, the burden of proof is still on us.

F. L. Hisaw: About starting a relaxin registry at Harvard, I hope this is not a serious thought, if Dr. Stone has me in mind. All I know about relaxin clinically is what I read. That is, I happen to belong to the monkey fraternity rather than the human fraternity with respect to these things. I am very well satisfied with leaving this in the hands of the clinicians where there seems to be a wholesome amount of skepticism and sound judgment, and things not understood now will finally be worked out, no doubt, and will fall eventually into their proper place.

B. Steinetz: May I make a comment with reference to a possible objective human end point regarding whether or not relaxin injections induce softening of the cervix. We have done some recent animal experiments that might possibly be applied to a human study. In these experiments the animals (rats) were treated similarly to those described by Dr. Kroc. In other words, they were first primed with estrogen and then received daily dosages of relaxin in a repository agent.

We then injected Evans Blue I.V. and measured the uptake of Evans Blue by the uterus and cervix. This has been taken by various people to be an indication of increased capillary permeability and may also indicate "depolymerization of the connective tissue ground substance."

In these studies we found that relaxin definitely did increase the Evans Blue uptake by the cervix and the uterus. I don't know how these data will fit with Dr. Szego's remarks yesterday about histamine liberation (due to estrogen treatment), but, as you know, histamine liberators also increase Evans Blue uptake by tissues. I wonder if such an end point could perhaps be used to determine objectively the effect of relaxin on the human cervix?

F. Hisaw: Dr. Stone, I don't know whether you want to reply to that. I might make a reply for you with regard to monkeys and then you can add any remark that you wish as it applies to the human being.

I might have mentioned in the discussion that I gave with the slides I showed you, that when estrogen is high, that is, when estriol was given in large doses with the progesterone treatment plus relaxin, there is a definite softening of the tissue in the symphysis pubis. Mobility may be pronounced; but in the absence of a large dose of estrogen this reaction did not occur. Nor did it occur in the absence of relaxin. That is, in the controls it didn't occur. In some animals there was rupture of small blood vessels and the symphyseal cartilages were bloodshot as is often seen in guinea pigs following an injection of relaxin. I have no knowledge as to how this might apply to the human being.

R. Kroc: I suggest that we get away from the idea that nature is necessarily built on only a "unitarian" ground. By that I mean the tendency to think that one hormone, relaxin, or another progesterone, will solve any particular abnormality. Perhaps it is time we considered the possibility that individuals vary in their balance. Possibly an answer to the apparent, but probably not real, difference between monkey and man referred to by Drs. Stone and Hisaw is that the balance achieved with three hormones in Dr. Hisaw's monkeys was not achieved by the administration of just one of the ovarian hormones in many of the patients treated.

C. G. Hartman: Do we not need to look for other effects of relaxin than the specific ones already alluded to, more subtle effects, applicable to all species that produce relaxin, from elasmobranchs to man, as Dr. Hisaw has pointed out?

It is easy to see that the guinea pig with its large young at term needs relaxin. As to the sow, however, the ovaries of which are our chief source of relaxin at this time, I have seen a 600-pound sow give birth to a dozen young while asleep. Perhaps the sow needs relaxin for other reasons than the guinea pig.

F. HISAW: Well, there are two things in connection with this that I might say. One is, I am, you know, a Professor of Natural History, not obstetrics and gynecology; and the other point is that from an evolutionary standpoint relaxin existed long before viviparity became a problem among mammals. In this connection, it should be mentioned that the ovaries of the pregnant sow are at present the principal source of relaxin, so it may be that by virtue of this was Hartman's sow able to perform the remarkable Morphean feat he describes.

R. NESBITT: I think that it might be worth while to emphasize that rigidity of maternal soft parts, particularly consistency of the cervix, is only one of several factors capable of influencing the outcome of labor. These factors include general maternal condition, size and morphology of the bony pelvis, presentation, station and size of the fetus, moldability of the fetal head, and particularly, the character of the powers of labor. These factors are difficult to define and to control in statistical data. Patients who deliver after comparable periods of labor are at best a heterogenous group, and this heterogenicity is increased when the labors have been artificially induced because of specific medical indications. These several enigmas should be taken into account when interpreting clinical data which pertain to the outcome of labor.

I should like to call your attention also to the fact that failure in uterine power may take one of several clinical forms. Certain patients fail to achieve satisfactory progress in labor despite palpable uterine contractions and considerable abdominal discomfort. Since the cervix in these patients frequently fails to dilate or efface satisfactorily, the assumption has been made, particularly in past years, that some type of cervical dystocia must be the primary factor impeding the progress of labor. Thus, any drug or procedure that improves the consistency of the cervix should promote effective labor. Current knowledge of uterine physiology, however, indicates that ordinarily the converse is true and the tardy dilatation of the cervix is the direct result of faulty uterine contractions. Only rarely, when the cervix has been partially amputated, chronically infected, and/or repeatedly cauterized, is rigidity of the cervix of primary concern. More frequently, these deliveries are complicated by incoordinated uterine contractions. These uterine dysfunctions may be characterized by a complete reversal of gradient whereby the mid-zone of the uterus contracts with equal or greater force than the fundus or by an apparent lack of synchronism in the fundus. These uterine dysfunctions are difficult to distinguish clinically, and I suspect that, in certain of these cases, there is too much emphasis placed upon the physical characteristics of the cervix as a possible deterrent to the progress of labor. One should not expect relaxin, by merely softening the cervix, to expedite labor in these patients to any appreciable extent. Delivery will not occur until an effective, coordinated labor is established, regardless of the dilatability of the cervix. I should be very much interested to hear Dr. Stone's remarks on this point.

I have been considerably interested in hearing Dr. Stone's splendid success rate in inducing labor in patients with unfavorable cervices. These results suggest that, with the use of relaxin, we may have considerable more latitude with this procedure in the management of specific medical and obstetrical complications than we have heretofore enjoyed. One of the chief hazards of manipulating patients with unfavorable cervices has been the increased incidence of inert labor. I should like to ask Dr. Stone if inert labor was a significant problem in his group of induced patients.

M. STONE: Dr. Nesbitt's points are well taken. Any of us who have been under the influence of Dr. Hellman doubt the existence of a condition called cervical dystocia and feel that the inability of the cervix to dilate is secondary to ineffectual uterine contractions, even though they may make the patient uncomfortable. They are just not the right kind of contractions. That is why I said in the paper that I don't think relaxin is causing inertia, I don't think the use of oxytocin is causing the inertia. I said in the paper that relaxin will soften the cervix clinically. This does not mean that it dilates the cervix or effaces the cervix; and as for uterine contractions, we still need oxytocin, either endogenous or exogenous.

Neurohypophyseal Control of Parturition

B. A. CROSS

*Sub-Department of Veterinary Anatomy, University of Cambridge,
Cambridge, England*

I. Introduction

The extent to which secretion of oxytocin by the neurohypophysis enters in the mechanism of labor has long been debated. No one doubts the ability of the hormone to induce rhythmic contractions in the estrogen-dominated uterus of many species; but as more than one author has emphasized, parturition is a complex process in which uterine contractions constitute only one of several participating mechanisms. For this and other reasons there has been a reluctance to ascribe to the neurohypophysis a physiological role in parturition. There is another function of oxytocin, however, that is now generally accepted, namely its lactational role in the milk-ejection reflex during suckling (11, 13,

16). Milk ejection is independent of a motor innervation to the mammary glands, and the only hormones known to induce the response are those of the neurohypophysis, of which oxytocin is five or six times more active than vasopressin (19, 46). Milk ejection can therefore be used as an indicator for circulating oxytocin, whether of endogenous or exogenous origin. This has enabled new evidence to be gathered on the secretion of oxytocin during parturition. Another gain from present knowledge of the milk-ejection mechanism is that it allows an independent evaluation of the capacity of animals with experimental interferences in the hypothalamo-hypophyseal region to secrete oxytocin. For example, if such an animal undergoes labor but fails to eject milk during suckling in the ensuing lactation, it is likely that delivery of the young was effected without the help of oxytocin.

II. Evidence for Neurohypophyseal Participation in Labor

A. Effect of Destruction of the Neurohypophysis

Fisher et al. (26) justly criticized much of the earlier work in which apparently normal delivery of young followed experimental removal of the pituitary gland. Such experiments were subject to three limitations: loss of anterior pituitary tissue, failure to remove the neurohypophyseal tissue of the median eminence, and inadequate evaluation of parturitional performance. In their own experiments in seven cats, Fisher et al. placed electrolytic lesions in the supraopticohypophyseal (SOH) tract behind the optic chiasma. The completeness of neurohypophyseal ablation was assessed by the resulting diabetes insipidus and by histological examination post mortem. Four cats died during protracted labors and the fetuses were macerated. Two animals survived prolonged labor but lost their young. The remaining cat delivered a viable litter and reared it despite a diabetes insipidus. Dey et al. (22) obtained comparable results in guinea pigs. More than half the animals with diabetes insipidus suffered dystocia of varying severity and most of the young were born dead. Approximately one-third of the animals, however, managed to deliver their litters normally.

In the human subject, also, diabetes insipidus has sometimes been associated with difficulty in labor (38, 39). But it is apparent that many women with diabetes insipidus experience no serious impairment of parturition (2, 21).

Recent work on rats has indicated that a chronic state of mild diabetes insipidus following section of the pituitary stalk (12) or removal of the neural lobe of the pituitary (6) may not interfere with labor or with milk ejection during the subsequent lactation. Evidently a deficiency of antidiuretic hormone production does not necessarily imply a corresponding deficiency of oxytocin. Some of the results with diabetic animals described above may be explained on the assumption that some oxytocin was available to assist in labor. However, the fact that some animals exhibit normal labor but in the ensuing lactation show inability to eject milk during suckling (18, 30) supports the view that oxytocin may not be indispensable to labor. Nonneurohypophyseal mechanisms (Section III) probably effect the delivery of young in such cases. Nevertheless, there is sufficient evidence from the results of neuro-hypophyseal ablations to indicate that oxytocin plays an important part in many labors.

B.   Ability of Oxytocin to Induce Labor

Over thirty years ago Knaus (35) demonstrated the induction of labor in rabbits by injection of posterior pituitary extract. The observation has been many times confirmed in a variety of species including man. There is little doubt that the effect is due to oxytocin rather than vasopressin, for the latter has minimal stimulating effects on the intact uterus (14). Purified oxytocic extract or synthetic oxytocin are very effective in inducing labor in near-term rabbits (7, 20), and such labors closely resemble natural parturition in this species (15, 27). Moreover, injection of physiological doses of oxytocin into rabbits under conditions in which maternal spinal reflexes and fetal movements are abolished (Nembutal and spinal anesthesia) can produce labors which in most respects are as efficient as in conscious unrestrained rabbits (15).

Synthetic oxytocin has also been shown to induce labor in women (24), and oxytocin intravenous drip is being increasingly employed in obstetrical practice (34, 44). From quantitative studies on the human pregnant uterus it has been estimated that infusion of oxytocin at the rate of 1–8 mU. (milliunits) per minute produces in near-term subjects similar uterine activity to that observed in the first stage of natural labor (8). These recent findings in rabbits and women are highly suggestive of a physiological role for oxytocin in parturition.

C.   Electrical Stimulation of the Neurohypophysis

Haterius and Ferguson (31) showed that electrical stimulation of the infundibular stem in anesthetized post-partum rabbits elicits greatly augmented uterine contractions. The response approximated to that produced by injection of 0.5 U. Pitocin and was not affected by eliminating all nervous connections from the head to the rest of the body (25).

The capacity of endogenous neurohypophyseal hormone to evoke uterine contractions has been confirmed in conscious rabbits by Harris (29), using his remote-control stimulating technique. Effective stimuli were located within 1/2 mm. of the SOH tract. The writer (14), working with spayed estrogenized rabbits under Nembutal anesthesia, stimulated various parts of the hypothalamus and obtained uterine responses of two distinct types. One, which resembled the effect of injecting 1–5 µg. adrenaline (epinephrine) intravenously was elicited by stimuli in the dorsal, lateral, and posterior hypothalamic areas. The response was abolished by spinal transection or spinal anesthesia. These procedures did not interfere with the second type of response, which resembled that produced by injection of 10–50 mU. Pitocin and which followed stimulation of the supraoptic and paraventricular nuclei and of the SOH tract. It is significant that in all the studies just mentioned neuro-hypophyseal stimulation more closely duplicated the effects of oxytocin than of vasopressin. Kurotsu *et al.* (37) also reported enhanced uterine motility following electrical stimulation of various hypothalamic nuclei in the rabbit, but these workers did not establish the neurohypophyseal origin of the uterine responses. From the standpoint of the parturition mechanism all these studies have the disadvantage that the uteri were empty. However, recently it has been demonstrated that electrical stimulation of the SOH tract also activates the full-term gravid uterus of the rabbit, with the result that delivery of the litter quickly follows (15). There can be no doubt, therefore, that parturition can be induced by endogenous neurohypophyseal hormone.

D. Assay of Oxytocin Content of Neurohypophysis and Body Fluids

Two groups of workers have shown that the neurohypophysis of rats is depleted of oxytocin immediately following parturition (1, 23). Acher and Fromageot (1) found that the glands contained only about 50% of the normal content of oxytocic and vasopressor activities and that 24 hours after parturition the content of both hormones had returned to normal. During the subsequent lactation the vasopressor activity remained constant but the oxytocin content was once again decreased, giving a vasopressin:oxytocin (V/O) ratio of 3:1 instead of the normal 1:1 ratio. It is not clear why the V/O ratio should differ in parturition and lactation, though evidently both conditions impose demands on neurohypophyseal reserves of oxytocin. Interestingly, parturition does not apparently deplete the neural lobe of Gomori-positive neurosecretory material though suckling does (43).

Early experiments indicated the presence of substances with oxytocic activity in the blood (4, 5) and urine (9) of parturient subjects. Modern work, however, casts serious doubt on the neurohypophyseal origin of this activity (45). Using more acceptable methods of extraction and assay, Hawker and Robertson (32) failed to detect any increase in the concentration of oxytocin in the blood of women in labor compared with earlier stages of pregnancy. There may be many reasons why this measure of neurohypophyseal functioning should fail to complement the evidence from the posterior pituitary gland assays in laboratory animals referred to in the last paragraph. Not least among them is the fact that the neurohypophyseal content of oxytocin reflects the balance of synthesis and release, whereas blood assays reflect the balance of secretion and destruction of the hormone. Neither procedure affords an accurate check on the secretory output of the neurohypophysis in labor.

E.   Evidence from Milk-Ejection Studies

It is well known in agricultural circles that several of the domesticated animals commonly exhibit milk ejection ("let-down") during parturition. Milk drips from the teats of cows in labor, and in pigs this is the only time, apart from suckling, when milk can readily be withdrawn from the udder. A recent lactational study in pigs (17) disclosed that the mammary alveoli in biopsy samples obtained during labor were virtually devoid of colostrum and showed the marked elongation of the lining epithelial cells with associated infolding of the alveolar walls which characterize oxytocin-induced alveolar contraction. The histological appearance differed greatly from the distended alveoli with flattened epithelial cells seen in biopsy samples obtained a few hours before the onset of labor. The observations of Gunther (28) indicate that ejection of milk from the breast may also occur in women in parturition.

There is reason to believe that the release of oxytocin in the above circumstances results from a reflex excitation of the neurohypophysis by stimuli originating in the female genital tract. Andersson (3) reported that mechanical stimulation of the cervix in goats induces milk ejection, and a similar phenomenon has been described in cows (33). These findings recall the experiments of Ferguson (25) in which mechanical dilatation of the empty uterus or cervix in post-partum rabbits elicited augmented uterine contractions which were abolished by electrolytic cautery of the pituitary stalk.

Further experiments in rabbits (15) have provided direct evidence that a reflex excitation of the neurohypophysis occurs in labor. Near-term rabbits under Nembutal had labor induced by injection of Pitocin or stimulation of the SOH tract (Section II, B and C). Kymographic records obtained from cannulated mammary glands showed that during the course of labor additional releases of oxytocin occurred, as evidenced by the resulting milk-ejection responses. In one case the magnitude of the endogenous response exceeded that produced by intravenous injection of 50 mU. Pitocin, and following it eight young were born in 5 minutes. Evidently in these experiments stimuli from the birth canal evoked the release of sufficient neurohypophyseal hormone to expedite delivery of young (Fig. 1A).

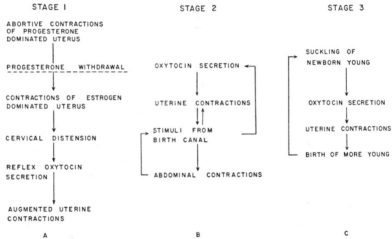

STAGE 1

ABORTIVE CONTRACTIONS OF PROGESTERONE DOMINATED UTERUS

PROGESTERONE WITHDRAWAL

CONTRACTIONS OF ESTROGEN DOMINATED UTERUS

CERVICAL DISTENSION

REFLEX OXYTOCIN SECRETION

AUGMENTED UTERINE CONTRACTIONS

A

STAGE 2

OXYTOCIN SECRETION

UTERINE CONTRACTIONS

STIMULI FROM BIRTH CANAL

ABDOMINAL CONTRACTIONS

B

STAGE 3

SUCKLING OF NEWBORN YOUNG

OXYTOCIN SECRETION

UTERINE CONTRACTIONS

BIRTH OF MORE YOUNG

C

FIG. 1. Diagrams showing three stages of uterine activity involving secretion of oxytocin during parturition in the rabbit. A. Oxytocin secretion in response to cervical distension. B. Oxytocin secretion secondary to reflex abdominal contractions. C. Oxytocin secretion in response to suckling of newborn young.

III. Nonneurohypophyseal Mechanisms in Labor

A. EVACUATION OF THE UTERUS

1. Intrinsic Contractility of the Parturient Uterus

Ferguson (25) found that the postparturient uterus of the rabbit displays spontaneous rhythmic contractions essentially similar to those of estrous or estrogenized animals (14, 29). Other studies (20, 42) have shown that the occurrence of this myometrial activity in the rabbit corresponds in time with the withdrawal of progesterone restraint, which commences about 48 hours before the onset of parturition. From this point on, the uterus becomes progressively more dominated by estrogen until maximal contractile power is developed at labor. During the same period the threshold dose of oxytocin for activation of the uterus progressively falls. Csapo (20) has offered good evidence that the restraint on myometrial activity in this species in late pregnancy is due to locally acting progesterone from the placentas. When terminal degenerative changes occur in these structures, the placental sites no longer serve as brakes on myometrial contractility and coordinated rhythmic contractions of the whole uterus become possible.

Experiments in spayed estrogenized rabbits have shown that the neurohypophysis is not essential for rhythmic uterine contractions (14). They continue for many hours after removal of the forebrain and pituitary gland. Similar rhythmic activity has long been known to occur *in vitro* (40, 41). Injection of oxytocin enhances the contractions, but even in the absence of the hormone their effect in the intact organ is to expel foreign bodies placed in the uterus. The writer found it necessary in recording uterine motility by the balloon technique to put a clip on the cervix to prevent extrusion of the balloons by the spontaneous contractions of estrogen-dominated uteri. It seems likely, therefore, that once a conceptus has become detached from the uterine wall there would be a tendency for it to be slowly pushed toward the cervix. If the cervix itself is suitably relaxed there would be no obstacle to the expulsion of the fetus into the vagina. Clearly such an operation would be much less efficient than one in which the expulsive force of the uterus was augmented by circulating oxytocin. However, the experiments of Kurdinowski (36), who obtained delivery of fetuses from gravid full-term uteri of rabbits after they had been removed from the animals and perfused with Locke solution, demonstrate that extrinsic hormonal or nervous mechanisms are not indispensable to evacuation of the uterus.

2. Mechanical Excitation of the Uterus

Contractions can be initiated in the estrogenized uterus by mechanical stimuli (14). The response occurs within 1 second of the stimulus, and since it is unaffected by spinal anesthesia it probably represents a direct activation of the myometrium. It is possible that movements of the fetuses might sometimes elicit similar effects during labor and thereby augment the rhythmic contractions discussed above.

3. Spinal Reflex Excitation of the Uterus

In those species possessing a motor innervation to the uterus, e.g., the rabbit, it is possible that spinal reflex mechanisms participate in uterine activity in labor. Mechanical dilatation of the vagina induces a sharp contraction of the uterus in post-partum (25) or estrogenized (14) rabbits. The response, which resembles the effect of injection of small doses of adrenaline or noradrenaline, survives spinal transection in the thoracic region but is abolished by spinal anesthesia. Ferguson (25) suggested that the reflex might operate in labor as a sphincterlike mechanism to prevent extrusion of further fetuses from the uterus until vaginal fetuses (initiating the reflex response) have been delivered. This view was based on the fact that the circular muscle of the cervical segment of the uterus is most affected by adrenaline. However, the writer observed no great difference in the spacing of young when labor occurred under spinal anesthesia as compared with deliveries occurring with intact spinal reflexes (15). It is even possible that the vaginal stimulus might help to expel a fetus lodged in the cervical portion of the uterus. Injection of 5 μg. adrenaline was shown to induce a powerful contraction of the estrogenized uterus which rapidly expelled a balloon placed in the cervical segment (14).

B. Evacuation of the Vagina

1. Reflex Vaginal Contractions

Another spinal reflex effect of vaginal distension observed by Ferguson (25) in post-partum rabbits concerned the vagina itself. The response consisted of a strong peristaltic wave of contraction sweeping in the direction of the vestibule. If such a mechanism operates during labor, its effect would be to hasten the passage of the fetus through the lengthy vagina of the rabbit, and, thus, to expedite delivery.

2. Reflex Abdominal Contractions

A further response to dilatation of the vagina in rabbits is a reflex contraction of the abdominal muscles (14, 15, 25) similar to the "bearing down" movements in human labors. This effect, which occurs in conscious and anesthetized animals is obliterated by spinal anesthesia but not by section of the thoracic spinal cord.

Observations on the parturitional performance of a series of near-term rabbits in which labor was induced by injection of 50–200 mU. Pitocin (15) revealed that reflex straining movements preceded the delivery of every fetus. When straining was abolished by spinal anesthesia some rabbits had difficulty in extruding young from the vagina. This was particularly noticeable in cases where the fetuses were large, suppression of abdominal contractions was that the last member of the or dry from early loss of fetal membranes. Another consequence of the litter was usually retained in the vagina. Retention of the last fetus has also been observed in rats with diabetes inspidus and denervation of the abdominal muscles (10). It would seem, then, that reflex straining is an important mechanism for the efficient delivery of young in these species.

3. Movements of the Mother and Young

In the rabbit parturition studies (15) referred to in the last section, it was noted that the time from first appearance of the fetus at the vulva to final extrusion was very short (< 30 seconds) in conscious rabbits. When the animals were under Nembutal anesthesia the duration of labor was often no longer, but extrusion of individual fetuses from the vulva sometimes required as much as 2 minutes, despite the occurrence of strong reflex straining. There appeared to be two possible reasons for this discrepancy. First, a voluntary component of the straining movements in the conscious does rendered them more coordinated and purposeful. Delivery was assisted by the posture of the mother and by nuzzling of the young as they emerged from the vulva. Second, the pups themselves were very active at the moment of birth and their exertions seemed to quicken delivery. By contrast, the does under Nembutal were lying on their sides and the young were born in a torpid condition.

4. Vis a Tergo from Uterine Contractions

That none of the mechanisms so far discussed are essential for delivery of the fetuses from the vagina was shown by experiments in which labor was induced in rabbits under Nembutal, combined with spinal anesthesia (15). In these animals spinal reflexes were eliminated and both maternal and fetal movements absent. Nevertheless parturition proved to be remarkably efficient. In several cases delivery of young was as rapid as in conscious animals. Following injection of 100 mU. Pitocin one doe delivered nine pups in 21 minutes, another produced seven pups in 15 minutes, and a third, six pups in 16 minutes. In these experiments it seems clear that the motive force derived from the contractions of the uterus and that the fetuses were simply shunted through the vagina from the rear (Fig. 2). This would account for the retention of the last fetus in the vagina which was mentioned previously. Since, as we have seen, oxytocin is not a prerequisite for uterine contractions at term, it is possible that such a shunt mechanism could operate in animals lacking a functional neurohypophysis.

IV. Mechanism of Labor in the Rabbit

Assuredly many variations in detail characterize parturition in different mammals. Variations in litter size, in relative development of the young at birth, and in the anatomical features of the female genital tract no doubt determine many species differences in parturitional performance and behavior. There may be physiological differences too, e.g., in the nature of myometrial activity, in the regulation of cervical function, and in the relative contributions of intrinsic contractile mecha-

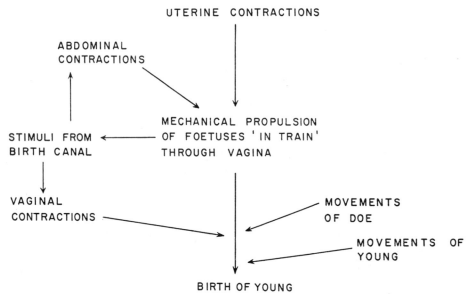

UTERINE CONTRACTIONS

ABDOMINAL
CONTRACTIONS

STIMULI FROM
BIRTH CANAL

MECHANICAL PROPULSION
OF FOETUSES 'IN TRAIN'
THROUGH VAGINA

VAGINAL
CONTRACTIONS

MOVEMENTS
OF DOE

MOVEMENTS OF
YOUNG

BIRTH OF YOUNG

FIG. 2. Diagram showing mechanisms by which fetuses are delivered from the vagina in the rabbit.

nisms and hormonal or nervous effects. It is probably true that no two labors are alike, even in the same individual. The rabbit has perhaps been studied more than any other species and is the animal whose parturition mechanism is best understood. In what follows, an attempt is made to summarize the principal events occurring in an average labor in the rabbit.

Parturition is inaugurated by the removal of progesterone restraint on myometrial activity and the consequent intensification of rhythmic contractions in the uterus—now under the dominating influence of estrogen (Section III A,1; Fig. 1A). Eventually we may suppose that these contractions cause detachment of one or more conceptuses from the endometrium. The fetus with its placenta is then propelled toward the cervix by the peristaltic movements of the uterus. When the fetus engages the cervix, the force applied by the uterine contractions dilates the cervical canal. At this point, if not sooner, a reflex excitation of the neurohypophysis occurs, with the result that oxytocin is released into the circulation to enhance the frequency and force of the uterine contractions. As the fetus passes into the vagina, reflex straining movements of the abdominal muscles are initiated. These speed the passage of the fetus through the vagina and at the same time assist the action of the uterus in propelling other fetuses toward the cervix. Thus, in addition to mechanically facilitating transport of the young, the reflex straining probably also helps to stimulate the release of more oxytocin from the neurohypophysis, and by this means indirectly favors augmented uterine activity (Fig. 1B). If the amniotic sac has not ruptured and the fetus is of a size to permit ready conveyance through the birth canal, this may be effected by reflex vaginal peristaltic waves set up by the presence of the fetus in the vagina, aided by minimal maternal straining. An oversized or dry fetus, on the other hand, which encounters resistance in the vagina, has its progress accelerated by more vigorous reflex straining and by the force of augmented uterine contractions exerted via the fetus or fetuses in its rear (Fig. 1B; 2). If the forelegs and head are presented first, the pup assists its own delivery by struggling movements. In the reverse case delivery may be aided by the mother nuzzling the pup as it emerges from the vulva. After birth the pup is licked by the doe and the placenta eaten. Then the pup tries to find a teat to suckle. This activity of newborn young probably initiates a third stage of uterine activity (Fig. 1C), for the suckling stimulates the neurohypophysis to release further oxytocin and, thus, to expedite delivery of the remaining members of the litter (15).

V. Conclusion

There are good grounds for the belief that secretion of neurohypophyseal oxytocin plays a prominent part in labor. Equally good evidence exists that various other mechanisms also contribute to the delivery of young. Some experiments suggest that these latter mechanisms may sometimes support labor in the absence of a functional neurohypophysis, while others indicate that the neurohypophyseal system can operate successfully without help from supplementary mechanisms. Somewhat analogous situations apply to other accepted neurohypophyseal functions. Antidiuretic hormone is an important, but not the exclusive, means of regulating water balance in the body, nor is the neurohypophyseal milk-ejection mechanism involving oxytocin the sole agency through which milk is removed from lactating mammary glands during suckling. It would seem, therefore, that no good reason remains for denying a physiological role for neurohypophyseal oxytocin in the mechanism of parturition.

References

1. Acher, R., and Fromageot, C., *in* "The Neurohypophysis" (H. Heller, ed.), p. 39. Academic Press, New York, 1957.
2. Alexander, S. A., and Downs, J. T., *Obstet. and Gynecol.* **10**, 682 (1957).
3. Andersson, B., *Acta Physiol. Scand.* **23**, 1 (1951).
4. Bell, G. H., and Morris, S., *J. Physiol.* (*London*) **81**, 63 (1934).
5. Bell, G. H., and Robson, J. M., *J. Physiol.* (*London*) **84**, 351 (1935).
6. Benson, G. K., and Cowie, A. T., *J. Endocrinol.* **14**, 54 (1956).
7. Berde, B., Doepfner, W., and Konzett, H., *Brit. J. Pharmacol.* **12**, 209 (1957).
8. Caldeyro-Barcia, R., Sica-Blanco, Y., Poseiro, J. J., Gonzales Panizza, V., Méndez-Bauer, C., Fielitz, C., Alvarez, H., Pose, S. V., and Hendricks, C. H., *J. Pharmacol. Exptl. Therap.* **121**, 18 (1957).
9. Cockrill, J. R., Miller, E. G., and Kurzrok, R., *Proc. Soc. Exptl. Biol. Med.* **31**, 572 (1934).
10. Colfer, H. F., and Harris, G. W., unpublished observations cited by G. W. Harris "Neural Control of the Pituitary Gland," p. 226. Williams & Wilkins, Baltimore, Maryland, 1955.
11. Cowie, A. T., and Folley, S. J., *in* "The Neurohypophysis" (H. Heller, ed.), p. 183. Academic Press, New York, 1957.
12. Cross, B. A., unpublished experiments cited by B. A. Cross and G. W. Harris, *J. Endocrinol.* **8**, 148 (1952).
13. Cross, B. A., *Brit. Med. Bull.* **11**, 151 (1955).
14. Cross, B. A., *J. Endocrinol.* **16**, 237 (1958).
15. Cross, B. A., *J. Endocrinol.* **16**, 261 (1958).
16. Cross, B. A., *in* "Milk: Its Physiology and Biochemistry" (A. T. Cowie and S. K. Kon, eds.). Academic Press, New York. In preparation.
17. Cross, B. A., Goodwin, R. F. W., and Silver, I. A., *J. Endocrinol.* **17**, 63 (1958).
18. Cross, B. A., and Harris, G. W., *J. Endocrinol.* **8**, 148 (1952).
19. Cross, B. A., and van Dyke, H. B., *J. Endocrinol.* **9**, 232 (1953).
20. Csapo, A., *Am. J. Anat.* **98**, 273 (1956).
21. Dandy, W. E., *J. Am. Med. Assoc.* **114**, 312 (1940).
22. Dey, F. L., Fisher, C., and Ranson, S. W., *Am. J. Obstet. Gynecol.* **42**, 459 (1941).
23. Dicker, S. E., and Tyler, C., *J. Physiol.* (*London*) **121**, 206 (1953).
24. Douglas, R. G., Boisnes, R. W., and du Vigneaud, V., *Obstet. and Gynecol.* **6**, 254 (1955).
25. Ferguson, J. K. W., *Surg. Gynecol. Obstet.* **73**, 359 (1941).
26. Fisher, C., Magoun, H. W., and Ranson, S. W., *Am. J. Obstet. Gynecol.* **36**, 1 (1938).
27. Franklin, K. J., and Winstone, N. E., *J. Physiol.* (*London*) **125**, 43 (1954).
28. Gunther, M., *Brit. Med. J.* **I**, 567 (1948).
29. Harris, G. W., *Phil. Trans. Roy. Soc. London* **B232**, 385 (1947).

30. Harris, G. W., and Jacobsohn, D., *Proc. Roy. Soc.* **B139**, 263 (1952).
31. Haterius, H. O., and Ferguson, J. K. W., *Am. J. Physiol.* **124**, 314 (1938).
32. Hawker, R. W., and Robertson, P. A., *Endocrinology* **60**, 652 (1957).
33. Hays, R. L., and Vandemark, N. L., *Endocrinology* **52**, 634 (1953).
34. Hellman, R. W., Harris, J. S., and Reynolds, S. R. M., *Am. J. Obstet. Gynecol.* **59**, 41 (1950).
35. Knaus, H., *J. Physiol.* (*London*) **61**, 383 (1926).
36. Kurdinowski, E. M., *Arch. Anat. u. Physiol.* (*Leipzig*) *Suppl.* **28**, 323 (1904).
37. Kurotsu, T., Kurachi, K., Takeda, M., and Ban, T., *Med. J. Osaka Univ.* **3**, 151 (1952).
38. McKenzie, C. H., and Swain, F. M., *Minn. Med.* **38**, 908 (1955).
39. Marañon, G., *Brit. Med. J.* **II**, 769 (1947).
40. Robson, J. M., *J. Physiol.* (*London*) **78**, 309 (1933).
41. Robson, J. M., *J. Physiol.* (*London*) **79**, 139 (1933).
42. Schofield, B., *J. Physiol.* (*London*) **138**, 1 (1957).
43. Stutinsky, F., *Ann. endocrinol.* (*Paris*) **14**, 722 (1953).
44. Theobald, G. W., Kelsey, H. A., and Muirhead, J. M. B., *J. Obstet. Gynaecol. Brit. Empire* **63**, 641 (1956).
45. van Dyke, H. B., Adamsons, K., Jr., and Engel, S. L., *Recent Progr. in Hormone Research* **11**, 1 (1955).
46. Whittlestone, W. G., *J. Endocrinol.* **8**, 89 (1952).

Discussion

CHAIRMAN: SIR S. ZUCKERMAN

H. HELLER: I was very much interested in the remarks of Dr. Cross on this curious situation in which an animal suffers from diabetes insipidus but is still able to secrete sufficient oxytocin. I call the situation "curious" because in the rabbit the glandular vasopressin:oxytocin ratio is usually 2 or 3 to 1. It would therefore appear that more oxytocin could be secreted from glandular tissue which contains larger amounts of vasopressin.

I am wondering whether the facilitation of oxytocin release which seems to be implied in the results which I discussed this morning would not perhaps explain this finding?

B. A. CROSS: As far as I know, Dr. Heller, there is no evidence in the rabbit, which has a 3:1 ratio, that this situation occurs. The reason is that the rabbit does not exhibit a typical diabetes insipidus—no one to my knowledge has ever succeeded in producing a permanent diabetes insipidus in the rabbit. Dr. G. W. Harris and I tried with supraopticohypophyseal lesion, and, I believe, Dr. Chandler Brooks tried before the war in a large series of rabbit stalk-section experiments and never obtained anything more than a temporary polyuria, which is all we ever got. So, the rabbit seems to be rather exceptional in respect to diabetes insipidus.

The evidence that I was quoting is mainly in the rat. Benson and Cowie's results seemed to me clearly indicative of deficient ADH secretion since the rats were producing I think, around 50 cc. of urine per day and yet milk ejection was apparently normal. I obtained similar results in G. W. Harris' laboratory some years ago, where stalk-sectioned rats which had mild diabetes insipidus of that order—about 50 cc. a day—showed normal pregnancy, normal labor, and normal lactation. However, animals which became severely diabetic with urine output up to 200 cc. a day never managed to rear litters.

H. HELLER: Thank you very much. I regret to hear that your attempts to produce permanent diabetes insipidus in rabbits were unsuccessful; but that does not alter the situation because you yourself, amongst others, have shown that the amounts of oxytocin released by a given stimulus are much greater than the amounts of ADH. So that, with a hormone ratio of 1:1 (as in the rat) the paradox, as it were, remains the same.

B. A. CROSS: Yes. The problem in my mind is how one can relate content of the principles in the lobe to what is coming out. If I knew more about that, I might be in a position to answer you more effectively.

S. ZUCKERMAN: May I put a question to you? Do I understand you to imply that the oxytocin acts directly on the myoepithelial elements in the mammary gland?

B. A. CROSS: Yes.

S. ZUCKERMAN: Does oxytocin act on myoepithelial elements in other glands of the body?

B. A. CROSS: The only evidence I know of is that concerning the parotid salivary gland of the sheep. This was work done in Cambridge by Kay. Large doses of oxytocin would produce expression of saliva from the parotid gland and this was related to the presence of myoepithelial cells. I don't think there is any evidence that oxytocin stimulates the contraction of the so-called myoepithelial cells that have been described in sweat glands. The mammary myoepithelium, as perhaps was apparent in the section I showed, seems to be a unique tissue with rather different histological and physiological characteristics from myoepithelial cells in other organs.

C. G. HARTMAN: I believe that in the rabbit it is impossible to produce contraction of the uterus during pregnancy. In the human it is also unlikely that you can cause an abortion during early stages of pregnancy. The reason I bring this up is because of the wide acceptance of the Knausian theory of the time of ovulation and the so-called "safe period" of the menstrual cycle. This is based on a phenomenon that holds 100% for the rabbit but not at all for man—that is the refractoriness of the myometrium in the presence of the corpus luteum. Nixon and Moir in England, Dahle in Oslo, Carlson in Stockholm, Woodbury in this country, have demonstrated that in man the corpus luteum does not prevent the response of the uterus to oxytocin. In over thirty monkeys containing 6–10-day corpora lutea I have never failed to produce powerful uterine contractions of the uterus. I think that Knaus' world-wide propaganda is based on a wrong premise.

S. ZUCKERMAN: The law of compensating errors must have operated in this instance. The theory about the time of ovulation and the safe period may have been partly based on the work of Knaus, but it was substantiated by a great deal of other work, especially on the monkey.

C. G. HARTMAN: Knaus' assumption that the corpus luteum has a life span of exactly and invariably 14 days is likewise unfounded, for above and other reasons.

E. EICHNER: I just want to make the point that we saw these excellent slides today of what happens in the rabbit in which a single injection of oxytocin, endogenous or otherwise, produces a very rapid delivery response.

Unfortunately, in the human, that is not so. I have one slide, which was prepared especially for this meeting, of the result of overstimulation of the uterus by oxytocin.

This was on induction. There is an increased tonus with the base line going up at one point, where the increased intrauterine tone—this is measured by bags in the uterus—is above the diastolic pressure of the patient. The injection was discontinued and contractions recurred shortly thereafter at a normal rate, membranes were ruptured, and a precipitate delivery occurred. We were fortunate in the outcome of the infant.

B. A. CROSS: I can only say with regard to the differences in the rabbit, that in these beasts, whether conscious or anesthetized when the rapid deliveries occurred, no case of uterine trauma resulted from oxytocin and the animals were so fit a few hours after the experiments, that they were ready to mate again. So I was able to do another experiment in the ensuing pregnancy.

I. ROTHCHILD: I would like to come to the defense of the effect of oxytocin on inducing rhythmic uterine contractions in human beings as well as in rabbits.

Dr. Charles Hendricks of the Department of Obstetrics and Gynecology at Western Reserve University has been able to produce predictable contractions of the human uterus in early labor with carefully timed and accurately graded doses of oxytocin administered I.V. by means of an infusion pump.

G. S. GREENWALD: I think that abortion can't be that easily induced in rabbits. It depends to a great extent on the time at which the treatment is begun.

For example, in the case of estrogen administration during the first half of pregnancy, the fetus will be killed but not evacuated from the uterus. There is a morphological basis for this difference depending on the time at which treatment is begun. As shown by Hammond, rabbit placenta is extremely adherent up until the 21st or 22nd day of pregnancy. It is only after this time that there is a sufficient separation between the fetal and maternal parts of the placenta. Treatment with estrogen or high dosages of oxytocin past this point will result in abortion. But before this time treatment will only kill the fetus and resorption will occur.

One point that I have always been curious about that Dr. Cross might be able to elucidate: At parturition, is there any orderly sequence in which the uterus is evacuated in the rabbit? Is one horn emptied before the other; or is it a random affair?

B. A. CROSS: My impression is that it has a certain randomness about it. If you make a window in the flank of the rabbit and watch the actual evacuation of the two uteri, you will find that three or four fetuses from one horn may be delivered and then one from the other and then perhaps two from the first, and so on. The actual factors that determine this are a mystery to me, and if anyone knows the answer, I shall be very glad to have it.

In regard to your first point, I think it is true that the amounts of oxytocin one needs to give to produce an abortion even at the 22nd day are pretty high; that it is only when you get to the last 48 hours of pregnancy that it is possible to induce a physiologically normal labor with a physiological dose. Presumably, just at the time when labor would occur naturally anyway, as little as 5 milliunits of oxytocin would probably produce some acceleration. According to how far away you are from the terminal point, you have to give increasingly large doses. But I was satisfied that our doses were within the physiological range by comparison with the output of oxytocin from the rabbit neurohypophysis during suckling.

Recent Developments in Endocrine Studies on Mammary Growth and Lactation

G. K. Benson, A. T. Cowie, S. J. Folley, and J. S. Tindal

National Institute for Research in Dairying, Shinfield, Reading, England

I. Mammary Growth

A. Mammogenic Effects of Estrogen and Progesterone in Animals with Intact Pituitaries

Although there has been a vast amount of work on the experimental induction of mammary growth by ovarian hormones during the past thirty years, much still remains to be done, especially on the hormone ratios necessary for optimal development, since such work is of considerable practical interest in dairy husbandry, and perhaps also in the clinical field. The subject has been reviewed a number of times (see for instance, 63), and the broad conclusion arising from previous work is as follows. While estrogen alone in physiological doses causes mainly duct growth, the combination of estrogen plus progesterone is necessary to obtain full lobule-alveolar growth. There are species differences in this response, however, and experimental animals can be classified in three broad categories according to whether in physiological doses, (a) estrogen alone causes duct development and relatively little alveolar growth (mouse, rat, rabbit); (b) estrogen alone causes both duct development and extensive lobule-alveolar development (monkey, guinea pig, cow, goat); (c) estrogen alone induces only slight growth of the mammary duct system (dog).

In the first of these categories, the allometric growth of the duct system in the normal virgin female rat could be quantitatively mimicked in the ovariectomized female by the initial injection of 0.1 µg. estradiol dipropionate on alternate days from the twenty-first day of life, and stepwise increase of dose with the body weight (138). Later, T. C. Smith (140) reported that doses of 1.0 µg. estradiol dipropionate plus 3–5 mg. progesterone were near optimum for lobule-alveolar growth in the spayed rat. In spayed mice of the CHI strain, 0.055 µg. estrone daily was required to attain the total mammary areas of comparable intact mice (56). Recently, Blair and associates (21) have investigated the mammary response to estrone and progesterone of castrated male mice of various cancer-prone strains and hybrids. The one strain which possessed neither the genetic susceptibility to mammary tumor formation, nor the mammary tumor agent, showed the least alveolar response to the hormonal combination used. They concluded that within the strains and hybrids under study, the mammary tumor agent appears to influence the extent of alveolar development under the hormonal treatment, but shows little relation to over-all gland growth.

In the second category, the goat has been studied more extensively than other ruminants, and the earlier observations of Mixner and Turner (113) that estrogen alone caused abnormal udder development in the spayed goat, were extended by Cowie et al. (31). The latter workers showed that in the spayed virgin goat, udders grown by hexestrol alone exhibited a variety of histological abnormalities, probably the most significant one being a deficiency in the total alveolar surface area [see also the work of Richardson (126) on the contralateral udder-halves from this experiment]. In later work in our laboratory (12), the histological abnormalities previously observed in glands developed with relatively high estrogen dosage, even when to some extent counterbalanced with progesterone, did not occur when lower levels of estrogen were administered with sufficient progesterone (e.g., 0.5 mg. hexestrol plus 70 mg. progesterone daily for 150 days, i.e., 1:140 by weight). Such alveolar tissue was of fairly uniform porosity (the index of porosity is defined as the alveolar surface area per unit volume of tissue), and the total alveolar surface area of half-udders removed from these experimental goats at the peak of lactation, although not as large as in goats with naturally developed udders (cf. 126), gave a high correlation with the milk yields of these half udders. A large component of this correlation was due to udder size, but the partial correlation between

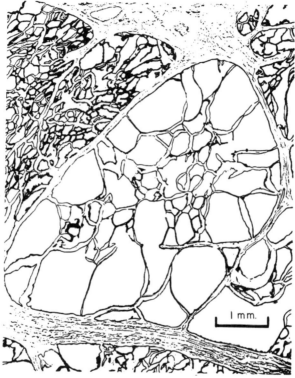

Fig. 1. Alveolar tissue from a goat mammary gland experimentally developed by daily doses of 0.25 mg. hexestrol. The field shows two adjacent lobules, one consisting of cystic alveoli and the other of alveoli of nearly normal size. From Benson *et al.* (12).

surface area and milk yield, with one method of assessment, amounted to 0.58. Surprisingly it was found that treatment with relatively low doses of estrogen alone (0.025–0.25 mg. per day for 140 days) resulted in histological abnormalities similar to those observed after high estrogen dosage (see Fig. 1). In the cow progesterone is also essential for normal udder development, and when estrogen is given alone, histological abnormalities of the udder occur, as in the goat (122, 145).

It has been the belief until recently, that progesterone was unnecessary for experimental mammary growth in the guinea pig, and that exogenous estrogen alone was capable of eliciting full mammary development in the ovariectomized animal. However, in this laboratory, utilizing both objective and subjective methods of assessment, this has proved not to be so (13), for over a wide range of estrogen dosage, greater mammary development was elicited in the spayed guinea pig by estrone plus progesterone than by estrone alone, maximal lobule-alveolar development being observed with a daily dose of 10–50 µg. estrone plus 1000 µg. progesterone. Progesterone alone caused considerable mammary development [as in the rat, mouse, and monkey; see (63) for references]. It is interesting to note that the guinea pig differs from the goat in that histological abnormalities do not occur with estrogen at supraoptimal levels; however, slight abnormalities were found with estrogen at suboptimal levels. The fact that suboptimal doses of estrogen may cause growth of mammary tissue which is histologically abnormal, has not, as far as we know, been reported previously, and is of course of considerable interest, possibly from the point of view of the genesis of mammary cancer. Benson et al. (13) concluded that the degree of mammary development was dependent on the absolute amounts of estrogen and progesterone administered. The estrogen:progesterone ratio had no significance per se, since altering the amounts of hormones, yet maintaining the same ratio, caused entirely different responses.

While the estrogen:progesterone ratio within a species seems to be of little account, is there any similarity in this respect between species (see Table I)? Benson et al. (13) obtained optimal mammary

TABLE I

RATIO OF ESTROGEN:PROGESTERONE (E:P) FOR OPTIMAL MAMMARY DEVELOPMENT

Animal	E:P Ratio	Estrogen	References
Rat	1:3000–5000	Estradiol	Elliot and Turner (51a)
	1:1000–5000	Estradiol	Kirkham and Turner (87)
	1:3000–5000	Estradiol	Smith (140)
Mouse	1:75–250	Estrone	Mixner and Turner (113)
	1:6000–10,000	Stilbestrol	Yamada et al. (154)
Rabbit	1:10–40	Estrone	Lyons and McGinty (102)
			Scharf and Lyons (132)
	1:67	Estradiol	Yamamoto and Turner (155)
Guinea pig	1:20–100	Estrone	Benson et al. (13)
Goat	1:140	Hexestrol	Benson et al. (12)

growth responses in the guinea pig with an estrone:progesterone gravi-metric ratio of 1:20–100. The optimal ratio in the rabbit given estrone and progesterone is 1:10–40 (102, 132), while the estradiol:progesterone ratio is said to be 1:67 (155). In the rat, optimal mammary growth has been obtained with a ratio of estradiol:progesterone of 1:1000–5000 (87), and 1:3000–5000 (140). The ratio for estrone:progesterone in the mouse lies between 1:75 and 1:250 (113), while the diethylstilbestrol:progesterone ratio in this species is between 1:6000 and 1:10,000 (154). Benson *et al.* (13) concluded from the available evidence that there was in fact no great constancy between species, and stressed the point that when making interspecific comparisons, the particular estrogen used should be stated, since in the immature rat, estradiol is thirty times, and hexestrol is sixty times as potent as estrone in causing mammary duct development (121). It is interesting to note in passing, that in the species in which estrogen alone causes little or no lobule-alveolar development (mouse and rat) the estrogen:progesterone ratios are wider than in the species where estrogen causes considerable lobule-alveolar development as well as duct growth (goat and guinea pig).

B. MAMMOGENIC EFFECTS OF ADRENAL CORTICOIDS IN ANIMALS WITH INTACT PITUITARIES

Experiments with adrenalectomized animals have provided little evi-dence that the presence of the adrenal cortex is necessary for mammary growth. This may not be universally true, however, for in the guinea pig, exogenous estrogen appears to synergize with progesterone pro-duced by the adrenals, as Höhn (77) has shown that in the absence of the ovaries and adrenals, exogenous estrogen elicits only duct growth. This may explain the considerable lobule-alveolar development caused by estrogen alone in a number of species. However, mammogenic effects have been obtained by administration of corticoids, but results are con-flicting. In our laboratory, deoxycorticosterone acetate (DCA) syner-gized with estrogen to cause mammary duct growth in spayed mice of the CHI strain, while DCA given alone caused stunted duct growth in about half the mice receiving the steroid (57). As regards the gluco-corticoids, cortisone and cortisol decreased the mammogenic action of both exogenous and endogenous estrogen (57). Also corticotropin (ACTH) was not mammogenic in intact mice (61).

In striking contrast to these results, Selye (135) showed that in fe-male rats, cortisone and cortisol elicited considerable mammary gland development and secretion in adrenalectomized-ovariectomized animals simultaneously treated with small doses of estradiol; if the adrenals were intact, ACTH was as effective as cortisol (136). Selye's findings have been confirmed for the intact female rat by Johnson and Meites (81). These completely different effects of corticoids in rats on the one hand, and mice on the other, may be due to species differences or, as Ahrén and Jacobsohn (3) have suggested, they may lie in the different hormonal balance of the experimental animals. The latter view seems more likely to be the correct one since at the relatively low level of 12.5 µg. daily, cortisol acetate stimulated mammary development in ovariectomized and ovariectomized estrone-treated mice, while at higher dosage rates (25 µg. and 50 µg. daily) it was without effect (115). In conclusion, the discordant results of adrenal steroid administration do not seem to invalidate the view that the adrenal cortex plays little part in normal mammary development (29), except perhaps, as already mentioned, in the guinea pig.

C. Mammogenic Effects of Anterior-Pituitary Hormones

Following the discovery of Stricker and Grueter (142) that anterior-pituitary extracts had a lactogenic effect, and the identification of this activity with the pigeon-crop stimulating hormone (prolactin, lactogenic hormone) by Riddle and co-workers (127), it was shown by several workers that anterior-pituitary extracts had a mammogenic effect in the ovariectomized animal. W. R. Lyons was prominent among those who regarded these effects as being due to prolactin, and the first unequivocal evidence on this point was obtained by Lyons (93). Virgin ovariectomized rabbits, pretreated with estrone and progesterone to obtain good lobule-alveolar growth, were injected via the galactophores (i.e., intraductally) with prolactin, causing lactogenesis to occur in the injected sectors of the gland, while uninjected sectors remained unaffected. It was also observed that the prolactin caused active growth of the alveolar epithelium. The lactogenic effect of intraductally administered prolactin in the rabbit has been confirmed by Meites and Turner (111) and also in our laboratory by Bradley and Clarke (22), who attempted to adapt this technique into a specific assay method for prolactin. In the ovariectomized rabbit whose mammary gland had been partially developed by estrogen, the nature of the mammogenic action of intraductally injected prolactin was found by Mizuno and colleagues (114) to be dependent on the existing degree of development. Thus, duct growth was elicited in glands showing only a rudimentary duct system, while in more highly developed glands, lobule-alveolar formation, and even milk secretion, occurred. It thus appears that prolactin can exert a direct mammogenic effect, at least in the rabbit with an intact pituitary.

During the past fifteen years, W. R. Lyons and his collaborators have continued their classical studies on the relationship between the anterior-pituitary hormones and mammary growth (94–97, 99–101). Briefly, the position can be summarized as follows: In the immature hypophysectomized-ovariectomized (i.e., doubly-operated) Long-Evans rat normal duct development could be induced by a combination of somatotropin (STH) plus estrone. Incomplete lobule-alveolar growth resulted from treatment with prolactin, estrone, and progesterone, while complete lobule-alveolar development typical of late pregnancy was elicited by the quartet of STH, prolactin, estrone, and progesterone. In similar experiments using the same hormone combination, duct growth and then full lobule-alveolar growth was obtained in the immature hypophysectomized-castrated male rat. In the immature hypophysectomized-ovariectomized-adrenalectomized (i.e., triply-operated) Long-Evans rat, although estrone and STH led to some duct development, the addition of DCA to this pair of hormones was necessary to obtain duct growth typical of the puberal state. In such rats receiving these three hormones for 10 days, lobule-alveolar development occurred after a further 20 days treatment with estrone, progesterone, prolactin, STH, and DCA. Some of the rats on this regime died, but further deaths were prevented by adding prednisolone acetate, thus substituting two hormones from each of the ablated endocrine glands. It would appear that the function of the adrenal corticoids was to restore the triply-operated animals toward the normal condition, since, in earlier work, estrone, progesterone, prolactin, and STH had produced full lobule-alveolar growth in triply operated animals given 1% saline to drink (98). Many of these observations on the hormonal requirements for mammogenesis (and lactogenesis) in the Long-Evans rat have recently been confirmed in our laboratory for the Hooded Norway rat (Cowie and Lyons, unpublished).

One important question arising from this work is whether STH acts indirectly, or whether it is a true, i.e., direct, mammogen. The work of Lyons and collaborators (97) on the effect of hormone pellets implanted over individual mammary glands of doubly or triply-operated rats would indicate that in fact STH does have some direct effect on mammary duct growth. Results in harmony with this concept are those of Flux (59), who showed that STH caused increased mammary duct growth in ovariectomized mice. Thus it appears that this hormone can exert a direct mammogenic effect, as well as probably influencing mammogenesis by its general effect on bodily metabolic processes.

It is interesting to note that in the hypophysectomized weanling male mouse (Strong A_2G strain), estrone and progesterone, at dose levels capable of inducing proliferation of the duct system in the intact weanling, failed to induce any duct growth unless prolactin was also administered; prolactin by itself was also inactive (71). On the other hand, in adult female hypophysectomized-ovariectomized mice of the C_3H strain, mammary duct growth has been observed after the local injection of prolactin alone (55).

Although in the above-mentioned experiments of W. R. Lyons full lobule-alveolar development was obtained in the triply-operated rat with estrone, progesterone, prolactin, and STH, it must be borne in mind that in the intact pregnant animal, neither of these two pairs of hormones need originate entirely in the ovary or pituitary gland, respectively, since in the advanced stages of pregnancy the placenta may be the source of some or all of these hormones. In the rat, the placenta is rich in a substance having all the well-defined properties of prolactin, but it is not known whether this substance is identical with prolactin of pituitary origin (8, 24, 120). In addition, there is some indication that a substance similar to STH may also be secreted by the placenta (120). The problem of how, and to what extent, the placental hormones influence mammary development, and the exact identity of such substances, requires further investigation.

D. ROLE OF INSULIN IN MAMMOGENESIS

It is important to remember that after removal of the pituitary and perhaps other endocrine glands, other hormones apart from the tetrad estrogen, progesterone, prolactin, and STH may be necessary for full mammary development. These hormones are probably not direct mammogens, but their role will be concerned with restoring the general metabolic milieu of the mammary tissue to normal. One such hormone appears to be insulin, since it re-established rapid growth in hypophysectomized rats, thus acting as a substitute for STH (129, 130). Salter and Best's results led Ahrén and Jacobsohn (2) to investigate the possible mammogenic effect of insulin in the hypophysectomized rat. The latter workers observed mammary growth in hypophysectomized rats treated with estrone, progesterone, and long-acting insulin, but not with insulin alone, and concluded that insulin acted by generally improving the metabolic condition of the operated animal and not by virtue of a direct mammogenic effect. In later work, Ahrén and Jacobsohn (3) found that injection of cortisone into hypophysectomized-ovariectomized rats treated with estrone, progesterone, and long-acting insulin, while decreasing the mammogenic effect of insulin, caused enlargement and proliferation of the epithelial cells lining the inner walls of the ducts, an effect which also occurred in the presence of exogenous estrone and progesterone in the absence of insulin. This work is important because it opens up a new viewpoint on the hormonal control of mammary growth, since it has shown that estrogen and progesterone in the absence of the pituitary, can cause some appreciable mammary duct growth.

II. Milk Secretion

A. Theories of Lactation Initiation

Having considered the role of hormones in mammary growth, it is appropriate to turn to the hormonal mechanism responsible for lactogenesis. Although there is some synthesis and some storage of milk before parturition, there has been much speculation on what causes the copious flow of milk occurring at, or soon after, parturition.

On the basis of assays of pituitary prolactin content, Meites and Turner (110, 112) put forward the theory that the absence of milk secretion during pregnancy was due to low prolactin production. They believed that estrogen evokes prolactin secretion by the pituitary, but is prevented from doing so during pregnancy by progesterone, and that at full-term, when the body-levels of progesterone fall, estrogen is then able to increase prolactin secretion and initiate lactation. However, when mammary growth was elicited in ovariectomized rabbits by treatment with estrone and progesterone, the concomitant administration of prolactin did not result in lactogenesis in the presence of both estrone and progesterone (108). When prolactin was given in conjunction with *either* steroid alone, lactation was not inhibited to any significant degree. This clearly does not agree with the Meites-Turner theory, according to which the prolactin should have been equally active in the presence or absence of the steroids. Work in our laboratory on induced mammary growth and lactation in the goat (12) and also that of others on rats (101) indicates that a combination of estrogen and progesterone is an effective inhibitor of lactation. In their later work, Meites and Sgouris (109) found that the inhibitory effect of estrone plus progesterone on lactation could be overcome by increasing the dose of prolactin. These results have led Meites (103) to modify the original Meites-Turner theory, and he now considers that lactogenesis does not occur during pregnancy, not only because of low levels of circulating prolactin, but also because of the combined inhibitory action of estrogen and progesterone on the mammary gland, making it refractory to prolactin. On this basis, lactating animals which become pregnant are enabled to continue lactating for a time by virtue of the high levels of circulating prolactin overriding the inhibitory effect of the rising titers of estrogen and progesterone.

The original Meites-Turner theory was criticized by Folley (63), first, on the relevance of pituitary prolactin content to prolactin release, and second, on the accuracy of the assay procedure used. His later views of the situation (66, 67) are that (a) low circulating levels of estrogen activate the lactogenic function of the anterior pituitary, while higher levels inhibit lactation; this was put forward as the "double threshold" theory of Folley and Malpress (68); (b) lactogenic doses of estrogen may be rendered inhibitory by suitable doses of progesterone, this being the normal inhibitory influence during pregnancy; and (c) the fall in ratio of progesterone:estrogen at parturition removes the inhibition which is replaced by the positive "lactogenic" effect of estrogen acting unopposed.

B. Endocrine Factors in Lactation Maintenance

Since hypophysectomy results in a rapid cessation of milk secretion, even with oxytocin therapy to ensure milk ejection (27) (see Fig. 2),

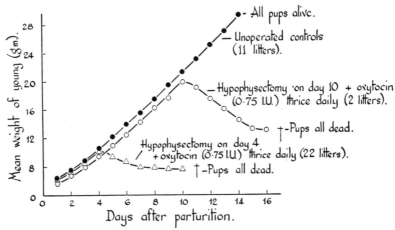

FIG. 2. Effect of hypophysectomy on the fourth or tenth day after parturition in the rat. Nursing rats were injected with oxytocin (0.75 I.U. three times daily). From Cowie, unpublished.

it is clear that the hormones of the anterior pituitary are of primary importance in the maintenance of lactation. After treating hypophysectomized-ovariectomized-adrenalectomized rats (given 1% saline to drink) with estrone, progesterone, prolactin, and STH to obtain full lobule-alveolar development, Lyons et al. (96, 98) were able to elicit milk secretion by stopping the injections of estrone and progesterone and continuing injections of prolactin and STH plus either cortisone or cortisol. In animals with intact adrenals, ACTH could be given instead of the adrenal steroids. In the rat, therefore, the basic hormonal requirements for the initiation of lactation, probably identical with the lactogenic complex postulated by Folley and Young (69), appear to be

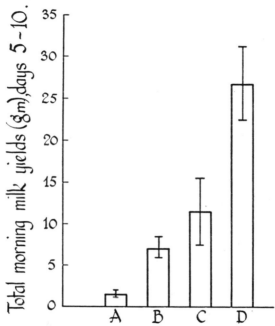

Fig. 3. Effect of replacement therapy in hypophysectomized lactating rats. Nursing rats were injected with oxytocin (0.75 I.U. three times daily), and mean total weight gains after morning suckling period only, from days 5–10, are given. Vertical lines represent the standard errors of the mean. A, Hypophysectomy plus oxytocin; B, hypophysectomy plus oxytocin plus prolactin (25 I.U. twice daily); C, as for B, plus GH (0.5 mg. twice daily); D, as for B, plus ACTH (2 I.U. per day). From Cowie, unpublished.

prolactin, STH, and ACTH (if the adrenals are intact). It does not, however, necessarily follow from this that the same hormonal combination is responsible for the *maintenance* of milk secretion. Cowie (27) hypophysectomized rats on the fourth day of lactation and observed some maintenance of milk secretion with prolactin alone, but none with either STH or ACTH alone. In a few cases, considerable maintenance was obtained with prolactin plus ACTH (see Fig. 3) and synergistic effects of STH and ACTH in combination with prolactin were also noted.

It was impossible, however, to achieve complete maintenance of lactation, and it was seldom better than 30% of normal. There is little doubt, then, that prolactin is necessary for the maintenance of milk secretion, and similar conclusions have been reported by Bintarningsih et al. (20) and Lyons et al. (101) in which prolactin plus cortisol or prednisolone acetate were found to be the minimum hormonal requirements for the maintenance of lactation in the hypophysectomized rat. In an attempt to speed recovery after hypophysectomy, Cowie and Tindal (35) administered Terramycin and glucose (cf. 70), but did not observe any beneficial effect of the treatment on lactational performance in the hypophysectomized rat receiving replacement therapy.

The question of the hormonal requirements for the maintenance of lactation in the hypophysectomized animal has also been studied in our laboratory by experiments involving pituitary transplants. The classical experiments of Harris and Jacobsohn (73), confirmed and extended by Nikitovitch-Winer and Everett (118), showed that when the pituitary was grafted away from its normal site, its gonadotropic function was reduced, or even abolished, but when grafted under the median eminence virtually full function was restored, presumably due to the re-establishment of vascular connections between the graft and the hypophyseal portal blood vessels. There are indications, however, that when the pituitary is grafted in sites remote from the pituitary capsule, the output of prolactin is unimpaired (46, 48) or even increased (53, 54). In view of this, Cowie and Tindal (35) thought it would be interesting to see if pituitary implants under the kidney capsule could maintain lactation in the hypophysectomized rat. Lactating rats were implanted under the kidney capsule with either three or six of their 7-day-old pups' pituitaries, and were mated again as soon as possible. The animals were allowed to litter a second time and were hypophysectomized on the fourth day of lactation. Oxytocin was injected thrice daily, to enable the pups to obtain any milk secreted and the gain in weight of the litters at the morning suckling period was recorded. As shown in Fig. 4, the grafts alone achieved a slight, though significant, replacement effect over the ungrafted hypophysectomized controls, while STH increased this effect slightly, and ACTH increased it significantly. These findings are in harmony with the view that such grafts secrete prolactin and that prolactin and ACTH seem to be the most important endocrine factors for the maintenance of milk secretion in this species.

Another way of investigating the hormonal requirements for lactation maintenance is to study galactopoietic effects of anterior-pituitary hormones, since the hormone constellations regulating galactopoiesis and normal lactation maintenance are probably related. It is understandable that the effect of pituitary hormones on established lactation should have been investigated in intact ruminants, not only from the academic standpoint, but also from that of the possibility of practical application, both in medicine and dairy husbandry. Results with prolactin have been disappointing, and the only really positive results, apart from the well-known galactopoietic effect of thyroxine, discussion of

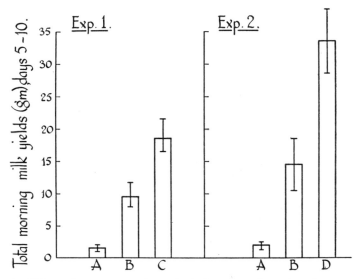

Fig. 4. Effect of pituitary grafts under kidney capsule and replacement therapy in hypophysectomized lactating rats. Nursing rats were injected with oxytocin (0.75 I.U. three times daily), and mean total weight gains after morning suckling period only, from days 5–10, are given. Vertical lines represent the standard errors of the mean. A, Hypophysectomy without grafts; B, hypophysectomy plus grafts in kidney; C, as for B, plus GH (0.5 mg. twice daily); D, as for B, plus ACTH (4 I.U. per day). From Cowie and Tindal, unpublished.

which is outside the scope of this paper, have been with STH and ACTH. The early work of Folley and Young [see (62) for review] indicated that crude anterior-pituitary extracts were galactopoietic in the cow, and this activity was subsequently shown to be mainly due to their content of STH (25). The galactopoietic effect of STH was later confirmed by other workers for both the cow and the sheep (66).*
Recently, in our laboratory, Hutton (79) studied the effect of single injections of STH (ranging from 6.25 to 200 mg.) on the yield and com-

---

* This reference is a review article.

position of cow's milk, and found a highly significant linear relationship between log dose of STH and the increase in milk yield (see Fig. 5). Also, increasing the dose of STH increased the yield of milk fat, relative to the yield of nonfatty solids. Hutton also obtained evidence that STH increased the efficiency of conversion of food constituents to milk. In contrast to the action of STH, ACTH depresses milk yield in the cow (25, 60, 137). This does not, however, detract from the importance of

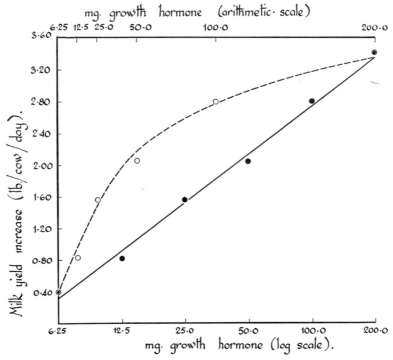

FIG. 5.   Increases in milk yield obtained in the cow after single injections of growth hormone (STH), plotted on arithmetic scale (o – – – o), and plotted on logarithmic scale (●————●). From Hutton (79).

ACTH as a member of the galactopoietic complex; it presumably implies a sufficiently high circulating level of the hormone in the animals under study, and any increase over this optimum level has a detrimental effect on milk secretion. It must be borne in mind that species differences in responses to hormones are very common, and in this connection it is interesting to note that whereas prolactin and ACTH are not galactopoietic in the cow, they are in the rat (82, 83), while STH has no galactopoietic effect in rats (28, 105). Turner (148) has recently put forward a hypothesis concerning the galactopoietic effects of pituitary hormones. He believes that if a cow in declining lactation responds to a given pituitary hormone by an increased milk yield, then the animal's inherited genetic make-up is such that insufficient of that hormone is produced for maximum milk production. The implication to be drawn from this might be that one should strive to breed cows which show no galactopoietic response to prolactin or STH. For reasons of space, the arguments for and against this hypothesis cannot be gone into here.

The importance of the pituitary-adrenal axis in the maintenance of lactation, referred to above, is illustrated by the severe decline in lactation following adrenalectomy, known for some years [for references, see (65)]. In our strain of rat, milk yield is not totally abolished by adrenalectomy alone, probably because of progesterone from the ovaries, and replacement experiments indicated that the ovaries exerted a lactation-maintaining effect equivalent to that of about 3.1 mg. progesterone daily. When the ovaries, as well as the adrenals, are removed, the inhibition of lactation is much more severe (58). After adrenalectomy in the rat, almost complete restoration of mammary function can be achieved by giving cortisone and DCA (26), or 9α-chlorocortisol (100 μg. per day). 9α-Fluorocortisol and cortisol at the same dose-levels, or aldosterone (50 μg. per day) were not as effective (33). Llaurado (91) has studied the effect of chlorocortisol and fluorocortisol on the survival and growth of adrenalectomized rats and found the halogenated corticoids to be as effective as aldosterone. In agreement with the findings of Cowie and Tindal (33), Llaurado (92) also showed that chlorocortisol allowed pregnancy and subsequent lactation to proceed normally in adrenalectomized rats. More recently, as shown in Fig. 6, fluorocortisol has been shown to give almost complete replacement in the adrenalectomized as well as in the adrenalectomized-ovariectomized lactating rat at a dose-level of 200 μg. per day (35). In our laboratory, therefore, fluorocortisol would appear to have about half the potency of chlorocortisol (weight for weight) to maintain lactation in the adrenalectomized rat.

Since most of the work on the effects of adrenal deficiency on lactation has been carried out in small animals, it seemed important to extend the studies to the ruminant, where possible changes in milk composition could be conveniently studied. It has already been shown (32) that bilateral adrenalectomy in the goat leads to the death of the animal, and Cowie and Tindal (34) continued this work by investigating the effect of adrenalectomy on survival and milk secretion in the lactating goat. Adrenalectomy resulted in a progressive rise in plasma potassium and a progressive fall in plasma sodium, as occurs in other species, and the mean survival period of twelve goats after removal of the second adrenal was between 7 and 8 days. In our Hooded Norway rats, as mentioned above, adrenalectomy results in a fall in lactational per-

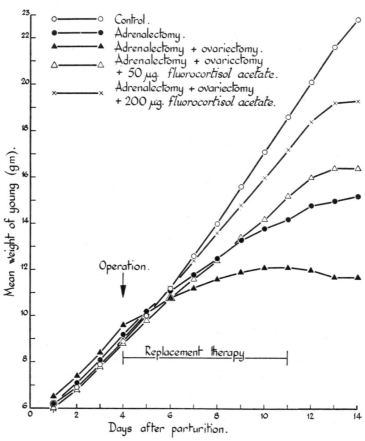

FIG. 6. Effect on lactation in the rat of adrenalectomy, adrenalectomy plus ovariectomy, and adrenalectomy plus ovariectomy plus fluorocortisol acetate at two dose-levels. Cowie and Tindal, unpublished.

formance, but milk secretion does continue at a reduced level, enabling the pups to grow, albeit slowly. In the goat, however, removal of both adrenals causes a rapid and complete inhibition of milk secretion. Partial to complete maintenance of lactation in adrenalectomized goats was achieved by implanting tablets of cortisone and DCA. It was found that a daily absorption of at least 6–12 mg. cortisone and 2.5 mg. DCA was required. DCA appeared to be the more critical component of the combination, since, after removal of the DCA tablets, leaving the cortisone, there was an abrupt cessation of milk secretion, and death ensued

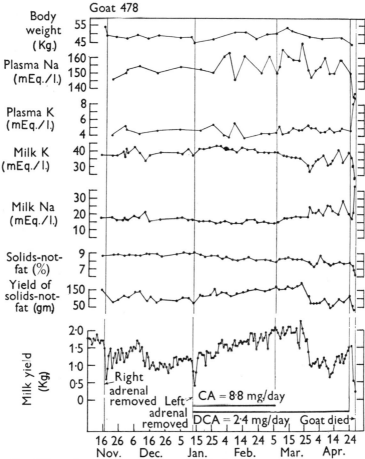

FIG. 7.   Effect of replacement therapy with deoxycorticosterone acetate (DCA) and cortisone acetate (CA) on milk yield and concentration of sodium and potassium in the milk and blood plasma after adrenalectomy in the goat. Duration of replacement therapy (tablet implantation) is indicated by horizontal lines, and name of steroid and mean daily absorption are given above each line. From Cowie and Tindal (34).

after 3 days, while after removal of the cortisone tablets, leaving the DCA, the milk yield either dropped slightly, or remained at the same level for some time (see Fig. 7). This would indicate that cortisone, ineffective by itself at the dose-levels given, synergizes with DCA. After removal of all hormone implants, the animals died within a few days. During replacement therapy, when the daily milk yield had become relatively steady, the composition of the milk (fat and solids-not-fat percentages), and the sodium and potassium concentrations in the milk were within the preoperative ranges. The technique adopted in this work, of implanting the animals with corticoid tablets under the skin at the time of operation, is particularly useful since it enables the adrenalectomized animal to achieve a steady state of milk secretion. When such a state is reached, the true effects of adrenal deficiency can be observed by removing the implants, uncomplicated by the prior starvation and surgical trauma of adrenalectomy, since the trivial amount of trauma involved in removing the implants under local anesthesia can be discounted.

III. Neural Influences

A. Milk-Ejection Reflex

Having considered the secretion of milk, we now turn to the removal of milk from the mammary gland. This can be regarded as consisting of two components: first, passive withdrawal; and second, milk ejection; it is this second component which we propose to discuss. The milk-ejection reflex [a term recommended by Cowie et al. (30)] is an active, though unconscious, process on the part of the lactating animal. The reflex manifests itself by a sudden rise in the milk pressure in the gland after stimulation of the sensory nerve endings in the nipple by the suckling or milking stimulus. It may be noted that the milk-ejection reflex can also be evoked by activation of other neural pathways, such as the stimulus of coitus (see 23, 74) or massage of the uterus (cf. 23). The latter observation might offer an explanation for the fact that among South African native tribes it is a custom, just before milking cows, to blow air into the vagina by mouth, presumably to evoke the milk-ejection reflex.

The milk-ejection reflex is known to occur in a wide variety of species, and is probably general throughout the Mammalia, except perhaps aquatic mammals. Like other reflexes, it can be conditioned, the best-known example being in the cow where it becomes conditioned to the external stimuli associated with the milking routine, and conditioning has been reported in lactating women (150). In this connection, mention should be made of the recent findings of Hawker and Roberts (75) that the level of oxytocic activity in the blood of the lactating cow and goat is not increased just after the beginning of milking. They suggest that oxytocin is released into the blood, not as a result of a reflex evoked by manipulation of the udder, but by a reflex initiated from association areas, that is, a conditioned reflex. Like other conditioned reflexes, it can be inhibited by emotionally disturbing stimuli as shown experimentally in the cow (52, 151), in woman (116), and in the rabbit (39).

1. Evidence for the Neuroendocrine Nature of the Reflex Arc

Although the reflex path was originally thought to be purely neural, it was later shown that a neuroendocrine arc was probably involved (52). The terminal link was believed to involve secretion of a principle by the neurohypophysis which caused contraction of an effector tissue around the alveoli, impelling the milk from the alveoli and causing an increase in intramammary pressure shortly after the start of suckling or milking.

In our laboratory, we tried to obtain evidence for the involvement of the posterior pituitary in the milk-ejection reflex. Macaulay [cited by Folley (64)] sought to show a depletion of oxytocin in the neurohypophysis of goats during milking, but could not find any appreciable difference in the concentrations of either the oxytocic or the antidiuretic principles in the neurohypophysis before and after milking, nor could Whittlestone et al. (152) in the cow. In smaller animals (rat, guinea pig, and cat) Dicker and Tyler (49), however, found less oxytocic activity in the posterior pituitary in lactating than in nonlactating animals, and this was confirmed in the dog by van Dyke et al. (149). The negative results in the cow and goat are not surprising, since we now know that the amounts of oxytocin which evoke milk ejection are extremely small. Cowie [cited by Folley (64)] obtained definite evidence in the anesthetized goat of milk ejection with intravenous doses of oxytocin as low as 5 mU. (milliunits), although 1 I.U. was required to give a response comparable in duration with that obtained during normal milking. Andersson (6) also reported a similar minimum dose for the goat, while Denamur and Martinet (45) obtained milk-ejection responses in the anesthetized goat with as little as 1 mU. oxytocin. In anesthetized lactating rabbits, definite milk-ejection responses were obtained by Cross and Harris (41) after an intravenous injection of 5–200 mU. posterior-pituitary extract. In the anesthetized lactating rat, hungry pups were able to obtain milk after the nursing rat had been given a single intraperitoneal injection of 250 mU. oxytocin [Cowie, cited by Folley (64)], and in the lactating rat whose posterior pituitary had been removed, 750 mU. oxytocin injected three times daily enabled the pups to grow at almost the normal rate (11). It is interesting to note that in an investigation of women unable to feed their babies but whose breasts were engorged with milk, Haeger and Jacobsohn (72) observed that during 10 minutes' suckling after an injection of 2 I.U. oxytocin into the mother, the child obtained three times more milk than during the 5-minute period prior to injection. Haeger and Jacobsohn concluded that milk ejection had not occurred in most of these cases.

Perhaps the most direct evidence was obtained by experiments involving electrical stimulation of, or placing of electrolytic lesions in, the supraopticohypophyseal system. Andersson (4, 5) obtained milk-ejection responses in the lactating sheep and goat by electrical stimulation of hypothalamic areas adjacent to the supraoptic nuclei, responses being obtained in denervated udder-halves and during sacral anesthesia, thus pointing to a terminal hormonal component of the reflex. In the anesthetized lactating rabbit, electrical stimulation of the pituitary stalk region resulted in ejection of milk comparable to that after intravenous injection of 50–200 mU. posterior-pituitary extract (40), and similar results were obtained by electrical stimulation of the supraopticohypophyseal tract (41). It is important to note that the response to stimulation was typical of humorally mediated effects, because of the long latency and the fact that the effects outlasted the stimulus. Cross and Harris (41) also showed that electrolytic lesions could be placed in the supraopticohypophyseal tract in such a way as to prevent suckling young from obtaining milk, and to interfere with the response to electrical stimulation, presumably after degeneration of the tract had occurred. The young, however, could obtain milk after the injection of posterior-pituitary extract. On the other hand, in those rabbits in which there was no disturbance of milk ejection following placement of lesions, electrical stalk stimulation still evoked the milk-ejection response.

Evidence as to the neuroendocrine nature of the milk-ejection reflex arising from experiments on the removal of the neurohypophysis has been conflicting. On the one hand, P. E. Smith (139) observed in rats, and Houssay (78) observed in bitches, that removal of the posterior lobe had no apparent effect on the functioning of the reflex. On the other hand, however, both Harris and Jacobsohn (73) and Cowie [cited by Folley (64)] observed that destruction of neural lobe function, or removal of the lobe in lactating rats, interfered with the milk-ejection reflex and the sucklings obtained little or no milk unless oxytocin were injected into the mother prior to nursing. However, the work of Benson and Cowie (11) may offer an explanation of these findings. They observed that when posterior-lobectomized rats became pregnant a second time, parturition was normal, and the milk-ejection reflex was sufficiently restored to enable the rats to rear their litters without the administration of exogenous oxytocin. In the Long-Evans strain of rat posterior-lobe function must evidently return as quickly as 10 days after hypophysectomy because Bintarningsih et al. (20) found that rats hypophysectomized on the twelfth day of pregnancy, and given hormonal replacement, will rear their pups without exogenous oxytocin. In the animals of Benson and Cowie's experiments, an increase in size of the cut end of the neural stalk occurred [also observed by Stutinsky (143) and Billenstein and Leveque (19) after hypophysectomy in the rat], and these results are in agreement with the theory that the posterior-lobe hormones are carried down the axones of the hypothalamohypophyseal tract into the neural lobe (133). Supporting evidence for the view that the milk-ejection reflex involves activation of the posterior pituitary was obtained from observations of an antidiuretic effect occurring in water-loaded lactating subjects shortly after application of the milking or suckling stimulus. This was observed in the cow (119), in the rabbit (36), in woman (85), and in the bitch (86).

2. Inhibitory Influences

While investigating emotional effects on the milk-ejection reflex in rabbits suckled under restraint, Cross (39) found that in about 80% of his experiments the milk yield obtained by the young was reduced by 20–100%, compared with normal suckling periods, and that there was a correlation between the size of the reflex response, measured by pressure recordings on a kymograph, and the amount of milk withdrawn. Normal milk removal was associated with a reflex response corresponding to about 50 mU. injected oxytocin; half the normal yield with a response equivalent to 5–10 mU. of oxytocin; and less than 15% of the milk yield with complete absence of any reflex milk ejection. Emotional inhibition of oxytocin release was accompanied in a few cases by a peripheral inhibitory effect in the mammary glands, as shown by the failure of an injection of 50 mU. oxytocin to restore normal milk ejection. In such cases, the recorded milk-ejection response to the injected oxytocin was reduced in size by an amount similar to that produced by an intravenous dose of 1 µg. adrenaline (epinephrine) given just before 50 mU. of oxytocin. It seems highly probable that the peripheral block occurring in these cases involved a mammary vasoconstriction due to activation of sympatheticoadrenal pathways from the hypothalamus (37, 38). In this connection Linzell (90) observed capillary vasoconstriction when adrenaline was topically applied to the living mammary gland of the mouse, but such treatment did not prevent topically applied oxytocin causing contraction of the alveoli. Cross concluded that while activation of the sympatheticoadrenal system can occur, the main factor in the emotional disturbance of the milk-ejection reflex is a partial or complete inhibition of oxytocin release from the posterior-pituitary gland.

3. Nature of the Milk-Ejection Hormone

We come now to the nature of the milk-ejection hormone. Earlier work indicated that it was probably oxytocin, and this was placed beyond reasonable doubt by the assays carried out by Cross and van Dyke (42) and van Dyke et al. (149) (see Table II), using the highly purified natural, and later, the synthetic polypeptides, made possible by the classical work of du Vigneaud and his colleages [for review see (51)]. It is clear from these results that although ADH-vasopressin has some

TABLE II

POTENCY OF PURIFIED OXYTOCIN AND VASOPRESSIN IN TERMS OF U. S. P. STANDARD[a,b]

	Oxytocic (rat uterus)	Avian depressor (fowl)	Milk-ejecting (rabbit)	Pressor (rat)	Anti-diuretic (dog)
Oxytocin	500	500	500	7	3
Vasopressin	30	85	100	600	600

[a] From van Dyke et al. (149).
[b] All figures are U.S.P. units per milligram.

inherent milk-ejection activity, oxytocin is the natural milk-ejection hormone, and the reports of Cross (36), that the release of ADH-vasopressin which occurs in response to the suckling stimulus in the rabbit is insufficient to exert any effect on milk ejection, and of Peeters and Coussens (119), that while mild fright inhibits the antidiuretic response to milking in the cow, it has no effect on milk ejection, are in harmony with this view. It is of interest that recently, an analog of oxytocin has been synthesized containing an L-valyl residue in place of an L-isoleucyl residue and this valyloxytocin has twice the milk-ejection activity (measured on the rabbit mammary gland), and only a third of the oxytocic activity (measured on the rat uterus in vitro) of normal synthetic oxytocin (18). The apparent partial separation of milk-ejection and oxytocic activities exhibited by this compound is of great interest (see further below).

In women, both natural and synthetic oxytocin were found to have cqual milk-ejection potency (117). However, Hawker and Robertson (76) claim that there may be another oxytocic substance in the blood of lactating women that may be different from oxytocin as we know it, and similar results were obtained with lactating cows and goats, and also with hypothalamic extracts of cows, oxen, cats, rats, and mice (75, 128). The possible bearing of this on the milk-ejection reflex requires further investigation.

4. The Contractile Effector Tissue of the Mammary Gland

The nature of the contractile effector tissue concerned in the milk-ejection reflex has recently been made clear by the elegant work of Richardson (123–125), who was able to demonstrate, for the first time convincingly, myoepithelial cells surrounding the alveoli in the goat and in man. He considers that the histological appearance of these cells before and after milking agrees with the view that they contract actively during milking. This work was confirmed by Linzell (89), who later was able to observe under the microscope the actual contraction of alveoli in the mammary gland of the anesthetized mouse, after topical application of oxytocin (90).

B. PHYSIOLOGICAL INTEGRATION OF TWO PHASES OF LACTATION— MILK SECRETION AND MILK EJECTION

Evidence has been accumulating that the suckling stimulus has two principal effects. First, as we have already seen, the suckling stimulus evokes the release of oxytocin, which causes contraction of the mammary alveoli, and second, as indicated by the earlier work of Selye (134), it can retard involution of the mammary glands of the rat, from which milk removal is prevented by ligation of galactophores. This latter observation suggested to Selye that the stimulus was causing release of prolactin, thus maintaining, partially at least, the structural integrity of the mammary gland—a conclusion which was later supported by Williams (153), who showed that prolactin could retard mammary involution in mice after weaning at day 1. It occurred to us, as to others, that these neurohormonal reflexes may share the same pathway as far as the neurohypophysis, and that oxytocin may be the humoral agent causing release of prolactin, and perhaps, other galactopoietic hormones, from the anterior lobe of the pituitary. If this were true, one would expect oxytocin to retard the involution of the unsuckled mammary gland. In our laboratory, this has been found to be the case, as Benson and Folley (14–16) found that injections of oxytocin, natural or synthetic, can strikingly retard mammary regression in the rat after weaning at the fourth day (see Fig. 8)—an effect identical with that following injection of prolactin. These observations have been confirmed by Stutinsky (144) and Meites (106).* To explain this oxytocin effect, there appear to be two main alternatives. Either this effect is due to a direct action of oxytocin on the mammary epithelium (for which, as yet, there is no evidence), or else oxytocin evokes the release of prolactin, and perhaps other hormones, from the anterior pituitary. Benson and Folley (16) favored the latter interpretation, but emphasized that the evidence for it is not yet conclusive. However, there are a number of other facts in harmony with this view. Thus, traumatization of the uterus gave a deciduoma reaction in rats to which oxytocin had been administered during diestrus (47, 48); oxytocin caused mucification of the vagina in lactating rats (16, 144), and the repeated administration of oxytocin was found to cause what appeared to be true galactopoietic effects (i.e., increases in the rate of milk secretion) in cows (1, 7, 50, 141) and goats (44). Finally, it may be noted that recent experiments in our laboratory (17) designed to determine whether the above-mentioned effect on mammary involution is bound up with the well-known direct effect of oxytocin on the mammary myoepithelium (the milk-ejection response) provided no evidence that this was so. A quantitative comparison, at two dose-levels (measured by the oxytocic effect on the rat uterus *in vitro*), was made between the effectiveness of valyloxytocin and synthetic oxytocin, as regards their action on mammary involution in the rat, and no difference was found with the doses used. If the two responses were related, valyloxytocin should have been many times more potent than oxytocin itself.

However, in our laboratory, it has not yet been possible to induce milk secretion in pseudopregnant rabbits with oxytocin, whereas in the same situation prolactin is highly effective. It is obvious, therefore, that further work is needed in this field to clarify the mode of action of oxytocin and to find out what factors affect the response. In this connection it has already been shown that the presence of the pituitary is essential, since oxytocin cannot prevent mammary regression in lactating rats after

---

* Our observations have also been confirmed by McCann, S. M., Mack, R., and Gale, C., *Federation Proc.* 17, 107 (1958) in a communication which we saw after this paper had been submitted for publication.

FIG. 8. Sections from left abdominal mammary glands of lactating rats treated with (a) synthetic oxytocin (1 I.U. three times daily) and (b) saline, for 9 days after removal of pups on fourth day of lactation. Involution is retarded after treatment with oxytocin. From Benson and Folley (16).

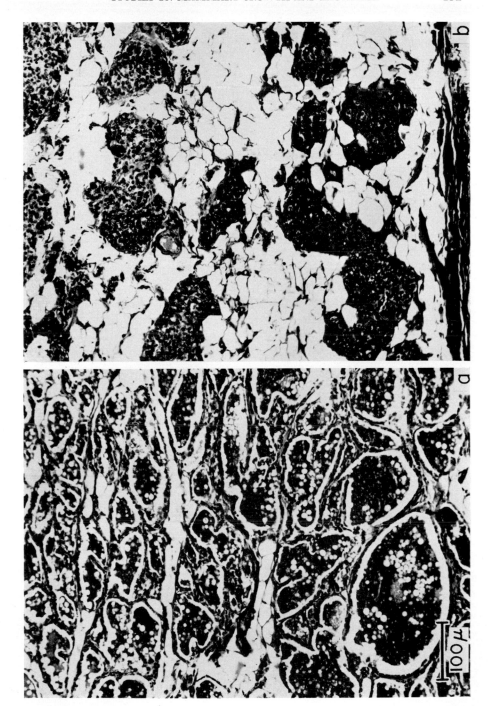

hypophysectomy and removal of pups at the fourth day, while it does so in sham-operated controls (15, 16). The role of the adrenal cortex in these phenomena must also be taken into account, since oxytocin shows no effect in retarding mammary involution in the adrenalectomized rat whose pups are removed at the fourth day of lactation, although the activity is restored in the presence of 9α-fluorocortisol (9). By contrast, prolactin shows some mammary-involution-retarding activity in the adrenalectomized rat, and the effect is not increased by treatment with 9α-fluorocortisol. In the adrenalectomized, as in the intact, rat, there is a marked synergism in this respect between prolactin and STH (see Fig. 9), but ACTH and fluorocortisol show only relatively slight mammary-involution-retarding effects in the intact rat. It would appear therefore that the interpretation of the oxytocin effect may be more complex than was originally thought, since the pituitary-adrenal axis seems to be involved to some extent. Nevertheless, the role of the latter does not appear to be so important and clear-cut as Meites (107) and Johnson and Meites (84) have suggested.

Even if it could be shown with certainty that oxytocin causes the release of prolactin under our experimental conditions, it does not necessarily follow that this is the mechanism which obtains during normal suckling. However, in this connection, it is interesting to note that direct vascular connections from the posterior to the anterior lobe of the pituitary have been demonstrated in the rat (43, 88) and dog (80), so the situation is favorable for blood, highly charged with oxytocin, to reach the anterior lobe of the pituitary. These considerations make it understandable why rather unphysiological doses of oxytocin were necessary in our experiments, since the oxytocin was administered systemically.

C.   Reserpine and the Mammary Gland

We feel it appropriate to conclude this section on neural influences by mentioning some recent work on the relation between tranquilizing drugs and lactation, since considerable interest has recently been focused on the effects of reserpine on mammary gland function. There have been reports in the literature of psychotic women developing galactorrhea after treatment with this drug, and these interesting but rather puzzling findings stimulated several workers to investigate the effects of reserpine on mammary growth and function in experimental animals. Both Sawyer (131) and Meites (104) were able to initiate lactation in virgin rabbits with reserpine, after suitable priming with estrogen, and Meites (104) achieved the same result in the pseudopreg-

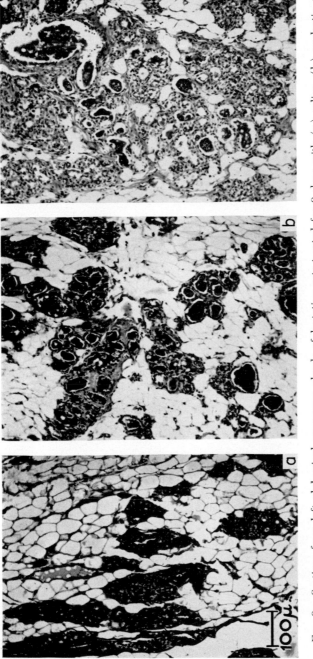

Fig. 9. Sections from left abdominal mammary glands of lactating rats treated for 9 days with (a) saline, (b) prolactin (100 I.U. daily), and (c) prolactin (100 I.U.) plus STH (1 mg. daily) after adrenalectomy and removal of pups on fourth day of lactation. Benson and Folley, unpublished.

nant rabbit; also Tuchmann-Duplessis and Mercier-Parot (147) claim that reserpine will induce lobule-alveolar development in the virgin rat. In our laboratory, however, Tindal (unpublished) could obtain no mammogenic or lactogenic effects with this drug (see Table III); it was not lactogenic in the pseudopregnant rabbit over a range of dose-

TABLE III

RESERPINE AND LACTATION[a]

Animal	Reserpine (daily dose)	Effect
Hooded Norway rat	50 µg., 12th–20th day of pregnancy	No effect on subsequent lactation
	50 µg., 2nd–13th day of lactation	Affected nursing rats adversely; reduced food intake
	Virgin rats, 50 µg. for 8 days; killed 9th day	No mammary development
Dutch rabbit	100 µg. or 200 µg., from 10th–16th day of pseudopregnancy; killed on 17th day	No lactogenesis
	1 mg./kg. once, on 15th day of pseudopregnancy; killed 5 days later	No lactogenesis
Goat	Lactating goats, 0.25 mg., twice daily for 10 days	No effect on milk yield
	Lactating goats, single injection, 12.5 mg.	No effect on milk yield
Pigeon	Either 60 µg., 120 µg., 180 µg., or 240 µg./kg. for 6 days; killed on 7th day	No effect on crop gland
	Either 0.125 mg., 0.25 mg., or 0.5 mg. for 6 days; killed on 7th day	No effect on crop gland

[a] From Tindal, unpublished.

levels, nor was it galactopoietic in the lactating rat, nor mammogenic in the virgin rat; it did not affect milk yield in the lactating goat, and had no stimulating effect on the crop gland of the pigeon over a wide dose-range. All these experiments except those in the virgin rat and the pigeon, were carried out before either Sawyer or Meites published their findings (cf. 146), and when they did so, the work on rabbits and goats was repeated in our laboratory, still with negative results.* These contradictory results are difficult to understand and cannot be explained as yet. However, it may be worth noting that the effects of reserpine (and

---

* See Addendum, page 496.

chlorpromazine) on pituitary function seem to be similar in certain respects to the effect of transplanting the pituitary away from the median eminence, particularly in that prolactin secretion, far from being reduced, is if anything, increased. Were it not that the present position is rather complicated, one might be tempted to ask whether the effect of reserpine on the mammary gland is bound up with the lifting of a hypothalamic restraint on the secretion of prolactin, and perhaps other galactopoietic hormones, by the anterior pituitary. In this connection, recent results in our laboratory are interesting, since Benson (10) has shown that reserpine is strikingly active in retarding mammary involution in the lactating rat after weaning at the fourth day (see Fig. 10), the effect being of such a magnitude as has only so far been equaled by the combination of prolactin and STH (16).

Acknowledgments

We are indebted to the following for material used in unpublished experiments reported in this paper: Dr. Irby Bunding (Armour Laboratories, Chicago) for prolactin and somatotropin, Dr. W. J. Tindall (Organon Laboratories, Ltd., London) for ACTH, Dr. Aleck Borman (Squibb Institute for Medical Research, New Brunswick, New Jersey) for fluorocortisol, Mr. C. W. S. Taylor (CIBA Laboratories, Horsham, Sussex) for reserpine, and Dr. H. Holgate (Sandoz Products Ltd.) for Syntocinon and valyloxytocin.

References

1. Adams, H. P., and Allen, N. N., *J. Dairy Sci.* **35**, 1121 (1952).
2. Ahrén, K., and Jacobsohn, D., *Acta Physiol. Scand.* **37**, 190 (1956).
3. Ahrén, K., and Jacobsohn, D., *Acta Physiol. Scand.* **40**, 254 (1957).
4. Andersson, B., *Acta Physiol. Scand.* **23**, 1 (1951).
5. Andersson, B., *Acta Physiol. Scand.* **23**, 8 (1951).
6. Andersson, B., *Acta Physiol. Scand.* **23**, 24 (1951).
7. Armstrong, D. T., and Ward, G. M., *Proc. Western Div. Am. Dairy Sci. Assoc.* (1957) (*Dairy Sci. Abstr.* **20**, 128, 1958).
8. Averill, S. C., Ray, E. W., and Lyons, W. R., *Proc. Soc. Exptl. Biol. Med.* **75**, 3 (1950).
9. Benson, G. K., *J. Endocrinol.* **17**, xvii (1958).
10. Benson, G. K., *Proc. Soc. Exptl. Biol. Med.* **99**, 550 (1958).
11. Benson, G. K., and Cowie, A. T., *J. Endocrinol.* **14**, 54 (1956).
12. Benson, G. K., Cowie, A. T., Cox, C. P., Flux, D. S., and Folley, S. J., *J. Endocrinol.* **13**, 46 (1955).
13. Benson, G. K., Cowie, A. T., Cox, C. P., and Goldzveig, S. M., *J. Endocrinol.* **15**, 126 (1957).
14. Benson, G. K., and Folley, S. J., *Nature* **177**, 700 (1956).
15. Benson, G. K., and Folley, S. J., *J. Endocrinol.* **14**, xl (1957).
16. Benson, G. K., and Folley, S. J., *J. Endocrinol.* **16**, 189 (1957).
17. Benson, G. K., and Folley, S. J., unpublished results.
18. Berde, B., Doepfner, W., and Konzett, H., *Brit. J. Pharmacol.* **12**, 209 (1957).

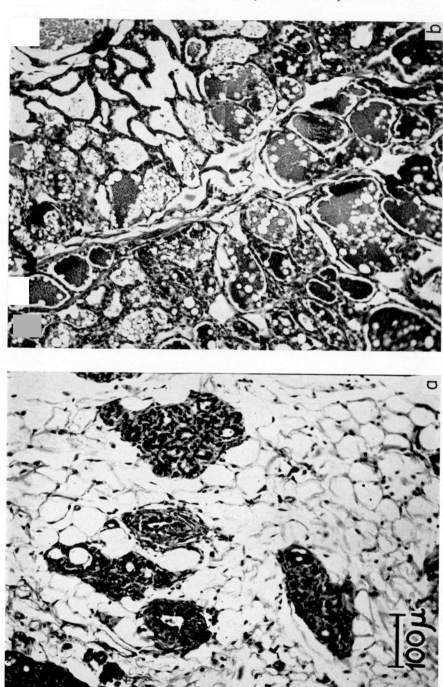

FIG. 10. Sections from left abdominal mammary glands of lactating rats treated with (a) saline and (b) reserpine (100 µg. daily) for 9 days after removal of pups on fourth day of lactation. Involution is retarded after treatment with reserpine. Benson (10).

19. Billenstein, D. C., and Leveque, T. F., *Endocrinology* **56**, 704 (1955).
20. Bintarningsih, Lyons, W. R., Johnson, R. E., and Li, C. H., *Anat. Record* **127**, 266 (1957).
21. Blair, S. M., Blair, P. B., and Daane, T. A., *Endocrinology* **61**, 643 (1957).
22. Bradley, T. R., and Clarke, P. M., *J. Endocrinol.* **14**, 28 (1956).
23. Campbell, B., and Petersen, W. E., *Human Biol.* **25**, 165 (1953).
24. Canivenc, R., and Mayer, G., *Compt. rend. soc. biol.* **147**, 1067 (1953).
25. Cotes, P. M., Crichton, J. A., Folley, S. J., and Young, F. G., *Nature* **164**, 992 (1949).
26. Cowie, A. T., *Endocrinology* **51**, 217 (1952).
27. Cowie, A. T., *J. Endocrinol.* **16**, 135 (1957).
28. Cowie, A. T., Cox, C. P., and Naito, M., unpublished results.
29. Cowie, A. T., and Folley, S. J., *Endocrinology* **40**, 274 (1947).
30. Cowie, A. T., Folley, S. J., Cross, B. A., Harris, G. W., Jacobsohn, D., and Richardson, K. C., *Nature* **168**, 421 (1951).
31. Cowie, A. T., Folley, S. J., Malpress, F. H., and Richardson, K. C., *J. Endocrinol.* **8**, 64 (1952).
32. Cowie, A. T., and Stewart, J., *J. Endocrinol.* **6**, 197 (1949).
33. Cowie, A. T., and Tindal, J. S., *Endocrinology* **56**, 612 (1955).
34. Cowie, A. T., and Tindal, J. S., *J. Endocrinol.* **16**, 403 (1958).
35. Cowie, A. T., and Tindal, J. S., unpublished results.
36. Cross, B. A., *J. Physiol. (London)* **114**, 447 (1951).
37. Cross, B. A., *J. Endocrinol.* **9**, 7 (1953).
38. Cross, B. A., *J. Endocrinol.* **12**, 15 (1955).
39. Cross, B. A., *J. Endocrinol.* **12**, 29 (1955).
40. Cross, B. A., and Harris, G. W., *J. Physiol. (London)* **113**, 35P (1951).
41. Cross, B. A., and Harris, G. W., *J. Endocrinol.* **8**, 148 (1952).
42. Cross, B. A., and van Dyke, H. B., *J. Endocrinol.* **9**, 232 (1953).
43. Daniel, P. M., and Prichard, M. M. L., *Quart. J. Exptl. Physiol.* **41**, 215 (1956).
44. Denamur, R., *Compt. rend. soc. biol.* **147**, 88 (1953).
45. Denamur, R., and Martinet, J., *Compt. rend. soc. biol.* **147**, 1217 (1953).
46. Desclin, L., *Ann. endocrinol. (Paris)* **11**, 656 (1950).
47. Desclin, L., *Compt. rend. soc. biol.* **150**, 1489 (1956).
48. Desclin, L., *Ann. endocrinol. (Paris)* **17**, 586 (1956).
49. Dicker, S. E., and Tyler, C., *J. Physiol. (London)* **121**, 206 (1953).
50. Donker, J. D., Koshi, J. H., and Petersen, W. E., *J. Dairy Sci.* **37**, 299 (1954).
51. du Vigneaud, V., *Harvey Lectures Ser.* **50**, 1 (1956).
51a. Elliott, J. R., and Turner, C. W., *Missouri Univ. Agr. Expt. Sta. Research Bull.* **537** (1953).
52. Ely, F., and Petersen, W. E., *J. Dairy Sci.* **24**, 211 (1941).
53. Everett, J. W., *Endocrinology* **54**, 685 (1954).
54. Everett, J. W., *Endocrinology* **58**, 786 (1956).
55. Ferguson, D. J., *Surgery* **39**, 30 (1956).
56. Flux, D. S., *J. Endocrinol.* **11**, 223 (1954).
57. Flux, D. S., *J. Endocrinol.* **11**, 238 (1954).
58. Flux, D. S., *J. Endocrinol.* **12**, 57 (1955).
59. Flux, D. S., *J. Endocrinol.* **15**, 266 (1957).
60. Flux, D. S., Folley, S. J., and Rowland, S. J., *J. Endocrinol.* **10**, 333 (1954).

61. Flux, D. S., and Munford, R. E., *J. Endocrinol.* **14**, 343 (1957).
62. Folley, S. J., *Brit. Med. Bull.* **5**, 135 (1947).
63. Folley, S. J., *in* "Marshall's Physiology of Reproduction" (A. S. Parkes, ed.), 3rd ed. Vol. 2, Chap. 20. Longmans, Green, London, 1952.
64. Folley, S. J., *Recent Progr. in Hormone Research* **7**, 107 (1952).
65. Folley, S. J., *in* "The Suprarenal Cortex" (J. M. Yoffey, ed.), p. 85. Butterworths, London, 1953.
66. Folley, S. J., *Brit. Med. Bull.* **11**, 145 (1955).
67. Folley, S. J., *in* "The Physiology and Biochemistry of Lactation," p. 34. Oliver & Boyd, Edinburgh and London, 1956.
68. Folley, S. J., and Malpress, F. H., *in* "The Hormones" (G. Pincus and K. V. Thimann, eds.), Vol. 1, Chap. 16, p. 745. Academic Press, New York, 1948.
69. Folley, S. J., and Young, F. G., *Lancet* **240**, 380 (1941).
70. Fortgang, A., and Simpson, M. E., *Proc. Soc. Exptl. Biol. Med.* **84**, 663 (1953).
71. Hadfield, G., *Lancet* **272**, 1058 (1957).
72. Haeger, K., and Jacobsohn, D., *Acta Physiol. Scand.* **30**, Suppl. 111, 152 (1953).
73. Harris, G. W., and Jacobsohn, D., *Proc. Roy. Soc.* **B139**, 263 (1952).
74. Harris, G. W., and Pickles, V. R., *Nature* **172**, 1049 (1953).
75. Hawker, R. W., and Roberts, V. S., *Brit. Vet. J.* **113**, 459 (1957).
76. Hawker, R. W., and Robertson, P. A., *J. Clin. Endocrinol. and Metabolism* **17**, 448 (1957).
77. Höhn, E. O., *J. Endocrinol.* **16**, 227 (1957).
78. Houssay, B. A., *Compt. rend. soc. biol.* **120**, 476 (1935).
79. Hutton, J. B., *J. Endocrinol.* **16**, 115 (1957).
80. Jewell, P. A., *J. Endocrinol.* **14**, xxiv (1956).
81. Johnson, R. M., and Meites, J., *Proc. Soc. Exptl. Biol. Med.* **89**, 455 (1955).
82. Johnson, R. M., and Meites, J., *J. Animal Sci.* **15**, 1288 (1956).
83. Johnson, R. M., and Meites, J., private communication.
84. Johnson, R. M., and Meites, J., *Endocrinology* **63**, 290 (1958).
85. Kalliala, H., and Karvonen, M. J., *Ann. Med. Exptl. et Biol. Fenniae* (*Helsinki*) **29**, 233 (1951).
86. Kalliala, H., Karvonen, M. J., and Leppänen, V., *Ann. Med. Exptl. et Biol. Fenniae* (*Helsinki*) **30**, 96 (1952).
87. Kirkham, W. R., and Turner, C. W., *Proc. Soc. Exptl. Biol. Med.* **87**, 139 (1954).
88. Landsmeer, J. M. F., *Acta Anat.* **12**, 83 (1951).
89. Linzell, J. L., *J. Anat.* **86**, 49 (1952).
90. Linzell, J. L., *J. Physiol.* (*London*) **130**, 257 (1955).
91. Llaurado, J. G., *Proc. Univ. Otago Med. School* **33**, 2 (1955).
92. Llaurado, J. G., *Endocrinology* **57**, 516 (1955).
93. Lyons, W. R., *Proc. Soc. Exptl. Biol. Med.* **51**, 308 (1942).
94. Lyons, W. R., *in* "Essays on Biology in Honor of Herbert M. Evans," p. 317. University of California Press, Berkeley, 1943.
95. Lyons, W. R., *Colloq. intern. centre natl. recherche sci.* (*Paris*) **32**, 29 (1951).
96. Lyons, W. R., Johnson, R. E., Cole, R. D., and Li, C. H., *in* "The Hypophyseal Growth Hormone, Nature and Actions" (R. W. Smith, Jr., O. H. Gaebler, and C. N. H. Long, eds.), p. 461. McGraw-Hill, New York, 1955.
97. Lyons, W. R., Johnson, R. E., and Li, C. H., *Anat. Record* **127**, 432 (1957).

98. Lyons, W. R., Li, C. H., Cole, R. D., and Johnson, R. E., *J. Clin. Endocrinol. and Metabolism* **13**, 836 (1953).
99. Lyons, W. R., Li, C. H., and Johnson, R. E., *J. Clin. Endocrinol. and Metabolism* **12**, 937 (1952).
100. Lyons, W. R., Li, C. H., and Johnson, R. E., *J. Clin. Endocrinol. and Metabolism* **16**, 967 (1956).
101. Lyons, W. R., Li, C. H., and Johnson, R. E., *Recent Progr. in Hormone Research* **14**, 219 (1958).
102. Lyons, W. R., and McGinty, D. A., *Proc. Soc. Exptl. Biol. Med.* **48**, 83 (1941).
103. Meites, J., *Ann. endocrinol. (Paris)* **17**, 519 (1956).
104. Meites, J., *Proc. Soc. Exptl. Biol. Med.* **96**, 728 (1957).
105. Meites, J., *Proc. Soc. Exptl. Biol. Med.* **96**, 730 (1957).
106. Meites, J., private communication.
107. Meites, J., private communication.
108. Meites, J., and Sgouris, J. T., *Endocrinology* **53**, 17 (1953).
109. Meites, J., and Sgouris, J. T., *Endocrinology* **55**, 530 (1954).
110. Meites, J., and Turner, C. W., *Endocrinology* **30**, 711, 719, 726 (1942).
111. Meites, J., and Turner, C. W., *Am. J. Physiol.* **150**, 394 (1947).
112. Meites, J., and Turner, C. W., *Research Bull. Missouri Agr. Expt. Sta. No.* **415** (1948).
113. Mixner, J. P., and Turner, C. W., *Research Bull. Missouri Agr. Expt. Sta. No.* **378** (1943).
114. Mizuno, H., Iida, K., and Naito, M., *Endocrinol. Japon.* **2**, 163 (1955).
115. Munford, R. E., *J. Endocrinol.* **16**, 72 (1957).
116. Newton, M., and Newton, N. R., *J. Pediat.* **33**, 698 (1948).
117. Nickerson, K., Bonsnes, R. W., Douglas, R. G., Condliffe, P., and du Vigneaud, V., *Am. J. Obstet. Gynecol.* **67**, 1028 (1954).
118. Nikitovitch-Winer, M., and Everett, J. W., *Nature* **180**, 1434 (1957).
119. Peeters, G., and Coussens, R., *Arch. intern. pharmacodynamie* **84**, 209 (1950).
120. Ray, E. W., Averill, S. C., Lyons, W. R., and Johnson, R. E., *Endocrinology* **56**, 359 (1955).
121. Reece, R. P., *Proc. Soc. Exptl. Biol. Med.* **73**, 284 (1950).
122. Reineke, E. P., Meites, J., Cairy, C. F., and Huffman, C. F., *Proc. Book Am. Vet. Med. Assoc.* **89**, 325 (1952).
123. Richardson, K. C., *Proc. Roy. Soc.* **B136**, 30 (1949).
124. Richardson, K. C., *J. Endocrinol.* **6**, xxv (1949).
125. Richardson, K. C., *Colloq. intern. centre natl. recherche sci. (Paris)* **32**, 167 (1951).
126. Richardson, K. C., *J. Endocrinol.* **9**, 170 (1953).
127. Riddle, O., Bates, R. W., and Dykshorn, S. W., *Am. J. Physiol.* **105**, 191 (1933).
128. Robertson, P. A., and Hawker, R. W., *Nature* **180**, 343 (1957).
129. Salter, J. M., and Best, C. H., *Brit. Med. J.* **II**, 353 (1953).
130. Salter, J. M., Davidson, I. W. F., and Best, C. H., *Can. J. Biochem. and Physiol.* **35**, 913 (1957).
131. Sawyer, C. H., *Anat. Record* **127**, 362 (1957).
132. Scharf, G., and Lyons, W. R., *Proc. Soc. Exptl. Biol. Med.* **48**, 86 (1941).
133. Scharrer, E., and Scharrer, B., *Recent Progr. in Hormone Research* **10**, 183 (1954).

134. Selye, H., *Am. J. Physiol.* **107**, 535 (1934).
135. Selye, H., *Acta Endocrinol.* **17**, 394 (1954).
136. Selye, H., *Rev. Can. biol.* **13**, 377 (1954).
137. Shaw, J. C., Chung, A. C., and Bunding, I., *Endocrinology* **56**, 327 (1955).
138. Silver, M., *J. Endocrinol.* **10**, 17 (1953).
139. Smith, P. E., *Am. J. Physiol.* **99**, 345 (1932).
140. Smith, T. C., *Endocrinology* **57**, 33 (1955).
141. Sprain, D. G., Smith, V. R., Tyler, W. J., and Fosgate, O. T., *J. Dairy Sci.* **37**, 195 (1954).
142. Stricker, P., and Grueter, F., *Compt. rend. soc. biol.* **99**, 1978 (1928).
143. Stutinsky, F., *Compt. rend. assoc. anat.* **38**, 942 (1952).
144. Stutinsky, F., *Compt. rend.* **244**, 1537 (1957).
145. Sykes, J. F., and Wrenn, T. R., *J. Dairy Sci.* **34**, 1174 (1951).
146. Tindal, J. S., *Ann. Rept. Natl. Inst. Research Dairying*, p. 56 (1956).
147. Tuchmann-Duplessis, H., and Mercier-Parot, L., *Compt. rend. soc. biol.* **151**, 656 (1957).
148. Turner, C. W., *U.S. Atomic Energy Comm. Rept. TID-7512*, p. 403 (1956).
149. van Dyke, H. B., Adamsons, K., Jr., and Engel, S. L., *Recent Progr. in Hormone Research* **11**, 1 (1955).
150. Waller, H., in "Clinical Studies in Lactation." Heinemann, London, 1938.
151. Whittlestone, W. G., *New Zealand J. Sci. Technol.* **A32**, 1 (1951).
152. Whittlestone, W. G., Bassett, E. G., and Turner, C. W., *J. Dairy Sci.* **35**, 889 (1952).
153. Williams, W. L., *Anat. Record* **93**, 171 (1945).
154. Yamada, J., Nagai, J., and Naito, M., *Endocrinol. Japon.* **1**, 63 (1954).
155. Yamamoto, H., and Turner, C. W., *Proc. Soc. Exptl. Biol. Med.* **92**, 130 (1956).

Discussion

CHAIRMAN: SIR S. ZUCKERMAN

I. ROTHCHILD: There are many, many things in Dr. Folley's beautiful paper that I would like to discuss, but I will try to keep my comments down to just two points. One concerns the question of the participation of ACTH and growth hormone in the maintenance of lactation. In the experiments in which the pup's pituitaries were transplanted to the mother, and the mother's pituitary was removed at the second lactation, it took ACTH as a supplement in one group and growth hormone, in another group, to get a fairly decent milk yield, which was still far from that characteristic of the intact animal.

In the Sprague-Dawley strain of rats, after hypophysectomy and pituitary auto-transplantation under the kidney capsule on the fifth day post partum, I have found that merely injecting oxytocin at the rate of a half unit every 4 hours, around the clock, without any supplementary ACTH or growth hormone, yielded a litter growth equivalent to 60–75% of that seen with the control intact mothers. I question whether ACTH is involved, although I have very little doubt that growth hormone is involved in the maintenance of lactation because these animals with autotransplanted pituitaries show several signs of at least partial secretion of the growth hormone from the transplanted pituitary.

The other point concerns the role of oxytocin in the maintenance of prolactin or luteotropin secretion from the transplanted pituitary. In these experiments one can study the factors that are concerned in the maintenance of at least the one hormone that this graft is capable of producing in fairly normal amounts, and this hormone is prolactin or luteotropin.

Oxytocin was capable of maintaining lactation in animals with autotransplanted pituitaries. The evidence from Drs. Benson and Folley's experiments, which was so beautifully presented here, on the delay in mammary involution with oxytocin, led me to think also that oxytocin had stimulated some luteotropin secretion from these transplanted pituitaries, perhaps in amounts above those secreted by the untreated gland. However, in fact, cycling rats injected with oxytocin in doses of up to 5 units a day in 6 divided doses every 4 hours around the clock for as long as 2 weeks showed no effect whatsoever on the maintenance of normal estrous cycles. In other words, they did not become pseudopregnant as one would have expected them to if the oxytocin were capable of stimulating luteotropin secretion.

There was also no delay in the regeneration of ovarian grafts transplanted to the kidneys of castrated animals treated with oxytocin in the same regime. This stands in sharp contrast to the time taken for an ovarian graft to regenerate in a suckling castrated animal. In these, the regeneration time is usually as long as the suckling itself. Again, if oxytocin were capable of stimulating luteotropin or pro-lactin secretion, one would have expected a similar result to be obtained here as in the castrated suckler.

S. J. FOLLEY: I was very interested in your statement that you could obtain about 70% maintenance of lactation by autotransplants of the mothers' pituitaries. That is certainly a very excellent result. I presume oxytocin was given as well. In our laboratory, Drs. Cowie and Tindal have so far been able to get about 40–50% maintenance with grafts of the pituitaries of the young supplemented with ACTH; in isolated cases the degree of maintenance was as high as 70–80%, but this was not achieved regularly.

With regard to your comment about your failure to prevent rats cycling by injections of oxytocin, I should say that we have tried the effect of oxytocin on the estrous cycles of mice and inhibited them in our first experiment. This proved to be an illustration of the adage that one should never repeat a successful experiment, for in subsequent experiments we were never able to confirm it.

S. ZUCKERMAN: I wonder if Professor Heller would care to make any observations about the conclusions drawn by Dr. Cowie about the resumption of oxytocic activity in rats in their second postoperative lactation, and if you could relate this to the fact that diabetes insipidus persists in many animals following the destruction of the neurohypophysis? For example, in monkeys diabetes insipidus may certainly continue for over a year—and by "diabetes insipidus" I mean diabetes insipidus.

H. HELLER: I am sorry, I think I would rather not comment on this subject. Evidence that vasopressin and oxytocin may be released differentially has only recently been forthcoming and this may imply that the two hormones are formed in cytologically different sites which may in turn be differently influenced by hypophysectomy. I feel therefore that long-term studies on the oxytocin content (and release?) of the hypothalamus and the residual neurohypophyseal tissue of diabetes insipidus animals are needed before the problem can be discussed further.

S. LEONARD: Dr. Folley, I was quite impressed with the results obtained in the hypophysectomized rats given insulin and estrogen noting improved mammary growth. In a test to repeat Best's work in inducing body growth in hypophysectomized rats by giving insulin with his diet, we were unable to do this in the female, but in the male it worked beautifully; yet the female is what I presume you used to get this mammary growth effect. Perhaps you could comment upon that.

Secondly, have you ever been able to increase mammary growth in hypophysectomized rats with estrogen if you force-fed them improved diets so they will grow, because it is believed actually that the insulin causes this increased somatic growth by greater food intake. By force-feeding them, as Dr. L. Samuels did years ago, you might be able to get duplicate results by that method.

S. J. FOLLEY: First I should make it clear that the work on mammary growth in hypophysectomized rats treated with insulin is not our own work, but was done by Dr. Dora Jacobsohn of Lund. I was merely quoting it and the slide I showed was taken from her paper with Åhrén.

We have never carried out any experiments on the forced feeding of hypophysectomized rats, and the only work I know of was that you yourself cited, which was carried out some years ago by L. T. Samuels, R. M. Reinecke, W. E. Petersen (*Proc. Soc. Exp. Biol. Med.* **46**, 379, 1941), in which they did claim, if I remember rightly, that force-fed hypophysectomized rats did respond with some degree of mammary growth to estrogen and progesterone; but we have never tried it ourselves.

C. H. SAWYER: I, too, should like to express my appreciation for Dr. Folley's beautiful review. There are one or two points I would like to raise. First, in connection with the failure to get lactation with reserpine, Dr. Folley tells me that he and his colleagues used small Dutch rabbits while we were using large New Zealand Whites. I think we shall have to invoke breed differences as an explanation here, inasmuch as not only Dr. Meites but also Dr. Leathem and Dr. Gaunt have confirmed our findings. I wonder whether Dr. Folley has used, as a control oxytocin experiment, animals with their spinal cords cut to eliminate afferent nerves from the mammary glands. It would seem that this might eliminate the possibility of setting up a reflex in which oxytocin might work peripherally.

Another possible mechanism I should like to propose is that oxytocin itself may work centrally in an inhibitory manner. We propose this because of our findings with Kawakami, that in the rabbit oxytocin does change thresholds in the rhinencephalon, and we proposed the other day that it might act as a feedback to the pituitary to inhibit further LH release. The French neurophysiologist Fauré has also found similar threshold changes in the amygdala on the use of oxytocin.

S. J. FOLLEY: We have considered the possibility of doing experiments involving section of the spinal cord, but so far have not had the opportunity of doing them. In fact, neurophysiologists, whom we have consulted, have told us that it would be extremely difficult to denervate the mammary gland of the rat.

What was your third point again, please?

C. H. SAWYER: Changes in thresholds within the central nervous system which would indicate that oxytocin may exert direct effects on the nervous system. Since oxytocin has shown this effect—we are reasoning somewhat backwards from that observation—that it may block in the same manner in which reserpine acts to release the pituitary from inhibition.

S. J. FOLLEY: Yes, that is an interesting suggestion, and in that connection one might recall the experiments carried out some years ago by Petersen which did indicate that oxytocin was capable of exerting a feed-back effect on the neurohypophysis in that, when he gave oxytocin regularly to cows over a long period, the natural milk-ejection reflex was inhibited after the injections ceased and took a few days to re-establish itself. This might indicate perhaps that oxytocin is capable of exerting some inhibitory effect on the neurohypophysis.

J. H. LEATHEM: Just to support the comments that Dr. Sawyer made, we have repeated his experiments with reserpine successfully in the rabbit and can only leave this question at this point; except to add to it that our efforts to gain lactational release in guinea pigs have failed in guinea pigs that have been brought into mammary development by estrogen alone, estrogen plus progesterone, or by natural means. Under these circumstances the guinea pigs have been uncooperative.

May I ask one or two other questions, Dr. Folley, and that is in relationship to your animals which were hypophysectomized on the fourth day of lactation, I presume that you considered undoubtedly whether food consumption in these animals has in any way affected the lactation. If you have considered the nutritional intake of these animals, it may also very well be possible that the so-operated animal on a diet that we consider adequate for a normal animal may still not be the diet which is completely adequate for these animals; we find in our experience that a diet that has been devised by a nutritionist as excellent for the normal proves to have definite deficiencies for an animal that has been hypophysectomized.

You also presented information on replacement therapy for lactation in animals that were subjected to the combination of ovariectomy and adrenalectomy. I presume that these animals in terms of lactation are not influenced by ovariectomy alone. Also, I wonder if anyone has attempted in adrenalectomized animals, but with ovaries intact, to study the influence of administered gonadotropins on the lactational performance of the animal.

S. J. FOLLEY: Your suggestion about the diet of the hypophysectomized lactating rat is very interesting, and this is a thing we must pay attention to. However, in the preliminary stages at least, we feel that complete replacement of the pituitary should mean restoration of the normal appetite.

As regards your second point, removal of the ovaries does not affect lactation— at any rate in our rats.

Lastly, I know of no experiments in which pituitary gonadotropins were administered to adrenalectomized lactating rats.

C. G. HARTMAN: Since among the flood of tranquilizers that are now coming out, all have different points of attack on the central nervous system, I would think that this fact might be used further to analyze certain reproductive functions, lactation included.

I believe the psychic phase in lactation has not yet been touched on, not being on Dr. Folley's agenda. I might briefly call attention to two phenomena: One, if you add a strange cow to your herd of 20 milkers, these are no longer "contented cows," become upset, and as a consequence give less milk for a few days. Two, in case of fright or sudden sorrow, as after a fire or a sudden death in the family, the lactating woman often "dries up" instantly. Is this due to adrenaline?

S. J. FOLLEY: Yes. I think Dr. Hartman's observations are very true and I feel that future research on the neurohormonal mechanisms governing lactation may throw some light on what it is that interferes with lactation in these women.

S. SEGAL: Comparing the endocrine role of the rat placenta, for example, to that of the human placenta it is apparent that important differences exist. In the human, there is a high degree of fetal independence from maternal hormonal levels as the placenta assumes a rather complex endocrine function. Are there differences among mammalian forms with regard to the role played by the placenta, as a source of hormones, in the preparation for an initiation of lactation?

S. J. FOLLEY: I believe that in all mammalian forms studied, with the possible exception of the monotremes, which seem to be rather peculiar, one sees a somewhat similar dependence of the mammary glands on endocrine factors operating during pregnancy. What has happened during the process of evolution is that nervous and psychological factors have come to assume a greater importance in the functioning of the mammary gland after lactation has been initiated.

Dr. Hartman pointed out that women sometimes cease lactation because of being involved in a fire or some other disaster. We get a similar sort of thing in cows, but in lower animals, such as the rat, it is rather difficult to stop them lactating short of removing their pituitaries. Frightening them or just opening up the pituitary fossa without taking out the pituitary does not seem to have the slightest effect.

I would envisage the picture as a rather unified one with regard to the endocrine control of lactation, but involving increasing dependence on the nervous system with respect to the initiation and maintenance of lactation as we ascend the evolutionary scale.

G. S. GREENWALD: I wonder whether the failure to induce pseudopregnancy in cycling rats with oxytocin could be due to the different hormonal status during lactation in contrast to the estrous cycle. At 4 days post partum, the levels of estrogen are probably extremely low in contrast to the amounts present during the normal estrous cycle. High levels of estrogen can act to prevent luteotropic release. Could this additional estrogen be a factor in the failure to elicit pseudopregnancy during the estrous cycle?

S. J. FOLLEY: Yes, I think that is an interesting possibility which we might investigate.

I should like to say here that I have heard of some unpublished experiments carried out at Cornell in which high doses of oxytocin have been given to cows. In fact, I have been told that these results have been published in abstract. I have not seen the abstract myself, but I understand that high doses of oxytocin were injected for 6 or 7 days following estrus into cows exhibiting normal 21-day cycles. After the injections were stopped the cows came into estrus within 2 or 3 days. This was rather the obverse of stopping the cycle, but the oxytocin certainly upset the cyclic condition of these animals. This may fit into the general picture.

D. T. ARMSTRONG: Since I am responsible for the work at Cornell to which Dr. Folley referred, I would like to comment upon it.

We have found, since the work was reported at the Federation Meetings in Philadelphia (Armstrong, D. T. and Hansel, W., *Federation Proc.* **17**, 6 (1958)), that the early return to estrus does not depend upon withdrawal of oxytocin treatment, since two cows have returned to estrus even though daily oxytocin injections were not discontinued. We have been able to prevent this response to oxytocin by means of concomitant reserpine treatment, as well as removal of the uterus prior to oxytocin treatment. Because of this, we are wondering if the effect of oxytocin which we have observed was due to some peripheral action rather than a direct effect on the anterior pituitary. One possibility may be that oxytocin-induced contractions of the reproductive tract send sensory impulses to the hypothalamus which may in some way inhibit the release of luteotropin from the anterior pituitary, thereby causing inhibition of normal corpus luteum function. This is borne out by the observation that the corpora lutea in these oxytocin-treated cows never attain the size of those in normally cycling cows.

C. W. LLOYD: In the neurohypophysectomized rats which lactated well during the second lactation, what happened to the diabetes insipidus?

S. J. FOLLEY: Dr. Cross, I believe, pointed out that immediately after posterior lobectomy there was a fairly severe diabetes insipidus, though not as severe as that which results, according to some authors, from more complete interference with the neurohypophysis caused by placing lesions in the SOH tract.

At the time of the second lactation, when the milk-ejection reflex, as you saw on the slide, was virtually restored, so that the pups grew almost at the normal rate, there was still a marked, though one would say, comparatively mild, diabetes insipidus. I have forgotten the actual figure, but it had regressed somewhat from what it had been immediately after the operation. Nevertheless it was significant, perhaps three or four times the normal urine volume.

E. M. RAY: Dr. Segal's earlier comment that the fetus, or the total conceptus, produces its "own," hormonally speaking, would be supported by studies from Dr. William Lyons' laboratory some time ago. Pregnancy could be maintained in the hypophysectomized rat by the injection of rat placentas subcutaneously, demonstrating that the pituitary's gonadotropic triad, FSH, ICSH, and lactogenic hormone can be replaced by the placenta. Similarly, regarding the mammary gland, lobuloalveolar development could be induced in the hypophysectomized-oophorec-tomized rat with large amounts of placenta alone, implying that the placenta in itself contains the estrogenic, progestogenic, and mammotropic requirements Dr. Folley has discussed.

J. McARTHUR: I would like to ask Dr. Folley if from his very large animal experience, he can hazard any interpretation of the experiment of nature that we, as clinicians, occasionally see—namely women, who after parturition, are unable to stop lactation. Their genitalia may become atrophic and a state of amenorrhea and sterility persists indefinitely unless in some manner their cycles can be restarted.

S. J. FOLLEY: I am afraid I cannot hazard any real explanation of Dr. Mc-Arthur's observations. They do seem reminiscent of a rather shadowy syndrome one has heard of, called the Chiari-Frommel syndrome. I looked up the literature on this some years ago.

The syndrome appears to consist of persistent lactation associated with amenor-rhea and uterine involution and, I think, ovarian hypoplasia. I believe cases have been described in which lactation persisted for years.

It has been postulated that this syndrome is associated with a minute lesion in the hypothalamus, but I don't know of any cases in which this has been actually proved. Further study of this aspect in any cases that may come to post-mortem, might throw light on this.

Some years ago there were two famous cows that seemed to me to be bovine cases of the Chiari-Frommel syndrome. Both were cows which had lactated for years, having had, I believe, one calf, and had given quite large volumes of milk over this period. One of them was in New Zealand, and I wrote to a veterinarian who was in contact with the owner suggesting that when this cow was slaughtered it might be interesting to have a neuroanatomist look at the brain, but I think that was never done.

Addendum (See page 484)

These, and the rabbits used in the previous experiments, all with negative results, were of the Dutch breed. Since this paper was submitted for publication further experiments have been carried out in our laboratory on New Zealand White rabbits (Tindal, unpublished), in which females, either primed with estrogen or made pseudopregnant, were given reserpine. Of eight rabbits treated in this way, five subsequently showed macroscopic evidence of lactation within 5 to 7 days after reserpine treatment. It would appear, therefore, that there may be breed differences in the response of rabbits to the lactogenic action of reserpine.

Closing Remarks by Sir Solly Zuckerman

S. ZUCKERMAN: Since we have to abide by a timetable, I am afraid that it is now necessary to close the general discussion on this paper, at the same time as I transmit to Dr. Folley our best thanks for his extraordinarily lucid and informative paper. Like all the previous reviews of the subject of lactation which he has provided, his present one will no doubt continue to guide our thoughts until the next occasion when he can be persuaded to produce a synthesis of the very complex field of knowledge in which he is so eminent.

As Chairman of the final session of the Conference, it is my privilege—and I believe that this is what Dr. Lloyd also expects me to do—to say some words in winding up the whole meeting. The first thing I should say is that we all owe an immense debt of gratitude to Dr. Lloyd for the initiative he took in calling this conference, and for the vast labors that he accepted in bringing us together here. He arranged a program that has progressed logically from ovulation, through fertilization and implantation, on to parturition, and so to lactation. And he chose as his main participants those who could provide an up-to-date account of knowledge in their particular fields of interest—so that others who came to listen, such as myself, find themselves greatly indebted to those who came to speak. I am sure that this sentiment also applies to the wider audience which will be able to read the account of the conference when it is published. Our thanks are due to all the contributors to the program. They have sustained our interest to the very end.

Like many conferences, this one has permitted the renewal of old friendships and the making of new ones. It is of the utmost value to meet people whom presumably one knows only by their writings, and to discover through conversation and discussion the way their minds work.

Three of us in this hall this morning—there are only two this afternoon—participated in what I believe was the first international conference on the Physiology of Reproduction. I am referring to the Singer-Polignac Colloquium which took place in Paris in 1937. Dr. Carl Hartman, Dr. Frederick Hisaw, and myself were fortunate enough to be both of the small number who took part in this French meeting and of the larger one of the present conference. On several occasions during the past few days my mind has drifted back over the twenty years that have intervened, and I have kept asking myself how one could categorize the differences between the two meetings. Obviously, we now have at our disposal innumerably more facts about endocrinology. It is also clear that our endocrinological knowledge today has a much firmer chemical basis than it had in the middle '30's. Then we were at the beginning of the exploration of the steroid molecule; and we knew practically nothing about the chemistry of the other hormones, or about the chemistry of hormonal reactions. The cooperation and collaboration of the chemist over the past twenty years has undoubtedly meant an enormous transformation of our subject. That seems to me to be the big difference between today and twenty years ago. The chemist has provided us with the basis for firm generalization in many parts of the endocrinological field. Equally, there is no doubt that the interests of the clinician have opened up for the attention of the experimentalist many problems of major interest.

At the same time, it is difficult not to be struck by the fact that today, no less than twenty years ago, endocrinologists are always impelled by an irresistible urge to generalize widely and to over-simplify in their explanations. I cannot avoid asking myself whether we do not try too often to comprehend too much in too few terms. Because of this, I ask whether the area of our ignorance today is really smaller than it appeared in the '30's. Many of the endocrine reactions which we are trying to understand have evolved over a period of hundreds of millions of years. Are we not sometimes beguiling ourselves if we think we can understand them by means of far-reaching, even if elegant, generalizations? Most of us are guilty of this habit. Have we not, for example, gone full-circle when we refer to the action of histamine as the first essential mechanism in the process of estrogenic action, for this idea, which has emerged today as a novelty, was also there twenty-five years ago. This is just an arbitrary example of what I have in mind. Our tendencies to generalize and to simplify need to be disciplined. Almost every series of facts lends itself to alternative explanations, the choice between which depends on the results of further experimental work. One might call this the stage of first-order speculation. One sets up a hypothesis, and one attempts to test it positively. The danger with endocrinology is that since it intrudes into so many fields of biological and scientific knowledge, first-order speculations readily lend themselves to second-order speculations in another field of study, and one might mistakenly take these—the second-order speculations—as a basis for experimental studies, forgetting that there may be a wide gap between them and the alternative explanations from which they spring. Sometimes, too, we are inclined to treat negative findings as possessing an equal validity to positive observations in the testing of hypotheses.

One of the newer branches of endocrinological study in which discipline seems to be urgently called for is the area where neurology and endocrinology meet. Neuroendocrinology is the new fashion; and the hypothalamus, which clearly is implicated in a general way in a variety of visceral functions, is appealed to in a specific way to explain many ill-defined endocrinological reactions. I cannot avoid thinking that since the biochemist has made so big a difference to the content of endocrinology over the last twenty years, the experimental neurologist should be able to do the same over the next twenty years. We endocrinologists step in where, I imagine, some neurologists would fear to tread. But we are not likely to achieve unanimity in our ideas about neuroendocrinology until we bring to this borderline subject not only the disciplines of endocrinology but also those of neurology. Again, when I say this, I am speaking not least for myself!

It only remains for me to thank, on your behalf, all those institutions which, by grants-in-aid, made it possible for those of us who have come from far afield to attend this meeting. I have also to thank the State University of New York Upstate Medical Center for having made the conference possible. This is the Dedication Year of a new medical school. To Dr. Lloyd, and to the President of the Medical Center, Dr. Carlyle Jacobsen, we extend our very best wishes, in the certainty that their College, in the years ahead, will continue to flower even more magnificently than it has in the past.

Author Index

Numbers in parentheses are reference numbers and are included to assist in locating the reference where the authors' names are not mentioned in the text. Numbers in italics refer to the page on which the reference is listed.

A

Abitbol, M. M., 430, *433*

Abrahams, V. C., 366, *383*

Abramowitz, A. A., 399 (43, 44), 411 (43), *422*

Abramson, D., 429, *433*

Adair, F. L., *200*

Adams, C. E., 159 (57), *162*, 170, *175*, 215 (1, 21), 220 (1, 21), *223*, *224*

Adams, E. C., 109 (4), 110 (4), *122*

Adams, H. P., 480 (1), *485*

Adamsons, K., Jr., 371 (45), *385*, 445 (45), *453*, 475 (149), 478 (149), *490*

Addis, T., 182 (1), *195*

Adey, W. R., 8, *16*

Adler, A., 257 (1), *274*

Agersborg, H. P., Jr., 104 (3), *105*

Ahrén, K., 462, 464, *485*

Albert, A., 73, *78*, *125*, 300 (26), *315*

Albright, F., 69 (2), *78*

Aldman, B., 320 (1), *326*

Aldrich, T. B., 374 (30), *384*

Alexander, D. P., 228, *240*

Alexander, S. A., 442 (2), *452*

Aliaga, R., 104, *105*

Allen, N. N., 480 (1), *485*

Allen, W. M., 186 (75), *197*, 205 (2), *223*, 238 (2), *240*, 255, 259 (2), *274*, *275*

Alper, C., 359 (20), *360*

Altland, P. D., 98, *105*

Altschul, A. M., 320 (18), *327*

Alvarez, H., 443 (8), *452*

Anderson, D. H., 319 (66, 67), *328*

Anderson, E., 4 (41), 6 (3), 11, *16*, *17*

Anderson, H. K., 173 (16), *175*

Anderson, J., 143, 147 (1), *161*

Andersson, B., 445, *452*, 475, 476, *485*

Andiada, J. A., 112 (5), *122*

Andrews, M. C., 300 (12), *314*

Anlyan, A. T., 311 (8), *314*

Aoki, I., 257 (30), *275*

Archer, R., 369, 371, 374 (3), 376 (2), 380 (50), *383*, *385*, 444 (1), *452*

Armstrong, D. T., 480 (7), *485*, *494*

Arrillaga, F., 112 (5), *122*

Aschkenasy, A., 182 (2), 187 (3), 190 (4), *195*

Aschkenasy-Lelu, P., 182 (77), 186 (76), 187 (3, 76), 190 (4), *195*

Asdell, S. A., 27 (1), *42*, 144 (41), *162*, 189 (5), *195*

Assenmacher, I., 2, *16*, 22 (13), 30 (13), *42*

Astwood, E. B., 318 (2, 63), *326*, 328, 408 (1, 2), 409, *421*

Atkins, J., 98, *106*

Atkinson, W. B., *425*

Austin, C. R., 132, 143, 145 (5), 150 (2, 3), *152*, *161*

Averill, R. L. W., 222 (22), *224*

Averill, S. C., 464 (8, 120), *485*, *489*

Axelrod, J., 347 (4), *360*

B

Babcock, J. C., *244*

Bagby, B. B., Jr., 72 (3), *78*

Baird, J. A., 104 (4), *105*

Balfour, W. E., 263, *274*

Ball, E. G., 325 (3), *326*

Ball, J., 32 (2), *42*

Ball, Z. B., 184 (6), 186 (6, 26), *196*

Ban, T., 3 (40), *17*, 444 (37), *453*

Barber, Y. K., 359 (2), *360*

Bard, P., 6, *16*, 32 (4, 73), 33 (3, 5, 6, 7), 34, 35, *42*, *44*

Barker, S. B., 193 (7), *196*

Barlow, G., 104, *105*

499

Subject Index

A

Acrosome
  loss in capacitation of sperm, 152-153
Adrenal
  estrogen production, 127, 128-129
Adrenal cortex
  fetal zone of adrenal and steroid pro-
    duction, 123
  and gonadal anlagen, 122-123
Adrenal steroids
  effect on lactation maintenance, 471-
    474
    on mammary growth, 461-462
    on vasopressin, 371
  excretion, increase at high altitude, 106
  in metabolic studies of pregnancy, 349,
    352, 359
  in placental perfusion, 302-311
    from C^{14}-labeled acetate, 306, 307
    conjugated material, 303-306, 311
    Porter-Silber chromogen production,
      302-310
  placental production, 310-311
Adrenaline, see Epinephrine
Adrenocorticotropic hormone (ACTH)
  effect on lamb size in ewes not exposed
    to heat during pregnancy, 88
  in perfused placenta, 285, 311
  on placental incubation, 296
  galactopoiesis, 470
  half-life, 382
  increased production due to hypoxia
    and temperature changes, 104
  in lactation initiation, 467
  in lactation maintenance, 467, 468, 490
  and mammary growth, 461-462
  and ovulation, 19
  and progesterone production, 263
  and relaxin, 402
Agglutination
  of sperm, 145-146
Aldosterone
  excretion of, 345-346
    in pregnancy, 345-346

from placental incubation, 296
placental perfusion production, 363
secretion in pregnancy
  control by intravascular volume, 359,
    361-362
  and sweating, 361
17α-Allyl-19-nortestosterone
  maintaining pregnancy in spayed rats,
    236
Amenorrhea
  hormonal excretion patterns, 19-20
Amygdala, see also Hypothalamico-
    hypophyseal-ovarian function
  and hypersexuality, 20
  and ovulation, 9
Androgen, see also individual compounds
  oxidation-reduction reaction, 257
Δ4-Androstenedione
  conversion of progesterone by fetal
    adrenal tissue to, 280
  and testosterone as an oxidation-re-
    duction system, 257
Δ4-Androstene-3,17-dione
  produced by fetal adrenal, 123
6β-OH-Δ4-Androstene-3,17-dione   from
    perfused placenta, 295
Antidiuretic hormone (ADH), see also
    Vasopressin
  in estrous cycle, 365
  protein-bound, 379
  secretion and oxytocin, 453-454

B

Bilirubin
  conjugation by placenta, 315-316
Blastocyst, see Implantation
Brain stem reticular formation, 9-11
  EEG arousal threshold and estrous
    behavior, 14
  in ovulatory mechanisms, 10-11
17α-Butyl-19-nortestosterone
  maintaining pregnancy in spayed rats,
    236

N

Neurohypophysis
in estrous cycle, 365-369
vasopressin:oxytocin ratio and concentration in gland, 366-369, 386-387
and water metabolism, 368-369, 371, 386-387
fate of vasopressin and oxytocin in rats, 377-383
common pathway for metabolism of peptide hormones, 382-383
sites of clearance, 378-379, 382
hormone content and ratio
extraction methods, 371-376
in lactating rats, 371-376
inactivation of hormones *in vitro*, 385
and lactation, 474-485
oxytocin secretion and conception, 169-171, 175
participation in labor, 442-446, 451
effect of lesions, 442-443
electrical stimulation, 443-444
labor induced by administered oxytocin, 443
milk ejection studies, 445-446
non-hormonal mechanisms, 446-449
oxytocin content of gland and blood, 444-445
in pregnancy, 369-371
vasopressin:oxytocin ratio and release from gland, 453-454

Nitrogen
in metabolic studies of pregnancy, 349, 352, 357, 358, 362

Norethynodrel, *see* $\Delta^{5(10)}$-17α-Ethynyl-17-hydroxyestren-3-one

Norlutin, *see* $\Delta^{4(5)}$-17α-Ethynyl-19-nor-testosterone

Nutrition
effect on reproduction, 179-190
of high protein diets, 198
effect on seminal vesicle
on deficient diet, 199
effect on testis
Leydig cell atrophy on protein-deficient diet, 199
priority of tissue with higher metabolic rate, 198

O

Ovary
cyst
amount of estrogen in fluid, 199, 200
androgen in fluid, 199
biochemical changes, 194
cholesterol in cyst fluid, 199
progesterone in fluid, 199
estrogen production by granulosa cells, 128
follicular artesia, 125
polycystic due to constant estrus, 49
response to chorionic gonadotropin modified by diet and thiouracil, 194-195
response to gonadotropin
in cretin, 193
source of relaxin, 395

Oviduct, *see also* Fallopian tube
function of, 176

Ovulation, *see also* Hypothalamico-hypophyseal-ovarian function
blockage by atropine and other agents, 10
and capacitation, 150-151, 164
criteria for, 343
effect of ACTH, 19
effect of hypothalamic stimulation and lesion on
in the cat, 4-6
in guinea pig and rat, 6-8
in the rabbit, 3
effect of rhinencephalon on, 8-9
effect of testosterone, 14
and estrogen peak, 58-62
in humans
following thermal nadir, 73
mechanisms in
role of reticular formation, 11
processes involved in, 21
ripening of ovarian follicles, 21-27
rupture of ovarian follicles, 27-32
synchronization of estrous behavior and ovulation time, 32-41
in rats
inhibited by hypoxia, 101
inhibited by low or high body temperature, 100-101
reduction in acclimatized rats, 89